CALCULUS

for Business, Biology,
and The Social Sciences

CALCULUS

for Business, Biology, and The Social Sciences

BY DAVID G. CROWDIS

SUSANNE M. SHELLEY

BRANDON W. WHEELER

Sacramento City College

 GLENCOE PRESS

A division of Benziger Bruce & Glencoe, Inc.

Beverly Hills, California

Collier-Macmillan Publishers / London

GLENCOE PRESS
A Division of Benziger Bruce & Glencoe, Inc.
8701 Wilshire Boulevard
Beverly Hills, California 90211
Collier-Macmillan Canada, Ltd., Toronto, Canada

Library of Congress Catalog Card Number: 70–158942

Third printing, 1973

Contents

Preface

Mathematics does not exist in a vacuum. For most students mathematics is a tool which will help them gain insight into their own special fields through its concepts and symbolism. Traditionally mathematics, especially calculus, has been considered a subject for engineers or physical scientists. However, in recent years specialists in the social, management, and biological sciences have found that calculus is also extremely useful in their disciplines. It is toward students in these areas that this text is directed.

At the start it must be pointed out that this book is intended to be a mathematics text, not an introduction to economics, biology, or sociology. As such, it deals primarily with the basic concepts of a first course in calculus and is written for students whose mathematics training includes a strong four-year high school program or its college equivalent. The approach is intuitive rather than formal. An intuitive approach, however, does not mean a totally mechanical approach. It means that ideas are discussed and their underlying principles are examined for "reasonableness" without attempting to structure formal proofs. For example, the $\delta-\epsilon$ approach to the definition of a limit is discussed, but the application of this definition is not considered in depth.

The first six chapters of this text parallel the introductory calculus courses described in the reports of the Committee on Undergraduate Program in Mathematics (CUPM). The remaining three chapters introduce concepts of multiple-variable calculus and infinite series. In this way, the text is designed to meet the needs of a one-semester, daily, first course, or a two-semester, three-hour course for students who need multiple-variable topics. The text also lends itself to a two or three-quarter pattern.

The major difference between the material presented here and the more traditional approach to calculus lies in the applications chosen to illustrate the mathematical concepts rather than in the mathematics itself. Whenever possible, applications are taken from the social, management, and biological sciences rather than from engineering and physics. For example, the derivative is interpreted as marginal cost, an economic concept, and the area under a curve, found with integration, is interpreted as a probability, a concept with applications in the social sciences.

Every chapter has a set of chapter review exercises in addition to the exercises following each section, and answers to the odd-numbered exercises are supplied in the back of the book. The answers to the even-numbered exercises are available in a separate Teacher's Manual.

CALCULUS

for Business, Biology, and The Social Sciences

CHAPTER ONE   Sets, Functions,

and Limits

Calculus is built upon two great concepts, the derivative, which examines rates of change, and the integral, which deals with sums and, initially, areas. Both of these concepts have been known and worked with in various forms for many centuries. It remained for two of the greatest minds of the seventeenth century, Issac Newton and W. G. Leibnitz, to see that these two concepts were not separate but rather fit together to form one unified discipline. The study of these two concepts, their interrelation, and their application, forms the subject we call calculus.

It would be interesting to jump right in and examine how the rate of change, or derivative, relates economic concepts like the rate of change of profit to a change in sales, or how the rate of radioactive decay of carbon 14 helps the anthropologist date his finds, or how the sum concept of the integral relates to ideas of supply and demand or population growth. But first we must study the basic concepts of sets, functions, and limits.

Mathematicians know that the key to understanding the derivative and the integral lies in the limit. The limit concept is used for the examination of the behavior of one variable quantity as a second related variable approaches but does not reach a selected value. To develop the concept of a limit it will be necessary to examine the function concept, which formalizes relationships between variables. Careful notation can smooth the study of these concepts. Modern notation and approaches to these topics rest with the idea of sets. Many students will have encountered this idea in previous courses. One final word, calculus can be and is applied to complex numbers; however that application is beyond the scope of this text, which will restrict its discussion to real numbers.

1-1 SETS, SET NOTATION

Some of what follows will be familiar to many readers, for set concepts are now common topics in most elementary instruction in mathematics. However, since the background of students using this text is diverse, it is reasonable to begin with a uniform presentation of this basic topic.

A *set* is any well-defined collection of objects. The words *collection* and *object* shall be considered primitive terms (that is, they will be left undefined); and we specify that a set must be *well-defined* because, in theory at least, we must be able to determine whether or not a given object belongs to a given collection.

A set may be specified in two ways.

1. By *listing* each object, member, or element in the set.
2. By stating a *rule* for membership.

Examples of the listing method are

$$A = \{1, 2, 3, 4, 5\}$$

(read: "*A* is the set of elements 1, 2, 3, 4, and 5"), and

$$B = \{a, b, c, d\}$$

(read: "*B* is the set of elements a, b, c, and d").

The sets specified by the capital letters A and B will be used in the following discussion. In general, capital letters are used to name sets, and lower-case letters to denote elements. However, this is not necessarily so, as will be seen in later discussion. The elements of a set are always enclosed in braces. The symbol $\in$ stands for "is an element of," "is a member of," or "belongs to."

Thus $1 \in A$, $2 \in A$, $3 \in A$, $4 \in A$, and $5 \in A$; and $a \in B$, $b \in B$, $c \in B$, and $d \in B$.

It is often convenient to state a rule for set membership. Sets A and B could also be specified:

$$A = \{x \mid 1 \leq x \leq 5, x \text{ is a natural number}\}$$

(read: "*A* is the set of all numbers *x* such that *x* is greater than or equal to one and less than or equal to five, where *x* is a natural number.")

$B = \{x \mid x \text{ is one of the first four letters of the English alphabet}\}$.

A useful notation is the *partial listing* of the elements of a set. Thus the set $\{1, 2, 3, \ldots\}$ specifies the set of *all* natural numbers. The ellipsis, $\ldots$, implies the sequence continues in the manner indicated.

Example.   Use the listing method to specify the set of positive odd integers less than nine.
Solution. $\{1, 3, 5, 7\}$.

Example.   Use the rule method to specify the set of all positive odd integers.
Solution. $\{x \mid x = 2n - 1, n \text{ is a positive integer}\}$.

Example.   Use the partial listing method to specify the set of positive odd numbers less than 99.
Solution. $\{1, 3, 5, 7, \ldots, 97\}$.
The set which contains no elements is called "empty," "null," or "void" and is written either $\varnothing$ or $\{\ \}$. Thus the set

$$\{x \mid x = x + 1, x \text{ is a real number}\}$$

is $\varnothing$.

An important relation defined on sets is the *subset* relation. Consider the sets $S = \{1, 2, 3, 4, 5\}$, $T = \{1, 3, 5\}$, $U = \{2, 4\}$, and $V = \{3\}$. Since sets T, U, and V only have elements which are in S, they are subsets of S.

> **Definition.**   If S and T are sets, then T is a subset of S ($T \subseteq S$) if and only if for every $x \in T$, it is also true that $x \in S$.

The symbol $\subseteq$ denotes "is a subset of." The empty set, $\varnothing$, is a subset of every set. In the examples, T, U, and V are not the only subsets of S. Other subsets are $\{1, 2, 3\}$, $\{2\}$, $\{2, 3, 4\}$, and so forth.

The *equality* of two sets is defined as follows.

> **Definition.**   If S and T are sets, $S = T$ if and only if $S \subseteq T$ and $T \subseteq S$.

Thus, if $S = \{1, 2, 3\}$ and $T = \{2, 1, 3\}$, then $S \subseteq T$, $T \subseteq S$, and $S = T$. An important consequence of this definition is that the *order* of listing elements in a set is immaterial.

Two important set operations are union, $\cup$, and intersection, $\cap$.

> **Definition.**   If S and T are sets, then $S \cup T$ is the set of all elements in S or T.

Example. Let $S = \{a, b, c, d\}$ and $T = \{a, c, f\}$. Find $S \cup T$.
Solution. $S \cup T = \{a, b, c, d, f\}$.

Definition.   If S and T are sets, then $S \cap T$ is the set of all elements which are in both S and T.

Example. Let $S = \{a, b, c, d\}$ and $T = \{a, c, f\}$. Find $S \cap T$.
Solution. $S \cap T = \{a, c\}$.

1-1   Exercises

(1-8)   Use the listing method to specify each of the following sets.

1. $\{x | x = 2n + 1, n$ is a natural number$\}$
2. $\{x | -3 < x \le 2, x$ is an integer$\}$
3. $\{y | \,|y| \le 6, y$ is an integer$\}$
4. $\{p | p$ is a factor of 24, p is a prime number$\}$
5. $\{t | \,|t - 3| < 5, t$ is an integer$\}$
6. $\{x | \,|x + 2| > 4, x$ is an integer$\}$
7. $\{x | \,|x + 2| > 4, x$ is a natural number$\}$
8. $\left\{x \middle| x = \dfrac{1}{n}, n \text{ is a natural number}\right\}$

(9-16)   Use the rule method to specify each of the following sets.

9. $\{2, 4, 6, 8, 10\}$
10. $\{1, 3, 5, 7, \ldots\}$
11. $\{-4, -3, -2, -1, 0, 1, 2, 3, 4\}$
12. $\{1, 4, 9, 16, 25\}$
13. $\{4, 7, 10, 13, \ldots\}$
14. $\{1, 8, 27, 64, \ldots\}$
15. $\{\frac{2}{3}, \frac{1}{2}, \frac{2}{5}, \frac{1}{3}, \frac{2}{7}, \frac{1}{4}, \ldots\}$
16. $\{\ldots, -3, -2, -1, 0, 1, \ldots, 15\}$

(17-24)   Let $S = \{1, 2, 3, 4, 5\}$, $T = \{n | \,|n| < 3, n$ is an integer$\}$, $U = \{2, 4, 6\}$. List each of the following sets.

17. $S \cup T$
18. $S \cap T$
19. $S \cup U$
20. $T \cap U$

21. $S \cup (T \cap U)$

22. $S \cap (T \cup U)$

23. $(S \cup T) \cap (S \cup U)$

24. $(S \cap T) \cup (S \cap U)$

25. Let N be the set of natural numbers. Use the listing method and the rule method to specify five different subsets of N. For example,

$$E = \{2, 4, 6, 8, \ldots\} = \{x | x = 2n, n \in N\}; E \subseteq N.$$

1-2 FUNCTIONS

It is reasonable to assume that any model attempting to describe the profit made from the sales of an item should reflect in some manner the relationship between profit and the number of items produced. Suppose, on one hand, the more items produced, the cheaper it is to make each individual item and, on the other hand, the more of the item on the market, the lower the price consumers are willing to pay. In mathematical terms one would say that profit is a *function* of the number of items produced. In a similar way, a mathematical model attempting to describe voter willingness to pass a school bond may be found to depend on the current tax rate. Again in mathematical terms, the size of the favorable vote may be viewed as a function of the tax rate. The idea of two or more variables being dependent on each other is fundamental to any application of mathematical concepts to real life. Using sets one can formalize the idea of dependent variables and give an exact mathematical meaning to a function and functional relationships.

Although the concept of a *function* is fundamental to the study of calculus, there are several different ways in which the term *function* may be defined. The student has undoubtedly been exposed to some of these definitions.

Let us first consider two nonempty sets, S and T, and define the operation $\times$, called the "cross" or "Cartesian product," on these sets.

Definition. $S \times T = \{(x,y) | x \in S$ and $y \in T\}$. Each element of the set $S \times T$ consists of an *ordered pair*, that is, of two components contained in parentheses and separated by a comma, whose order is determined by the definition. For example, if

$$S = \{1, 2, 3\} \text{ and } T = \{a, b\}, \text{ then}$$

$$S \times T = \{(1, a), (1, b), (2, a), (2, b), (3, a), (3, b)\},$$

and $T \times S = \{(a, 1), (b, 1), (a, 2), (b, 2), (a, 3), (b, 3)\}$.

We observe that $S \times T$ is not the same set as $T \times S$, and the operation is not commutative.

Any set of ordered pairs is called a *relation*. The set of all x's such that (x,y) belongs to the relation is called the *domain* of the relation, and the set of all y's such that (x,y) belongs to the relation is called the *range*. In the language of sets, these definitions are stated as follows.

Definition.   Let R be a relation. Then $\{x|(x,y) \in R\}$ is the *domain* of the relation R, and $\{y|(x,y) \in R\}$ is the *range* of the relation R.

In the above example of the relation $S \times T$, S is the domain and T is the range. However, for the relation $T \times S$, the domain is T and the range is S. We are now ready to define a function.

Definition.   A *function* is a set of ordered pairs, (x,y), such that for every value of x in the domain there corresponds a unique value y in the range.

The single letters f, g, h, F, and G are often used to denote functions. Thus, $f = \{(1, 2), (3, 4), (2, 2)\}$ defines a function whose domain is $\{1, 2, 3\}$ and whose range is $\{2, 4\}$.

Example.   Which of the following relations are functions?
Solution. $R = \{(2, 4), (3, 6), (2, 5)\}$.
R is *not* a function, because two different elements in the range (4 and 5) correspond to the element 2 in the domain.

$$G = \{(1, 5), (2, 5), (3, 5)\}.$$

G is a function, because every element in the domain corresponds to one and only one element in the range.

Notation of the form $f(x)$, $g(x)$, or $h(x)$ is commonly used to denote the element in the range which corresponds to the element x in the domain of the function.

Example. $f(x)$ is used to denote the element in the range of the function f corresponding to x in the domain. $f(x)$ is read "f of x."

Example. $g(x)$ is the element in the range of the function g corresponding to x in the domain.

Example. $f(z)$ denotes the range element paired with the domain element z by the function f.

Definition.   Domain elements are called *arguments* of a function; range elements are called *images*.

Example. $f(x)$ denotes the image of the argument x under the function f.

Example. $f = \{(x, f(x))| f(x) = 2x + 1\}$, where the domain and range of f are all real numbers.

When a function is defined with an equation, the domain and range of the function should be specified separately. However, we shall agree that, unless specified otherwise, the domain of a function that is defined by an equation, such as $f(x) = 2x + 1$, shall be the set of all real numbers for which there is a meaningful application of the equation to produce a real number image. The range will consist of all such images.

Example. $g = \{(x,y)|y = \sin x\}$ defines a function. Since $\sin x$ is defined for any real number x, the domain of g is the set of real numbers. Since the corresponding images will all lie between -1 and $+1$, the range of this function is $\{y|-1 \leq y \leq 1, y \text{ is a real number}\}$.

Example.
$$f = \left\{(x,y)|y = \frac{1}{x-3}\right\}$$

The domain of f is $\{x|x \text{ is a real number and } x \neq 3\}$. 3 must be excluded, as replacement of x by 3 would result in division by zero. The range of f would be $\{y|y \text{ is a real number, and } y \neq 0\}$.

From this point on references to the fact that the numbers involved are real numbers will be dropped. It is understood that only real numbers are being considered.

Example.
$$g = \{(x,y)|y = \sqrt{x-4}\}$$

Here the domain of g is $\{x|x \geq 4\}$; this is required to produce real number images. The range of g, is $\{y|y \geq 0\}$.

A function is often called a *mapping* of the domain into the range, and is denoted by $f: x \rightarrow y$.

Example.   The function $f = \{(x,y)|y = 2x + 1\}$ can be denoted:

$$f: x \rightarrow 2x + 1.$$

This is read: "the image of the argument x defined by f is $2x + 1$."

In figure 1-1, the image of x under f is $f(x)$, the image of a is $f(a)$, and the image of $(x + h)$ is $f(x + h)$. Therefore, if $f: x \rightarrow 2x + 1$, then $f(x) = 2x + 1$, $f(a) = 2a + 1$, and $f(x + h) = 2(x + h) + 1$.

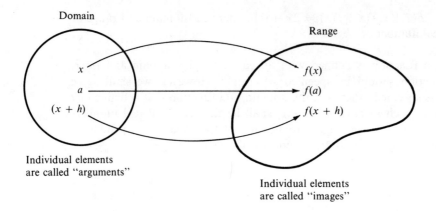

Domain

Range

x

$f(x)$

a

$f(a)$

$(x + h)$

$f(x + h)$

Individual elements
are called "arguments"

Individual elements
are called "images"

FIG. 1-1.   A Mapping f from the Domain
into the Range

Example.   Let x and y be real numbers. Define

$$f = \{(x,y) | y = 2x^2 + 3x + 1\}.$$

Since $y = f(x)$,

$$f(x) = 2x^2 + 3x + 1,$$

$$f(1) = 2(1)^2 + 3(1) + 1 = 6,$$

$$f(2) = 2(2)^2 + 3(2) + 1 = 15,$$

$$f(-2) = 2(-2)^2 + 3(-2) + 1 = 3,$$

$$f(x + 2) = 2(x + 2)^2 + 3(x + 2) + 1 = 2x^2 + 11x + 15, \text{ and}$$

$$f(x + h) = 2(x + h)^2 + 3(x + h) + 1 = 2x^2 + 4xh + 2h^2$$

$$+ 3x + 3h + 1.$$

Note that the value of y, or $f(x)$, depends on the value assigned to x. x is, therefore, called the *independent* variable, and y is the *dependent* variable.

A graph is a useful representation of relations.

The graph in figure 1-2 represents the function $y = x^2 + 2$, or $f(x) = x^2 + 2$. Since points on this graph are named as ordered pairs, (x,y), it is easily seen that for every x there exists a unique y, and the graph can be recognized as a function.

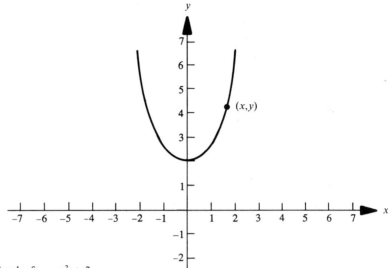

FIG. 1-2.   A Graph of $y = x^2 + 2$

Figure 1-3 is the graph of a relation which is *not* a function, since the points $(4, 2)$, $(4, -2)$, $(9, 3)$, and $(9, -3)$ belong to the relation. The relation

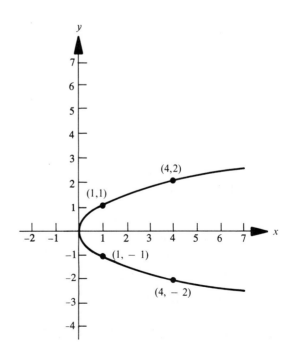

FIG. 1-3.   A Graph of $x = y^2$

$x = y^2$ may be defined as *two* functions: $y = \sqrt{x}$, the portion of the graph above the x axis, and $y = -\sqrt{x}$, the portion of the graph below the x axis. The point $(0,0)$ belongs to both functions. (See figure 1-4).

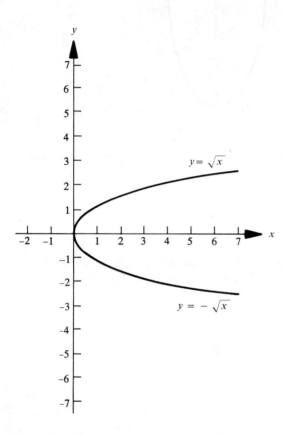

FIG. 1-4.   A Graph of $y = \pm\sqrt{x}$

1-2 Exercises

(1-10) Determine which of the following sets are functions. If the set is a function, determine its domain and range. If the set is not a function, justify your decision.

   1. $f = \{(1, 2), (3, 4), (5, 6), (7, 8)\}$
   2. $g = \{(2, 2), (3, 3), (4, 4), (-1, -1)\}$
   3. $h = \{(x,y)\,|\,y = 2x + 1\}$.
   4. $k = \{(1, 2), (1, 3), (1, 4), (1, 5)\}$

5. $F = \{(2, 1), (3, 1), (4, 1), (5, 1)\}$
6. $f = \{(x, f(x)) | f(x) = 2x^2 - 4x + 1\}$
7. $g = \{(x, y) | y = \sqrt{x^2 - 3}\}$
8. $G = \{(x, y) | y = \sin x\}$
9. $H = \{(x, y) | y = \tan^2 x\}$
10. $g = \{(x, y) | y = \pm\sqrt{16 - x^2}\}$

(11-17)   If $f(x) = 3x^2 - 2x + 1$, find:

11. $f(0)$
12. $f(2)$
13. $f(-1)$
14. $f(-3)$
15. $f(a)$
16. $f(x + h)$
17. $f(x + h) - f(x)$

(18-23)   If $f(x) = \frac{1}{3}x^3 - 2x + 4$, find:

18. $f(-3)$
19. $f(0)$
20. $f(1)$
21. $f(x + 1)$
22. $f(x + h)$
23. $\dfrac{f(x + h) - f(x)}{h}$

(24-31)   Graph each of the following relations and state whether they are functions.

24. $\{(x, y) | y = 2x + 1\}$
25. $\left\{(x, y) | y = \sin x, \ -\dfrac{\pi}{2} \le x \le \dfrac{\pi}{2}\right\}$
26. $\{(x, y) | y = |x + 1|\}$
27. $\left\{(x, y) | y = \dfrac{1}{x^2}\right\}$
28. $\{(x, y) | x^2 + y^2 = 1\}$
29. $\{(x, y) | y = \sqrt{x^2 + 4}\}$

30. $f(x) = \begin{cases} 1 \text{ when } x > 0 \\ 0 \text{ when } x = 0 \\ -1 \text{ when } x < 0 \end{cases}$

31. $f(x) = \dfrac{x^2 - 4}{x + 2}$ when $x \neq -2$, and $f(-2) = -4$.

32. Let $f(x) = \dfrac{x^2 - 9}{x + 3}$, and $g(x) = x - 3$. Compare the domain of $f(x)$ with the domain of $g(x)$.

33. If the Jingle Telephone Company charges 55¢ per three minutes for a coast-to-coast call, express the charge rate as a function of time.

34. A box manufacturing company wishes to design a lidless box of maximum volume from a 5 by 7 inch rectangular piece of cardboard by cutting equal-sized squares from each corner and folding the edges up. Express the volume of the box as a function of its depth.

35. A certain item manufactured by the Little Profit Manufacturing Company yields a profit expressed by the function

$$f(x) = -500 + 0.35x,$$

where x is the number of items manufactured. Determine the profit when $x = 1000, 10,000,$ or $100,000$. For what value of x is $f(x) = 0$? How would you interpret the statement $f(x) = 0$ in terms of profit and the number of items manufactured?

(36-39) The revenue produced from the sale of an item is a function of the number of items produced. In each case you are given an expression relating revenue, R, to the number of items produced, x. In each problem define the domain of the function based on the equation given and its real world domain, and sketch the function.

36. The revenue $R(x)$, in thousands of dollars from sales of a talking doll is given by $R(x) = 2.1x^2 - 2\sqrt{x^4 + 3}$, where x is in hundreds of dolls.

37. The revenue from vodka sales in Moscow in thousands of rubles is given by $R(x) = \frac{1}{3}x^2 - 2x + 4$, where x is in kiloliters.

38. The revenue of a store in London in pounds sterling from the sale of tobacco in 10-pound tins is given by $R(x) = 4(x + \sin x)$.

39. The revenue in dollars from the sales of Volkswagens in New York is given by $R(x) = 895x + 895\sqrt{x^2 - 400}$ where $x \geq 20$.

(40-44) In each problem the sketch of a possible function is given. Based on the information given by the sketch determine if there was a functional relation.

40.

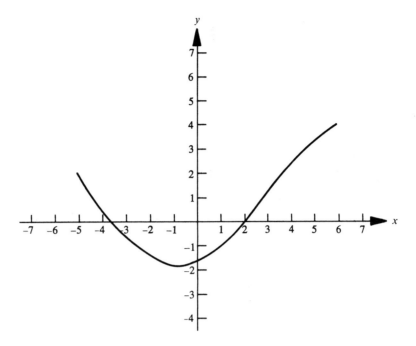

41.

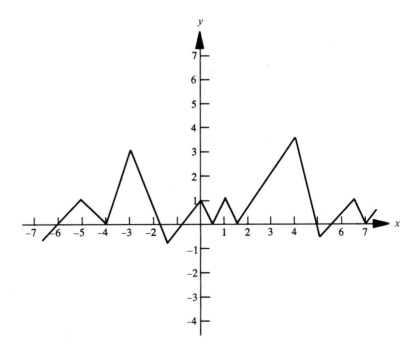

42.

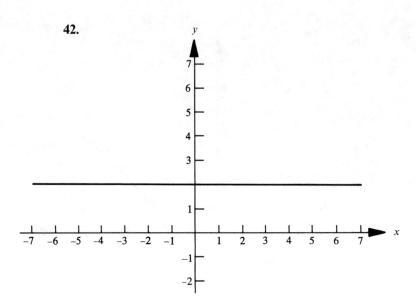

43.

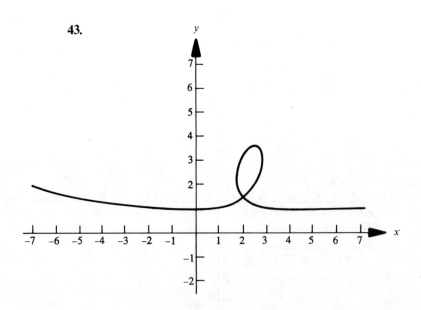

44.

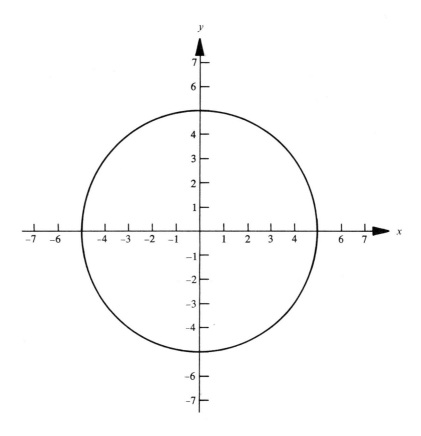

1-3 MORE ABOUT FUNCTIONS

It is reasonable to study complex functional relationships, such as one might find in constructing a mathematical model of profit or sales, by breaking them down into their simpler components. To see how this approach would work, it will be necessary to examine how complex functions can be built up from basic functions.

There are five operations defined on functions. They can be used to build up simple functions into more complex functions. Four of these operations are analogous to addition, subtraction, multiplication, and division as defined on numbers. The fifth operation, the *composition* of two functions, is somewhat unique and does not correspond to an operation on real numbers.

Definition.   Let f and g be functions. Then

$$(f + g)(x) = f(x) + g(x) \qquad\qquad sum$$

$$(f - g)(x) = f(x) - g(x) \qquad\qquad difference$$

$$(f \cdot g)(x) = f(x) \cdot g(x) \qquad\qquad product$$

$$\left(\frac{f}{g}\right)(x) = \frac{f(x)}{g(x)}, \text{ provided } g(x) \neq 0 \qquad\qquad quotient$$

The domain of each of these functions is the intersection of the domain of f and the domain of g. The domain of the quotient function excludes the values which result in a zero denominator.

Example.   Let $f(x) = \dfrac{1}{2x + 1}$ and $g(x) = \sqrt{1 - x}$. Find $f + g, f - g, f \cdot g,$

and $\dfrac{f}{g}$, and examine the domains.

Solution.

$$(f + g)(x) = \frac{1}{2x + 1} + \sqrt{1 - x},$$

$$(f - g)(x) = \frac{1}{2x + 1} - \sqrt{1 - x},$$

$$(f \cdot g)(x) = \frac{\sqrt{1 - x}}{2x + 1}, \text{ and}$$

$$\left(\frac{f}{g}\right)(x) = \frac{1}{(2x + 1)\sqrt{1 - x}}.$$

The domain of f, $D_f = \{x | x \neq -\frac{1}{2}\}$. The domain of g, $D_g = \{x | x \leq 1\}$. $D_f \cap D_g = \{x | x \leq 1, \ x \neq -\frac{1}{2}\}$. The domain of $\left(\dfrac{f}{g}\right)(x) = \{x | x < 1, \ x \neq -\frac{1}{2}\}$.

Definition.   Let f and g be functions. Then the *composite function, $f \circ g$*
(read, "f circle g"), is defined

$$(f \circ g)(x) = f(g(x)).$$

The domain of $f \circ g$ consists of all values of x in the domain of g for which $g(x)$ is in the domain of f.

In the terminology of mapping, $g(x)$ is the image of x under g, and $f(g(x))$

is the image of $g(x)$ under f. (See figure 1-5.) Let f and g be defined as in the preceding example.

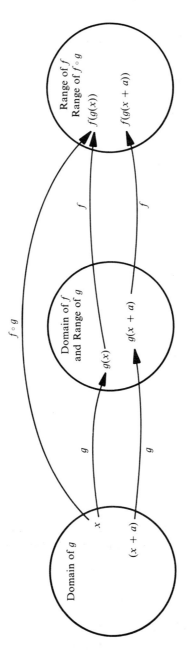

FIG. 1-5.   The Composite Function

$$f(x) = \frac{1}{2x + 1}, \quad g(x) = \sqrt{1 - x}.$$

Then, $$f(g(x)) = \frac{1}{2\sqrt{1 - x} + 1}.$$

The domain of $f \circ g$ is $\{x | x \le 1, x \text{ is a real number}\}$. Turning again to the mapping notation, we write

$$g : x \to \sqrt{1 - x} = g(x), \text{ and}$$

$$f : g(x) \to \frac{1}{2g(x) + 1} = \frac{1}{2\sqrt{1 - x} + 1} = f(g(x)).$$

Example. Let $f(x) = 2x^2 + 3x + 1$ and $g(x) = x + 2$. Evaluate $f(g(2))$, $g(f(2)), f(g(-2))$, and $g(f(-2))$.
Solution.

1. $g(2) = 4$;

   $f(g(2)) = f(4) = 2(4)^2 + 3(4) + 1 = 45$.

2. $f(2) = 2(2)^2 + 3(2) + 1 = 15$;

   $g(f(2)) = g(15) = 15 + 2 = 17$.

3. $g(-2) = -2 + 2 = 0$;

   $f(g(-2)) = f(0) = 1$.

4. $f(-2) = 2(-2)^2 + 3(-2) + 1 = 3$.

   $g(f(-2)) = g(3) = 3 + 2 = 5$.

1-3 Exercises

(1-5) Find the sum, difference, product, and quotient of the functions, f and g, and state the domains of the resultant functions.

1. $f(x) = x^2 + 3x, \quad g(x) = 2x + 1$

2. $f(x) = \dfrac{1}{1 - x}, \quad g(x) = \sqrt{x}$

3. $f(x) = \sqrt{x^2 - 1}, \quad g(x) = x + 2$

4. $f(x) = \sin x, \quad g(x) = 1 + \sqrt{x}$

5. $f(x) = 1 - \sqrt{x}, \quad g(x) = \cos x$

(6-10)   Find $f \circ g$ for each of the functions as defined in exercises (1-5), and state the domain of $f \circ g$ for each exercise.

(11-15)   Find $g \circ f$ for each of the functions as defined in exercises (1-5), and state the domain of $g \circ f$ for each exercise. Compare the answers with those of exercises (6-10). Is the composition operation commutative?

(16-22)   Let $f(x) = 1 - \sqrt{x}$, and $g(x) = \dfrac{1}{x}$. Evaluate each of the following.

16. $f(g(4))$

17. $g(f(4))$

18. $f(g(1))$

19. $g(f(1))$

20. $f(g(x + h)), h > 0$

21. $g(f(x + h)), h > 0$

22. $g(f(0))$

23. If $g(x) = \cos x$, find a function f such that $f(g(x)) = \csc x$.

24. If $f(x) = \dfrac{1}{1 + x^2}$, and $f(g(x)) = \cos^2 x$, find a function g which satisfies this composition.

25. The function $f(x) = [x]$ is called the *greatest integer function*, and the $[\ ]$ means that $f(x)$ is the greatest integer less than or equal to x. Thus $f(1) = 1, f(\frac{1}{2}) = 0, f(-\frac{1}{2}) = -1$, and $f(2.999) = 2$. Graph this function for $-2 \le x \le 5$.

26. If $f(x) = [x]$, and $g(x) = [x + 1]$, find the value of
 (a) $(f + g)(2.3)$
 (b) $(f - g)(2.3)$
 (c) $(f \cdot g)(2.3)$
 (d) $\left(\dfrac{f}{g}\right)(2.3)$
 (e) $f(g(2.3))$

27. The greatest integer function can be used to solve this problem: A taxi charges 25 cents for the first mile of fare, and 10 cents for each subsequent half mile or part thereof. Graph this function for a journey of five miles, and from your graph evaluate the fare for the first 4.3 miles of travel.

1-4 INCREMENTS AND RATE OF CHANGE

If an auto maker increases his production by 1,000 cars a month he expects to produce a corresponding change in his costs, revenue, and, hopefully, his profits. He is especially interested in the relative change in these quantities. That is, he will want to know how much his profits increase (or decrease) with each additional unit he produces. Along a similar line, a doctor might be interested in a patient's blood pressure drop in response to a given dose of a new drug. In a classic problem of this type, auto experts want to know the increase in stopping distance for a given increase in speed. To a student of calculus, all of these problems are part of the more general study of rates of change of a function, the change of a function's image per unit change in the function's argument, and the related concept of a limit. These are the mathematical ideas which will be examined in this section and the next.

The concept of change in a function image $f(x)$ with a change in x is basic to calculus. In fact it is one of the primary differences between calculus and other types of mathematics. This means, for example, we will consider not only the cost of production as a function of the number of units produced but also how the cost per unit changes as the number of units produced changes.

Suppose that $x_1 = 4$ and $x_2 = 5.7$. Then the change in x is 1.7. The Greek letter Δ (delta) is used to denote change in a variable. In this case, "the change in x is 1.7" is abbreviated to $\Delta x = 1.7$.

Definition.   The change in x from x_1 to x_2 will be called the *increment* of x and be denoted by Δx, where

$$\Delta x = x_2 - x_1.$$

Example.   If x changes from 7 to 9, then $\Delta x = 2$. If y changes from 1 to -2, then $\Delta y = -2 - 1 = -3$. The increment of $f(x)$, as $f(x)$ changes from 1.11 to 1.13, is $\Delta f(x) = .02$. If $x_2 = x + h$ and $x_1 = x$, then

$$\Delta x = x_2 - x_1 = x + h - x = h.$$

If $y = f(x)$, and an increment, Δx, is added to x, then y is changed by a corresponding increment Δy. Let $y_1 = f(x_1)$ and $y_2 = f(x_2)$. Then $\Delta y = y_2 - y_1 = f(x_2) - f(x_1)$. Solving $\Delta x = x_2 - x_1$ for x_2 gives $x_2 = x_1 + \Delta x$. Substituting $x_1 + \Delta x$ for x_2 gives $\Delta y = f(x_1 + \Delta x) - f(x_1)$. Since x_1 can be any element in the domain of f, the subscript becomes superfluous and the formula for the increment of y can be written:

$$\Delta y = f(x + \Delta x) - f(x).$$

Example.   If $f(x) = x^2 + 3$ find Δy when $x = 2$ and $\Delta x = 0.5$.
Solution.   Substituting the values specified for x and Δx in $\Delta y = f(x + \Delta x) - f(x)$ gives

$$\Delta y = f(2 + 0.5) - f(2)$$

$$= f(2.5) - f(2).$$

Substituting in $f(x)$,

$$\Delta y = [(2.5)^2 + 3] - (2^2 + 3)$$

$$= 6.25 + 3 - 4 - 3$$

$$= 2.25.$$

In this example, a 0.5 change in x resulted in a 2.25 change in y.

Example.   A painted sphere has a radius of exactly 6 inches. The old paint on the sphere is then ground off and it is repainted, with a net loss in radius of 0.1 of an inch. How much was the volume changed?
Solution.   The volume of a sphere is $V = \frac{4}{3}\pi r^3$. Let $r = 6$ and $\Delta r = -0.1$. Δr is negative because the radius was reduced. To find ΔV, evaluate the volume for $r + \Delta r$ and for r and find the difference between the volumes:

$$r + \Delta r = 6 - 0.1 = 5.9$$

$$\Delta V = \frac{4}{3}\pi(5.9)^3 - \frac{4}{3}\pi 6^3 = \frac{4}{3}(205.379 - 216)\pi$$

$$= -\frac{4}{3}(10.621)\pi$$

$$= \text{(approx.)} -45 \text{ cubic inches.}$$

Change stated in absolute terms as in the two examples discussed above or in more familiar phrases such as "I lost 20 pounds" or "My income has increased \$48" may not be as informative as relative change; relative change is stated in terms such as "I lost 20 pounds over the last six months" or "My income has increased \$48 per week." From the statement "I lost 20 pounds in the last six months" it is possible to compute the average change in weight per month. It is the change in weight divided by the number of months (change in time) or $\frac{20}{6} = 3\frac{1}{3}$ pounds per month. In an example, it was shown that $\Delta y = 2.25$ when $\Delta x = 0.5$. In this case, the average change in y as x changes from 2 to 2.5 is $\dfrac{\Delta y}{\Delta x} = \dfrac{2.25}{0.5} = 4.5$. This means that, for the indicated interval of x, the average rate of change of y is 4.5 units for each one unit change in x. For the painted sphere a change of -0.1 inches in the radius produced a -45 cubic inch change in the volume. The average rate of change of volume, as the radius goes from 6 to 5.9 is

$\dfrac{\Delta V}{\Delta r} = \dfrac{-45}{-0.1} = 450$ cubic inches/inch. Thus, the volume is changing at the average rate of 450 cubic inches per one inch change in radius.

Definition. The average rate of change of a function f over an interval of its domain, x to $x + \Delta x$, is:

$$\frac{\Delta y}{\Delta x} = \frac{f(x + \Delta x) - f(x)}{\Delta x}.$$

Example. Find the average rate of change of $f(x) = x^3$ as x changes from 4 to 6.

Solution.

$$\frac{\Delta y}{\Delta x} = \frac{f(6) - f(4)}{2} = \frac{6^3 - 4^3}{2} = \frac{216 - 64}{2} = \frac{152}{2} = 76.$$

Example. The distance, S, in feet, a body will fall (from rest) in a vacuum after t seconds is given by $S = 16t^2$. Find the average speed of such a falling body between times $t = 5$ and $t = 5\frac{1}{2}$ seconds.

Solution. The average speed is the change in distance with respect to change in time, $\dfrac{\Delta S}{\Delta t}$.

$$\frac{\Delta S}{\Delta t} = \frac{16(5\frac{1}{2})^2 - 16(5)^2}{\frac{1}{2}} = \frac{484 - 400}{\frac{1}{2}} = \frac{84}{\frac{1}{2}} = 168 \text{ ft/sec.}$$

Thus for the interval of time from 5 to $5\frac{1}{2}$ seconds the body has an average speed of 168 feet per second.

1-4 Exercises

(1-10) Find the increment of the function for the given interval of its domain.

1. $y = 2x + 5$, $x = 3$, $\Delta x = 0.1$
2. $y = x^2$, $x = 2$ to $x = 2.01$
3. $y = x - 5x^2$, $x = -3$ to $x = -2.5$
4. $g(t) = 1 - 3t^2$, $t = 0$, $\Delta t = 0.4$
5. $f(x) = x^2$, $x = a$, $\Delta x = h$
6. $h(x) = x^2 + 3x + 5$, x to $x + \Delta x$
7. $f(x) = 3x^2 + 2x$, x to $x + \Delta x$

8. $y = 2x - 3x^2$, x to $x + \Delta x$

9. $y = x^3$, x to $x + h$

10. $f(x) = x^3 + 3x^2$, a to $a + h$

(11-17)   Find the average rate of change of the function for the indicated interval of its domain.

11. $y = 2x + 5$, $x = 3$, $\Delta x = 0.1$

12. $f(x) = 4x^2$, $x = -2$, $\Delta x = \frac{1}{2}$

13. $f(x) = \sqrt{x}$, $x = 4$, $\Delta x = 0.25$

14. $y = x^2 + 5x + 6$, x to $x + \Delta x$

15. $y = ax^2 + bx + c$, x to $x + h$

16. $y = \dfrac{4}{x}$, $x = 2$ to $x = 2 + \Delta x$

17. $y = 2x^3$, a to $a + h$

(18-21)   The distance, S, a body initially at rest falls in a vacuum in t seconds is given by $S = 16t^2$. Find the average speed of the body for the given interval of time.

18. $t = 0$ to $t = 1$

19. $t = 3$ to $t = 6$

20. $t = 10$ to $t = 11$

21. $t = 3$ to $t = 3.001$

22. The cost, C, to produce x units is given by $C = 100x + \dfrac{1}{x}$. What is the average cost per unit (also known as the average marginal cost) for the units from $x = 16$ to $x = 20$?

23. A growing culture of bacteria weighs $10e^{t/3}$ grams at time t. Find the average rate of growth during the hours $t = 3$ to $t = 6$. Where $e = 2.7$ (approximately).

24. The price elasticity of demand for an item is defined to be

$$PE = -\frac{\text{percentage change in the quantity of the item demanded}}{\text{percentage change in the price of the item}}.$$

Discuss how this relates to increments and rates of change.

25. Using the expression given in problem 24, calculate the price elasticity if the sales of an item change from 10 to 15 units and the price goes from \$22,500 to \$21,800 per item.

26. The average cost of the production of an item is defined to be the total cost divided by the total number of items produced. Discuss how the average cost of production relates to the idea of increments and rates of change.

27. The total cost for producing 20 TV sets is \$900. What is the average cost (defined in problem 26) of production?

28. Referring to problems 26 and 27, the marginal cost is defined to be the additional cost attributable to the addition of one unit produced. That is, the marginal cost for $x = 16$ is the cost of the 16th item. If the total cost of producing 15 of the TV sets described in problem 27 was \$349.50, what was the marginal cost of the 16th set? Discuss the assumptions which had to be made in order to apply the definition of marginal cost.

29. Describe marginal cost in terms of rates of change as considered in this section.

1-5 LIMITS

To refine the idea of an average change it will be necessary to introduce the concept of a limit. This basic idea can be shown by a simple example: Suppose that you are sitting on one end of a bench and the object of your affections is sitting on the other end. Further suppose that your strategy is to halve the distance between you, then halve it again, and so on, over and over. A mathematician would say that the object of your affections is the limit of your moves, no matter how many you make. He would also realize that you would never reach her, which is an important part of the concept of "a limit."

The average rate of change of $f(x)$ for the interval a to $a + \Delta x$ is $\dfrac{f(a + \Delta x) - f(a)}{\Delta x}$. As Δx is successively assigned smaller and smaller values, the average rate of change of the function approaches the "instantaneous rate of change" of the function at a. In order to create simple techniques for computing such instantaneous rates of change we introduce *limits*.

The phrase, "The limit, as x approaches a, of $f(x)$ is L," will be abbreviated to $\lim\limits_{x \to a} f(x) = L$. Intuitively, this means that as x gets closer and closer to a, $f(x)$ approaches L. Thus $\lim_{x \to 6} (2x - 3) = 9$ says that as x approaches 6, $2x - 3$ approaches 9. Intuitively this seems correct, since $2(6) - 3 = 9$.

Statements such as "closer and closer" and "approaches" are too imprecise to be used to prove that certain values are limits of functions or to prove theorems about limits. However the idea of "closer and closer" can be denoted mathematically by examination of the absolute values of differences. If two numbers are close to the same value, their difference will be small. Thus, "x approaches a" will mean that $|x - a|$ is less than some small positive number δ. Absolute values are used around $|x - a|$, because the algebraic sign of the difference is not important. In the same manner the phrase "$f(x)$ approaches L" will mean that $|f(x) - L| < \epsilon$ for any positive ϵ no matter how small. Therefore the following:

Definition. $\lim_{x \to a} f(x) = L$ if and only if for any positive number ϵ (no matter how small) there is a positive number δ (function of ϵ) such that
$$|f(x) - L| < \epsilon$$
whenever
$$0 < |x - a| < \delta.$$

This means that if the statement $\lim_{x \to a} f(x) = L$ is true, then there is a δ such that $f(x)$ can be made as close to L as we please (*i.e.*, within ϵ of L), by substituting any value of x within a distance δ of a into $f(x)$. Notice that the definition of limits and the intuitive discussion about limits say nothing about $f(x)$ at a. That is, the function may not be defined at a, and in fact many important ones are not, but these functions can still have a limit as x approaches a. The statement $0 < |x - a| < \delta$, in the definition, requires that f be defined for all x close to a, but it need not be defined at a.

Example. Use the definition of limit to prove that $\lim_{x \to 6} 2x - 3 = 9$.

Solution. From the definition, we must find δ, a function of ϵ, such that for any positive ϵ no matter how small:
$$|(2x - 3) - 9| < \epsilon \text{ whenever } |x - 6| < \delta.$$
To show this we will write $(2x - 3) - 9$ as a function of $|x - 6|$.
$$|(2x - 3) - 9| < \epsilon$$
implies
$$|2x - 12| < \epsilon,$$
which implies
$$|2(x - 6)| < \epsilon.$$
Thus,
$$|x - 6| < \frac{\epsilon}{2}.$$

Therefore, $|(2x - 3) - 9| < \epsilon$ whenever $|x - 6| < \dfrac{\epsilon}{2}$. So take $\delta \leq \dfrac{\epsilon}{2}$, and the proof is complete. It shows that $2x - 3$ will be within ϵ of 9 whenever x is within $\frac{1}{2} \epsilon$ of 6.

Using the definition of a limit, theorems can be proved that expedite work with limits. The theorems are stated below without proof. Their proofs can be found in most standard engineering calculus texts.

Provided the following limits exist, then:

Theorem 1-1. $\lim\limits_{x \to a} x = a$.

IN WORDS: "The limit of the function x is a as x tends toward a."

Example. $\lim\limits_{x \to 3} x = 3$.

Theorem 1-2. $\lim\limits_{x \to a} [f(x) \pm g(x)] = \lim\limits_{x \to a} f(x) \pm \lim\limits_{x \to a} g(x)$.

IN WORDS: "The limit of a sum or difference is the sum or difference of the limits."

Example. If $\lim\limits_{x \to 3} x^3 = 27$ and $\lim\limits_{x \to 3} \dfrac{1}{x} = \frac{1}{3}$, then $\lim\limits_{x \to 3} \left(x^3 + \dfrac{1}{x} \right) = \lim\limits_{x \to 3} x^3$ $+ \lim\limits_{x \to 3} \dfrac{1}{x} = 27 + \frac{1}{3} = \frac{81}{3} + \frac{1}{3} = \frac{82}{3}$.

Theorem 1-3. $\lim\limits_{x \to a} [f(x) \cdot g(x)] = \left[\lim\limits_{x \to a} f(x) \right] \left[\lim\limits_{x \to a} g(x) \right]$.

IN WORDS: "The limit of a product is the product of the limits."

Example. If $\lim\limits_{x \to 3} x^3 = 27$, and $\lim\limits_{x \to 3} \dfrac{1}{x} = \frac{1}{3}$, then find $\lim\limits_{x \to 3} x^3 \left(\dfrac{1}{x} \right)$

Solution. $\lim\limits_{x \to 3} x^3 \left(\dfrac{1}{x} \right) = \left[\lim\limits_{x \to 3} x^3 \right] \left[\lim\limits_{x \to 3} \dfrac{1}{x} \right] = 27(\frac{1}{3}) = 9$.

Theorem 1-4. $\lim\limits_{x \to a} [f(x)^n] = \left[\lim\limits_{x \to a} f(x) \right]^n$ where n is a rational number.

IN WORDS: "The limit of a function raised to a rational power is the power of the limit of the function."

Example. Find $\lim\limits_{x \to 3} x^{5/7}$.

Solution. $\lim\limits_{x \to 3} x^{5/7} = 3^{5/7}$.

Theorem 1-5. $\lim\limits_{x \to a} \dfrac{f(x)}{g(x)} = \dfrac{\lim\limits_{x \to a} f(x)}{\lim\limits_{x \to a} g(x)}$, provided $\lim\limits_{x \to a} g(x) \neq 0$.

IN WORDS: "The limit of a quotient is the quotient of the limits, provided the limit of the denominator is not zero."

Example.   Find $\lim\limits_{x \to \pi} \dfrac{\sin x}{\sqrt{x^2 + 2}}$.

Solution. $\lim\limits_{x \to \pi} \dfrac{\sin x}{\sqrt{x^2 + 2}} = \dfrac{\lim\limits_{x \to \pi} \sin x}{\lim\limits_{x \to \pi} \sqrt{x^2 + 2}}$.

Theorem 1-6. $\lim\limits_{x \to a} c = c$, for c constant.

IN WORDS: "The limit of a constant is the constant itself."

Example.   Find $\lim\limits_{x \to 3} 2$.

Solution. $\lim\limits_{x \to 3} 2 = 2$.

Example.   Use the above theorems to find $\lim\limits_{x \to 5} (x^2 - 3x + 4)$.

Solution. $\lim\limits_{x \to 5} x^2 - 3x + 4 = \lim\limits_{x \to 5} x^2 - \lim\limits_{x \to 5} 3x + \lim\limits_{x \to 5} 4$ by Theorem 1-2.

$\qquad\qquad \lim\limits_{x \to 5} x^2 = 5^2$ by Theorem 1-4.

$\qquad\qquad \lim\limits_{x \to 5} 3x = (\lim\limits_{x \to 5} 3)(\lim\limits_{x \to 5} x)$ by Theorem 1-3.

$\qquad\qquad\qquad = 3 \cdot \lim\limits_{x \to 5} x$ by Theorem 1-6

$\qquad\qquad\qquad = 3(5) = 15$ by Theorem 1-1.

$\qquad\qquad \lim\limits_{x \to 5} 4 = 4$ by Theorem 1-6.

$\therefore \lim\limits_{x \to 5} (x^2 - 3x + 4) = 25 - 15 + 4 = 14$.

In practice the theorems are applied mentally. We will write them in the next example to show two applications that the previous example does not contain.

Example.   Use limit theorems to find $\lim\limits_{x \to -3} \dfrac{\sqrt{x^2 + 16}}{9x}$.

Solution. $\lim\limits_{x \to -3} \dfrac{\sqrt{x^2 + 16}}{9x} = \dfrac{\lim\limits_{x \to -3} \sqrt{x^2 + 16}}{\lim\limits_{x \to -3} 9x}$ by Theorem 1-5

$$= \frac{\sqrt{\displaystyle\lim_{x \to -3} (x^2 + 16)}}{\displaystyle\lim_{x \to -3} 9x} \qquad \text{by Theorem 1-4}$$

$$= \frac{\sqrt{\displaystyle\lim_{x \to -3} x^2 + \lim_{x \to -3} 16}}{\displaystyle\lim_{x \to -3} 9 \cdot \lim_{x \to -3} x} \qquad \begin{array}{l}\text{by Theorem 1-2 and} \\ \text{Theorem 1-3}\end{array}$$

$$= \frac{\sqrt{9 + 16}}{9(-3)} \qquad \begin{array}{l}\text{by Theorems 1-4 and 1-6, and} \\ \text{by Theorems 1-6 and 1-1}\end{array}$$

$$= \frac{5}{-27}.$$

Example.   Find $\displaystyle\lim_{x \to 4} \frac{2x^2 - 7x - 4}{x - 4}$.

Solution.   Theorem 1-5 cannot be applied because the limit of the denominator is 0. From the definition of limits we are only concerned with values of x close to but *different* from 4. Therefore the numerator may be divided by $x - 4$ since it is a small but nonzero number.

$$\lim_{x \to 4} \frac{2x^2 - 7x - 4}{x - 4} = \lim_{x \to 4} \frac{(2x + 1)(x - 4)}{x - 4} = \lim_{x \to 4} 2x + 1 = 9.$$

Example.   Find $\displaystyle\lim_{x \to 1} \frac{x - 1}{\sqrt{x} - 1}$.

Solution.   Once more Theorem 1-5 cannot be applied since the denominator tends to 0. Nor can the numerator be easily factored and divided by the denominator as in the last example. For limits involving radicals, rationalize the denominator.

$$\lim_{x \to 1} \frac{x - 1}{\sqrt{x} - 1} = \lim_{x \to 1} \frac{(x - 1)}{(\sqrt{x} - 1)} \frac{(\sqrt{x} + 1)}{(\sqrt{x} + 1)}$$

$$= \lim_{x \to 1} \frac{(x - 1)(\sqrt{x} + 1)}{x - 1}$$

$$= \lim_{x \to 1} (\sqrt{x} + 1),$$

$$= 2.$$

Example.   For $f(x) = x^2$, find $\displaystyle\lim_{\Delta x \to 0} \frac{\Delta f}{\Delta x}$ for the interval x to $x + \Delta x$, where Δf is defined by:

$$\Delta f = f(x + \Delta x) - f(x).$$

Solution. $\lim\limits_{\Delta x \to 0} \dfrac{\Delta f}{\Delta x} = \lim\limits_{\Delta x \to 0} \dfrac{f(x + \Delta x) - f(x)}{\Delta x}.$

Substituting in $f(x)$ yields:

$$\lim\limits_{\Delta x \to 0} \frac{\Delta f}{\Delta x} = \lim\limits_{\Delta x \to 0} \frac{(x + \Delta x)^2 - x^2}{\Delta x}$$

$$= \lim\limits_{\Delta x \to 0} \frac{x^2 + 2x\,\Delta x + (\Delta x)^2 - x^2}{\Delta x}$$

$$= \lim\limits_{\Delta x \to 0} \frac{2x\,\Delta x + \Delta x^2}{\Delta x}$$

$$= \lim\limits_{\Delta x \to 0} (2x + \Delta x)$$

$$= 2x.$$

The definition of limits implies that if a limit exists it is unique. If, as x approaches a, $f(x)$ approaches two different values, the limit, $\lim\limits_{x \to a} f(x)$, does not exist.

Example. Find $\lim\limits_{x \to 0} \dfrac{|x|}{x}$.

Solution. The function is not defined for $x = 0$. For x negative $\dfrac{|x|}{x} = -1$;

for x positive $\dfrac{|x|}{x} = +1$. Therefore if x approaches 0 from the negative

side $\dfrac{|x|}{x} = -1$; if it approaches 0 from the positive side $\dfrac{|x|}{x} = +1$. Since

the $\lim\limits_{x \to 0} \dfrac{|x|}{x}$ does not approach a unique number, no limit exists.

The last example was used to emphasize the uniqueness of limits. A more complete discussion of the techniques used is presented in the section on one-sided limits.

1-5   Exercises

1. Calculate $f(x) = 2x - 5$ for $x = 2.7$, 2.8, 2.9, 3.2, and 3.1.

2. Calculate $f(x) = x^2 + 2x$ for $x = 1$, 0.5, 0.1, 0.01, 0.001, 0.00001, -1, -0.5, -0.1, -0.01, -0.001, and -0.00001.

3. What is the limit implied in exercise 1?

4. What is the limit implied in exercise 2?

5. $\lim\limits_{x \to 3} (x - 3)$

15. $\lim\limits_{x \to -8} \dfrac{x^2 + 9x + 8}{x + 8}$

6. $\lim\limits_{x \to 5} (x^2 + 2x)$

16. $\lim\limits_{x \to 1} \dfrac{x^3 - 1}{x - 1}$

7. $\lim\limits_{x \to -2} \dfrac{x^2 + 5x + 4}{x + 1}$

17. $\lim\limits_{x \to 2} \dfrac{x^3 - 8}{x - 2}$

8. $\lim\limits_{x \to -3} \dfrac{x^2 + 5x}{\sqrt{x^2 + 16}}$

18. $\lim\limits_{x \to 0} \dfrac{x^2 + 3x + 7}{x}$

9. $\lim\limits_{x \to 6} (3x^2 + 5x - 6)$

19. $\lim\limits_{x \to 0} \dfrac{x^3 - 5x^2 + 7x + 4}{x}$

10. $\lim\limits_{x \to -a} \dfrac{x^2 - a^2}{x - a}$

20. $\lim\limits_{x \to 4} \dfrac{x - 4}{\sqrt{x - 2}}$

11. $\lim\limits_{x \to 1} \dfrac{x^2 - 1}{x - 1}$

21. $\lim\limits_{x \to a} \dfrac{\sqrt{x} - a}{x - a^2}$

12. $\lim\limits_{x \to 5} \dfrac{x^2 - 25}{x - 5}$

22. $\lim\limits_{\Delta x \to 0} \dfrac{\sqrt{2 + \Delta x} - \sqrt{2}}{\Delta x}$

13. $\lim\limits_{x \to -1} \dfrac{x^2 + x}{x + 1}$

23. $\lim\limits_{\Delta x \to 0} \dfrac{\Delta x}{\sqrt{a + \Delta x} - \sqrt{a}}$

14. $\lim\limits_{x \to 2} \dfrac{x^2 + 3x - 10}{x - 2}$

(24-30) A function $f(x)$ and a value for a are given. Compute

$$\lim\limits_{\Delta x \to 0} \dfrac{f(a + \Delta x) - f(a)}{\Delta x} \text{ for each of the following.}$$

24. $f(x) = 2x^2$, $a = 1$

25. $f(x) = x^2 + 5x$, $a = 3$

26. $f(x) = 3x^2 - 2x$, $a = -2$

27. $f(x) = 3x^2 + 6x - 7$, $a = 0$

28. $f(x) = 3x^2 + 9x$, $a = x$

29. $f(x) = x^3, a = x$

30. $f(x) = x^3 + 3x^2, a = x$

1-6   LIMITS OF TRIGONOMETRIC FUNCTIONS

Since trigonometric functions are important to the solution of many problems, it is essential to consider the application of limits to them. If a trigonometric function $f(x)$ is defined at a, then

$$\lim_{x \to a} f(x) = f(a).$$

Examples. $\lim_{x \to \pi} \sin x = \sin \pi = 0.$

$$\lim_{x \to \pi/4} \tan x = \tan \frac{\pi}{4} = 1.$$

But what happens to the limits of trigonometric functions when the functions are not defined at a? Recall that $\tan x$ does not exist for $x = \dfrac{\pi}{2}$; neither does $\lim_{x \to \pi/2} \tan x$ exist. Figure 1-6 shows the graph of $f(x) = \tan x$.

Notice that, as values of x are taken closer and closer to $\dfrac{\pi}{2}$ but *less than* $\dfrac{\pi}{2}$, $f(x)$ takes on successively larger positive values. If values of x are taken close to, but greater than $\dfrac{\pi}{2}$, $f(x)$ is a negative number with large absolute value. All of this can be noted as follows. If a function takes on larger and larger positive values without bound, we will say it approaches positive infinity, denoted by $+\infty$ or just ∞. $+\infty$ and $-\infty$ are not real numbers but are used to indicate the unbounded feature of the function. If $f(x)$ takes on successive negative values that have larger and larger absolute value, then $f(x)$ will be said to approach negative infinity, $-\infty$. To denote x approaching but always less than a, we will use $\lim_{x \to a^-}$. This can be read: "the limit as x approaches a from the left." The analogous "right-hand" case, $\lim_{x \to a^+}$, will mean that x is approaching a but is always greater than a.

Examples. $\lim_{x \to \pi/2^-} \tan x = \infty.$

$$\lim_{x \to \pi/2^+} \tan x = -\infty.$$

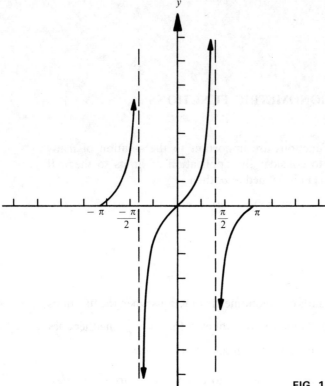

FIG. 1-6.   A Graph of $f(x) = \tan x$

$$\lim_{x \to 0^-} \csc x = -\infty.$$

$$\lim_{x \to 0^+} \frac{1}{x} = \infty. \qquad \text{(See figure 1-7.)}$$

$$\lim_{x \to 0^-} \frac{1}{x} = -\infty.$$

$$\lim_{x \to 1^+} \sqrt{1 - x} = \text{no limit}.$$

$$\lim_{x \to 1^-} \sqrt{1 - x} = 0.$$

In the last two examples above, $\lim \sqrt{1 - x}$ does not exist when $x \to 1^+$ because $1 - x$ is negative, when x is greater than 1. In this case, $\sqrt{1 - x}$ is imaginary. We say that the limit *does not exist* in the real numbers, because we wish to confine this text to functions of real variables, with real images.

It should be noted that the symbol ∞ in this text does not represent a real number, hence it cannot be manipulated algebraically, and technically, such expressions as $\lim\limits_{x \to a} f(x) = \pm\infty$ are not rigorously correct. They are, however, notationally convenient.

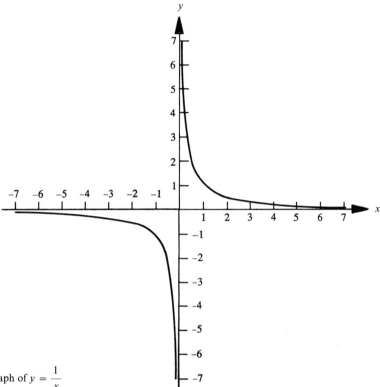

FIG. 1-7.   A Graph of $y = \dfrac{1}{x}$

The limit $\lim\limits_{\theta \to 0} \dfrac{\sin \theta}{\theta}$ will be important in the next chapter. To prove

that $\lim\limits_{\theta \to 0} \dfrac{\sin \theta}{\theta} = 1$, we will first show that $\lim\limits_{\theta \to 0^+} \dfrac{\sin \theta}{\theta} = 1$, and then that

$\lim\limits_{\theta \to 0^-} \dfrac{\sin \theta}{\theta} = 1$. Figure 1-8 is a circle with center at O and radius r. The

central angle θ is such that $0 < \theta < \dfrac{\pi}{2}$. Line segment $\overline{BC}$ is tangent to

the circle at B. $\overline{PA}$ is perpendicular to $\overline{OB}$.

The area of $\triangle OBC >$ the area of sector OPB which $>$ the area of

$\triangle OBP$. Since $\tan \theta = \dfrac{\overline{BC}}{\overline{OB}} = \dfrac{\overline{BC}}{r}$, the area of $\triangle OBC = \frac{1}{2}\overline{OB} \cdot \overline{BC} =$

$\frac{1}{2}r \cdot r \tan \theta = \frac{1}{2}r^2 \tan \theta.$

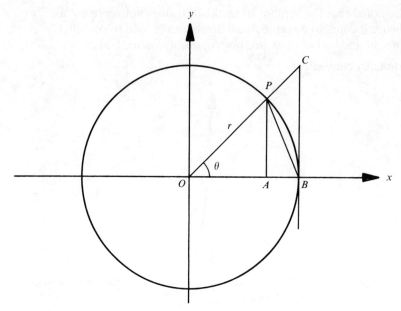

FIG. 1-8.

The area of sector $OPB = \dfrac{\theta}{2\pi} \cdot$ (area of circle) $= \dfrac{\theta}{2\pi} \cdot \pi r^2 = \dfrac{\theta r^2}{2}$.

The area of $\triangle OBP = \frac{1}{2}\overline{OB} \cdot \overline{PA} = \frac{1}{2} r \cdot r \sin \theta = \frac{1}{2} r^2 \sin \theta$. Therefore,

$$\tfrac{1}{2} r^2 \tan \theta > \frac{\theta r^2}{2} > \tfrac{1}{2} r^2 \sin \theta.$$

Multiplying all three terms by $\dfrac{2}{r^2}$ gives

$$\tan \theta > \theta > \sin \theta.$$

Since $\tan \theta = \dfrac{\sin \theta}{\cos \theta}$,

$$\frac{\sin \theta}{\cos \theta} > \theta > \sin \theta.$$

Multiplying by $\dfrac{1}{\sin \theta}$ yields

$$\frac{1}{\cos \theta} > \frac{\theta}{\sin \theta} > 1.$$

From algebra we know that if a and b are positive numbers and $a > b$,

then $\dfrac{1}{a} < \dfrac{1}{b}$. Since $\dfrac{1}{\cos \theta}$, $\dfrac{\theta}{\sin \theta}$, and 1 are positive numbers for

$0 < \theta < \dfrac{\pi}{2}$, taking their reciprocals results in

$$\cos\theta < \frac{\sin\theta}{\theta} < 1.$$

The $\lim\limits_{\theta\to 0^+} \sin\theta/\theta$ is between $\lim\limits_{\theta\to 0^+} \cos\theta$ and $\lim\limits_{x\to 0^+} 1$. However both the latter limits are 1. So:

$$\lim_{\theta\to 0^+} \frac{\sin\theta}{\theta} = 1.$$

By taking θ as a negative angle between 0 and $-\dfrac{\pi}{2}$, the same method as above can be used to show

$$\lim_{\theta\to 0^-} \frac{\sin\theta}{\theta} = 1.$$

Since the right- and left-hand limits are equal,

$$\lim_{\theta\to 0} \frac{\sin\theta}{\theta} = 1.$$

The name of the variable does not affect the limit so $\lim\limits_{x\to 0} \dfrac{\sin x}{x} = 1$, and $\lim\limits_{y\to 0} \dfrac{\sin 3y}{3y} = 1$. The $\lim\limits_{y\to 0} \dfrac{\sin 3y}{3y} = 1$, because as y approaches 0 so does $3y$.

The following identities are the most common ones from trigonometry, and they will be useful in doing the exercises in this section. Some have been used in the following examples.

$$\sin x = \frac{1}{\csc x}, \qquad\qquad \csc x = \frac{1}{\sin x},$$

$$\cos x = \frac{1}{\sec x}, \qquad\qquad \sec x = \frac{1}{\cos x},$$

$$\tan x = \frac{\sin x}{\cos x}, \qquad\qquad \cot x = \frac{\cos x}{\sin x},$$

$$\sin^2 x + \cos^2 x = 1, \qquad\qquad \tan^2 x + 1 = \sec^2 x,$$

$$1 + \cot^2 x = \csc^2 x.$$

Using the product theorem (Theorem 1-3) from the last section it can be shown that $\lim\limits_{x\to a} kf(x) = k \lim\limits_{x\to a} f(x)$ for k constant. This can be used to solve the following limits.

Example. Find $\lim\limits_{x \to 0} \dfrac{\sin 2x}{x}$.

Solution. $\lim\limits_{x \to 0} \dfrac{\sin 2x}{x} = \lim\limits_{x \to 0} \dfrac{2 \sin 2x}{2x} = 2 \lim\limits_{x \to 0} \dfrac{\sin 2x}{2x} = 2(1) = 2.$

A second important limit is

$$\lim\limits_{\theta \to 0} \frac{1 - \cos \theta}{\theta} = 0.$$

Proof. $\lim\limits_{\theta \to 0} \dfrac{1 - \cos \theta}{\theta} = \lim\limits_{\theta \to 0} \dfrac{1 - \cos \theta}{\theta} \cdot \dfrac{1 + \cos \theta}{1 + \cos \theta}$

$$= \lim\limits_{\theta \to 0} \frac{1 - \cos^2 \theta}{\theta(1 + \cos \theta)}$$

$$= \lim\limits_{\theta \to 0} \frac{\sin^2 \theta}{\theta(1 + \cos \theta)}$$

$$= \lim\limits_{\theta \to 0} \frac{\sin \theta}{\theta} \cdot \frac{\sin \theta}{1 + \cos \theta}$$

$$= \lim\limits_{\theta \to 0} \frac{\sin \theta}{\theta} \cdot \lim\limits_{\theta \to 0} \frac{\sin \theta}{1 + \cos \theta}$$

$$= (1) \frac{0}{1 + 1}$$

$$= (1)0$$

$$= 0.$$

Example. Find $\lim\limits_{\theta \to 0} \dfrac{1 - \cos \theta}{\theta^2}$.

Solution. Start by multiplying numerator and denominator by $1 + \cos \theta$.

$$\lim\limits_{\theta \to 0} \frac{1 - \cos \theta}{\theta^2} = \lim\limits_{\theta \to 0} \frac{1 - \cos \theta}{\theta^2} \cdot \frac{1 + \cos \theta}{1 + \cos \theta}$$

$$= \lim\limits_{\theta \to 0} \frac{1 - \cos^2 \theta}{\theta^2 (1 + \cos \theta)}$$

$$= \lim\limits_{\theta \to 0} \frac{\sin^2 \theta}{\theta^2 (1 + \cos \theta)}$$

$$= \lim\limits_{\theta \to 0} \frac{\sin^2 \theta}{\theta^2} \cdot \frac{1}{1 + \cos \theta}$$

$$= \lim_{\theta \to 0} \left(\frac{\sin \theta}{\theta} \right)^2 \frac{1}{1 + \cos \theta}$$

$$= 1^2 \left(\frac{1}{1 + 1} \right)$$

$$= \tfrac{1}{2}.$$

Example.   Find $\lim\limits_{x \to 0} \dfrac{2x^2 \cot^2 x}{x \csc x}$.

Solution. $\lim\limits_{x \to 0} \dfrac{2x^2 \cot^2 x}{x \csc x} = 2 \lim\limits_{x \to 0} x \cdot \dfrac{1}{\csc x} \cdot \cot^2 x$

$$= 2 \lim_{x \to 0} x \cdot \sin x \cdot \frac{\cos^2 x}{\sin^2 x}$$

$$= 2 \lim_{x \to 0} x \, \frac{\cos^2 x}{\sin x}$$

$$= 2 \lim_{x \to 0} \frac{x}{\sin x} \cdot \cos^2 x$$

$$= 2 \lim_{x \to 0} \frac{1}{\dfrac{\sin x}{x}} \cdot \cos^2 x$$

$$= 2(\tfrac{1}{1})1^2 = 2.$$

1-6   Exercises

(1-25)   Find the indicated limits.

1. $\lim\limits_{x \to \pi/4} 2 \tan x$

2. $\lim\limits_{\theta \to \pi/3} \dfrac{\sin \theta}{\theta}$

3. $\lim\limits_{y \to \pi} \dfrac{1 - \cos y}{y}$

4. $\lim\limits_{x \to \pi/6} \tan x \cot x$

5. $\lim\limits_{x \to \pi/2^+} \sec x$

6. $\lim\limits_{x \to 2\pi^-} \csc x$

7. $\lim\limits_{x \to 0^+} \cot x$

8. $\lim\limits_{x \to 3\pi/4^+} \sin x$

9. $\lim\limits_{x \to 0^+} \dfrac{|x|}{x}$

10. $\lim\limits_{x \to 0^-} \dfrac{|x|}{x}$

11. $\lim\limits_{x \to 0^+} \sqrt{x}$

12. $\lim\limits_{x \to 0^-} \sqrt{x}$

13. $\displaystyle\lim_{h\to 2^+} \frac{2+h}{2-h}$

14. $\displaystyle\lim_{h\to 2^-} \frac{2+h}{2-h}$

15. $\displaystyle\lim_{x\to 0} \frac{x}{\sin x}$

16. $\displaystyle\lim_{x\to 0} \frac{x}{1-\cos x}$

17. $\displaystyle\lim_{x\to 0} \frac{\sin 3x}{x}$

18. $\displaystyle\lim_{x\to 0} \frac{\sin 5x}{8x}$

19. $\displaystyle\lim_{x\to 0} \frac{\tan x}{x}$

20. $\displaystyle\lim_{x\to 0} \frac{-2x}{\tan 3x}$

21. $\displaystyle\lim_{x\to 0} \frac{\cot ax}{\cot bx}$, a and b constants

22. $\displaystyle\lim_{x\to 0} \frac{\tan 2x \sec x}{x}$

23. $\displaystyle\lim_{x\to 0} \frac{1-\cos x}{\sin x}$

24. $\displaystyle\lim_{x\to 0} \frac{1-\cos x}{\tan x}$

25. $\displaystyle\lim_{x\to 0} \frac{\sec x - \tan x}{\sin x}$

1-7   LIMITS AS X TENDS TO INFINITY

Now that we have examined the limits of functions as the independent variables tend to finite values, the next step is to examine the behavior of functions as the argument becomes indefinably large. Consider, for example, the function $\dfrac{1}{x}$. The value of $f(x) = \dfrac{1}{x}$ becomes progressively smaller for successively greater values of x. For example, if x has values 4, 5, 10, 100, and 1,000, $f(x)$ has corresponding values $\frac{1}{4}, \frac{1}{5}, \frac{1}{10}, \frac{1}{100}$, and $\frac{1}{1,000}$. As x becomes infinitely large, $f(x)$ approaches zero, denoted

$$\lim_{x\to\infty} \frac{1}{x} = 0.$$

Intuitively this limit seems obvious. In fact, intuition will serve very well to find most limits as x increases without bound, but it fails miserably in the proof of theorems. In order to deduce theorems for functions as x becomes great without bound, we need the following definition.

Definition.   If $f(x)$ is defined for all positive real numbers, then $f(x)$ approaches L as x tends to infinity, written $$\lim_{x \to \infty} f(x) = L,$$

if and only if for any positive number ϵ, no matter how small, there is a number N such that $|f(x) - L| < \epsilon$ whenever $x > N$.

This means that if L is the limit of $f(x)$ as $x \to \infty$, then $f(x)$ can be made as close to L as we please by substituting any value for x sufficiently large (greater than N). Using this definition it is possible to prove that limits of functions of x as x tends to infinity have many of the same properties as limits taken as x approaches a constant; that is, provided the limits exist. The reader should compare the following theorems with theorems 1-2–1-6.

Theorem 1-7. $\lim\limits_{x \to \infty} [f(x) \pm g(x)] = \lim\limits_{x \to \infty} f(x) \pm \lim\limits_{x \to \infty} g(x).$

Theorem 1-8. $\lim\limits_{x \to \infty} [f(x) \cdot g(x)] = \lim\limits_{x \to \infty} f(x) \cdot \lim\limits_{x \to \infty} g(x).$

Theorem 1-9. $\lim\limits_{x \to \infty} [f(x)]^n = [\lim\limits_{x \to \infty} f(x)]^n, n \in \text{rationals}.$

Theorem 1-10. $\lim\limits_{x \to \infty} \dfrac{f(x)}{g(x)} = \dfrac{\lim\limits_{x \to \infty} f(x)}{\lim\limits_{x \to \infty} g(x)}, \lim\limits_{x \to \infty} g(x) \neq 0.$

Theorem 1-11. $\lim\limits_{x \to \infty} c = c$, for c constant.

Example.   Find $\lim\limits_{x \to \infty} \dfrac{3x + 5}{x}$.

Solution.   Dividing by x gives

$$\lim_{x \to \infty} \frac{3x + 5}{x} = \lim_{x \to \infty} 3 + \frac{5}{x}$$

$$= \lim_{x \to \infty} 3 + 5 \lim_{x \to \infty} \frac{1}{x}$$

$$= 3 + 5(0)$$

$$= 3.$$

To solve the next example first divide the numerator and denominator by x^2.

Example.   Find $\lim\limits_{x \to \infty} \dfrac{5x^2 + 9}{3x^2 - 7}$.

Solution. $\lim\limits_{x\to\infty} \dfrac{5x^2 + 9}{3x^2 - 7} = \lim\limits_{x\to\infty} \dfrac{5 + \dfrac{9}{x^2}}{3 - \dfrac{7}{x^2}} = \dfrac{\lim\limits_{x\to\infty} 5 + \lim\limits_{x\to\infty} \dfrac{9}{x^2}}{\lim\limits_{x\to\infty} 3 - \lim\limits_{x\to\infty} \dfrac{7}{x^2}}$

$$= \frac{5 + 0}{3 - 0} = \frac{5}{3}.$$

Example. Find $\lim\limits_{x\to\infty} \dfrac{5x + 9}{3x^2 - 7}$.

Solution. Divide numerator and denominator by x.

$$\lim_{x\to\infty} \frac{5x + 9}{3x^2 - 7} = \lim_{x\to\infty} \frac{5 + \dfrac{9}{x}}{3x - \dfrac{7}{x}}$$

$$= \lim_{x\to\infty} \frac{5}{3x}$$

$$= 0.$$

Example. Find $\lim\limits_{x\to\infty} \dfrac{5x^2 + 9}{3x - 7}$.

Solution. Divide numerator and denominator by x.

$$\lim_{x\to\infty} \frac{5x^2 + 9}{3x - 7} = \lim_{x\to\infty} \frac{5x + \dfrac{9}{x}}{3 - \dfrac{7}{x}}$$

$$= \infty.$$

The $\lim\limits_{x\to\infty} \sin x$ has no limit because the sine function will take on the value of each real number between -1 and 1 for each 2π interval of its domain and approaches none of them. However $\lim\limits_{x\to\infty} \dfrac{\sin x}{x} = 0$, because for any C in the range of sine, $C \lim\limits_{x\to\infty} \dfrac{1}{x} = 0$.

Example. Find $\lim\limits_{x\to\infty} (3x + \cos x)$.

Solution. As x increases in value so does $3x$; however, $\cos x$ is bounded between -1 and 1. Thus the sum must increase. Therefore,

$$\lim_{x\to\infty} (3x + \cos x) = \infty.$$

Example. Find $\lim\limits_{x\to\infty} \dfrac{5x^3}{\sqrt{x^6 + 1}}$.

Solution. $\lim\limits_{x\to\infty} \dfrac{5x^3}{\sqrt{x^6 + 1}} = \lim\limits_{x\to\infty} \dfrac{5}{\dfrac{\sqrt{x^6 + 1}}{x^3}}$

$$= \lim_{x\to\infty} \frac{5}{\dfrac{\sqrt{x^6 + 1}}{\sqrt{x^6}}}$$

$$= \lim_{x\to\infty} \frac{5}{\sqrt{\dfrac{x^6 + 1}{x^6}}}$$

$$= \lim_{x\to\infty} \frac{5}{\sqrt{1 + \dfrac{1}{x^6}}}$$

$$= 5.$$

1-7   Exercises

(1-28)   Find the indicated limits.

1. $\lim\limits_{x\to\infty} \dfrac{1}{x^4}$

2. $\lim\limits_{x\to\infty} \dfrac{5}{x^3}$

3. $\lim\limits_{x\to\infty} \dfrac{4x + 7}{8x + 3}$

4. $\lim\limits_{x\to\infty} \dfrac{-x + 4}{x - 7}$

5. $\lim\limits_{x\to\infty} \dfrac{3x^2 + 5x + 2}{5x^2 + 2x + 7}$

6. $\lim\limits_{x\to\infty} \dfrac{ax^2 + bx + c}{cx^2 + bx + a}$,

a, b, and c are nonzero constants

7. $\lim\limits_{x\to\infty} \dfrac{-3x^2 + 2x - 1}{x^2 - 3x}$

8. $\lim\limits_{x\to\infty} \dfrac{x^2 - x}{-2x^2 + 5}$

9. $\lim\limits_{x\to\infty} \dfrac{2x^2 + 3x - 100}{4x + 9}$

10. $\lim\limits_{x\to\infty} \dfrac{4x + 9}{2x^2 + 3x - 100}$

11. $\lim\limits_{x\to\infty} \dfrac{13 - 4x^2}{5x^3 - 8x^2}$

12. $\lim\limits_{x\to\infty} \dfrac{-7x^4 + 5x^3}{3x^3 + 5x^2}$

13. $\lim\limits_{x\to\infty} \dfrac{-4x^5 + 5x^4 - 8}{-3x^4 + 12x^5 - 9}$

14. $\lim\limits_{x\to\infty} \dfrac{2x^2 - 3x^3 + x}{x - 2x^2 - x^3}$

15. $\lim\limits_{x \to \infty} \dfrac{\sqrt{4x^2 + 5}}{x}$

16. $\lim\limits_{x \to \infty} \dfrac{\sqrt{3x^2 + 2}}{x - 8}$

17. $\lim\limits_{x \to \infty} \dfrac{-5x^2 + x}{\sqrt{16x^4 - 8}}$

18. $\lim\limits_{x \to \infty} \dfrac{x^4 + x^3 + 5x^2}{\sqrt{x^6 - 2}}$

19. $\lim\limits_{x \to \infty} \dfrac{\sqrt{x + 2}}{\sqrt{x^2 - 5}}$

20. $\lim\limits_{x \to \infty} (x + \sin x)$

21. $\lim\limits_{x \to \infty} x \sin \dfrac{1}{x}$

22. $\lim\limits_{x \to \infty} x\left(1 - \cos \dfrac{1}{x}\right)$

23. $\lim\limits_{x \to -\infty} \dfrac{-2x^2 - 8}{5x^2 + 25}$

24. $\lim\limits_{x \to -\infty} \dfrac{x}{\sqrt{x^2 - 1}}$

25. $\lim\limits_{x \to -\infty} \dfrac{x^3 - 5x^2}{\sqrt{x}}$

26. $\lim\limits_{x \to -\infty} \dfrac{x^3}{\sqrt{1 - x^6}}$

27. $\lim\limits_{x \to -\infty} \dfrac{x^2 - 2x + 1}{-\sqrt{x^4 + 5x}}$

28. $\lim\limits_{x \to -\infty} \dfrac{\sqrt{x^3 + 80}}{x^2}$

29. State theorems 1-7 to 1-11 in words in the manner used in the text to illustrate theorems 1-1 to 1-6.

Chapter 1 REVIEW

(1-5) Use the listing method to specify each of the following sets.

  1. $\{x|\ |2x + 1| < 3, x \text{ is an integer}\}$
  2. $\{x|\ -2 < 3 - x < 5, x \text{ is an integer}\}$
  3. $\{p|p \text{ is a positive integer divisor of } 12\}$
  4. $\{x|\ |3x + 2| \geq 7, x \text{ is a negative integer}\}$
  5. $\left\{x|x = \dfrac{1}{n^2}, n \text{ is a natural number}\right\}$

(6-10) Let $A = \{2, 4, 6\}$, $B = \{1, 2, 3, 4\}$, $C = \{x|x = 2n + 1, 0 < n < 9$, n is an integer$\}$. List each of the following sets.

  6. $A \cup B$
  7. $B \cap C$
  8. $(A \cup C) \cap B$
  9. $B \cup (A \cap C)$
  10. $(A \cap B) \cup (A \cap C)$

(11-15) State the largest real domain and range for each of the following functions.

11. $f = \{(2,3), (3,4), (5,6), (7,8)\}$
12. $g = \{(x,y)|y = 3x - 2\}$
13. $f{:}x \rightarrow \sqrt{2x - 1}$
14. $g{:}x \rightarrow \dfrac{1}{x + 1}$
15. $\left\{(x,y)|y = \dfrac{|x|}{x}\right\}$

(16-20) If $f(x) = x^3 - 2x + 4$, find the following.

16. $f(2)$
17. $f(-1)$
18. $f(x + h)$
19. $f(x + h) - f(x)$
20. $f(\sqrt{x})$

(21-25) Let $f(x) = 3x^2 - x - 2$, and $g(x) = 3x + 2$.

21. Find $(f + g)(x)$, and state the domain of $f + g$.
22. Find $(f \cdot g)(x)$, and state the domain of $f \cdot g$.
23. Find $\left(\dfrac{f}{g}\right)(x)$, and state the domain of $\dfrac{f}{g}$.
24. Find $(f \circ g)(x)$, and state the domain of $f \circ g$.
25. Find $(g \circ f)(x)$, and state the domain of $g \circ f$.

(26-27) Find the increment of the function for the given interval of its domain.

26. $f(x) = x^2 - 3x + 7$, x to $x + \Delta x$
27. $y = x^3$, x to $x + 1$

(28-29) Find the average rate of change for the indicated interval.

28. $y = 3x - 6$, $x = 3$ and $\Delta x = 0.1$
29. $y = -4x^2$, b to $b + h$

(30-41) Evaluate.

30. $\displaystyle\lim_{x \to -\frac{1}{2}} \frac{x - 4}{2x^2 - 7x - 4}$

31. $\displaystyle\lim_{x \to 0} \frac{3x^2 - 5x + 8}{x}$

32. $\lim\limits_{x \to 9} \dfrac{x - 9}{\sqrt{x} - 3}$

33. $\lim\limits_{\Delta x \to 0} \dfrac{\sqrt{1 - \Delta x} - 1}{\Delta x}$

34. $\lim\limits_{x \to 0} \dfrac{x^2}{1 - \cos x}$

35. $\lim\limits_{h \to 0} \dfrac{\sin 5h}{2h}$

36. $\lim\limits_{x \to 0^-} \sqrt{x}$

37. $\lim\limits_{x \to 0^-} \csc x$

38. $\lim\limits_{x \to \infty} \dfrac{-2x^2 + 5x}{3x^2 - 8x + 7}$

39. $\lim\limits_{x \to -\infty} \dfrac{4x + 9}{2x^2 + 3x - 50{,}000}$

40. $\lim\limits_{x \to \infty} \dfrac{x + 8}{\sqrt{x^2 - 7}}$

41. $\lim\limits_{x \to -\infty} \dfrac{5x + 3}{\sqrt{x^2 - 1}}$

42. For $f(x) = x^2 - 3x$ find $\lim\limits_{\Delta x \to 0} \dfrac{f(x + \Delta x) - f(x)}{\Delta x}$.

43. Use the formula $S = 16t^2$ to find the average speed, between times $t = 4$ and $t = 4.1$ seconds, of a falling object initially at rest.

44. If $e = 2.7$ and a growing culture of bacteria weighs $5e^{t/4}$ grams at time t, find the average rate of growth between the hours $t = 8$ and $t = 12$.

CHAPTER TWO

The Derivative

In this chapter we will show how the ideas considered in Chapter 1 are used to develop the concept of the derivative. In the first chapter the ideas of increment and average rate of change were examined along with the idea of limit. The derivative is simply the limit of the average rate of change as the increment of x becomes small. The derivative has many applications in economics and science. The following demonstrates one possible use for the derivative. Suppose that a scientist wishes to know how fast a culture of bacteria is growing when it weighs 15 grams. He notes that it weighs 15 grams at 10 a.m. and later, at 12 noon, he finds that it weighs 55 grams. In two hours, then, its average rate of growth (change) is $\frac{40}{2}$ or 20 grams per hour. The scientist could then reason that the culture is growing at "about" 20 grams per hour when it weighs 15 grams. To improve this estimate all he need do is shorten the time period after 10 a.m. Suppose, once more, that the culture weighs 15 grams at 10 a.m. but at 10:30 a.m. it has increased to 16 grams. Now the average rate of growth (change) for the half hour time period from 10 a.m. to 10:30 a.m. is 1 divided by $\frac{1}{2}$ or 2 grams per hour. The scientist could now say, with greater conviction, that the culture is growing at "about" 2 grams per hour when it weighs 15 grams. As the average rate of change is taken for shorter time periods after 10 a.m. his estimate would become more accurate. This process of finding the average rate of change as the change in time becomes small is known as finding the derivative.

2-1 SLOPE AND MARGINAL COST

The average rate of change has been used to describe the growth rate of a population of bacteria and, at another time, to calculate speed. It can also be interpreted as marginal cost or, geometrically, as the slope of a line.

Definition. The slope, m, of the line segment between points (x_1,y_1) and (x_2,y_2) is

$$m = \frac{y_2 - y_1}{x_2 - x_1}.$$

If $x_1 = x_2$, the slope is undefined.

In figure 2-1, line BC is parallel to the y axis and AC is parallel to the

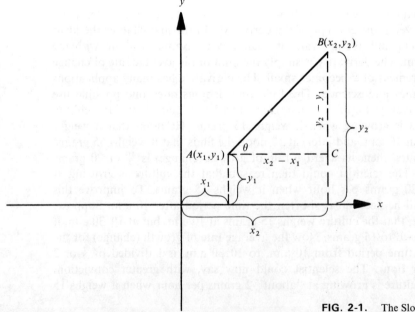

FIG. 2-1. The Slope of a Line

x axis. The slope of a line segment is sometimes defined as the tangent of the angle formed by the line segment and a line parallel to the x axis, in this example θ. In triangle ABC, side BC has length $y_2 - y_1$ and AC has length $x_2 - x_1$. Therefore,

$$\tan \theta = \frac{y_2 - y_1}{x_2 - x_1} = m.$$

Recall in Chapter 1 we found it convenient to use the relations $\Delta y = y_2 - y_1$, and $\Delta x = x_2 - x_1$. Thus, the slope is also the average rate of change of y as x changes from x_1 to x_2, since

$$m = \frac{y_2 - y_1}{x_2 - x_1} = \frac{\Delta y}{\Delta x}.$$

When computing the slope of a line segment, either point may be designated as (x_2, y_2), for the order of subtraction is not important.

$$m = \frac{y_2 - y_1}{x_2 - x_1}.$$

Multiplying numerator and denominator by -1.

$$m = \frac{-1(y_2 - y_1)}{-1(x_2 - x_1)}$$

$$= \frac{-y_2 + y_1}{-x_2 + x_1}$$

$$= \frac{y_1 - y_2}{x_1 - x_2}.$$

Example.   Find slope of the line segment between points $(-5,6)$ and $(3,-2)$.
Solution.   Arbitrarily let $(-5,6)$ be (x_2,y_2), $(3,-2)$ be (x_1,y_1), and apply the slope formula.

$$m = \frac{y_2 - y_1}{x_2 - x_1}$$

$$= \frac{6 - (-2)}{-5 - 3}$$

$$= \frac{6 + 2}{-8}$$

$$= \frac{8}{-8}$$

$$= -1.$$

   The slope of a straight line is, of course, constant. If three or more
points are on a single line, the slope computed by using any two of them
will be the same as that computed by using any other two.

Example.   In figure 2-2, points $(2,5)$, $(0,1)$ and $(-2,-3)$ are all on the
same line. Compute the slope.

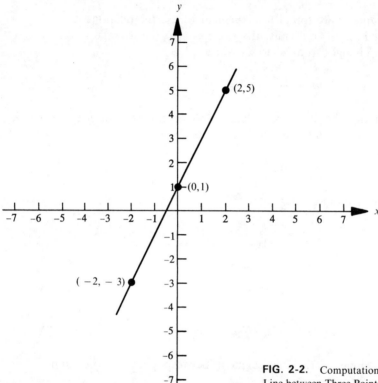

FIG. 2-2.   Computation of the Slope of the
Line between Three Points.

Solution.   If the slope is computed using $(2,5)$ and $(-2,-3)$ it is:

$$m = \frac{5 - (-3)}{2 - (-2)}$$

$$= \frac{8}{4}$$

$$= 2.$$

If the slope is computed using $(2,5)$ and $(0,1)$ it is:

$$m = \frac{5 - 1}{2 - 0}$$

$$= \frac{4}{2}$$

$$= 2.$$

If the slope, m, of a line and a point (x_1, y_1) on the line are known, the equation of the line can easily be found. If (x,y) is any other point on the line, then

$$\frac{y - y_1}{x - x_1} = m,$$

$$\text{and } y - y_1 = m(x - x_1).$$

This is called the *point-slope form* of a linear equation.

Example.   Find the equation of the line that has slope 6 and passes through $(4, -8)$.

Solution.   Substituting into the point-slope form of a linear equation:

$$y - y_1 = m(x - x_1)$$

$$y - (-8) = 6(x - 4)$$

$$y + 8 = 6x - 24$$

$$y = 6x - 32$$

If a line has slope m and intersects the y axis at $(0,b)$, we can use the point-slope form to find its equation:

$$y - y_1 = m(x - x_1)$$

$$y - b = m(x - 0)$$

$$y - b = mx$$

$$y = mx + b$$

$y = mx + b$ is called the *slope-intercept form* of the linear equation.

Example.   Find the slope and y intercept of the graph of $3x - 9y = 5$.

Solution.   Put the equation in the slope-intercept form. The coefficient of x will be the slope and the constant term the y intercept.

$$3x - 9y = 5$$

$$-9y = -3x + 5$$

$$y = \frac{-3x}{-9} + \frac{5}{-9}$$

$$y = \frac{1}{3}x - \frac{5}{9}$$

Therefore the slope is $\frac{1}{3}$, and the line crosses the y axis at $-\frac{5}{9}$.

If a linear equation represents the total cost of manufacturing a certain number of items, in terms of the number of items, then the economist's term for the slope of the graph of the equation is *marginal* cost per item. One further restriction is required to interpret a linear equation of cost. The domain must be restricted to the positive numbers, because it is unrealistic to talk about a negative number of items. The marginal cost when the equation is nonlinear will be considered later.

The equation $y = \frac{2}{3}x + 4$ is graphed in figure 2-3. Suppose y represents the cost in dollars of manufacturing x number of items. The point D, $(0,4)$, on the line means that the cost of producing 0 items is \$4. The reason that there is some cost before any items are produced is that there is some capital outlay before production can begin, for such things as supplies. Thus, the line segment OD, which represents \$4, is called *fixed cost*. The length of line segment AC represents the cost of manufacturing x items. The length of AB, which is equal to that of OD, also represents the fixed cost and that of BC is called the *variable cost for x items*. Thus, if $x = 3$, then the cost, $y = \frac{2}{3}(3) + 4 = \$6$; \$4 of the \$6 is fixed cost, and \$2 is the variable cost for 3 items. The ratio of BC to DB is the marginal cost per item (slope). In this case it is $\frac{2}{3}$ of a dollar.

The average cost per item is simply the total cost divided by the number of items produced. The average cost of producing 12 items is the total cost, \$12, divided by 12, or \$1 per item. The average cost of producing 30 items is the total cost, \$24, divided by 30, or \$0.80. The average cost per item

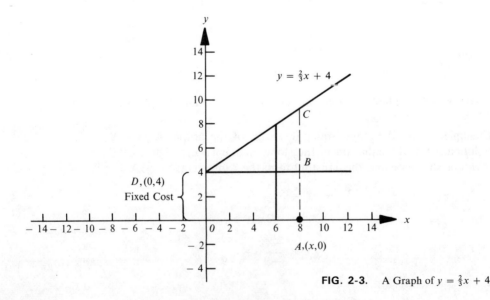

FIG. 2-3.   A Graph of $y = \frac{2}{3}x + 4$

for 30 items is lower than that for 12 items because the fixed cost is spread over a greater number of items.

2-1   Exercises

(1-6)   Find the slope of the line segments between points:

1. $(0,0)$ and $(4,5)$
2. $(-1,-1)$ and $(3,3)$
3. $(-5,4)$ and $(2,-1)$
4. $(4,3)$ and $(-2,3)$
5. $(-1,-2)$ and $(-1,6)$
6. $(4,3)$ and $(4,17)$

(7-12)   Find the slope and y intercept.

7. $y = -3x + 5$
8. $2x = 5y + 7$
9. $4x - 3y + 7 = 0$
10. $x = 4$
11. $y = 4$
12. $5x - 19y = 28$

(13-18)   Find the equation of the line with the given slope that contains the given point.

13. $m = 1, (3,3)$
14. $m = 5, (-2,4)$
15. $m = \frac{3}{4}, (1,4)$
16. $m = -2, (-3,-5)$
17. $m = 0, (-3,2)$
18. $m = -\frac{5}{8}, (-3,7)$

(19-26)   Find the equation of the line that contains the given points.

19. $(0,0), (2,2)$
20. $(3,4), (-1,3)$
21. $(1,-2), (-3,5)$
22. $(4,2), (-8,2)$
23. $(6,-5), (0,-5)$
24. $(1,0), (1,4)$
25. $(-5,2), (-5,-2)$
26. $(2,3), (7,-2)$
27.   What are the economist's terms for m and b in the equation $y = mx + b$?

(28-33)   In each of the following equations, y represents the cost in dollars of manufacturing x items. The number of items produced is given with each equation. Find the following for each equation.
a) the total cost
b) the average cost per item
c) the fixed cost
d) the variable cost
e) the marginal cost per item

28. $y = 5x + 40$, 100 items produced
29. $y = 5x + 40$, 10 items produced

30. $y = 8x + 10$, 40 items produced
31. $y = 8x + 10$, 80 items produced
32. $y = 50x + 1,000$, 90 items produced
33. $y = 50x + 1,000$, 120 items produced
34. Give four possible interpretations of average rate of change of a function over increments of its domain.

2-2 THE DERIVATIVE OF A FUNCTION

The derivative is the limit of the average rate of change as the increment of the independent variable becomes zero. The derivative will have similar interpretations to those of the average rate of change, except they will be "instantaneous." That is, the derivative will evaluate instantaneous velocity, instantaneous growth rate, and instantaneous marginal cost, rather than averages. This list of possible interpretations is by no means exhaustive. We will show you many more uses for the derivative, but before that is possible convenient methods for its evaluation are needed. This chapter will provide those methods.

To find the derivative of a function at a point in its domain, it is necessary that the function be continuous at the point. Intuitively, a continuous function is one whose graph has no breaks. In figure 2-4, $y = f(x)$ is discontinuous at $x = a$ and at $x = b$, where a single point is missing in its graph.

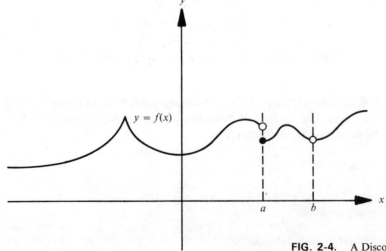

FIG. 2-4.   A Discontinuous Function

Definition. A function $f(x)$ is *continuous* at a if $\lim\limits_{x \to a} f(x) = f(a)$. If a function is continuous for all values of x in an interval from a to b, then it will be said to be *continuous on the interval*.

The definition requires three things: $f(a)$ must exist, $\lim\limits_{x \to a} f(x)$ must exist, and they must be equal.

Example. Is $f(x) = x^2 - 4$ continuous at $x = 3$?
Solution. Since $\lim\limits_{x \to 3} f(x) = 9 - 4 = 5 = f(3)$, the limit exists. Thus the function is continuous.

Example. Is $f(x) = \dfrac{1}{x}$ continuous at $x = 0$?

Solution. Since $\lim\limits_{x \to 0} \dfrac{1}{x}$ does not exist, $f(x) = \dfrac{1}{x}$ is discontinuous at $x = 0$. $f(x)$ is continuous on the interval $1 \le x \le 17$, or the interval $-2 \le x < 0$, but not over an interval that contains 0.

If the average rate of change of a function of x is taken over smaller and smaller intervals of its domain, it approaches "the instantaneous rate of change" of the function at x. Recall that the average rate of change had several interpretations; the instantaneous rate of change will also have many useful applications. In fact, because of the many potential applications, it is given a special name. Since its value is "derived" from the original function, it will be called the derivative of the function. Reference to the derivative as an "instantaneous rate of change" lies in the historic role the derivative has played in physical problems related to velocity and motion, where it refers to the instantaneous rate of change of position.

Definition. For $y = f(x)$, $f(x)$ a function, *the derivative of y with respect to x is*

$$\lim_{\Delta x \to 0} \frac{\Delta y}{\Delta x} = \lim_{\Delta x \to 0} \frac{f(x + \Delta x) - f(x)}{\Delta x}$$

provided the limit exists. When $\lim\limits_{\Delta x \to 0} \dfrac{\Delta y}{\Delta x}$ exists, y is said to be a *differentiable* function with respect to x. The derivative of $f(x)$ is a function of x, since its value depends on the value of x.

Example. Find the derivative of y with respect to x for $y = x^2 + 2x$.

Solution. $\lim\limits_{\Delta x \to 0} \dfrac{\Delta y}{\Delta x} = \lim\limits_{\Delta x \to 0} \dfrac{f(x + \Delta x) - f(x)}{\Delta x}$

$$= \lim_{\Delta x \to 0} \frac{[(x + \Delta x)^2 + 2(x + \Delta x)] - (x^2 + 2x)}{\Delta x}$$

$$= \lim_{\Delta x \to 0} \frac{x^2 + 2x \Delta x + (\Delta x)^2 + 2x + 2\Delta x - x^2 - 2x}{\Delta x}$$

$$= \lim_{\Delta x \to 0} \frac{2x \Delta x + (\Delta x)^2 + 2\Delta x}{\Delta x}$$

$$= \lim_{\Delta x \to 0} 2x + \Delta x + 2$$

$$= 2x + 2.$$

Therefore the derivative of y with respect to x is $2x + 2$.

The derivative has traditionally had many notations. They include y', $f'(x)$, $\frac{dy}{dx}$, $\frac{df}{dx}$, $\frac{d}{dx}f$, $D_x f$, and $D_x y$ for $y = f(x)$. Each of these notations reflects one or more special characteristics of the derivative. The choice of a particular form of notation depends on the meaning or characteristic most appropriate for a specific problem. The prime ($'$) notations are compact, and denote the new function has been derived from the old. The $\frac{dy}{dx}$ or $\frac{df}{dx}$ notations remind one of the $\frac{\Delta y}{\Delta x}$ from the average rate of change, and later will remind the user of some of the "fraction-like" properties of the derivative. The $D_x f$ will be used to indicate the operation of differentiation working on a function. For the time being, however, all of these notations will be used interchangeably.

In the last example, the derivative of y with respect to x for $y = f(x) = x^2 + 2x$ was found to be $2x + 2$. Using some of the many notations for derivatives, this could be written

$$y' = 2x + 2, \qquad\qquad \frac{df}{dx} = 2x + 2,$$

$$f'(x) = 2x + 2, \qquad\qquad D_x(x^2 + 2x) = 2x + 2,$$

$$\frac{dy}{dx} = 2x + 2, \quad \text{or} \qquad D_x y = 2x + 2.$$

Example. Find $f'(x)$ for $f(x) = \dfrac{1}{x}$.

Solution. $f'(x) = \lim_{\Delta x \to 0} \dfrac{f(x + \Delta x) - f(x)}{\Delta x}$

$$= \lim_{\Delta x \to 0} \frac{\dfrac{1}{x + \Delta x} - \dfrac{1}{x}}{\Delta x}$$

$$= \lim_{\Delta x \to 0} \frac{\dfrac{x - (x + \Delta x)}{x(x + \Delta x)}}{\Delta x}$$

$$= \lim_{\Delta x \to 0} \frac{x - x - \Delta x}{(\Delta x \cdot x)(x + \Delta x)}$$

$$= \lim_{\Delta x \to 0} \frac{-\Delta x}{(\Delta x \cdot x)(x + \Delta x)}$$

$$= \lim_{\Delta x \to 0} \frac{-1}{x(x + \Delta x)}$$

$$= \frac{-1}{x^2}.$$

For $y = f(x)$, the derivative at x is the instantaneous rate of change of y with respect to x. That is, it is the limit of the average rate of change as the interval of x, $\Delta x \to 0$. For instance, if y gives the amount of bacteria in a culture at time x, then the derivative is the growth rate at a specific time. It is also the slope of the tangent to a curve for any given x. In figure 2-5 points $P(x,y)$ and P_1 are located on the graph of $y = f(x)$. The slope of the

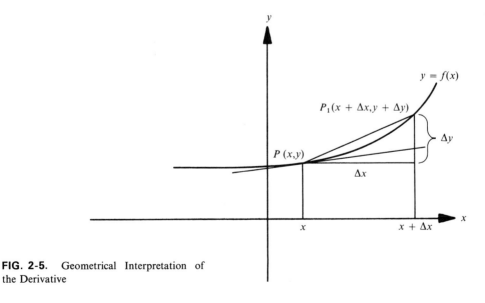

FIG. 2-5.   Geometrical Interpretation of the Derivative

line through P_1 and P is $\dfrac{\Delta y}{\Delta x}$. As Δx approaches zero, point P_1 moves closer to point P. The tangent line at P is the limiting position for the secant line.

Example. If $y = \sqrt{x}$, find the slope of the tangent line to the curve at $x = 4$. (See figure 2-6.)

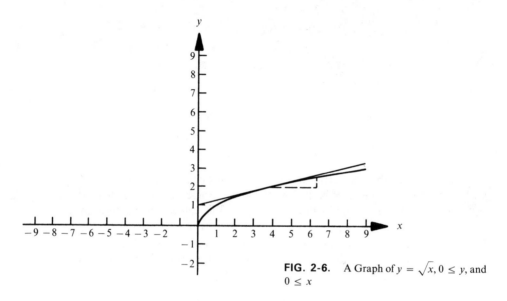

FIG. 2-6. A Graph of $y = \sqrt{x}, 0 \le y$, and $0 \le x$

Solution. The slope of the tangent is the derivative evaluated at $x = 4$.

$$y' = \lim_{\Delta x \to 0} \frac{\sqrt{x + \Delta x} - \sqrt{x}}{\Delta x}.$$

Rationalizing the numerator,

$$y' = \lim_{\Delta x \to 0} \left(\frac{\sqrt{x + \Delta x} - \sqrt{x}}{\Delta x} \right) \left(\frac{\sqrt{x + \Delta x} + \sqrt{x}}{\sqrt{x + \Delta x} + \sqrt{x}} \right)$$

$$= \lim_{\Delta x \to 0} \frac{x + \Delta x - x}{\Delta x (\sqrt{x + \Delta x} + \sqrt{x})}$$

$$= \lim_{\Delta x \to 0} \frac{1}{\sqrt{x + \Delta x} + \sqrt{x}}$$

$$= \frac{1}{\sqrt{x} + \sqrt{x}}$$

$$= \frac{1}{2\sqrt{x}}.$$

Since we now know the slope at $x = 4$ is y' at $x = 4$, the slope of this curve at $x = 4$ is

$$y'(4) = \frac{1}{2\sqrt{4}} = \frac{1}{4}.$$

2-2   Exercises

(1-4)   Find $\dfrac{dy}{dx}$ for the following.

1. $y = x^2$ **3.** $y = -6x + 2$

2. $y = 7x + 4$ **4.** $y = 3x^2$

(5-8)   Find $D_x y$ for the following.

5. $y = 7 - x^2$ **7.** $y = \dfrac{1}{x^2}$

6. $y = x^3 - 2x$ **8.** $y = \dfrac{1}{\sqrt{x}}$

(9-14)   Find the value of the derivative at the given point.

9. $f'(3)$ for $f(x) = \dfrac{x + 1}{x}$ **12.** $g'(4)$ for $g(\theta) = \theta^2 - 8\theta$

10. $f'(2)$ for $f(t) = 16t - t^2$ **13.** $f''(0)$ for $f(t) = 3t^3$

11. $h'(-1)$ for $h(z) = z^2 - 3z + 4$ **14.** $f'(1)$ for $f(x) = \dfrac{1}{x + 3}$

(15-18)   Find the slope of the tangent line at the value indicated.

15. $f(x) = \dfrac{1}{x + 1}$ at $x = 5$ **17.** $f(x) = \dfrac{x}{x + 1}$ at $x = 0$

16. $f(x) = \dfrac{x - 1}{x + 1}$ at $x = 0$ **18.** $f(x) = x^4$ at $x = 2$

19.   The cost of producing x items is given in dollars by $c = 500 + x + \dfrac{1}{x}$. If the marginal cost is redefined as $\dfrac{dc}{dx}$ find the marginal cost of producing the tenth item.

20. By setting $\dfrac{dy}{dx} = 0$, find the point on the graph of $4y = x^2 - 8x$ + 12 where the tangent is parallel to the x axis. Draw a figure to illustrate.

21. If $R = f(I)$, where R is the return on an investment of I amount then $\dfrac{dR}{dI}$ is called the marginal efficiency of investment. Find the marginal efficiency of investment if $R = 3I^2 - 2I$.

22. If P is the measure of production of x machines or workers (*i.e.*, $P = f(x)$) then $\dfrac{dP}{dx}$ is called the marginal physical productivity. Find the marginal physical productivity of a group of x lumberjacks, where P is given in thousands of board feet of lumber per day, and $P = 4x^2 - 10{,}000x$. According to this formula if there are 2,500 lumberjacks then $P = 0$; conjecture how such a large number of lumberjacks can result in no production.

2-3 THE DERIVATIVE OF POLYNOMIALS

The definition of the derivative from the last section can be used to find the derivative of any function. However, this process often involves considerably more labor than necessary. The objective of this and the next few sections is to develop simple formulas to facilitate finding derivatives.

Theorem 2-1. For $y = f(x) = C$, C constant, $y' = 0$.
Proof. $f(x) = C$ for any x. Therefore, $f(x + \Delta x) = C$. Then,

$$y' = \lim_{\Delta x \to 0} \frac{f(x + \Delta x) - f(x)}{\Delta x}$$

$$= \lim_{\Delta x \to 0} \frac{C - C}{\Delta x}$$

$$= 0.$$

This proves the theorem.

If we think of the derivative as the slope of the tangent line, the theorem becomes obvious. The graph of the equation $y = C$ for C constant is parallel to the x axis (see figure 2-7). Hence, its slope for all x is the same as the slope of its tangent, which is 0.

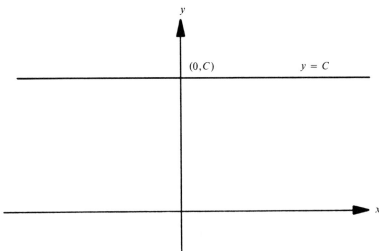

FIG. 2-7.   A Graph of $y = C$

Example.   If $f(x) = 7$, find $f'(x)$.
Solution.   From theorem 2-1, we know

$$f'(x) = 0 \text{ for all } x.$$

The next theorem is proved by use of the binomial theorem. The notation $n!$ is read "n factorial" and means $n(n - 1)(n - 2) \cdots 1$. Thus, $3! = 3(2)(1) = 6$, and $5! = 5(4)(3)(2)(1) = 120$. $1!$ is defined equal to 1.
The binomial theorem states that if a and b are numbers, and n is a positive integer, then,

$$(a + b)^n = a^n + \frac{na^{n-1}b^1}{1!} + \frac{n(n - 1)a^{n-2}b^2}{2!}$$

$$+ \frac{n(n - 1)(n - 2)a^{n-3}b^3}{3!} + \cdots + b^n$$

Example.   Use the binomial theorem to find $(a + b)^3$.

Solution. $(a + b)^3 = a^3 + \dfrac{3a^2b}{1!} + \dfrac{(3)2ab^2}{2!} + b^3$

$$= a^3 + 3a^2b + 3ab^2 + b^3$$

Theorem 2-2.   If $y = x^n$ for n a positive integer, then $y' = nx^{n-1}$.

Proof. By definition of the derivative from the last section,

$$y' = \lim_{\Delta x \to 0} \frac{(x + \Delta x)^n - x^n}{\Delta x}.$$

Using the binomial theorem to expand $(x + \Delta x)^n$ gives

$$y' = \lim_{\Delta x \to 0} \frac{\left(x^n + \dfrac{n \Delta x\, x^{n-1}}{1!} + \dfrac{n(n-1)(\Delta x)^2 x^{n-2}}{2!} + \cdots + (\Delta x)^n\right) - x^n}{\Delta x}$$

$$= \lim_{\Delta x \to 0} \frac{\dfrac{n \Delta x\, x^{n-1}}{1!} + \dfrac{n(n-1)(\Delta x)^2 x^{n-2}}{2!} + \cdots + (\Delta x)^n}{\Delta x}$$

$$= \lim_{\Delta x \to 0} \left[\frac{n x^{n-1}}{1!} + \frac{n(n-1)\Delta x\, x^{n-2}}{2!} + \cdots + (\Delta x)^{n-1}\right]$$

In the last line each term except the first contains at least one Δx as a factor. Therefore as $\Delta x \to 0$ each of these will vanish and the derivative is the first term.

$$y' = \frac{n x^{n-1}}{1!} = n x^{n-1}.$$

Example. Find the derivatives of $y = x^3$ and $y = x^5$.

Solution.   For $y = x^3$, $y' = 3x^2$.

For $y = x^5$, $y' = 5x^4$.

Theorem 2-2 was proved for n a positive integer. It is also true for all rational numbers. Proofs for negative integers will be given in the section on the derivative of the quotient of two functions and for rational numbers in the section on the chain rule.

Example. Find y' for $y = \dfrac{1}{x^2}$.

Solution. Write with negative exponent and apply theorem 2-2. $y = \dfrac{1}{x^2}$ is equivalent to $y = x^{-2}$. Therefore,

$$y' = -2x^{-2-1} = -2x^{-3} = \frac{-2}{x^3}.$$

Example. Find $f'(x)$ for $f(x) = \sqrt{x}$.
Solution. Write $\sqrt{x}$ as $x^{\frac{1}{2}}$ and apply theorem 2-2.

$$y = \sqrt{x} = x^{\frac{1}{2}}.$$

Therefore,

$$y' = \frac{1}{2}x^{\frac{1}{2}-1} = \frac{1}{2}x^{-\frac{1}{2}} = \frac{1}{2x^{\frac{1}{2}}} = \frac{1}{2\sqrt{x}}.$$

Example.   Find the derivative of $y = x^{\frac{2}{3}}$.

Solution.   For $y = x^{\frac{2}{3}}$, $y' = \frac{2}{3}x^{-\frac{1}{3}} = \frac{2}{3x^{\frac{1}{3}}}$.

Theorem 2-3.   If $y = cf(x)$ then $y' = cf'(x)$, which is to say the derivative of a constant times a function is the constant times the derivative of the function.

Proof.   We must prove that if $f(x)$ is a differentiable function, c is a constant, and $y = cf(x)$, then $y' = cf'(x)$.

$$y' = \lim_{\Delta x \to 0} \frac{cf(x + \Delta x) - cf(x)}{\Delta x}.$$

Applying limit theorems this becomes

$$y' = c \lim_{\Delta x \to 0} \frac{f(x + \Delta x) - f(x)}{\Delta x}$$

$$= cf'(x).$$

Example.   Find $D_x y$ for $y = 3x^2$.
Solution.   By theorem 2-3, $D_x y$ is 3 times the derivative of x^2, which is $2x$. Therefore,

$$D_x y = 6x.$$

Example.   Find the derivative of $y = cx^n$, where c is a constant and n is a rational number.
Solution. $y = cx^n$, then $y' = cnx^{n-1}$.

Theorem 2-4.   The derivatives of the sum of differentiable functions is the sum of the derivatives. If $f(x)$ and $g(x)$ are differentiable functions, and $y = f(x) + g(x)$, then $y' = f'(x) + g'(x)$.
Proof.   From the definition of y',

$$y' = \lim_{\Delta x \to 0} \frac{f(x + \Delta x) + g(x + \Delta x) - (f(x) + g(x))}{\Delta x}$$

$$= \lim_{\Delta x \to 0} \frac{f(x + \Delta x) - f(x) + g(x + \Delta x) - g(x)}{\Delta x}$$

$$= \lim_{\Delta x \to 0} \left\{ \frac{f(x + \Delta x) - f(x)}{\Delta x} + \frac{g(x + \Delta x) - g(x)}{\Delta x} \right\}$$

$$= \lim_{\Delta x \to 0} \frac{f(x + \Delta x) - f(x)}{\Delta x} + \lim_{\Delta x \to 0} \frac{g(x + \Delta x) - g(x)}{\Delta x}$$

$$= f'(x) + g'(x).$$

Example. Find y' when $y = x^2 + x^3$.
Solution. Since y' is the sum of the derivatives of x^2 and x^3,

$$y' = 2x + 3x^2.$$

Theorem 2-4 can be extended to the sum or difference of any number of terms. Using this theorem and the others, the derivative of a polynomial is easily found.

Example. Find the derivative of $y = 7x^2 - 8x + 3$.
Solution. The derivative of y is the sum of the derivatives of the three terms of the polynomial.

$$D_x(7x^2) = 2(7)x^1 = 14x.$$

$$D_x(-8x) = D_x(-8x^1) = (-8)(1)x^0 = -8.$$

$$D_x(3) = 0,$$

since the derivative of a constant is 0.

Therefore, $y' = 14x - 8.$

Example. Find the derivative of $y = 7x^5 + 3x^3 + 7x^2 - x + x^{-2}$.
Solution. Take the derivative of each term. The fourth term, x, has derivative 1, since $x = x^1$; and $D_x(x^1) = 1x^0 = 1$, since $x^0 = 1$. Therefore,

$$y' = 35x^4 + 9x^2 + 14x - 1 - 2x^{-3}.$$

Example. Find y' for $y = (x + 3)^2$.
Solution. First expand $(x + 3)^2$; then take the derivative term by term.

$$y = (x + 3)^2 = x^2 + 6x + 9.$$

$$y' = 2x + 6.$$

Example. Find y' if $y = \dfrac{3x^2 + 2}{\sqrt{x}}$.

Solution. $$y = \frac{3x^2 + 2}{\sqrt{x}}$$

$$= \frac{3x^2}{\sqrt{x}} + \frac{2}{\sqrt{x}}$$

$$= 3x^{\frac{3}{2}} + 2x^{-\frac{1}{2}}.$$

Thus,
$$y' = 3\left(\frac{3}{2}\right)x^{\frac{1}{2}} + 2\left(-\frac{1}{2}\right)x^{-\frac{3}{2}}$$

$$= \frac{9}{2}x^{\frac{1}{2}} - x^{-\frac{3}{2}}.$$

Once the form of the derivative has been found, the next natural step is the evaluation of the derivative for specific arguments.

Example.   If $f(x) = \dfrac{3x^2 + 2}{\sqrt{x}}$, find $f'(81)$.

Solution.   From the preceding example we know, if $f(x) = \dfrac{3x^2 + 2}{\sqrt{x}}$, then

$$f'(x) = \frac{9}{2}x^{\frac{1}{2}} - x^{-\frac{3}{2}}.$$

Thus, $f'(81) = \dfrac{9}{2}(81)^{\frac{1}{2}} - (81)^{-\frac{3}{2}}$

$$= \frac{9}{2}(9) - \frac{1}{(81)^{\frac{3}{2}}}$$

$$= \frac{81}{2} - \frac{1}{9^3}$$

$$= \left(\frac{81}{2}\right)\left(\frac{9^3}{9^3}\right) - \left(\frac{2}{2}\right)\left(\frac{1}{9^3}\right) = \frac{59049 - 2}{1458} = \frac{59047}{1458}.$$

Example.   If $f(x) = 3 - 4x + x^2$ find $f'(-1)$.
Solution. $f'(x) = -4 + 2x.$

Therefore, $f'(-1) = -4 + 2(-1)$

$$= -4 - 2 = -6.$$

2-3   Exercises

(1-10)   Find $\dfrac{dy}{dx}$ for each of the following functions.

1. $y = x^3$ 6. $y = -x^{-5}$
2. $y = x^2$ 7. $y = \sqrt{x}$
3. $y = 7x^5$ 8. $y = x^{4/5}$
4. $y = 4x^4$ 9. $y = 9x^{5/3}$
5. $y = 12x^{-3}$ 10. $y = -3x^{-4/3}$

(11-16) Find $D_x f$ for the following.

11. $f(x) = 3x^2 - 6x + 2$ **12.** $f(x) = 4 - 7x - 8x^3$

13. $f(x) = 3x^2 - 4x$

14. $f(x) = 4x^{12} + 5x^{11} - 6x^9 + 7000$

15. $f(x) = ax^2 + bx + c$, a, b, and c constants

16. $f(x) = 3ax^4 - \dfrac{bx^6}{6}$, a and b constants

(17-20) Evaluate the derivative for the indicated value of the function's domain.

17. $f'(\tfrac{1}{2})$ for $f(x) = x^{-1} + x^{-2}$ **19.** $f'(1)$ for $f(x) = \dfrac{1}{x} + \dfrac{1}{x^3}$

18. $f'(0)$ for $f(x) = \sqrt[3]{x^2}$ **20.** $f'(16)$ for $f(x) = \sqrt{x} + \dfrac{4}{\sqrt{x}}$

(21-26) Find $D_x y$ for the following.

21. $y = \dfrac{x^5 + 3x^2 + 1}{x^2}$ **24.** $y = (x + 4)^2$

22. $y = \dfrac{x + 1}{\sqrt{x}}$ **25.** $y = (x^2 + 3x)(x + 1)$

23. $y = \dfrac{x^3 + 3x^2 + x}{\sqrt{x}}$ **26.** $y = x(x + 1)(x - 1)$

(27-30) Solve for y, and find y'.

27. $xy + x = 2$ **29.** $x\sqrt{y} + 3x = 5$

28. $x^2 y + 3x = 4x^2$ **30.** $xy^2 = 16$

2-4 THE DERIVATIVE OF PRODUCTS AND QUOTIENTS

In the last section it was possible to change the products or the quotients of functions to polynomials. It is not always possible to do so.

Theorem 2-5. The derivative of the product of two functions is the first function times the derivative of the second plus the second function times the derivative of the first function. That is, if $v = v(x)$ and $u = u(x)$ are differentiable functions, then

$$\frac{d(uv)}{dx} = u\frac{dv}{dx} + v\frac{du}{dx}.$$

Proof. We apply the definition of the derivative to $uv = u(x)v(x)$.

$$\frac{d(uv)}{dx} = \lim_{\Delta x \to 0} \frac{u(x + \Delta x)v(x + \Delta x) - u(x)v(x)}{\Delta x}.$$

To the numerator, subtract and add a term $u(x + \Delta x)v(x)$.

$$\frac{d(uv)}{dx} = \lim_{\Delta x \to 0} \frac{u(x + \Delta x)v(x + \Delta x) - u(x + \Delta x)v(x) + u(x + \Delta x)v(x) - }{\Delta x}$$

$$\frac{u(x)v(x)}{\Delta x}$$

$$= \lim_{\Delta x \to 0} \frac{u(x + \Delta x)[v(x + \Delta x) - v(x)] + v(x)[u(x + \Delta x) - u(x)]}{\Delta x}$$

$$= \lim_{\Delta x \to 0} \left[u(x + \Delta x) \frac{v(x + \Delta x) - v(x)}{\Delta x} + v(x) \frac{u(x + \Delta x) - u(x)}{\Delta x} \right]$$

$$= u(x)v'(x) + v(x)u'(x)$$

$$= u \frac{dv}{dx} + v \frac{du}{dx}.$$

Example. Find y' for $y = (x + 4)(x^2 + 2)$.

Solution. Applying theorem 2-5 for the derivative of the product of two functions, $u(x)$ corresponds to $x + 4$ and $v(x)$ corresponds to $x^2 + 2$. Thus,

$$y' = u \frac{dv}{dx} + v \frac{du}{dx} = (x + 4) \frac{d(x^2 + 2)}{dx} + (x^2 + 2) \frac{d(x + 4)}{dx}$$

$$= (x + 4)2x + (x^2 + 2)(1)$$

$$= 2x^2 + 8x + x^2 + 2$$

$$= 3x^2 + 8x + 2.$$

In this example, it is possible to multiply the two functions and find the derivative term by term. This will not always be practical, but we do so now in case you are not convinced.

$$y = (x + 4)(x^2 + 2)$$

$$= x^3 + 4x^2 + 2x + 8,$$

and therefore,

$$y' = 3x^2 + 8x + 2.$$

Note that this checks with the result obtained using the first method.

Theorem 2-6. The derivative of the quotient of two differentiable functions is the denominator times the derivative of the numerator minus the numerator times the derivative of the denominator, all divided by the square of the denominator. That is, if $v = v(x)$ and $u = u(x)$ are two differentiable functions then

$$D_x\left(\frac{u}{v}\right) = \frac{vD_xu - uD_xv}{v^2}, \quad v \neq 0.$$

Proof. $D_x\left(\dfrac{u}{v}\right) = \lim_{\Delta x \to 0} \dfrac{\dfrac{u(x + \Delta x)}{v(x + \Delta x)} - \dfrac{u(x)}{v(x)}}{\Delta x}$

$$= \lim_{\Delta x \to 0} \frac{\dfrac{u(x + \Delta x)v(x) - u(x)\,v(x + \Delta x)}{v(x + \Delta x)\,v(x)}}{\Delta x}.$$

Subtract and add $u(x)v(x)$ to the numerator,

$$D_x\left(\frac{u}{v}\right) = \lim_{\Delta x \to 0} \frac{u(x + \Delta x)\,v(x) - u(x)\,v(x) - u(x)\,v(x + \Delta x) + u(x)\,v(x)}{\Delta x\,v(x + \Delta x)\,v(x)}$$

$$= \lim_{\Delta x \to 0} \frac{v(x)\dfrac{u(x + \Delta x) - u(x)}{\Delta x} - u(x)\dfrac{v(x + \Delta x) - v(x)}{\Delta x}}{v(x + \Delta x)\,v(x)}$$

$$= \frac{v(x)\,u'(x) - u(x)\,v'(x)}{[v(x)]^2}$$

$$= \frac{vD_xu - uD_xv}{v^2}, \quad v \neq 0.$$

Example. Find y' for $y = \dfrac{x^2 + 1}{x^4 + 3x}$.

Solution. $y' = \dfrac{(x^4 + 3x)D_x(x^2 + 1) - (x^2 + 1)D_x(x^4 + 3x)}{(x^4 + 3x)^2}$

$$= \frac{(x^4 + 3x)2x - (x^2 + 1)(4x^3 + 3)}{(x^4 + 3x)^2}$$

$$= \frac{2x^5 + 6x^2 - (4x^5 + 4x^3 + 3x^2 + 3)}{(x^4 + 3x)^2}$$

$$= \frac{2x^5 + 6x^2 - 4x^5 - 4x^3 - 3x^2 - 3}{(x^4 + 3x)^2}$$

$$= \frac{-2x^5 - 4x^3 + 3x^2 - 3}{(x^4 + 3x)^2}.$$

Because of the simplicity of the formula, we have used the fact that if $y = x^n$ then $y' = nx^{n-1}$ for n a rational number, but we have only proved it for positive integers. Using the formula for the derivative of the quotient of two functions it is easy to show that if $y = x^n$ then $y' = nx^{n-1}$ for n a negative integer. Suppose that n is a negative integer. Then $-n$ is positive. $y = x^n$ is equivalent to $y = \dfrac{1}{x^{-n}}$. Now we apply the formula for the derivative of the quotient of two functions to $y = \dfrac{1}{x^{-n}}$ with $v = x^{-n}$ and $u = 1$.

$$y' = \frac{x^{-n}D_x(1) - 1D_x(x^{-n})}{(x^{-n})^2}.$$

$D_x(1) = 0$, because the derivative of a constant is zero. $D_x(x^{-n}) = -nx^{-n-1}$, because $-n$ is positive integer, and the formula for the derivative of x to a positive integral power applies. Making these substitutions above:

$$y' = \frac{x^{-n}(0) - (-nx^{-n-1})}{x^{-2n}}$$

$$= \frac{nx^{-n-1}}{x^{-2n}}$$

$$= nx^{n-1}.$$

2-4   Exercises

(1-14)   Find the derivative with respect to the independent variable using the formula for the derivative of the product of two functions.

1. $y = (3x + 1)(5x + 2)$
2. $y = (7x - 3)(1 - 3x)$
3. $y = (t^2 + 4t)(t + 1)$
4. $y = (5t^2 - 3t)(2 - t)$
5. $f(x) = (3x^2 + 5x)(2x^2 + 4)$
6. $f(x) = (4x^2 - 6x)(3x^2 - 2)$
7. $f(t) = (3t^2 + 5t + 6)(4t^2 - 2t)$
8. $f(t) = (5t^2 - 6t + 4)(t^2 - 4t - 2)$
9. $y = (3x^3 + 7x^2 + x)(6x^3 - 3x^2 + 5x + 2)$
10. $y = (x^4 - x^3 + 3x + 2)(5x^4 + 3x^3 - x)$
11. $y = (t^3 + 3t)\left(1 + \dfrac{5}{t}\right)$
12. $y = \left(5t^2 + \dfrac{1}{t}\right)\left(1 - \dfrac{1}{t^2}\right)$
13. $y = x(x + 1)(x - 1)$
14. $y = 2x(2x + 1)(x - 3)$

(15-28)   Find the derivative using the quotient formula.

15. $y = \dfrac{x + 1}{x - 1}$

16. $y = \dfrac{2x + 3}{x + 2}$

17. $y = \dfrac{t}{t^2 + 1}$

18. $y = \dfrac{2t + 3}{t^2 - 1}$

19. $y = \dfrac{x^2 + 5}{x + 1}$

20. $y = \dfrac{3x^2 + 2x}{2x + 5}$

21. $y = \dfrac{t^2 + 2t + 1}{t^2 - 2t + 1}$

22. $y = \dfrac{3t^2 - 2t + 4}{2t^2 - 3t + 1}$

23. $y = \dfrac{x^3}{x^3 - 1}$

24. $y = \dfrac{x^4}{x^4 - 1}$

25. $y = \dfrac{t^{\frac{1}{3}}}{t^{\frac{1}{3}} - 1}$

26. $y = \dfrac{t^{\frac{1}{4}}}{t^{\frac{1}{4}} - 1}$

27. $y = \dfrac{1 - \sqrt{x}}{1 + \sqrt{x}}$

28. $y = \dfrac{1 - \sqrt[3]{x}}{1 + \sqrt[3]{x}}$

29. Find $\dfrac{dy}{dx}$ at $x = 3$ for $x + 2y - 3x^2y = 0$.

30. Find $\dfrac{dy}{dx}$ at $x = -7$ for $x^2 + yx + 7y = 4$.

2-5 THE DERIVATIVE OF COMPOSITE FUNCTIONS

A very important technique for finding derivatives is called the *chain rule*. It is used to find $\dfrac{dy}{dx}$ when y is a function of u and u is a function of x; that is, when y is the composite function $y = f(u(x))$. Such a function is $y = \sqrt{u}$ and $u = x^2 + 5x$ which can be written $y = \sqrt{x^2 + 5x}$.

Theorem 2-7 (Chain rule)   If y is a function of u and u is a function of x, and if y is differentiable with respect to u and u is differentiable with respect to x, then

$$\frac{dy}{dx} = \frac{dy}{du} \cdot \frac{du}{dx}.$$

Proof.   Since $y = f(u(x))$, a change of Δx in x causes a change of Δu in $u(x)$, which in turn causes a change of Δy in $y = f(u(x))$. If a change in x of Δx causes no change in u, that is $\Delta u = 0$, then there can be no change in y, that is $\Delta y = 0$, and $\dfrac{dy}{dx} = 0$. If Δx and Δu are both not zero, then we may write

$$\frac{\Delta y}{\Delta x} = \frac{\Delta y}{\Delta x} \cdot \frac{\Delta u}{\Delta u}$$

$$= \frac{\Delta y}{\Delta u} \cdot \frac{\Delta u}{\Delta x}.$$

Therefore,

$$\frac{dy}{dx} = \lim_{\Delta x \to 0} \frac{\Delta y}{\Delta x}$$

$$= \lim_{\Delta x \to 0} \left(\frac{\Delta y}{\Delta u} \cdot \frac{\Delta u}{\Delta x} \right)$$

$$= \left(\lim_{\Delta x \to 0} \frac{\Delta y}{\Delta u} \right) \cdot \left(\lim_{\Delta x \to 0} \frac{\Delta u}{\Delta x} \right).$$

Recall that $\dfrac{dy}{du} = \lim\limits_{\Delta u \to 0} \dfrac{\Delta y}{\Delta u}$ and $\dfrac{du}{dx} = \lim\limits_{\Delta x \to 0} \dfrac{\Delta u}{\Delta x}$.

Since $u(x)$ is a differentiable function, $\Delta u \to 0$ as $\Delta x \to 0$. Applying this information to the above,

$$\frac{dy}{dx} = \left(\lim_{\Delta x \to 0} \frac{\Delta y}{\Delta u} \right) \left(\lim_{\Delta x \to 0} \frac{\Delta u}{\Delta x} \right)$$

$$= \left(\lim_{\Delta u \to 0} \frac{\Delta y}{\Delta u} \right) \left(\lim_{\Delta x \to 0} \frac{\Delta u}{\Delta x} \right)$$

$$= \frac{dy}{du} \cdot \frac{du}{dx}.$$

Example.   Use the chain rule to find the derivative of $y = (2x + 3)^2$.
Solution.   The function is a composite function of the form $y = f(u(x))$ where $u = u(x) = 2x + 3$ and $y = u^2$. According to the chain rule, y' is the product of the derivative of y with respect to u times the derivative of u with respect to x. Since $y = u^2$, then $\dfrac{dy}{du} = 2u$; and since

$$u = 2x + 3, \frac{du}{dx} = 2;$$

therefore,

$$y' = \frac{dy}{du} \cdot \frac{du}{dx} = (2u)2.$$

Substituting $u = 2x + 3$,

$$y' = 2(2x + 3)2$$
$$= 4(2x + 3)$$
$$= 8x + 12.$$

In the preceding example, the derivative could have been found without resorting to the chain rule by first multiplying. That is, if $y = (2x + 3)^2$, then

$$y = 4x^2 + 12x + 9.$$

Therefore,

$$y' = 8x + 12.$$

This is the same answer found using the chain rule.

In the example, the derivative of y and u were found separately and then multiplied together according to the chain rule. Finally $(2x + 3)$ was substituted for u and the expression was simplified. It is not always necessary to write f as a function of u. Sometimes this process can be made more efficient by only identifying $f(u)$ mentally, as demonstrated in the following example. This is the same example we have already discussed in detail.

Example. Find y' for $y = (2x + 3)^2$.
Solution. Think of $y = (2x + 3)^2$ as $y = u^2$, where $u = 2x + 3$. Then $y' = 2u D_x u$. In operation it looks like this: If $y = (2x + 3)^2$, then

$$y' = \underbrace{2(2x + 3)}_{2u}\underbrace{2}_{D_x u} = 8x + 12.$$

In the last example, it was not necessary to use the chain rule to find the derivative. The chain rule is necessary when functions cannot be reduced to polynomials.

Example. Find $f'(x)$ for $f(x) = \sqrt[3]{x^4 + 5x^2 + 7}$.
Solution. $f(x) = (x^4 + 5x^2 + 7)^{\frac{1}{3}}$. Let $u = x^4 + 5x^2 + 7$, and $f(u) = u^{\frac{1}{3}}$. Therefore,

$$f'(x) = \frac{1}{3}(x^4 + 5x^2 + 7)^{-\frac{2}{3}} D_x(x^4 + 5x^2 + 7)$$

$$= \frac{1}{3}(x^4 + 5x^2 + 7)^{-\frac{2}{3}}(4x^3 + 10x)$$

$$= \frac{4x^3 + 10x}{3(x^4 + 5x^2 + 7)^{\frac{2}{3}}}.$$

We have proved that if $y = x^n$ then $y' = nx^{n-1}$ for any *integer n*. Using the chain rule, it is easy to prove this relation is true for any *rational number n*.

Theorem 2-8. If n is a rational number and $y = x^n$ then $y' = nx^{n-1}$.

Proof. Since n is a rational number, $n = \dfrac{p}{q}$, where p and q are integers, and $q \neq 0$. Thus,

$$\frac{dy}{dx} = \frac{d}{dx} x^n = \frac{d}{dx} (x^{p/q}).$$

Consider

$$\frac{d}{dx} (x^{1/q})^q = \frac{d}{dx} (x^{q/q}) = \frac{d}{dx} x = 1.$$

However, applying the chain rule

$$\frac{d}{dx} (x^{1/q})^q = q(x^{1/q})^{q-1} \frac{d}{dx} x^{1/q}.$$

Therefore,

$$q(x^{1/q})^{q-1} \frac{d}{dx} x^{1/q} = 1,$$

or

$$\frac{d}{dx} x^{1/q} = \frac{1}{q(x^{1/q})^{q-1}} = \frac{1}{q}(x^{1/q})^{1-q} = \frac{1}{q} x^{(1-q)/q}$$

$$= \frac{1}{q} x^{1/q - 1}$$

Then,

$$\frac{d}{dx} x^{p/q} = \frac{d}{dx} (x^{1/q})^p = p(x^{1/q})^{p-1} \frac{d}{dx} x^{1/q}$$

$$= p(x^{(p-1)/q}) \frac{1}{q} x^{1/q - 1}$$

$$= px^{p/q - 1/q} \frac{1}{q} x^{1/q - 1}$$

$$= \frac{p}{q} x^{p/q - 1/q + 1/q - 1} = \frac{p}{q} x^{p/q - 1}$$

$$= nx^{n-1}.$$

2-5 Exercises

(1-22) Use the chain rule to find the derivative of y with respect to x.

1. $y = (x + 5)^6$

2. $y = 3(x^2 + 4)^5$

3. $y = (2x + 1)^{\frac{1}{2}}$

4. $y = (x^2 + x)^{\frac{1}{2}}$

5. $f(x) = \sqrt{x^2 + 1}$

6. $f(x) = \sqrt[3]{x^3 - 3x^2}$

7. $f(x) = \dfrac{1}{(x + 4)^{\frac{2}{3}}}$

8. $f(x) = \dfrac{1}{(x^2 + 2x + 2)^{\frac{1}{2}}}$

9. $y = \dfrac{1}{\sqrt[3]{x^3 + 2x}}$

10. $y = \dfrac{1}{\sqrt[4]{x^3 + 5x}}$

11. $y = x\sqrt{3x + 2}$

12. $y = x^2\sqrt{3x + 2}$

13. $y = \dfrac{5x^2}{\sqrt{x^2 + 9}}$

14. $y = \dfrac{3x^2 + 2x}{\sqrt{x^3 + 2x}}$

15. $y = (x + \sqrt{x})^{\frac{1}{3}}$

16. $y = (x + \sqrt[3]{x})^{1/6}$

17. $f(x) = \dfrac{\sqrt{x^2 + 5}}{x + 2}$

18. $f(x) = \dfrac{\sqrt{x^3 + 3x}}{x^2 + 1}$

19. $f(x) = \dfrac{\sqrt[3]{x^3 + 1}}{\sqrt{x^2 - 1}}$

20. $f(x) = \dfrac{\sqrt[3]{x^2 + 5x}}{\sqrt{4x^2 - 2}}$

21. $y = \sqrt{2x + \sqrt{x^2 + 1}}$

22. $y = \sqrt{3x^3 + x\sqrt{x^2 + 1}}$

23. Find the slope of the tangent to the curve $9x^2 - 4y^2 = 36$ at the point $(2,0)$.

24. Find the slope of the tangent to the curve $16x^2 + 25y^2 = 400$ at the point $(-3, -\frac{16}{5})$.

25. Find $\dfrac{d}{dx}(x^{\sqrt{2}})$.

26. Find $\dfrac{d}{dx}(x^{\pi})$.

2-6   THE DERIVATIVE OF SIN U AND COS U

To find the derivative of $\sin x$, we can make use of the definition of the derivative of $f(x)$ and two facts about limits that were established earlier:
$\lim\limits_{\Delta x \to 0} \dfrac{\sin \Delta x}{\Delta x} = 1$ and $\lim\limits_{\Delta x \to 0} \dfrac{\cos \Delta x - 1}{\Delta x} = 0$. If $y = \sin x$, then by definition of $f'(x)$,

$$y' = \lim_{\Delta x \to 0} \frac{\sin (x + \Delta x) - \sin x}{\Delta x}.$$

Applying the trigonometric identity for the $\sin(\alpha + \beta)$,

$$\sin (\alpha + \beta) = \sin \alpha \cos \beta + \cos \alpha \sin \beta,$$

$$y' = \lim_{\Delta x \to 0} \frac{\sin x \cos \Delta x + \sin \Delta x \cos x - \sin x}{\Delta x}$$

$$= \lim_{\Delta x \to 0} \left[\frac{\sin x \cos \Delta x - \sin x}{\Delta x} + \frac{\sin \Delta x \cos x}{\Delta x} \right]$$

$$= \lim_{\Delta x \to 0} \left[\sin x \left(\frac{\cos \Delta x - 1}{\Delta x} \right) + \left(\frac{\sin \Delta x}{\Delta x} \right) \cos x \right].$$

Since $\lim\limits_{\Delta x \to 0} \dfrac{\cos \Delta x - 1}{\Delta x} = 0$, and $\lim\limits_{\Delta x \to 0} \dfrac{\sin \Delta x}{\Delta x} = 1$,

$$y' = (\sin x)0 + 1(\cos x).$$

$$y' = \cos x.$$

Therefore if $y = \sin x$, $y' = \cos x$. If u is a differentiable function of x then, by the chain rule,

$$D_x(\sin u) = \cos u \, \frac{du}{dx}.$$

We could also find the derivative of $\cos x$, by application of the definition, but instead we will make use of the chain rule. From trigonometry we have the identity

$$\cos x = \sin \left(\frac{\pi}{2} - x \right).$$

Therefore to find $D_x \cos x$, we take the derivative of $\sin u$, where $u = \dfrac{\pi}{2} - x$.

$$D_x \cos x = D_x \sin \left(\frac{\pi}{2} - x \right)$$

$$= \cos\left(\frac{\pi}{2} - x\right) D_x\left(\frac{\pi}{2} - x\right).$$

Since

$$\cos\left(\frac{\pi}{2} - x\right) = \sin x,$$

$$D_x \cos x = \sin x \cdot D_x\left(\frac{\pi}{2} - x\right)$$

since

$$D_x\left(\frac{\pi}{2} - x\right) = -1.$$

$$D_x \cos x = (\sin x)(-1)$$

$$= -\sin x.$$

If u is a differentiable function of x, then the chain rule applies, and

$$D_x(\cos u) = -\sin u \cdot \frac{du}{dx}.$$

Example.   If $y = \cos 2x$, then

$$y' = D_x \cos 2x$$

$$= -\sin 2x \cdot D_x(2x)$$

$$= -2 \sin 2x.$$

Example.   Find y' for $y = \cos 2x \sin x$.
Solution. y is the product of two functions: $\cos 2x$ and $\sin x$. Therefore, the formula for the derivative of the product of two functions applies. y' will be the first function, $\cos 2x$, times the derivative of $\sin x$ plus the second function, $\sin x$, times the derivative of $\cos 2x$.

$$y' = \cos 2x \cdot D_x \sin x + \sin x \cdot D_x \cos 2x$$

$$= \cos 2x \cdot \cos x + \sin x(-2 \sin 2x)$$

$$= \cos 2x \cos x - 2 \sin x \sin 2x.$$

Example.   Find $f'(x)$ when $f(x) = \sin^2 x$.
Solution.   The function, $f(x)$, is of the form $f(x) = u^2$, where $u = \sin x$. By the chain rule, $f'(x) = 2u D_x u$.

$$f'(x) = 2 \sin x \cdot D_x \sin x$$

$$= 2 \sin x \cos x$$

$$= \sin 2x.$$

2-6 Exercises

(1-24) Find the derivative of y with respect to x or t.

1. $y = \sin 5x$

2. $y = \sin(-3x)$

3. $y = \cos 4x$

4. $y = \cos(-2x)$

5. $y = 3 \sin t$

6. $y = -2 \sin 2t$

7. $y = -4 \cos 6t$

8. $y = -2 \cos(-t)$

9. $y = \sin x - \cos x$

10. $y = 4 \cos 3x + 5 \sin 2x$

11. $y = \cos^2 x$

12. $y = \cos x^2$

13. $y = x \cos x^2$

14. $y = x^2 \cos^2 x$

15. $y = \cos x \sin x$

16. $y = \cos^2 x \sin x$

17. $y = \sqrt{\sin x}, \; 0 \le x \le \dfrac{\pi}{2}$

18. $y = \sqrt[3]{\cos x}$

19. $y = \dfrac{\sin x}{x}$

20. $y = \dfrac{1 + \cos x}{\sin x}$

21. $y = \dfrac{1 - \sin t}{1 + \sin t}$

22. $y = \dfrac{\sin x + \cos x}{\sin x - \cos x}$

23. $y = \cos^2 \sqrt{x}$

24. $y = \sin^2 \sqrt{x^2 + 1}$

25. If the number of grams of bacteria in a population after t hours of growth is given by $y = t^2 \sin t$, find the rate of growth of the population at $t = \pi$ hours.

26. Find the growth rate of the population in exercise 25 at 6.28 hours.

27. If the income of a company is $(x^3 \cos 2x)10^3$ dollars in x years, find the rate of change of income in 3.14 years.

28. Find the rate of change of income of a company in 2 years, if income in x years is $(x^3 \sin 3x)10^3$ dollars.

29. Find the slope of the tangent line to the graph of $y = \sin x$ at $x = \dfrac{\pi}{2}$.

30. Find the slope of the tangent line to the graph of $y = \cos 2x$ when $x = \dfrac{\pi}{3}$.

2-7 DERIVATIVES OF TAN U, COT U, SEC U, AND CSC U

The derivatives of $\tan x$, $\cot x$, $\sec x$, and $\csc x$ are found by writing each in terms of $\sin x$ and $\cos x$, and then applying the formula for the derivative of the quotient of two functions or the chain rule.

If $y = \tan x$, then to find y'.

$$y' = D_x \tan x = D_x\left(\frac{\sin x}{\cos x}\right).$$

Applying the quotient formula,

$$y' = \frac{\cos x(D_x \sin x) - \sin x(D_x \cos x)}{\cos^2 x}$$

$$= \frac{\cos x(\cos x) - \sin x(-\sin x)}{\cos^2 x}$$

$$= \frac{\cos^2 x + \sin^2 x}{\cos^2 x}.$$

But

$$\cos^2 x + \sin^2 x = 1$$

$$y' = \frac{1}{\cos^2 x}$$

$$= \sec^2 x.$$

Therefore,

$$D_x(\tan x) = \sec^2 x.$$

If $y = \cot x$, then y' can be found as follows:

$$D_x(\cot x) = D_x\left(\frac{\cos x}{\sin x}\right)$$

$$= \frac{\sin x\, D_x \cos x - \cos x\, D_x \sin x}{\sin^2 x}$$

$$= \frac{\sin x(\ \sin x)\quad \cos x(\cos x)}{\sin^2 x}$$

$$= \frac{-\sin^2 x - \cos^2 x}{\sin^2 x}$$

$$= \frac{-(\sin^2 x + \cos^2 x)}{\sin^2 x}$$

$$= \frac{-1}{\sin^2 x}$$

$$= -\csc^2 x,$$

and $\qquad D_x(\cot x) = -\csc^2 x.$

To find the derivative of sec x, it is written as $\dfrac{1}{\cos x}$ and the quotient formula can be used.

$$D_x(\sec x) = D_x\left(\frac{1}{\cos x}\right)$$

$$= \frac{(\cos x)(0) - 1(-\sin x)}{\cos^2 x}$$

$$= \frac{\sin x}{\cos^2 x}$$

$$= \frac{1}{\cos x} \cdot \frac{\sin x}{\cos x}$$

$$= \sec x \tan x.$$

The derivative for csc x is established in the same way as that for the sec x.

$$D_x(\csc x) = D_x\left(\frac{1}{\sin x}\right)$$

$$= \frac{(\sin x)(0) - 1 \cos x}{\sin^2 x}$$

$$= \frac{-\cos x}{\sin^2 x}$$

$$= \frac{-1}{\sin x} \cdot \frac{\cos x}{\sin x}$$

$$= -\csc x \cot x.$$

If u is a differentiable function of x, these four derivatives can be stated:

$$D_x \tan u = \sec^2 u \cdot D_x u,$$

$$D_x \cot u = -\csc^2 u \cdot D_x u,$$

$$D_x \sec u = \sec u \tan u \cdot D_x u, \text{ and}$$

$$D_x \csc u = -\csc u \cot u \cdot D_x u.$$

Example. Find y' for $y = \tan 3x$.

Solution. We use the formula for the derivative of tan u, where $u = 3x$.

$$y' = \sec^2 3x \cdot D_x 3x$$

$$= (\sec^2 3x)3$$

$$= 3 \sec^2 3x.$$

Example. Find y' for $y = \sec^2 x$.
Solution. The function y is in the form u^2 where $u = \sec x$.

$$y' = D_x \sec^2 x$$

$$= 2 \sec x \cdot D_x \sec x$$

$$= 2 \sec x \cdot \sec x \tan x$$

$$= 2 \sec^2 x \tan x.$$

Example. Find y' for $y = x^2 \cot 2x$.
Solution. We use the formula for the derivative of the product of two functions.

$$y' = x^2 \cdot D_x(\cot 2x) + D_x(x^2) \cot 2x$$

$$= x^2(-2 \csc^2 2x) + 2x \cot 2x$$

$$= -2x^2 \csc^2 2x + 2x \cot 2x.$$

2-7 Exercises

(1-20) Find the derivative.

1. $y = \sec 3x$
2. $y = 4 \sec 2x$
3. $y = 3 \tan 2x$
4. $y = \tan 9\, x$
5. $y = \cot x^2$
6. $y = \cot \sqrt{x}$
7. $y = -4 \csc x^2$
8. $y = x \csc x$
9. $f(t) = \tan^2 t$
10. $f(t) = \sqrt{\tan t}$
11. $f(t) = 3t^2 + 7t + \sec t^2$
12. $f(t) = \sec(t^3 + 5t)$
13. $f(t) = t^2 \csc \sqrt{t}$

14. $f(x) = x \cot^3(x^2 + 5)$
15. $f(t) = \tan(\sin t)$
16. $f(t) = \sin(\sec t)$
17. $f(x) = \dfrac{\sin 2x}{\tan x}$
18. $f(x) = \dfrac{\cot 2x}{\sec 3x}$
19. $f(x) = \dfrac{\tan x - 1}{\tan x + 1}$
20. $f(x) = \dfrac{\sec x - \tan x}{\sec x + \tan x}$

2-8 HIGHER ORDER DERIVATIVES

The derivative of a function is a function and is itself often differentiable. If $y = f(x)$ is a differentiable function and $f'(x)$ is also differentiable, then the derivative of $f'(x)$ is called the *second derivative* of f, and is denoted as $f''(x)$. The third derivative of f is the derivative of f'' and is called f'''. f'' is read "f double prime." f''' is read as "f triple prime." The "prime" notation is not used after the third derivative. Symbols for the fourth derivative are

$$y^{(4)}, f^{(4)}(x), D_x^4 y, \text{ and } \frac{d^4 y}{dx^4}.$$

The nth derivative is denoted

$$y^{(n)}, f^{(n)}(x), D_x^n y, \text{ and } \frac{d^n y}{dx^n}.$$

Higher order derivatives are used in curve sketching and in curve approximations. In certain circumstances, they can also be interpreted as change in the growth rate, change in the marginal cost per item, or instantaneous acceleration.

Example.   If $y = x^3 - 7x^2 - 2x$, find the successive derivatives of y.

Solution. $y' = 3x^2 - 14x - 2$.

$y'' = 6x - 14$.

$y''' = 6$.

$y^{(4)} = 0$.

$y^{(5)} = 0$.

$y^{(6)} = 0$.

All the derivatives after the fourth derivative will be zero, since each is the derivative of zero, a constant.

Example.   Find $\dfrac{d^2 y}{dx^2}$ for $y = \sqrt{x^2 + 1}$.

Solution. $y = \sqrt{x^2 + 1} = (x^2 + 1)^{\frac{1}{2}}$. Therefore,

$$\frac{dy}{dx} = \tfrac{1}{2}(x^2 + 1)^{-\frac{1}{2}}(2x)$$

$$= \frac{x}{\sqrt{x^2 + 1}}.$$

$\dfrac{d^2 y}{dx^2}$ is the derivative of $\dfrac{dy}{dx}$. We use the formula for the derivative of the quotient of two functions.

$$\frac{d^2 y}{dx^2} = \frac{(\sqrt{x^2 + 1}) \cdot 1 - x \cdot \frac{1}{2}(x^2 + 1)^{-\frac{1}{2}} 2x}{x^2 + 1}$$

$$= \frac{\sqrt{x^2 + 1} - x^2(x^2 + 1)^{-\frac{1}{2}}}{x^2 + 1}$$

Multiplying numerator and denominator by $(x^2 + 1)^{\frac{1}{2}}$ gives

$$\frac{d^2 y}{dx^2} = \frac{x^2 + 1 - x^2}{(x^2 + 1)^{\frac{1}{2}}(x^2 + 1)}$$

$$= \frac{1}{(x^2 + 1)^{\frac{3}{2}}}.$$

Example.   Find $D_x^2 y$ when $y = \sec x$.
Solution. $D_x y = \sec x \tan x$.

$$D_x^2 y = \sec x \cdot D_x(\tan x) + \tan x \cdot D_x(\sec x)$$

$$= \sec x \cdot \sec^2 x + \tan x \cdot \sec x \tan x$$

$$= \sec^3 x + \sec x \tan^2 x.$$

2-8   Exercises

(1-14)   Find $D_x^2 y$ for the given functions.

1. $y = 3x$

2. $y = 28x$

3. $y = 2x^2 + 5x + 3$

4. $y = 5x^3 - 2x^2 + 7x$

5. $y = \dfrac{1}{x}$

6. $y = \dfrac{x}{x + 1}$

7. $y = 3x + \sin x$

8. $y = x \cos x$

9. $y = \sqrt{x^2 + 1}$

10. $y = \sqrt[3]{x^3 + 2}$

11. $y = \dfrac{x + 4}{x - 2}$

12. $y = \dfrac{x^2 + 2}{\sin x}$

13. $\sqrt{x} + \sqrt{y} = 4$

14. $y^2 - \sin x - 2x = 0, \, y \geq 0, \, x \geq 0$

(15-22)   Find $f'''(x)$ for each function.

15. $f(x) = 4x^3 + 2x^2 - x + 3$

16. $f(x) = 7x^2 + 8x + 2$

17. $f(x) = \dfrac{1}{x - 1}$

18. $f(x) = \sqrt{x + 2}$

19. $f(x) = \dfrac{x}{x + 1}$

20. $f(x) = \sin x$

21. $f(x) = \cos x$

22. $f(x) = \tan x$

23. Find $D_x^{(100)} y$ for $y = \sin x$.

24. Find $D_x^{(99)} y$ for $y = \cos x$.

25. Find the nth derivative of $y = x^a$ when $n < a$ and when $n > a$, n and a integers.

26. Find the nth derivative of $y = x^n$.

27. Graph $y = x^3 - 3x^2$ and draw tangents to the graph at the points where $f'(x) = 0$ and where $f''(x) = 0$.

28. Graph $y = x^2 - \dfrac{x^3}{6}$ and draw tangents to the curve at the points where $f'(x) = 0$ and where $f''(x) = 0$.

Here is a list of the derivative formulas from this chapter. Let $u = u(x)$ and $v = v(x)$.

$$D_x C = 0 \qquad \text{for } C \text{ constant}$$

$$D_x(u^n) = nu^{n-1} \frac{du}{dx}$$

$$D_x(u + v) = \frac{du}{dx} + \frac{dv}{dx}$$

$$D_x(u \cdot v) = u \frac{dv}{dx} + v \frac{du}{dx}$$

$$D_x\left(\frac{u}{v}\right) = \frac{v \dfrac{du}{dx} - u \dfrac{dv}{dx}}{v^2}$$

$$D_x \sin u = \cos u \frac{du}{dx}$$

$$D_x \cos u = -\sin u \frac{du}{dx}$$

$$D_x \tan u = \sec^2 u \frac{du}{dx}$$

$$D_x \cot u = -\csc^2 u \frac{du}{dx}$$

$$D_x \sec u = \sec u \tan u \frac{du}{dx}$$

$$D_x \csc u = -\csc u \cot u \frac{du}{dx}$$

Chapter 2   REVIEW

(1-5) The total cost of manufacturing x items is $C = 3x + 20$. If 70 items are produced find:

1. The fixed cost.

2. The variable cost.

3. The marginal cost.

4. The average cost per item.

5. The total cost.

(6-15) Find the first derivative.

6. $y = 3x^2 + 5x + \dfrac{1}{x^2} + \dfrac{3}{\sqrt{x}}$ **11.** $y = \dfrac{\sin x}{x^2}$

7. $xy^2 = 4, y > 0$ **12.** $y = \tan^2 x^2$

8. $y = \dfrac{x + 3}{x + 2}$ **13.** $y = \sec^2 3x$

9. $y = (t^3 + 3t)\sqrt{t^2 + 1}$ **14.** $y = \csc x^2$

10. $y = (1 - \sqrt{x})(1 + \sqrt{x})$ **15.** $y = \tan x \cot x$

(16-17) Find the second derivative.

16. $y = \sqrt{x^2 + 4}$ **17.** $y = \tan x$

(18-19) Find the third derivative.

18. $y = \cot x$ **19.** $y = \sqrt{x^2 + 1}$

20. The cost of producing x items is given, in dollars, by $C = 500 + \sqrt{x} + \dfrac{1}{x}$. Find the marginal cost $\dfrac{dC}{dx}$ of producing the 100th item.

21. If the number of grams of bacteria in a population after t hours is given by $y = t^2 \cos t$, find the growth rate of the population after 45 minutes.

CHAPTER THREE  **More about**

Derivatives and Their Applications

This chapter will consider some of the applications of the derivative to economics, business, social science, and biological science as well as some additional methods for finding derivatives.

3-1 NEWTON'S METHOD OF ROOT APPROXIMATION

Suppose in the process of determining the price to charge for a season ticket for a pro football team, a consulting mathematical management specialist discovers he must find a solution to the equation $\cos x - 5x + 6 = 0$. Unfortunately, this equation is not a type we know how to solve. In this section, we will examine how the derivative can be used to assist us to find a numerical solution. These problems require that we find the roots of nonlinear, nonquadratic equations. As the pro football example illustrates, it is not always possible to solve equations analytically.

Fortunately there are a number of methods for approximating roots of these difficult equations. The method that will be presented here was developed by Sir Isaac Newton about 1670. It can involve much tedious arithmetic when used for manual calculation of roots. However, it is extremely well suited for use by computers.

The roots of a function $y = f(x)$ are the values of x that, when substituted into the function, make its value zero. In figure 3-1, the function crosses the x axis at a, b, and c. Since the range values of a function are zero for every point on the x axis, $x = a$, b, and c are roots of the function and $f(a) = f(b) = f(c) = 0$. Therefore the problem of solving $f(x) = 0$ for x can be viewed as finding the points at which $y = f(x)$ crosses the x axis, which is exactly what Newton's method does.

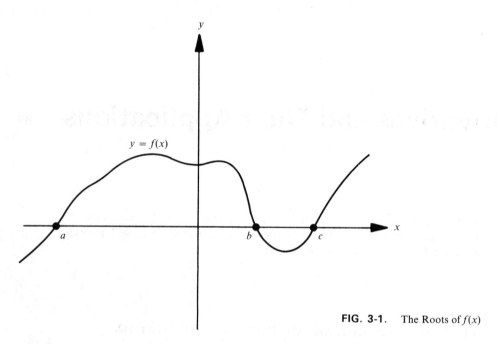

FIG. 3-1.   The Roots of $f(x)$

Newton's method of root approximation involves guessing a root and then improving the accuracy of the guess. In figure 3-2, f is a continuous differentiable function. When b is substituted for x in $f(x)$, $f(b)$ is negative; but $f(x_1)$ is positive. Therefore, since the functional value changes from positive to negative, there is a real root of $f(x) = 0$ somewhere between b and x_1. This root is denoted as a in figure 3-2. We will arbitrarily take x_1 as the first estimate of a. An improved estimate is x_2 which is the x intercept of the tangent line at $(x_1, f(x_1))$. A third estimate is x_3, which is the x intercept of the tangent line at $(x_2, f(x_2))$. By repeated applications of this process, the root can be estimated to any desired degree of accuracy.

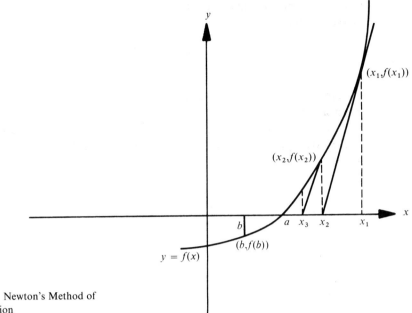

FIG. 3-2.   Newton's Method of
Approximation

We use the point-slope form of a linear equation to find the equation
of the line tangent to $y = f(x)$ at $(x_1, f(x_1))$. You should remember that
the point-slope form of a linear equation is

$$y - y_1 = m(x - x_1),$$

where m is the slope of the line. x_1 is our first estimate for the root. $y_1 = f(x_1)$, and the slope, m, is $f'(x_1)$. Thus, the equation of the tangent line is

$$y - f(x_1) = f'(x_1)(x - x_1).$$

To find x_2, note that the ordinate of any point on the x axis is 0. Therefore,
we substitute 0 for y and solve for $x = x_2$.

$$0 - f(x_1) = f'(x_1)(x_2 - x_1),$$

which implies $$\frac{-f(x_1)}{f'(x_1)} = x_2 - x_1$$

and, finally $$x_2 = x_1 - \frac{f(x_1)}{f'(x_1)}.$$

After x_2 is computed, it can be used to find x_3 by replacing x_2 by x_3 and
x_1 by x_2. That is,

$$x_3 = x_2 - \frac{f(x_2)}{f'(x_2)}.$$

In general the nth approximation can be found by using the $(n-1)$th approximation.

$$x_n = x_{n-1} - \frac{f(x_{n-1})}{f'(x_{n-1})}.$$

Example.   Use Newton's method to find a real root of $x^2 - 5x - 2 = 0$.
Solution. $f(x) = x^2 - 5x - 2$, and $f'(x) = 2x - 5$. By trial and error we find that $f(5) = -2$, and $f(6) = 4$. Therefore, there is a root between 5 and 6. We could choose either 5 or 6 or some number between them for x_1. We choose $x_1 = 5$.

$$x_2 = x_1 - \frac{f(x_1)}{f'(x_1)}$$

$$= 5 - \frac{f(5)}{f'(5)}$$

$$= 5 - \left(\frac{-2}{5}\right)$$

$$= 5 + 0.4$$

$$= 5.4.$$

Applying Newton's method a second time to find x_3,

$$x_3 = 5.4 - \frac{f(5.4)}{f'(5.4)}$$

$$= 5.4 - \frac{0.16}{5.8}$$

$$= 5.4 - 0.028$$

$$= 5.372.$$

Using the quadratic formula to solve the equation shows that, to three decimal places, $x = 5.373$. Thus after just two applications of Newton's method, x_3 differs from the root by about .001.

Newton's method fails if $f'(x_1) = 0$ where x_1 is an estimate of the root. Geometrically, this means that the slope of the tangent line is zero (see figure 3-3). A line with a slope of zero is parallel to the x axis. Hence, it cannot intersect the x axis to yield a new and better estimate of the root. Certain specific curves (see figure 3-4) are such that Newton's method does not improve an estimate of the root.

Newton's method can be used to find decimal estimates of irrational numbers.

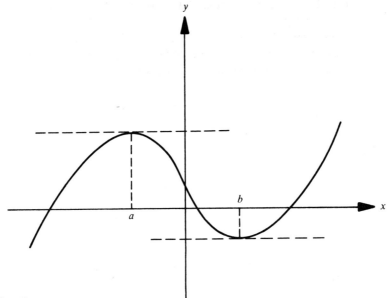

FIG. 3-3. $f'(x) = 0$

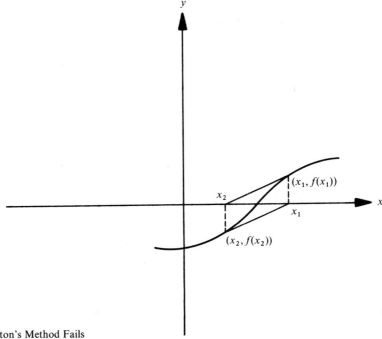

FIG. 3-4.   Newton's Method Fails

Example. Find a decimal approximation for $\sqrt{2}$ that is accurate to three decimal places.

Solution. Let $x = \sqrt{2}$, then $x^2 = 2$, and $x^2 - 2 = 0$. Use Newton's method to estimate a root of $f(x) = x^2 - 2$. The arithmetic is often simplified by applying the general formula before substituting constants.

$$x_2 = x_1 - \frac{f(x_1)}{f'(x_1)}$$

$$= x_1 - \frac{x_1^2 - 2}{2x_1}$$

$$= \frac{2x_1^2 - x_1^2 + 2}{2x_1}$$

$$= \frac{x_1^2 + 2}{2x_1}.$$

Since $f(1) = -1$ and $f(2) = 2$ there is a root between 1 and 2. Take $x_1 = 1$, then

$$x_2 = \frac{1 + 2}{1(2)} = \frac{3}{2}.$$

Find x_3 by substituting $\frac{3}{2}$ in $x_3 = \frac{x_2^2 + 2}{2x_2}.$

$$x_3 = \frac{\frac{9}{4} + 2}{2(\frac{3}{2})}$$

$$= \frac{9 + 8}{12}$$

$$= \frac{17}{12}.$$

Find x_4 by substituting $\frac{17}{12}$ in $x_4 = \frac{x_3^2 + 2}{2x_3}.$

$$x_4 = \frac{(\frac{17}{12})^2 + 2}{2(\frac{17}{12})}$$

$$= \frac{\frac{289}{144} + 2}{\frac{17}{6}}$$

$$= \frac{289 + 288}{24(17)}$$

$$= \frac{577}{408}$$

$$= 1.414.$$

3-1 Exercises

If a desk calculator is available, use it to solve these problems.

(1-4) Use two applications of Newton's method to estimate the following irrational numbers.

1. $\sqrt{3}$

3. $\sqrt[3]{10}$

2. $\sqrt[3]{2}$

4. $\dfrac{1}{\sqrt{2}}$

(5-12) Find all real roots of the given equations accurate to two decimal places.

5. $3x^2 + 5x - 8 = 0$

9. $x^3 - 8x^2 + 4x + 7 = 0$

6. $x^4 - 5 = 0$

10. $x^3 + x^2 + x + 1 = 0$

7. $x^2 + x + 1 = 0$

11. $\sin x + x + 8 = 0$

8. $5x^2 + 2x + 5 = 0$

12. $\cos x - 5x + 6 = 0$

(13-16) A root for $f(x) = 0$ can be estimated by using the x intercept of the secant line formed between the two points on $y = f(x)$, one above and the other below the x axis. The equation of such a secant is

$$y - y_2 = \frac{y_2 - y_1}{x_2 - x_1}(x - x_2),$$

where (x_1, y_1) and (x_2, y_2) are on opposite sides of the x axis. To find an estimate for a root let $y = 0$ and solve the above equation for x. The first estimate of the root, r_1, can then be used to find a second estimate by finding the x intercept of the secant line between $(r_1, f(r_1))$ and either (x_1, y_1) or (x_2, y_2), whichever is on the opposite side of the x axis from $(r_1, f(r_1))$.

For the following problems estimate the root between the indicated values of x using two applications of the "secant" method and also by using two applications of Newton's method.

13. $x^2 - 8 = 0$, between $x = 2$ and $x = 3$

14. $10 - x^2 = 0$, between $x = 3$ and $x = 4$

15. $x^3 - 4x^2 + 3x + 2 = 0$, between $x = -1$ and $x = 0$

16. $x^3 - x^2 - x - 4 = 0$, between $x = 2$ and $x = 3$

3-2   CURVE ANALYSIS

Functions can, of course, be used as mathematical models of many things. They may be used to relate supply to demand, sales to profit, or effectiveness of differing amounts of fertilizer to crop yield. In each case, the user of the model is primarily interested in how the dependent quantity relates to a set of values of the independent variable. Often, the simplest way to analyze relations is with a graph of the function involved. The derivative gives us a fundamental tool for the production of such sketches.

First and second derivatives can be used to sketch curves. In most applications an exact graph of a curve is not necessary, as long as the general shape is preserved. One criterion used to establish the "general shape" is simply whether the function is decreasing or increasing for some interval of x.

Definition.   A function is *increasing* over an interval of its domain if, for every x_1 and x_2 in the interval, $f(x_2) > f(x_1)$ whenever $x_2 > x_1$.

Definition.   A function is *decreasing* over an interval if, for every x_1 and x_2 in the interval, $f(x_2) < f(x_1)$ whenever $x_2 > x_1$.

Note that the definitions conform to an intuitive idea of increasing and decreasing functional values. An increasing function is such that the functional value increases as x increases (figure 3-5a), while a decreasing function is one where the functional images decrease when x increases (figure 3-5b).

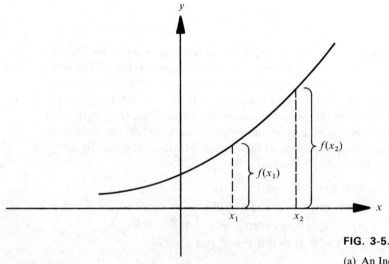

FIG. 3-5.

(a) An Increasing Function

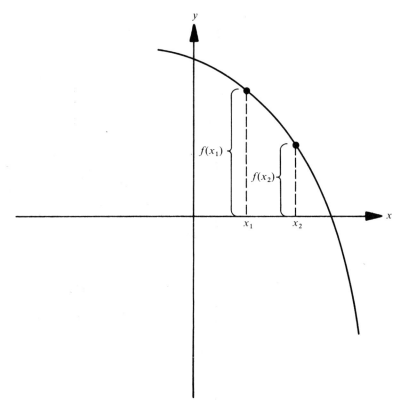

(b) A Decreasing Function

It is not usually convenient to apply the definitions to determine the intervals of x for which a given function increases or decreases. A better method uses the first derivative. Recall that $f'(x) = \lim\limits_{\Delta x \to 0} \dfrac{\Delta y}{\Delta x}$. Therefore, if a function is increasing, as in figure 3-6a, both Δx and Δy will be positive or both negative. Thus their ratio is positive, and

$$\lim_{\Delta x \to 0} \frac{\Delta y}{\Delta x} = f'(x) > 0.$$

If a function is decreasing, as in figure 3-6b, Δx and Δy are of different signs so their ratio is negative. Therefore,

$$\lim_{\Delta x \to 0} \frac{\Delta y}{\Delta x} = f'(x) < 0.$$

This leads to the following theorem, which will be stated without proof.

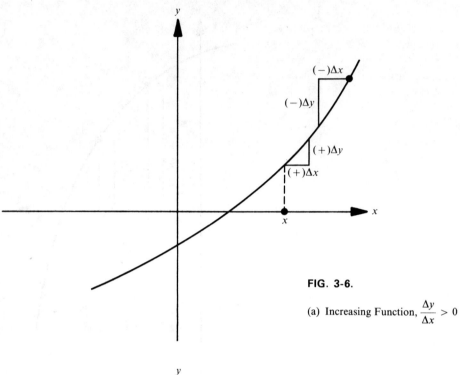

FIG. 3-6.

(a) Increasing Function, $\dfrac{\Delta y}{\Delta x} > 0$

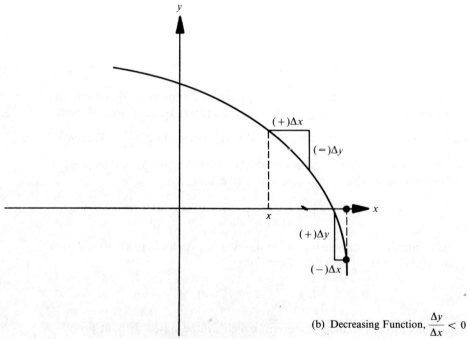

(b) Decreasing Function, $\dfrac{\Delta y}{\Delta x} < 0$

Theorem 3-1.   If $f'(x) > 0$ for all x such that $a < x < b$, then $f(x)$ is increasing on the interval from a to b. If $f'(x) < 0$ for all x such that $a < x < b$ then $f(x)$ is decreasing on the interval from a to b.

Example.   Find the values of x for which $f(x) = x^2$ is increasing and those for which it is decreasing.
Solution. $f'(x) = 2x$; so $f'(x) > 0$ for all positive numbers and $f'(x) < 0$ for all negative numbers. Thus, by the above theorem, the function increases for x positive and decreases for x negative. This is clearly shown by the graph of the function in figure 3-7.

When $f'(x) = 0$ the slope of the tangent line is 0 and the tangent is parallel to the x axis. In this case the function is neither increasing nor decreasing. In the last example, $f'(x) = 0$ when $x = 0$.

The intervals of x for which a function is increasing or decreasing are slightly more difficult to find when the equation is cubic or higher in degree.

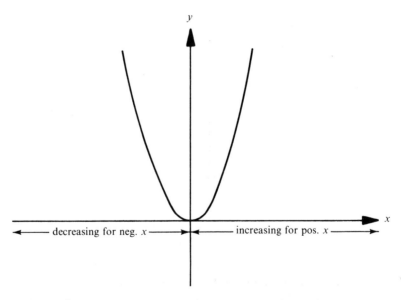

FIG. 3-7.   A Graph of $y = x^2$

Example.   Find the values of x for which $f(x) = 2x^3 + 3x^2 - 72x$ is increasing and decreasing.
Solution. $f'(x) = 6x^2 + 6x - 72$ which, in factored form, is $f'(x) = 6(x + 4)(x - 3)$. By the above theorem, the function is increasing when

$f'(x) > 0$ and decreasing when $f'(x) < 0$. The sign of the derivative can be determined by examining the signs of its factors: if the factors are both positive or both negative, the derivative is positive; if one factor is positive and the other is negative the derivative is negative. The derivative is zero when $x = -4$ or $x = 3$. To determine the sign of the derivative we test in succession, values of x less than -4, between -4 and 3, and greater than 3. If $x < -4$, then $(x + 4) < 0$, and $(x - 3) < 0$; hence, $f'(x) = 6(x + 4) \cdot (x - 3) > 0$. If $-4 < x < 3$, then $x + 4 > 0$, and $x - 3 < 0$; therefore, $f'(x) = 6(x + 4)(x - 3) < 0$. If $x > 3$, then $x + 4 > 0$, and $x - 3 > 0$; therefore, $f'(x) > 0$. The function is increasing when $x < -4$ or $x > 3$ and decreasing when $-4 < x < 3$; see figure 3-8.

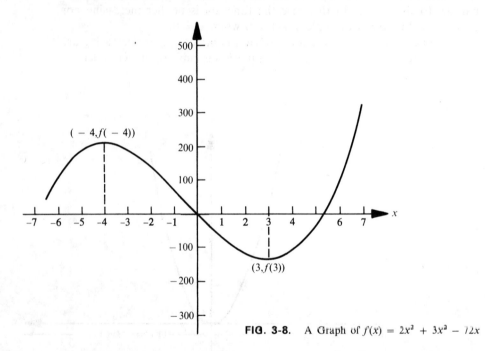

FIG. 3-8.   A Graph of $f(x) = 2x^3 + 3x^2 - 12x$

A second characteristic of curves, which is easily examined by use of derivatives (second derivatives to be exact), is called *concavity*. The first derivative, $f'(x)$, of a function is also a function. For certain values of x, $f'(x)$ will be an increasing function, for others decreasing. To discover the values of x for which $f'(x)$ is increasing (or decreasing), examine its derivative. This is the second derivative of $f(x)$. If $f''(x) > 0$, then $f'(x)$ is increasing; if $f''(x) < 0$, then $f'(x)$ is decreasing. $f'(x)$ is the slope of the line tangent to the curve $y = f(x)$ at the point $(x, f(x))$. If $f'(x)$ is increasing, the slope of the tangent line is increasing; if $f'(x)$ is decreasing, the slope of the tangent line is decreasing. Figure 3-9 shows a curve such that the

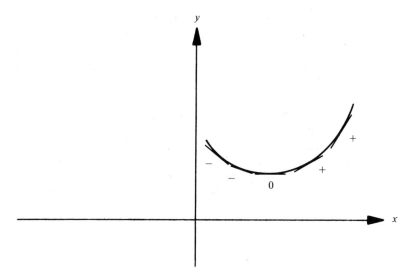

FIG. 3-9. Concavity Upward

slope of the tangent lines increases from negative values to zero to positive values as x increases. Such a curve is said to be *concave upward*.

Figure 3-10 illustrates a curve that is concave downward. Note that the slope of successive tangent lines decreases from positive to zero to negative values.

Therefore, a curve is concave upward for values of x for which its first derivative is an increasing function. This happens when $f''(x) > 0$. By

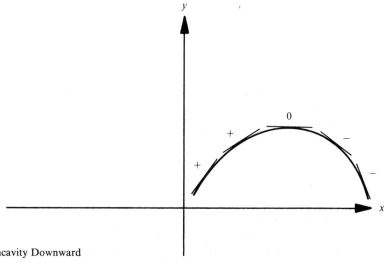

FIG. 3-10. Concavity Downward

similar reasoning, a curve is concave downward for values of x for which $f''(x) < 0$. The point where a curve changes from concave downward to concave upward is called a *point of inflection*. Similarly, a point where a curve changes from concave upward to concave downward is also a point of inflection.

Given a function $y = f(x)$, if the second derivative exists on an interval that contains a point of inflection, $(a, f(a))$, then $f''(a) = 0$. This follows from the fact that the curve is concave downward on one side of a point of inflection and concave upward on the other. Therefore the second derivative is negative on one side of a point of inflection and positive on the other. Then the second derivative must equal zero *at* the point of inflection, since by hypothesis it exits there. In figure 3-11 a tangent line is drawn at the point of inflection.

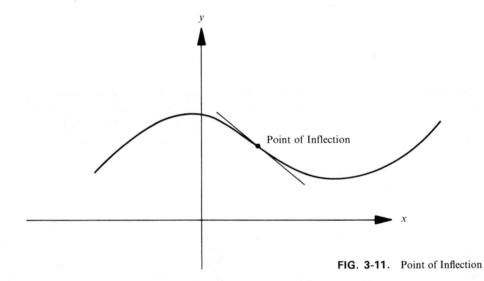

FIG. 3-11. Point of Inflection

Example. Find the points of inflection and values of x for which $f(x) = x^3 + 3x^2$ is concave upward and those for which it is concave downward.

Solution. $f'(x) = 3x^2 + 6x$, and $f''(x) = 6x + 6$. To find the point of inflection, set $f''(x)$ equal to zero, and solve for x.

$$6x + 6 = 0$$

$$6x = -6$$

$$x = -1.$$

The second derivative, $6x + 6$, is negative for $x < -1$ and positive for $x > -1$. Therefore, $f(x)$ is concave downward for $x < -1$ and concave upward for $x > -1$; it has a point of inflection at $x = -1$, $y = 2$. Figure 3-12 is the graph of the curve.

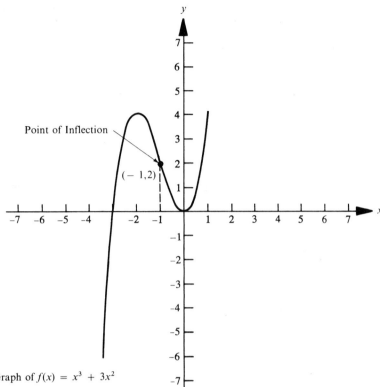

Point of Inflection

$(-1,2)$

FIG. 3-12. A Graph of $f(x) = x^3 + 3x^2$

3-2   Exercises

(1-12)   Is the given function increasing or decreasing, and is it concave upward or concave downward for the indicated values of x?

1. $f(x) = 3x^2 + 15x,\ x = -3$

2. $f(x) = 4x^2 - 28x + 7,\ x = -10$

3. $f(x) = 8x^3 + 9x^2 - 18x + 15,\ x = 0$

4. $f(x) = x^5 + x^3 - x^2 + x,\ x = -3$

5. $y = x^5 + 5x^3 + 18x^2,\ x = 0$

6. $y = x^3 + 3x^2 + 14,\ x = -2$

7. $y = 4x - 14,\ x = 7$

8. $y = -3x + 9,\ x = -2$

9. $y = x^2 + \dfrac{1}{x^2},\ x = 0$

10. $y = \sqrt{x^2 + 25},\ x = -1$

11. $y = x^2 \cos x,\ x = \dfrac{\pi}{4}$

12. $y = \tan x \sec x,\ x = \dfrac{\pi}{4}$

(13-18)   Find the values of the independent variable for which the function is increasing or decreasing and for which it is concave upward or downward. Sketch the function.

13. $f(x) = x^2 + 2x + 1$

14. $f(x) = 3x^2 - 8x + 14$

15. $f(t) = 4t^3 - 45t^2 + 150t$

16. $f(t) = \frac{4}{3}t^3 + 4t^2 - 45t + 100$

17. $xy = 6$

18. $xy = 1$

(19-22) Find the points of inflection.

19. $y = x^3$

20. $y = x^{10} + x^8$

21. $y = \sqrt[3]{x}$

22. $y = x^{\frac{2}{3}}$

23. Sketch a continuous function with the following properties: $f(0) = 0$; $f(5) = -3$; $f'(5) = 0$; $f''(-1) = 0$; $f''(11) = 0$; $f''(x) < 0$ for $x < -1$ or $x > 11$, and $f''(x) > 0$ for $-1 < x < 11$.

24. Sketch a continuous function with the following properties: $f(-2) = f'(-2) = f''(-2) = 0$; $f'(x) < 0$ for $x \neq -2$; $f''(x) > 0$ for $x < -2$; $f''(x) < 0$ for $x > -2$.

3-3 MAXIMA—MINIMA

One of the most useful applications of the derivative is to find the largest and smallest values a function can take on over its domain. Consider the problem of the manufacture of a container designed to hold a fixed volume; by using the minimum amount of material necessary the cost of manufacture can be held to a minimum, and hopefully the profit can be maximized. In a like manner, a farmer's profit depends on his costs, and he is interested in maximizing profits by minimizing costs. If we assume that the quantities to be dealt with can be placed in some kind of functional relation, then the derivative can supply us with tools to find the maximum or minimum. This section will examine the mathematical theory necessary to solve these types of problems; the next section will apply the theory to specific problems.

Definitions. If $f(a) > f(x)$ for all x near a, then $f(a)$ is called a *relative maximum* value of f. If $f(a) < f(x)$ for all x near a, then $f(a)$ is called a *relative minimum* value of f. If $f(a)$ is greater than $f(x)$ for all other values of x for which the function is defined then $f(a)$ is the *absolute maximum* value of f. In the same manner if $f(a)$ is less than all other images of f then $f(a)$ is the *absolute minimum*.

In figure 3-13, points P_1, P_3, and P_6 are relative maximum points. Point P_6 is also the absolute maximum of the function. Points P_2 and P_4 are relative minima. There is no absolute minimum. Point P_5 is neither a relative maximum nor a relative minimum point.

The words "relative" and "absolute" are usually dropped. Thus a minimum or maximum value of a function will mean either a relative or an absolute minimum or maximum value. An *extremum* of a function is a relative maximum or a relative minimum value. *Extrema* is the plural of extremum.

If $f'(a) = 0$ or $f'(a)$ is undefined, then a is called a *critical value*. Maxima and minima are found by examining critical values. If all critical values yielded either a maximum or a minimum value of the function, our problem would be greatly simplified. However, they do not. In figure 3-13, the domain element of P_5 is a critical value since the slope of the tangent at P_5 is zero, but P_5 is neither a maximum nor a minimum value of the function. It is a point of inflection. If the behavior of a curve is known through studying its derivatives, its maxima and minima can easily be found. We can use a simple example to illustrate this.

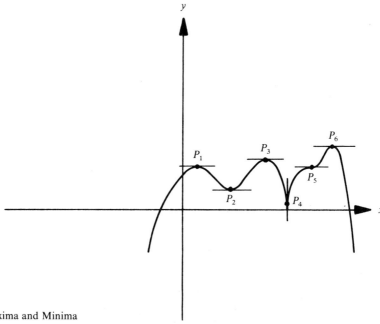

FIG. 3-13.   Maxima and Minima

Example.   Find the extrema for $y = x^2 - 2x$.
Solution.   Since $y = x^2 - 2x$ is the equation of a parabola, it will have a single maximum or minimum point. In fact, since it is concave upward,

the point we are looking for will be a minimum point. To find it we examine critical values, values of x that cause $y' = 2x - 2$ to equal zero or be undefined. Since y' is defined for all x, we need only set it equal to zero and solve for x.

$$2x - 2 = 0$$

$$2x = 2$$

$$x = 1.$$

Substituting 1 for x in the original equation,

$$y = 1^2 - 2(1)$$

$$= -1.$$

Thus the minimum value for y is -1, and the extremum is at the point $(1, -1)$. Figure 3-14 shows the graph of the function and its minimum point. The tangent line at the minimum point has slope zero.

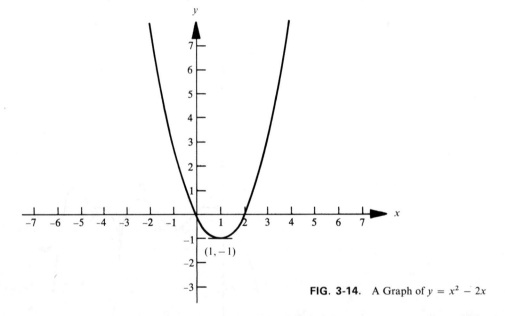

FIG. 3-14. A Graph of $y = x^2 - 2x$

The problem of finding maximum or minimum points is more difficult if the general shape of the curve of the function is not well known. In this case it is difficult to tell if a certain critical value is at a maximum point, minimum point, or neither. Of course, it is usually possible to test a critical value by substituting it into the equation of the function, then comparing the functional value with two others found by substituting values slightly greater and slightly less than the critical value into the function. In this manner we can determine whether the critical value yields a functional value greater than or less than those produced by values of x close to the critical value. An alternative and better method is to examine the first or second derivatives near the critical value.

In the graph of a relative maximum point, figure 3-15a, note that the slope of the tangent line changes from a positive slope to zero slope and finally to a negative slope as x increases in value. In the graph of a relative minimum point, figure 3-15b, the slope of the tangent line changes from negative to zero and then to positive. For points that are neither relative maxima nor relative minima, figure 3-15c, the tangent lines on either side of critical values both have positive slopes or both have negative slopes. These properties are summarized in the following test:

THE FIRST DERIVATIVE TEST FOR EXTREMA: If $x = a$ is a critical number and if f is continuous on an interval about a;

1. If $f'(x)$ changes sign from positive to negative as x increases in value over an interval containing a, then $f(a)$ is a maximum value of f.
2. If $f'(x)$ changes in sign from negative to positive as x increases in value over an interval containing a, then $f(a)$ is a minimum value of f.
3. If $f'(x)$ does not change sign as x increases in value over an interval

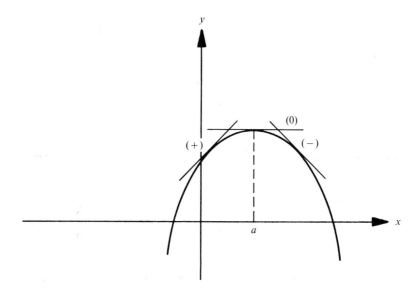

FIG. 3-15.   (a) Relative Maximum $[+, 0, -]$

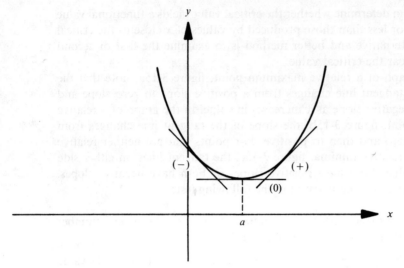

(b) Relative Minimum $[-,0,+]$

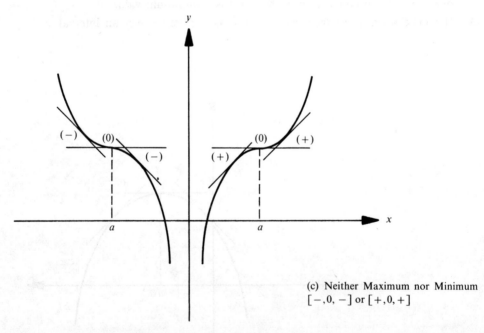

(c) Neither Maximum nor Minimum
$[-,0,-]$ or $[+,0,+]$

that contains a, then $f(a)$ is neither a maximum nor a minimum value of f.

Example. Examine $y = 2x^3 + 3x^2 - 72x$ for maximum and minimum values.

Solution.   We find critical values by taking the first derivative, setting it equal to zero, and solving for x.

$$y' = 6x^2 + 6x - 72 = 0$$

$$6(x^2 + x - 12) = 0$$

$$6(x + 4)(x - 3) = 0$$

$$x = -4, \text{ or } x = 3.$$

The question is: What kinds of points are produced by the critical values, -4 and 3?

We apply the first derivative test to y' for an interval about -4. If x is slightly less than -4, then the factor $(x + 4)$, from $y' = 6(x + 4)(x - 3)$, is negative and the factor $(x - 3)$ is also negative. The derivative is the product of two negatives and, hence, is positive. If x is slightly greater than -4 then $(x + 4)$ is positive while $(x - 3)$ is negative. The derivative is negative. Therefore, as x increases in value over an interval that contains -4, the slope of the tangent line changes from positive to negative. By the first step of the first derivative test, $(-4, f(-4))$ is a maximum point.

Applying the first derivative test to $x = 3$, if x is slightly less than 3, then $(x + 4)$ is positive while $(x - 3)$ is negative. In this case the derivative is the product of a positive number and a negative number and is negative. If x is slightly greater than 3, then both $(x + 4)$ and $(x - 3)$ are positive and the derivative is positive. Thus as x increases in value over an interval that contains 3, the first derivative changes sign from negative to positive. By the second step of the first derivative test, $(3, f(3))$ is a minimum point on the graph of f. The function $y = 2x^3 + 3x^2 - 72x$ is graphed in figure 3-8.

The second derivative is often easier to use to test for maxima and minima since the concavity at any point is indicated by the second derivative. Recall that if the second derivative is negative at some point, the curve is concave downward there, and if the second derivative is positive at a point then the curve is concave upward at that point. One type of maximum point, where the derivative exists, can be described as a point where the slope of the tangent line is zero and the curve is concave downward while some minima, again where the derivative exists, are points where the tangent line has zero slope and the curve is concave upward.

THE SECOND DERIVATIVE TEST FOR EXTREMA: If $f'(x)$ and $f''(x)$ exist for an interval that contains a, and if $f'(a) = 0$, then:

1. If $f''(a) < 0, f(a)$ is a maximum value of f.
2. If $f''(a) > 0, f(a)$ is a minimum value of f.

The second derivative test cannot be used to describe the curve when $f''(a) = 0$. If $f''(a) = 0$, the point $(a, f(a))$ could be a point of inflection.

However, for certain special curves it could also be a maximum or minimum value. When the second derivative is zero, the second derivative test fails and we must resort to the first derivative test.

Example.   Examine $y = 2x^3 + 3x^2 - 72x$ for maximum and minimum values.

Solution.   This is the same problem posed in the last example. The curve is drawn in figure 3-8. The first and second derivatives are:

$$y' = 6x^2 + 6x - 72, \text{ and}$$

$$y'' = 12x + 6.$$

The critical values were found to be $x = -4$ and $x = 3$ in the last example. By inspecting the second derivative, it is easy to see that $y'' < 0$ when $x = -4$, and $y'' > 0$ when $x = 3$. Therefore, by the second derivative test, $x = -4$ yields a maximum point, and $x = 3$ yields a minimum.

Example.   Examine $y = x^{\frac{2}{3}}$ for maximum and minimum points.

Solution. $y' = \frac{2}{3}x^{-\frac{1}{3}} = \dfrac{2}{3\sqrt[3]{x}}.$ y' cannot equal zero and is undefined when $x = 0$. Therefore $x = 0$ is a critical point. To test it, we apply the first derivative test: If x is negative, $y' = \dfrac{2}{3\sqrt[3]{x}}$ is negative. If x is positive, y' is positive. Therefore y' changes from negative to positive as x increases. The critical value, $x = 0$, is at a minimum point. This is clearly seen in the graph of the curve, figure 3-16. Since y' is undefined at $x = 0$, the slope

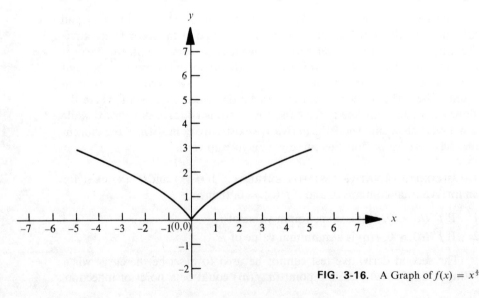

FIG. 3-16.   A Graph of $f(x) = x^{\frac{2}{3}}$

of the tangent at that point is undefined, and the tangent is vertical at the origin. Also, the second-derivative test shows the curve to be concave downward for all values of x except $x = 0$.

3-3   Exercises

(1-21)   Find the maximum and minimum points for each of the following functions.

1. $y = 2x^2 + 8x + 3$

2. $y = 16 - 3x - 9x^2$

3. $y = 4x + 9$

4. $y = -8x + 2$

5. $y = x^3$

6. $y = 2x^3 - 6x$

7. $y = 4x^3 - 12x$

8. $y = x^3 + 3x^2 - 1$

9. $y = 2x^3 - 3x^2 - 36x + 4$

10. $y = x^4 - 2x^2$

11. $f(x) = x^4 - 2x^2 + 12$

12. $f(x) = x^5$

13. $f(x) = x^7$

14. $f(x) = x^4$

15. $f(x) = x + \dfrac{1}{x}$

16. $f(x) = 4x + \dfrac{16}{x}$

17. $f(x) = 3(x^{\frac{2}{3}} - x^{\frac{1}{3}})$

18. $f(x) = \dfrac{x - 1}{x + 1}$

19. $f(x) = x\sqrt{x - 1}$

20. $f(x) = \dfrac{x^2}{x - 1}$

21. $f(x) = x^{\frac{2}{3}} + x$

(22-23)   Use one application of Newton's method to estimate the maximum or minimum point for each of the following functions (this method will facilitate the solution of the cubic equation which results when $y' = 0$).

22. $y = x^4 + 8x^2 + x$

23. $y = x^4 - 10x^3 + x^2 + x$

3-4   APPLICATIONS OF MAXIMUM-MINIMUM

The difficulty with the application of any mathematical theory, including the one presented here, to the solution of problems is that questions are usually stated in words rather than in equations. The problem of creating an equation is especially difficult in maximum-minimum problems, because any single exercise may use a number of different formulas. The key point is this: *The quantity to be maximized or minimized must be written as a function of some independent variable.* For instance, if income is to be maximized then income must be written as a function of some independent variable such as the number of items produced. If surface area is to be minimized then it must be written as a function of an independent variable such as length or width.

Example.   Divide 36 into two parts whose product is maximum.
Solution.   The product must be written as a function of one of the parts of 36. Let x be one the parts of 36. Then $(36 - x)$ is the other part of 36. Let p represent the product.

$$p = x(36 - x)$$
$$= 36x - x^2.$$

To maximize p, find the critical values of x by taking the first derivative of p with respect to x, setting it equal to zero, and solving for x.

$$p' = 36 - 2x = 0$$
$$-2x = -36$$
$$x - 18, \text{ and } 36 - x - 18.$$

Since $p = 36x - x^2$ is a parabola opening downward, we know that the critical value is at a maximum point. Therefore, the two numbers 18 and 18 are the parts of 36 that give the maximum product.

Example.   Suppose that a rancher has 100 feet of chicken wire to make a chicken yard. One side of the yard will be formed by the side of a barn so no wire will be needed there. What are the dimensions of the yard if it is to be rectangular in shape and contain maximum area?
Solution.   Since area is to be maximized, we need an equation for it. Let w be the width of the yard and l the length, as in figure 3-17. Then, if A represents area,

$$A = wl, \text{ and } 2w + l = 100.$$

In order to maximize area we need to describe it as a function of a single

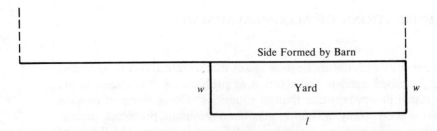

FIG. 3-17.   Area of Yard

variable. Therefore, we solve $2w + l = 100$ for l and substitute into the formula for area:

$$l = 100 - 2w \quad \text{and,}$$

$$A = wl = w(100 - 2w),$$

so

$$A = 100w - 2w^2.$$

To maximize A, take its derivative, set the derivative equal to zero, and solve for w.

$$A' = 100 - 4w = 0$$

$$-4w = -100$$

$$w = 25.$$

Substitute $w = 25$ into $l = 100 - 2w$, and solve for l.

$$l = 100 - 2(25)$$

$$= 100 - 50$$

$$= 50.$$

The yard should be 25 feet wide and 50 feet long in order to have maximum area.

Example.   A certain television set manufacturer will, on the average, sell 1,000 television sets per month at $500 per set, and he can sell an additional 100 sets per month for each $20 decrease in price. What priced set will bring the greatest income?

Solution.   Let the price of the television set be x dollars. Since the income is to be maximized, we need an expression for income in terms of the independent variable, price. It is clear that the income will be equal to the price per TV set times the number of sets sold. If I stands for the income then,

$$I = (\text{price per set})(\text{number of sets sold}).$$

But x stands for the price per set, so income is

$$I = x(\text{number of sets sold}).$$

The number of sets sold will be 1,000 sets plus 100 more sets for each $20 price reduction from $500. The price reduction is the original price of $500 minus the new price of x dollars or $500 - x$. For each $20 in the reduction 100 more sets will be sold. The question is, how many units of $20 each is the reduction, $500 - x$? The answer is $\dfrac{500 - x}{20}$. Thus the number of sets sold in excess of 1,000 will be

$$100\left(\frac{500 - x}{20}\right).$$

Therefore, the total number of sets sold will be 1,000 plus the extra sets sold because of the price reduction, or

$$1,000 + 100\left(\frac{500 - x}{20}\right).$$

Since the income, I, is the price per set times the number of sets sold,

$$I = x\left[1,000 + 100\left(\frac{500 - x}{20}\right)\right]$$
$$= x[1,000 + 5(500 - x)]$$
$$= x[1,000 + 2,500 - 5x]$$
$$= x[3,500 - 5x]$$
$$= 3,500x - 5x^2.$$

Taking the derivative, setting it equal to zero, and solving for x gives:

$$I' = 3,500 - 10x = 0.$$
$$-10x = -3,500.$$
$$x = 350.$$

The price that will yield maximum income is $350.

3-4 Exercises

1. Find two numbers whose sum is 30 and whose product is maximum.
2. Find two numbers whose sum is 30 and the sum of their squares is minimum.
3. Find two numbers whose sum is 30 and the sum of the square of one plus ten times the other is minimum.
4. Find the dimensions of the open box with the largest volume that can be made from a 12-inch, square piece of cardboard by cutting equal squares from the corners and turning up the sides.
5. Find the volume, to the nearest one tenth of a cubic inch, of the open box with the greatest volume that can be made from an 8-inch by 15-inch rectangular piece of sheet metal by cutting equal squares from the corners and folding up the sides.
6. What are the dimensions of the rectangular field with maximum area that has a perimeter of 1,000 feet?

7. A rectangular garden is to be created using 600 feet of fencing. At one corner of the garden and at right angles to each other there will be a 20-foot shed and a 20-foot gate. Find the dimensions of the garden with maximum area if no fencing is needed for the spaces occupied by the shed and the gate.

8. Find the volume of the box with the greatest volume that can be made from 1,200 square inches of material if the box is to be rectangular with a square base and no top.

9. A rectangular box with a square base is to contain 540 cubic inches. If the top costs $0.30 per square inch of material, the bottom $0.20 and the sides $0.10, find the dimensions of the box so that the cost is minimum.

10. A poster is to contain 200 square inches of illustrations and instructions. The top and bottom margins are to be 4 inches wide while the side margins are 2 inches wide. Find the length and width of the poster that would use the least amount of paper.

11. Answer exercise 10 for a poster that is to contain 100 square inches of printed material with the same margins.

12. What dimensions of a cylindrical coffee can would require the least amount of metal if the can is to contain 64 cubic inches of coffee?

13. In making a cylindrical tin can to contain 64 cubic inches of coffee, there is no waste involved in making the vertical side of the can. However, the circular top and bottom are cut from squares of material with the corner parts of the square wasted. What are the height and radius of the most economical can?

14. An ammonia tank is to hold c cubic feet. It is constructed of a cylinder capped on each end by a hemisphere. Find the dimensions of the most economical tank if the cylindrical part costs $10.00 per square foot to build while the hemispheres cost $15.00 per square foot.

15. The cross section of a culvert is in the shape of an isosceles triangle with vertex downward. The equal sides of the triangle are 10 feet long. Such a culvert will handle maximum water flow when it has maximum cross sectional area. At what angle should the equal sides be to one another in order for the culvert to handle maximum water flow?

16. The culvert of exercise 15 is to be made in the shape of an isosceles trapezoid with shorter base downward. The equal sides and the short base are all 10 feet long. How long should the other base be so that the culvert will carry maximum water flow?

17. A golf pro-shop operator has found that he can sell 500 sets a year of his top grade clubs at $300 per set. For each $5.00 he drops the price, he will sell 10 more sets of clubs. What price would give him the largest gross income?

18. A resort hotel will provide a dinner, dance and drinks for a local organization at $50 a couple, with the agreement that there be at least 100 couples attending. However, it is also agreed that the price will be reduced $2.00 per couple for each 10 couples in excess of 100. How many couples will maximize the hotel's total revenue?

19. The board of directors of the organization described in exercise 18 agreed to the $50 but thought that the price should be reduced $0.20 per couple for each couple in excess of 100. Now how many couples will it take to maximize the hotel's gross revenue?

20. When traveling at s miles per hour, the cost per hour of operating a truck is $12 + \dfrac{s^2}{48}$, which includes the driver's wages, depreciation, cost of fuel, maintenance, insurance, etc. At what speed is the cost minimum during a 96-mile trip?

21. At what speed is the cost minimum for the truck in exercise 20 if the cost per hour is $20 + \dfrac{s^2}{100}$ and the trip is 500 miles?

22. A power line runs due north. Town A is 2 miles due east from point c on the power line. Town B is 10 miles due east from point d on the power line. Points c and d are 5 miles apart. At what point between c and d on the power line should a transformer be located so that when power lines are run from it to towns A and B, they will be of minimum length?

23. Three towns are located at the vertices of an isosceles triangle. Towns B and C are at the base angles while A is at the vertex of the triangle. The distance from B to C is 16 miles and the altitude through A is 10 miles. How far from A, along the altitude through A, should a well be located so that it will use minimum pipe when supplying water to all three towns?

24. A printer has contracted to print 500,000 campaign posters. He could set in type a large number of metal copies of the poster so that each impression of his printing press would create a number of posters, or he could set a single metal copy of the poster and use 500,000 impressions of his printing press. A single metal copy of the poster costs $0.80 to set in type. It costs $5.00 per hour to run the printing press. How many metal copies of the poster should be set to minimize the cost of printing if the press runs 1,000 impressions per hour?

25. For a certain commodity, x items will be sold per week when the price is $P = 100 - 0.10x$ dollars. The cost of x items is $C = 50x + 1,000$ dollars. How many should be produced each week in order to maximize profits?

26. Answer exercise 25 for a price $P = 8,000 - 7x$ dollars and a cost $C = 25x + 950$ dollars.

3-5   THE DIFFERENTIAL

To this point, the symbol $\dfrac{dy}{dx}$ $\left(\text{or } \dfrac{df}{dx}\right)$ has simply denoted the first derivative of a function with respect to x. However, it is useful to be able to think of $\dfrac{dy}{dx}$ as the quotient of the two symbols dy and dx. The following definitions will allow us to think of $\dfrac{dy}{dx}$ as either the derivative of a function with respect to x or the ratio of dy and dx. This will in turn, expand possible interpretations of the derivative.

> **Definition.**   If $y = f(x)$ is a differentiable function of x, then the *differential*, dx, is an increment of x. That is, $dx = \Delta x$. The differential $dy = f'(x)dx$.

Example.   If $y = 2x^3 + 7x$, find the differential of y.

Solution. $dy = f'(x)dx$, but $f'(x) = 6x^2 + 7$,

so, $dy = (6x^2 + 7)dx$.

The differential dy is also denoted by df. Therefore, $df = dy = f'(x)dx$. Note that if both sides of

$$dy = f'(x)dx$$

are divided by dx, we have

$$\frac{dy}{dx} = f'(x), \ dx \neq 0.$$

Thus, $\dfrac{dy}{dx}$ can be thought of as the symbol for the first derivative of $f(x)$, or as the quotient of differentials.

Although it is useful to consider $dx = \Delta x$, in general, $dy \neq \Delta y$. This can be seen in figure 3-18.

The line through points A and D is tangent to the curve at point A. The derivative evaluated at point A gives the slope of the tangent line. But, the ratio of the lengths of line segments $\overline{DC}$ to $\overline{AC}$ is also the slope of the tangent line. Therefore,

$$f'(x) = \frac{\overline{DC}}{\overline{AC}}.$$

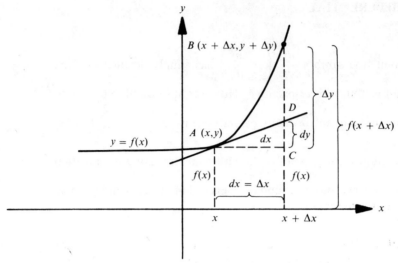

FIG. 3-18.   The Differential

But the length of $\overline{AC}$ is dx; therefore dy must equal the measure of $\overline{DC}$ since

$$f'(x) = \frac{\overline{DC}}{\overline{AC}} = \frac{\overline{DC}}{dx}.$$

$$\overline{DC} = f'(x)dx = dy.$$

Now for any change, Δx, in x, $\Delta y = f(x + \Delta x) - f(x)$. This is also shown in figure 3-18, where the difference between Δy and dy given by the line segment $\overline{BD}$. Although dy is not equal to Δy, it is a good estimate of Δy when dx is small. To see this, note that in figure 3-18, if dx were made very small, then the difference between dy and Δy would also become very small. The fact that dy is a good estimate of Δy is useful, because dy is usually much easier to compute than Δy.

Example.   Find Δy and dy for $y = f(x) = x^2 + 4x$ when $x = 3$ and $\Delta x = .2$.

Solution. $\Delta y = f(x + \Delta x) - f(x)$

$$= f(3 + 0.2) - f(3)$$

$$= f(3.2) - f(3)$$

$$= (3.2)^2 + 4(3.2) - [3^2 + 4(3)]$$

$$= 10.24 + 12.8 - (9 + 12)$$

$$= 23.04 - 21$$

$$= 2.04.$$

To compute $dy = f'(x)dx$, we note that $dx = \Delta x = 0.2$, and $f'(x) = 2x + 4$; so,

$$dy = f'(3)dx$$
$$= [2(3) + 4](0.2)$$
$$= (10)(0.2)$$
$$= 2.$$

Thus $\Delta y = 2.04$ and $dy = 2$. They differ by 0.04.

Example.   Use differentials to find an estimate for $\sqrt[3]{8.1}$.

Solution.   This problem is asking us to find y for the function $y = \sqrt[3]{x}$ when $x = 8.1$. Since we do not know the cube root of 8.1, we will evaluate the function at $x = 8$, a number whose cube root is known, and then estimate the change in y caused by adding 0.1 to 8. That is, we will use differentials to estimate Δy when $x = 8$ and $dx = 0.1$.

$$dy = f'(x)dx$$

$$= \frac{1}{3} x^{-\frac{2}{3}} dx$$

$$= \frac{dx}{3x^{\frac{2}{3}}}$$

$$= \frac{0.1}{3(8)^{\frac{2}{3}}}$$

$$= \frac{0.1}{(3)(4)}$$

$$= \frac{0.1}{12}$$

$$= \frac{1}{120} \approx 0.0083.$$

Now the value of $y = \sqrt[3]{8.1}$ is the value of $y = \sqrt[3]{8} = 2$ plus the change in y caused by adding 0.1 to 8. That is, the value we are looking for is $y + \Delta y$ which is approximately $y + dy = 2 + \frac{1}{120}$.

So $\sqrt[3]{8.1} \approx 2\frac{1}{120} \approx 2.0083$

Example.   Find an approximation for the maximum possible error in calculating the volume of a sphere when its radius is 5 inches with a possible error of ± 0.01 inch.

Solution. We are being asked what effect an error in the radius of a sphere will have on its volume. The volume of a sphere is $V = \frac{4}{3}\pi r^3$. The change in V is approximately the differential of the volume where r is the independent variable, V is the dependent variable, $r = 5$, and $dr = \pm 0.01$,

$$dV = V'dr, \text{ but } V' = 4\pi r^2.$$

$$dV = 4\pi r^2\, dr$$

$$= 4\pi(5)^2\,(\pm 0.01)$$

$$= 100\pi(\pm 0.01)$$

$$= \pm\pi \approx \pm 3.14 \text{ cubic inches.}$$

Thus an error of ± 0.01 in the radius produces an error of π cubic inches in the volume.

Formulas for differentials can be obtained by multiplying derivative formulas by dx. Recall that if u and v are differentiable functions of x, and $y = \dfrac{u}{v}$, then

$$\frac{dy}{dx} = \frac{v\,\dfrac{du}{dx} - u\,\dfrac{dv}{dx}}{v^2}.$$

To find the differential of y, dy, multiply both sides by dx.

$$dy = \frac{v\,du - u\,dv}{v^2}.$$

Other formulas can be found in a similar manner. For instance, if u and v are functions of x and c is a constant, then

$$dc = 0,$$

$$d(u^n) = nu^{n-1}\,du, \text{ for } n \text{ a rational number,}$$

$$d(u + v) = du + dv,$$

$$d(u \cdot v) = u\,dv + v\,du,$$

$$d(\sin u) = \cos u\,du, \text{ and so forth.}$$

These formulas are important in integration, the second major concept of calculus, which will be introduced later. For the time being the differential of the dependent variable is easily found using the definition

$$dy = f'(x)dx.$$

3-5   Exercises

(1-8)   Find dy for the given functions.

1. $y = 8x^2$
2. $y = 5x^3 + 7x^2 + 8$

3. $y = \sqrt{x^2 + 25}$

4. $y = -\sqrt{16 - x^2}$

5. $y = \tan x \sec x$
6. $y = \sin x + \cos x$

7. $y = \dfrac{x}{x + 1}$

8. $y = \dfrac{5x^2}{3x^3 + 4}$

(9-12)   Evaluate df for the given function and the given values of x and dx.

9. $f(x) = x^3 + 2x, \; x = 2, \; dx = 0.01$
10. $f(x) = \sqrt[5]{x}, \; x = -32, \; dx = 3$
11. $f(x) = \dfrac{1}{x}, \; x = 10, \; dx = -0.003$

12. $f(x) = \cot x, \; x = \dfrac{\pi}{2}, \; dx = -0.01$

(13-16)   Find dy and Δy for the given functions and the given values of x and dx.

13. $y = x^2, \; x = 5, \; dx = 0.2$
14. $y = x^2 + 7x + 2, \; x = -3, \; dx = 0.01$
15. $y = x^3, \; x = 2, \; dx = 0.1$
16. $y = x^3, \; x = 2, \; dx = -0.1$

(17-20)   Use differentials to approximate the indicated roots.

17. $\sqrt[3]{28}$
18. $\sqrt[4]{620}$

19. $\sqrt{37}$
20. $\sqrt[5]{33}$

21.   Use differentials to estimate the volume of a cube that is 6.1 inches on a side.

22.   A small adding machine is sold with the following instruction for finding the square root of a number near 16.

$$\sqrt{16 + dx} = 4 + \frac{dx}{8}.$$

What is the corresponding instruction for finding the square root of a number near 25?

23.   Answer exercise 22 for a number near 100.

24.   A cubical metal box has an interior measurement of exactly 5 inches

along each edge. If the metal sides and the top and bottom of the box are all 0.5 inches thick use differentials to approximate the volume of metal used in constructing the box.

25. The radius of a sphere is to be measured and that measurement is to be used to compute the volume of the sphere. However, the radius can only be measured to within $\pm\frac{1}{4}$ of an inch of its actual length but the volume can be in error by at most 12 cubic inches. What is, approximately, the radius of the largest sphere whose volume will be in error by at most 12 cubic inches when its radius is in error $\pm\frac{1}{4}$ of an inch?

3-6 IMPLICIT DIFFERENTIATION

Functions may be regarded as a pairing of variables by some rule. Consider the equations $2x + 2y - 3 = 0$ and $y = \dfrac{3 - 2x}{2}$. Actually both define identical functions. Any pair of values which satisfies one will satisfy the other. To differentiate between the two types of definitions, we say that y as a function of x defined by $y = \dfrac{3 - 2x}{2}$ is an *explicit function*, whereas the equation $2x + 2y - 3 = 0$ implies y is an *implicit function* of x.

Similarly, expressions, such as $y = x^2$ or $y = \sqrt{x^2 + 5x} + \sin x$, define explicit functions of x, whereas expressions such as $x^2 + y^2 = 1$ and $x^4 y^5 + 3xy + y^3 + 5 = 0$ define implicit functions of x. This means that the expressions can either be solved for y in terms of x or, if this is impractical or impossible, the set of ordered pairs that satisfy the expression form a function of x. In practice it is often necessary to restrict our attention to certain intervals of x or y in order to insure a functional relationship. The expression $x^2 + y^2 = 1$ implies two functions of x,

$$y = \sqrt{1 - x^2} \text{ and } y = -\sqrt{1 - x^2}.$$

Many implicit functions cannot readily be solved for y in terms of x. However, it may not be difficult to find $\dfrac{dy}{dx}$ for such functions. The method is called *implicit differentiation*. We will assume that y is implicitly a function of x in any expression containing x and y. Thus if the term of y^2 is encountered, we can take its derivative with respect to x by assuming y is an implicit function of x and applying the chain rule,

$$D_x(y^2) = 2y\frac{dy}{dx}.$$

Example.   Use implicit differentiation to find $\frac{dy}{dx}$ for $x^2 + y^2 = 1$.

Solution.   Take the derivative of each side with respect to x and solve for $\frac{dy}{dx}$.

$$D_x(x^2) + D_x(y^2) = D_x(1).$$

$$2x + 2y\frac{dy}{dx} = 0.$$

$$2y\frac{dy}{dx} = -2x.$$

$$\frac{dy}{dx} = -\frac{x}{y}.$$

Example.   Find y' for $xy = 1$.

Solution. $y' = \frac{dy}{dx}$. The derivative of 1, the right side of the equation, is zero. The left side of the equation, xy, is the product of x and a function of x, namely, y. Therefore, we take x times the derivative of y and y times the derivative of x, the rule for finding the derivative of the product of two functions of x.

$$D_x(xy) = D_x(1).$$

$$x\frac{dy}{dx} + y(1) = 0.$$

$$x\frac{dy}{dx} = -y.$$

$$\frac{dy}{dx} = -\frac{y}{x},$$

or

$$y' = -\frac{y}{x}.$$

Solving $xy = 1$ for y gives $y = \dfrac{1}{x}$. If we substitute $y = \dfrac{1}{x}$ in $y' = -\dfrac{y}{x}$, we get $y' = -\dfrac{1}{x^2}$, which is the same result that comes from finding y' for

$y = \dfrac{1}{x}$.

Example. Find $\dfrac{dy}{dx}$ for $2x^4 - 3x^2y^2 + y^4 = 0$.

Solution. Take the derivative with respect to x term by term. Note that the middle term will be treated as the product of two functions of x.

$$D_x(2x^4) - 3D_x(x^2y^2) + D_x(y^4) = 0.$$

$$8x^3 - 3\left(2x^2y\frac{dy}{dx} + 2xy^2\right) + 4y^3\frac{dy}{dx} = 0.$$

$$8x^3 - 6x^2y\frac{dy}{dx} - 6xy^2 + 4y^3\frac{dy}{dx} = 0.$$

Solving for $\dfrac{dy}{dx}$,

$$4y^3\frac{dy}{dx} - 6x^2y\frac{dy}{dx} = 6xy^2 - 8x^3.$$

$$(4y^3 - 6x^2y)\frac{dy}{dx} = 6xy^2 - 8x^3.$$

$$\frac{dy}{dx} = \frac{6xy^2 - 8x^3}{4y^3 - 6x^2y}$$

$$= \frac{3xy^2 - 4x^3}{2y^3 - 3x^2y}.$$

Example. Find the slope of the tangent line to the ellipse $4x^2 + 9y^2 = 40$ at the point $(1,2)$.

Solution. To find the slope we need only evaluate y' at the point $(1,2)$. We could solve the equation for y and then find y'. However it is easier to find y' by implicit differentiation.

If $4x^2 + 9y^2 = 40,$

then $8x + 18y(y') = 0.$

$$18y(y') = -8x.$$

$$y' = \frac{-8x}{18y} = \frac{-4x}{9y}.$$

We now substitute the values 1 and 2 for x and y.

$$y' = \frac{-4x}{9y}$$

$$= \frac{-4(1)}{9(2)}$$

$$= -\frac{2}{9}.$$

The slope is $-\frac{2}{9}$.

It is also possible to find second derivatives by implicit differentiation.

Example. Find y'' for $xy^3 = 1$.
Solution. First we find y'.

$$xy^3 = 1.$$

$$3xy^2 \cdot y' + y^3 = 0.$$

$$3xy^2 \cdot y' = -y^3.$$

$$y' = \frac{-y^3}{3xy^2}$$

$$= -\frac{y}{3x}.$$

Now we take the derivative of y' to get y''.

$$y'' = -\frac{1}{3}\left[\frac{x \cdot y' - y}{x^2}\right]$$

Substituting $y' = -\dfrac{y}{3x}$ in y'' and simplifying,

$$y'' = -\frac{1}{3}\left[\frac{x\left(\dfrac{-y}{3x}\right) - y}{x^2}\right]$$

$$= -\frac{1}{3}\left[\frac{-\dfrac{y}{3} - y}{x^2}\right]$$

$$= -\frac{1}{3}\left[\frac{-\dfrac{4}{3}y}{x^2}\right]$$

$$= \frac{4y}{9x^2}.$$

3-6   Exercises

(1-12)   Find $\dfrac{dy}{dx}$ by implicit differentiation.

1. $x^2 - y^2 = 1$ 7. $y\sqrt{x + 1} = 4$
2. $4x^2 + 25y^2 = 100$ 8. $x\sqrt{y} = y\sqrt{x}$
3. $xy + x = 2$ 9. $x = \sin y$
4. $3xy^2 + xy = 1$ 10. $x = \cos y$
5. $x^3 - xy + y^2 = 0$ 11. $x \cos xy = 1$
6. $x^{\frac{1}{3}} + y^{\frac{1}{3}} = 4$ 12. $x \tan xy = 1$

(13-18)   Find the slope of the tangent line to the given function at the given point.

13. $x^2 + y^2 = 25, (-4,3)$ 15. $xy^2 = 12, (3, -2)$
14. $x^2 + 4x - y^2 = 3, (2,3)$ 16. $x^2 y = -18, (3, -2)$
17. $2xy - 2x + y + 14 = 0, (2, -2)$
18. $x^3 - 2x^2 + 3y^2 - 4xy + 2x + y - 58 = 0, (4, -1)$

(19-26)   Find y''.

19. $x^2 - y^2 = 1$ 23. $y^2 = x^2$
20. $x^2 y^2 = 1$ 24. $y^2 - xy + 2 = 0$
21. $4x^2 + 9y^2 = 36$ 25. $3x^2 + 4xy + y^2 = 0$
22. $x^{\frac{1}{2}} + y^{\frac{1}{2}} = 1$ 26. $x^{\frac{1}{3}} + y^{\frac{1}{3}} = 1$

3-7   RELATED RATES, IMPLICIT FUNCTIONS OF TIME

In many physical and economic applications of mathematics variables are implicit functions of time. For instance, if $C = f(x)$ is a function that relates cost, C, to the number of items sold, x, it may also be true that both x and C are functions of time. That is, we might expect to sell 25 items per hour, which in turn might give a cost of $100 per hour, which means that over a definite number of hours, N, we will sell $25N$ items and incur $100N$ dollars of cost.

The instantaneous rate of change in x per unit of time is noted by $\dfrac{dx}{dt}$,

and the instantaneous rate of change in cost per unit of time is denoted

$\dfrac{dC}{dt}$. If some value for x and $\dfrac{dx}{dt}$ at a specific time can be computed, then

we can find $\dfrac{dC}{dt}$ at that time.

Example.   The cost in dollars of selling x items is given by $C = 500 + x + \dfrac{1}{x}$. When the 50th item is sold, it is noted that the rate of sales is 20 items per hour. What is the rate of change of the cost with respect to time at that moment?

Solution.   We are given $\dfrac{dx}{dt} = 20$ and $x = 50$ and are asked to find $\dfrac{dC}{dt}$.

C and x are both implicit functions of time. Therefore, we use the chain rule to take the derivative with respect to time of both sides of $C = 500 + x + \dfrac{1}{x}$.

$$\frac{dC}{dt} = \frac{d(500)}{dt} + \frac{dx}{dt} + \frac{d\left(\dfrac{1}{x}\right)}{dt}$$

$$= 0 + \frac{dx}{dt} + \left(-\frac{1}{x^2}\right)\frac{dx}{dt}$$

$$= \frac{dx}{dt} - \frac{1}{x^2}\frac{dx}{dt}$$

$$= \left(1 - \frac{1}{x^2}\right)\frac{dx}{dt}.$$

Substituting 50 for x and 20 for $\dfrac{dx}{dt}$ gives

$$\frac{dC}{dt} = \left(1 - \frac{1}{50^2}\right)20$$

$$= \left(1 - \frac{1}{2,500}\right)20$$

$$= \frac{2,499}{2,500}(20)$$

$$= \frac{2,499}{125} \approx \$20/\text{hr}.$$

This means that the cost at the time the 50th item is sold is increasing at the rate of about \$20 per hour.

In this example, the cost per hour is a function of both the number of items sold and the rate of sales. If the rate of sales is 5 items per hour at the time the second item is sold, then the cost per hour is only \$3.75, which is computed as follows.

$$x = 2, \quad \frac{dx}{dt} = 5, \text{ and } \quad \frac{dC}{dt} = \left(1 - \frac{1}{x^2}\right)\frac{dx}{dt}, \text{ so}$$

$$\frac{dC}{dt} = \left(1 - \frac{1}{4}\right)5$$

$$= \frac{3}{4}(5)$$

$$= 3.75.$$

The cost per hour is a function of the number of items sold as well as the rate of sales because an increase in the number of items sold causes greater production costs, and an increase in the rate of sales causes greater sales cost due to a need for more salesmen, delivery personnel, and so forth.

In physical problems, the most common example of an instantaneous rate of change of a variable with respect to time is velocity, because velocity is the rate of change of distance with respect to time, and physical problems often involve movement over distances.

Example. Suppose that a 13-foot ladder, figure 3-19, is leaning against a

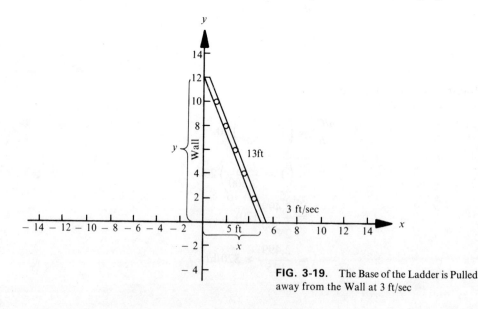

FIG. 3-19. The Base of the Ladder is Pulled away from the Wall at 3 ft/sec

vertical wall with the foot of the ladder on a horizontal surface. The foot of the ladder is drawn away from the wall at the rate of 3 feet per second. How fast is the top of the ladder moving down the wall when the foot of the ladder is 5 feet from the wall?

Solution.   Let the height of the ladder as measured along the wall be y and the distance of the foot of the ladder from the wall be x. Since the ladder is 13 feet long, Pythagoras' theorem gives

$$x^2 + y^2 = 13^2.$$

Our problem is to find $\dfrac{dy}{dt}$ when $x = 5$ and $\dfrac{dx}{dt} = 3$. Implicit differentiation with respect to time gives

$$2x\frac{dx}{dt} + 2y\frac{dy}{dt} = 0.$$

$$\frac{dy}{dt} = -\frac{x}{y}\frac{dx}{dt}.$$

We need the value of y when $x = 5$.

$$x^2 + y^2 = 169.$$

$$25 + y^2 = 169.$$

$$y^2 = 144.$$

$$y = 12.$$

Therefore,

$$\frac{dy}{dt} = -\frac{x}{y}\frac{dx}{dt}$$

$$= -\frac{5}{12}(3)$$

$$= -\frac{5}{4} = -1.25 \text{ ft/sec.}$$

The top of the ladder is moving down the wall at -1.25 feet per second. The negative sign in -1.25 indicates that the y value is decreasing.

In the last example, it was necessary to find $\dfrac{dy}{dt}$ when $x = 5$. Many students make the error of substituting 5 for x before taking the implicit derivative of the function. Since 5 is a constant and the derivative of constants is zero, this causes the derivative of the x terms to be zero which, in turn, leads to some nonsense conclusion, such as $\dfrac{dy}{dt} = 0$. Therefore, *substitute values after implicit differentiation.*

3-7   Exercises

1. The cost of selling x items in dollars is given by $C = 0.75x + 1,000$. What is the rate of change in the cost with respect to time at the instant that the 100th item is sold if the items are selling at the rate of 4 per hour?

2. Find the rate of change in cost, when the cost in dollars is given by $C = 700 + 8\sqrt{x}$ and the 36th item is sold, if the items are selling at the rate of 50 per hour.

3. Find the rate of change per week in cost, when the cost in dollars is given by $C = 100 + 2x + \dfrac{1}{x^2}$ and the first item is sold, if the items are selling at 1 a week.

4. Find the rate of change of cost, if the cost in dollars is given by $C = 800 + 9x^3$, when the 8th item is sold, and the items are selling at the rate of 100 per day.

5. Find the rate of change in cost, where cost is given by $C = 0.0002x^3 - 0.05x^2 + 20x + 20,000$, when the 1,000th item is sold, if the rate of sales is 50 per day.

6. What is the rate of change in profit, given by $P = 4x^2 + 5x - 1,000$, at the time the 100th item is sold, given that the items are selling at the rate of 70 a day?

(7-9)   The profit, P, resulting from the sales of x data-wacks is given by $P = x^2 + 500x - 100$, and exactly two data-wacks are sold every day.

7. How is the profit changing when the 100th data-wack is sold?

8. How is the profit changing when the 125th data-wack is sold?

9. How is the profit changing when the 150th data-wack is sold?

10. A 26-foot ladder is leaning against a vertical wall with its foot on a horizontal floor. The foot of the ladder is being moved away from the wall at the rate of 5 feet/second. Find the rate at which the top of the ladder is moving down the wall when the foot of the ladder is 24 feet from the wall.

11. If the radius of a circle is decreasing at the rate of $\frac{1}{2}$ an inch per minute, at what rate is its area changing when the radius is 12 inches? When the radius is 2 inches?

12. The base of a triangle is increasing at the rate of 2 feet per second while the height is decreasing at 4 feet per second. How is the area of the triangle changing when its base is 10 feet and its height is 6 feet?

13. The volume of a sphere is $V = \frac{4}{3}\pi r^3$. Suppose that a balloon retains a spherical shape as it is being blown up. How fast is the radius of the balloon increasing at the instant it is 3 inches, if air is being pumped into the balloon at 5 cubic inches per second?

14. Two ships leave the same port at the same time. One ship steams directly north at 15 knots. The other steams due west at 20 knots. How fast is the distance between them increasing 3 hours after they leave port?

15. One ship leaves port and steams due north at 10 knots. Three hours later another ship leaves the same port and steams due west at 30 knots. How fast is the distance between them increasing when the first ship has been out of port for 5 hours?

16. At what rate is the shadow of a 6-foot tall man shortening as he walks at 8 feet/second toward a street light that is 20 feet above the pavement?

17. Water is pouring into an inverted cone-shaped tank at the rate of 20 cubic feet per minute. The tank is 10 feet high with a circular top of radius 4 feet. The volume of a cone is $V = \frac{1}{3}\pi r^2 h$. How fast is the height of the water increasing when it is 5 feet deep?

3-8 INVERSE FUNCTIONS

In Chapter 1 the concept of a relation was introduced. There, any set of ordered pairs was viewed as defining a relation. Associated with each relation there is a second relation, a second set of ordered pairs, produced by interchanging domain and range elements. For example, consider the relation $R = \{(1,2), (2,4), (3,5), (4,1), (1,7)\}$. In the case of R this relation would be $\{(2,1), (4,2), (5,3), (1,4), (7,1)\}$. This second relation is called the *inverse* of the original relation.

> **Definition.** For a given relation R the *inverse relation*, denoted by R^{-1}, is the relation formed by interchanging the elements in the ordered pairs forming R.

Example. If $R = \{(1,3), (6,2), (5,4), (0,2)\}$, find R^{-1}.
Solution. $R^{-1} = \{(3,1), (2,6), (4,5), (2,0)\}$.

Example. If $R = \{(x,y)|y^2 = x^6\}$ then find R^{-1}.
Solution. $R^{-1} = \{(x,y)|x^2 = y^6\}$. This is found by interchanging the roles of x and y in the defining equation.

Since all functions are also relations it follows that associated with every function f there is a *inverse relation* f^{-1}. However, a few examples will illustrate the fact that the inverse of a function is not always a function.

Example. $\{(1,3),\ (5,6),\ (8,3),\ (4,6)\}$ is a function; is its inverse?
Solution. $\{(3,1),\ (6,5),\ (3,8),\ (6,4)\}$ is not a function, because the domain element 3 is paired with two different range elements in $(3,1)$ and in $(3,8)$.

Example. $\{(x,y)|y = x^2\}$ is a function; is its inverse?
Solution. $\{(x,y)|y^2 = x\}$ is not a function, since a domain element, such as 4, could be paired with either $+2$ or -2.

Example. $\{(1,2),\ (2,3),\ (3,4),\ (4,5)\}$ is a function; is its inverse?
Solution. $\{(2,1),\ (3,2),\ (4,3),\ (5,4)\}$ is also a function.

Example.   If $f = \{(x,y)|y = 3x + 4\}$, find f^{-1}.
Solution.   Interchanging x and y in $y = 3x + 4$ gives

$$x = 3y + 4.$$

Now, solving for y

$$3y = x - 4, \text{ and}$$

$$y = \frac{x - 4}{3}.$$

Therefore,

$$f^{-1} = \left\{(x,y)|y = \frac{x - 4}{3}\right\}.$$

By substituting $x = 0$, 1, and -1 in $y = 3x + 4$ we find that $(0,4)$, $(1,7)$ and $(-1,1)$ are elements of f and by substituting 4, 7, and 1 for x in $y = \frac{x - 4}{3}$ we find that $(4,0)$, $(7,1)$ and $(1,-1)$ are elements of f^{-1}. f^{-1} does reverse the order of the elements of f. In this case f^{-1} is also a function.

If the inverse, f^{-1}, of a function f is also a function, the f^{-1} is called the inverse function of f. f and f^{-1} are referred to as an *inverse functional pair*.

The "-1" in f^{-1} is a notational device and does not mean the function is to be raised to the -1 power. If it should be necessary to raise $f(x)$ to the negative first power it will be written $[f(x)]^{-1}$.

Example.   Find f^{-1} for $y = f(x) = x^3$.
Solution.   We interchange x and y in $y = x^3$ and solve for y.

$$x = y^3$$

$$y = \sqrt[3]{x}.$$

Since $y = \sqrt[3]{x}$ is a function,

$$f^{-1}(x) = \sqrt[3]{x}.$$

Example.   Find f^{-1} for $y = f(x) = x^2$.
Solution.   We will find f^{-1} and then check to see if it is a function,

$$y = x^2,$$

becomes

$$x = y^2.$$

$$y = \pm\sqrt{x}.$$

Therefore, since $f^{-1}(x) = \pm\sqrt{x}$, the function has no inverse.

In the last example, $f(x) = x^2$ had no inverse. However, an inverse can be found for a restricted version of this function. If

$$f = \{(x,y)|y = x^2 \text{ and } x \geq 0\}, \text{ then}$$

$$f^{-1} = \{(x,y)|y = \sqrt{x} \text{ and } y \geq 0\}.$$

The set f^{-1} results from interchanging x and y in f. Note that x is changed to y in f^{-1}. In the last example, we found that the inverse of $f(x) = x^2$ is $f^{-1}(x) = \pm\sqrt{x}$. But from the restriction $y \geq 0$, the $\pm$ sign is not necessary because y must be positive and f^{-1} is now a function.

The concept of restricting the domain of a function to create the inverse function will be used often with the trigonometric functions. When finding derivatives or later, when doing integration, it is necessary that each domain element be paired with a unique image; in short, that f^{-1} be a function.

The graphs of a function and its inverse are symmetric about the line $y = x$. This can be seen in figure 3-20, which contains the graphs of $y = f(x)$ $= 3x + 4$ and its inverse function $y = f^{-1}(x) = \dfrac{x - 4}{3}$. In the general case, if the point (a,b) is an element of f then (b,a) is the corresponding point of f^{-1}.

If we can show that these two points are symmetric about the line $y = x$ then every pair of such points must be; and, thus, the entire graph of a function and its inverse must be symmetric about the line $y = x$. To show that two points are symmetric about a line it is sufficient to show that the line is the perpendicular bisector of the line joining the two points. In figure 3-21 the points $A(a,b)$ and $B(b,a)$ are graphed. To prove they are symmetric about the line $y = x$, we must show that $y = x$ is the perpendicular bisector of $\overline{AB}$. Triangles $\triangle BCD$ and $\triangle ACD$ are congruent because they have side

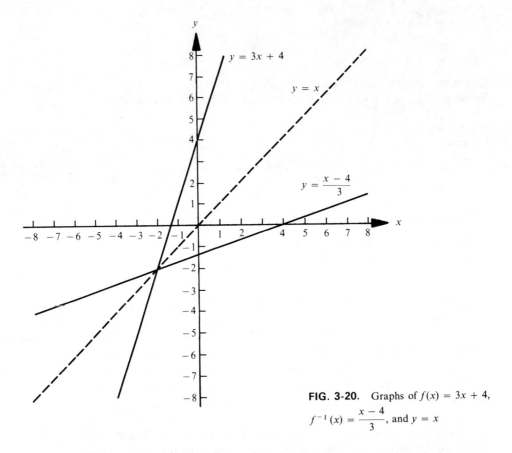

FIG. 3-20. Graphs of $f(x) = 3x + 4$, $f^{-1}(x) = \dfrac{x-4}{3}$, and $y = x$

CD in common, angles α and β are both 45°, and the lengths of sides BC and AC are $a - b$. Therefore, the line $y = x$ is the perpendicular bisector of $\overline{AB}$. This shows that a function and its inverse are symmetric about the line $y = x$.

The inverse of the sine function is

$$\text{sine}^{-1} = \{(x,y)\,|\,x = \sin y\}.$$

We have formed this inverse by interchanging x and y in the equation $y = \sin x$. Up to this point we have, after interchanging x and y, solved for y. We cannot, algebraically, solve $x = \sin y$ for y. However, we will adopt a notation that allows the defining equation of the inverse to have y as a function of x, its domain element. It is important to note that $x = \sin y$ is not a function of x unless we restrict the domain, for if $x = 1$ in $x = \sin y$, y could be $\dfrac{\pi}{2}$, $\dfrac{5\pi}{2}$, or $-\dfrac{3\pi}{2}$. Any value of x can be paired with any number of values for y. In order to form the inverse function we must restrict

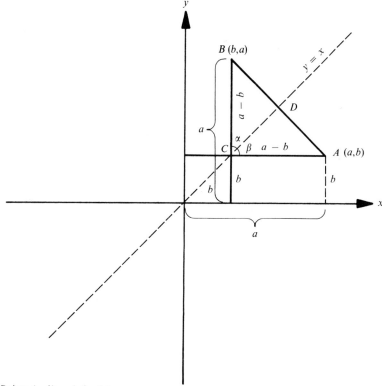

FIG. 3-21.   The Points (a, b) and (b, a) Are
Symmetric about the Line $y = x$

the domain of sine. The restricted domain must be such that each value of
x is paired with one and only one value of y, so that when we interchange
x and y, the inverse will be a function, and there must be a domain element
for each y such that $-1 \leq y \leq 1$. Figure 3-22 shows the graph of $y = \sin x$
and a restricted interval of x. The interval $-\dfrac{\pi}{2} \leq x \leq \dfrac{\pi}{2}$ is called the
principal value domain for the sine function.

We can now define Sine (spelled with a capital "S") so that it will have
an inverse function Sine^{-1}.

$$\text{Sine} = \left\{ (x,y) \middle| y = \sin x \text{ and } -\frac{\pi}{2} \leq x \leq \frac{\pi}{2} \right\}.$$

Then the inverse of the Sine function is

$$\text{Sine}^{-1} = \left\{ (x,y) \middle| x = \text{Sin } y \text{ and } -\frac{\pi}{2} \leq y \leq \frac{\pi}{2} \right\}.$$

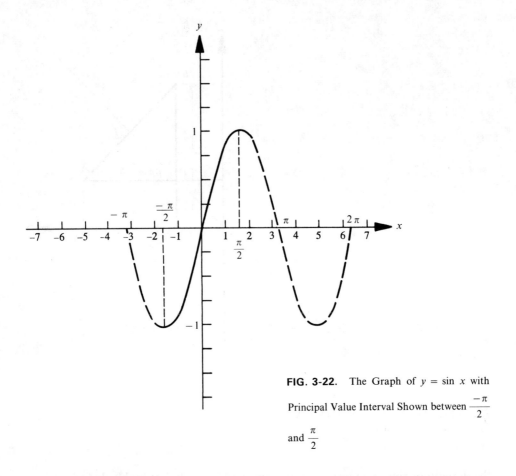

FIG. 3-22. The Graph of $y = \sin x$ with Principal Value Interval Shown between $\dfrac{-\pi}{2}$ and $\dfrac{\pi}{2}$

The graph of Sine^{-1} is shown in figure 3-23. Note that it is a function. It was drawn by using the fact that the graph of a function and its inverse is symmetric about the line $y = x$.

There is an alternate notation to the set notation used above for the Sine^{-1}. We could simply use $x = \mathrm{Sin}\ y$ but to show y as a function of its domain element x, we adopt the following.

Definition. $y = \sin^{-1}x$ if and only if $x = \mathrm{Sin}\ y$.

The capital "S" in $x = \mathrm{Sin}\ y$ means that $-\dfrac{\pi}{2} \le y \le \dfrac{\pi}{2}$. The expression $y = \sin^{-1}x$ can be read "y equals the inverse sine of x" or "y equals the arc sine of x" or "y is the angle whose sine is x." The last phrase, "y is the angle whose sine is x," gives the intuitive meaning to $y = \sin^{-1}x$. When asked to evaluate sine^{-1} for certain values of x it is sometimes useful to recall that y is now taking the place of the "angle."

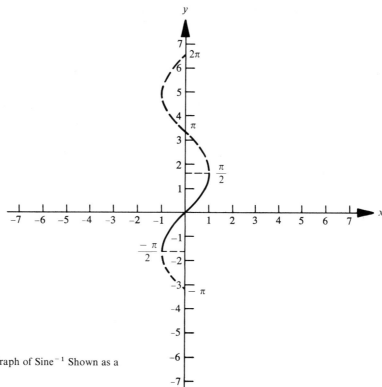

FIG. 3-23.   A Graph of Sine^{-1} Shown as a
Solid Line

Example.   Evaluate $\sin^{-1} \dfrac{1}{\sqrt{2}}$.

Solution.   By definition $y = \sin^{-1} x$ if and only if $x = \text{Sin } y$; if we let $y = \sin^{-1} \dfrac{1}{\sqrt{2}}$, then $\dfrac{1}{\sqrt{2}} = \text{Sin } y$. This means, "$y$ is the number whose sine is $\dfrac{1}{\sqrt{2}}$." Since we are restricted to $-\dfrac{\pi}{2} \leq y \leq \dfrac{\pi}{2}$, $y = \dfrac{\pi}{4}$. Therefore,

$$\sin^{-1} \frac{1}{\sqrt{2}} = \frac{\pi}{4}.$$

Example.   Evaluate $\sin^{-1}(-1)$.

Solution.   Many students answer incorrectly, $\dfrac{3\pi}{2}$. Remember, the Sine^{-1} is defined only for $-\dfrac{\pi}{2} \leq y \leq \dfrac{\pi}{2}$. Therefore,

$$\sin^{-1}(-1) = -\frac{\pi}{2}.$$

Example. Evaluate $\sin^{-1}(\frac{1}{2})$ and $\sin^{-1}(-\frac{1}{2})$.

Solution. $\sin^{-1}(-\frac{1}{2}) = -\dfrac{\pi}{6}$ and $\sin^{-1}(\frac{1}{2}) = \dfrac{\pi}{6}$.

The same method as that used in developing Sine^{-1} is used with the other trigonometric functions. Figures 3-24 and 3-25 show the graphs of the inverse cosine and tangent functions. These were graphed by graphing the standard cosine and tangent functions then "reflecting" these graphs across the $y = x$ line.

Using capital letters to indicate functions with restricted domains, we define

$$\text{Cosine} = \{(x,y)|y = \cos x \text{ and } 0 \leq x \leq \pi\}, \text{ and}$$

$$\text{Tangent} = \left\{(x,y)|y = \tan x \text{ and } -\frac{\pi}{2} < x < \frac{\pi}{2}\right\}.$$

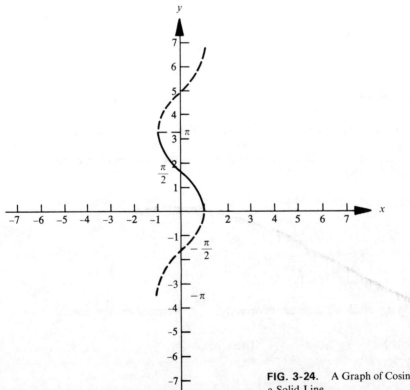

FIG. 3-24. A Graph of Cosine^{-1} Shown as a Solid Line

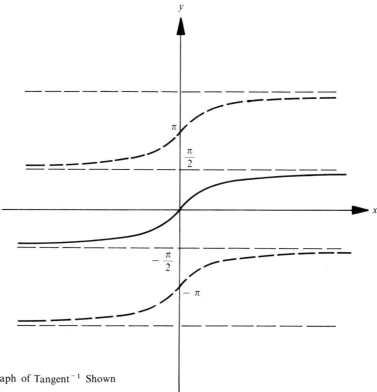

FIG. 3-25.   A Graph of Tangent^{-1} Shown
as a Solid Line

Now the inverse functions can be defined.

$$\text{Cosine}^{-1} = \{(x,y)|x = \text{Cos } y \text{ and } 0 \leq y \leq \pi\}, \text{ and}$$

$$\text{Tangent}^{-1} = \left\{(x,y)|x = \text{Tan } y \text{ and } -\frac{\pi}{2} < y < \frac{\pi}{2}\right\}.$$

Definition. $y = \cos^{-1}x$ if and only if $x = \text{Cos } y$.

$$y = \tan^{-1}x \text{ if and only if } x = \text{Tan } y.$$

The capital "C" in $x = \text{Cos } y$ and the capital "T" in $x = \text{Tan } y$ indicate
the cosine and tangent functions have restricted domains. Thus, $y = \cos^{-1}x$
is a function with domain $-1 \leq x \leq 1$ and range $0 \leq y \leq \pi$; whereas
$y = \tan^{-1}x$ has domain $-\infty < x < \infty$ and range $-\frac{\pi}{2} < y < \frac{\pi}{2}$.

Example.   Evaluate $\cos^{-1}(1)$, $\cos^{-1}(-1)$, $\cos^{-1}\left(\frac{\sqrt{3}}{2}\right)$, $\cos^{-1}\left(-\frac{\sqrt{3}}{2}\right)$,

$\tan^{-1}(1)$ and $\tan^{-1}\left(-\frac{1}{\sqrt{3}}\right)$.

Solution. $\cos^{-1}(1) = 0,$

$$\cos^{-1}(-1) = \pi,$$

$$\cos^{-1}\left(\frac{\sqrt{3}}{2}\right) = \frac{\pi}{6},$$

$$\cos^{-1}\left(-\frac{\sqrt{3}}{2}\right) = \frac{5\pi}{6},$$

$$\tan^{-1}(1) = \frac{\pi}{4}, \text{ and}$$

$$\tan^{-1}\left(-\frac{1}{\sqrt{3}}\right) = -\frac{\pi}{6}.$$

FOLLOWING THE ESTABLISHED PATTERN:

1. $y = \cot^{-1}x$ Domain, $\{x \mid x \text{ is real}\}$
    Range, $\{y \mid 0 < y < \pi\}$
2. $y = \sec^{-1}x$ Domain, $\{x \mid x \leq -1 \text{ or } x \geq 1\}$
    Range, $\left\{y \mid 0 \leq y \leq \pi, y \neq \frac{\pi}{2}\right\}$
3. $y = \csc^{-1}x$ Domain, $\{x \mid x \leq -1 \text{ or } x \geq 1\}$
    Range, $\left\{y \mid -\frac{\pi}{2} \leq y \leq \frac{\pi}{2}, y \neq 0\right\}$

Example.   Evaluate $\cot^{-1}(1)$, $\cot^{-1}(-1)$, $\csc^{-1}(\sqrt{2})$, $\csc^{-1}(-\sqrt{2})$, $\sec^{-1}(2)$, and $\sec^{-1}(-2)$.

Solution. $\cot^{-1}(1) = \frac{\pi}{4}.$

$$\cot^{-1}(-1) = \frac{3\pi}{4}.$$

$$\csc^{-1}(\sqrt{2}) = \frac{\pi}{4}.$$

$$\csc^{-1}(-\sqrt{2}) = -\frac{\pi}{4}.$$

$$\sec^{-1}(2) = \frac{\pi}{3}.$$

$$\sec^{-1}(-2) = \frac{2\pi}{3}.$$

Example.   Find $\sin\left[\cos^{-1}\left(\dfrac{\sqrt{3}}{2}\right)\right]$.

Solution.   This asks for the sine of the number whose cosine is $\dfrac{\sqrt{3}}{2}$.

$\cos^{-1}\left(\dfrac{\sqrt{3}}{2}\right) = \dfrac{\pi}{6}$. Therefore,

$$\sin\left[\cos^{-1}\left(-\dfrac{\sqrt{3}}{2}\right)\right] = \sin\dfrac{\pi}{6}$$

$$= \dfrac{1}{2}.$$

3-8   Exercises

(1-12)   Find the inverse of the given functions.

1. $y = x$
2. $y = x + 8$

4. $y = 7x - 13$
5. $y = -6x + 1$

3. $y = 4x + 5$

6. $y = -\dfrac{x}{3} + 9$

7. $y = \sqrt{x + 25}$. State the restrictions on the domain and range of the inverse function.

8.   Repeat exercise 7 for $y = \sqrt{3 - x}$.

9. $y = (x + 4)^2$
10. $y = x^5$

11. $y = x^{\frac{3}{2}}$
12. $y = (x - 5)^2$

(13-30)   Evaluate.

13. $\sin^{-1}(1)$
14. $\sin^{-1}(0)$

18. $\tan^{-1}(-1)$
19. $\tan^{-1}(0)$

15. $\sin^{-1}\left(-\dfrac{\sqrt{3}}{2}\right)$

20. $\sec^{-1}\left(\dfrac{2}{\sqrt{3}}\right)$

16. $\cos^{-1}\left(-\dfrac{\sqrt{3}}{2}\right)$

21. $\csc^{-1}(-2)$

17. $\cos^{-1}\left(-\dfrac{1}{\sqrt{2}}\right)$

22. $\cot^{-1}(-\sqrt{3})$

23. $\sin\left[\cos^{-1}\left(\dfrac{\sqrt{3}}{2}\right)\right]$

27. $\sin^{-1}\left(\sin\dfrac{\pi}{2}\right)$

24. $\cos\left[\sin^{-1}\left(\dfrac{\sqrt{3}}{2}\right)\right]$

28. $\cos^{-1}\left(\cos\dfrac{\pi}{4}\right)$

25. $\tan(\sin^{-1}1)$

29. $\tan(\tan^{-1}(-1))$

26. $\cot(\cos^{-1}1)$

30. $\cot(\cot^{-1}1)$

(31-32) Find f^{-1} for the given function then give the value of $f(f^{-1}(x))$.

31. $y = 3x + 2$

32. $y = 4x - 1$

(33-42) The exponential and logarithmic functions are a pair of inverses. That is, the inverse of $y = a^x$, $a > 0$, $a \neq 1$ is written $y = \log_a x$.

33. Graph $y = 2^x$ and $y = \log_2 x$ on the same set of coordinate axes.
34. Repeat exercise 33 for $y = 10^x$ and $y = \log_{10} x$.

(35-42) Evaluate.

35. $\log_2 4$

39. $\log_{10} 10^6$

36. $\log_{10} 100$

40. $10^{\log_{10} 100}$

37. $\log_{10} 10^3$

41. $10^{\log_{10} 1,000}$

38. $\log_{10} 10^4$

42. $10^{\log_{10} b}$

43. Prove that $\log_b xy = \log_b x + \log_b y$. Start by letting $u = \log_b x$ and $v = \log_b y$.

3-9 DERIVATIVES OF THE INVERSE TRIGONOMETRIC FUNCTIONS

The derivatives of the inverse trigonometric functions are found by using the definition of these functions and implicit differentiation.

Find $D_x(\sin^{-1}x)$. If $y = \sin^{-1}x$ then by definition $x = \operatorname{Sin} y$. Taking the derivative of both sides of $x = \operatorname{Sin} y$ with respect to x,

$$1 = \cos y\,\frac{dy}{dx}.$$

$$\frac{dy}{dx} = \frac{1}{\cos y}$$

We want $\dfrac{dy}{dx}$ as a function of x rather than y, as it is now. From the identity $\cos^2 y + \sin^2 y = 1$, we have $\cos y = \pm\sqrt{1 - \sin^2 y}$. But $y = \sin^{-1} x$ requires $-\dfrac{\pi}{2} \leq y \leq \dfrac{\pi}{2}$, and for these values of y, $\cos y$ is positive. Therefore, $\cos y = \sqrt{1 - \sin^2 y}$. Since $x = \sin y$, we substitute x^2 for $\sin^2 y$ and have $\cos y = \sqrt{1 - x^2}$. Thus,

$$\frac{dy}{dx} = \frac{1}{\cos y} = \frac{1}{\sqrt{1 - x^2}},$$

and
$$D_x(\sin^{-1} x) = \frac{1}{\sqrt{1 - x^2}}.$$

Find $D_x(\tan^{-1} x)$. If $y = \tan^{-1} x$, then by definition $x = \operatorname{Tan} y$. Taking the derivative of both sides of $x = \operatorname{Tan} y$ with respect to x gives

$$1 = \sec^2 y \frac{dy}{dx}.$$

$$\frac{dy}{dx} = \frac{1}{\sec^2 y}.$$

But $\sec^2 y = 1 + \tan^2 y$. Since $x = \tan y$, we can substitute x^2 for $\tan^2 y$ and $\sec^2 y = 1 + x^2$. Therefore,

$$\frac{dy}{dx} = \frac{1}{\sec^2 y} = \frac{1}{1 + x^2},$$

and
$$D_x(\tan^{-1} x) = \frac{1}{1 + x^2}.$$

Find $D_x(\sec^{-1} x)$. If $y = \sec^{-1} x$ then $x = \operatorname{Sec} y$. Taking the derivative of both sides of $x = \operatorname{Sec} y$ gives

$$1 = \sec y \tan y \frac{dy}{dx}.$$

$$\frac{dy}{dx} = \frac{1}{\sec y \tan y}.$$

In the above equation we wish to replace $\sec y$ and $\tan y$ with equivalent functions of x. $\operatorname{Sec} y$ is easy, since it equals x. From the identity $1 + \tan^2 y = \sec^2 y$, we have $\tan y = \pm\sqrt{\sec^2 y - 1}$, and substituting x^2 for $\sec^2 y$ gives $\tan y = \pm\sqrt{x^2 - 1}$. Then,

$$\frac{dy}{dx} = \frac{1}{\sec y \tan y} = \frac{1}{x(\pm\sqrt{x^2 - 1})}.$$

In order to decide about the ambiguous $\pm$ sign, note that it depends upon tan y. For $y = \sec^{-1}x$, x must be greater than 1 or less than -1. When x is positive ($x > 1$), $0 < y < \dfrac{\pi}{2}$, and tan y is positive. In this case x is positive and the positive part of $\pm\sqrt{x^2 - 1}$ applies. When x is negative, $x < -1$, $\dfrac{\pi}{2} < y < \pi$, and tan y is negative. In this case, x is negative, and so is $\sqrt{x^2 - 1}$. Therefore, the product $x\sqrt{x^2 - 1}$ is always positive. To show this we use absolute value symbols.

$$D_x(\sec^{-1}x) = \frac{1}{|x|\sqrt{x^2 - 1}}.$$

The derivative of the three remaining inverse trigonometric functions are found in the same way. Their proofs are left as exercises. Below are the derivatives of the six inverse trigonometric functions of u, where u is a function of x.

$$D_x(\sin^{-1}u) = \frac{1}{\sqrt{1 - u^2}} \cdot \frac{du}{dx}$$

$$D_x(\cos^{-1}u) = \frac{-1}{\sqrt{1 - u^2}} \cdot \frac{du}{dx}$$

$$D_x(\tan^{-1}u) = \frac{1}{1 + u^2} \cdot \frac{du}{dx}$$

$$D_x(\cot^{-1}u) = \frac{-1}{1 + u^2} \cdot \frac{du}{dx}$$

$$D_x(\sec^{-1}u) = \frac{1}{|u|\sqrt{u^2 - 1}} \cdot \frac{du}{dx}$$

$$D_x(\csc^{-1}u) = \frac{-1}{|u|\sqrt{u^2 - 1}} \cdot \frac{du}{dx}.$$

Example.   Find $D_x(\sin^{-1}3x)$.

Solution. $D_x(\sin^{-1}3x) = \dfrac{1}{\sqrt{1 - (3x)^2}} \cdot D_x(3x)$

$$= \frac{3}{\sqrt{1 - 9x^2}}.$$

Example.   Find y' for $y = x\tan^{-1}x$.

Solution.   Treat $x \tan^{-1}x$ as any other product of two functions of x.

$$y' = x \frac{1}{1 + x^2} + (\tan^{-1}x)(1)$$

$$= \frac{x}{1 + x^2} + \tan^{-1}x.$$

3-9   Exercises

1.   Prove $D_x(\cos^{-1}x) = \dfrac{-1}{\sqrt{1 - x^2}}$

2.   Prove $D_x(\cot^{-1}x) = \dfrac{-1}{1 + x^2}$

3.   Prove $D_x(\csc^{-1}x) = \dfrac{-1}{|x|\sqrt{x^2 - 1}}$

(4-13)   Find y'.

4. $y = \sin^{-1}(5x)$

5. $y = \sin^{-1}(x^2)$

6. $y = \tan^{-1}(3x^2 + 2x)$

7. $y = \tan^{-1}(3x - 4x^3)$

8. $y = x \cot^{-1}x$

9. $y = x^2 \cot^{-1}(2x)$

10. $y = \sec^{-1}(\cos x)$

11. $y = \sec^{-1}(\sec x)$

12. $y = [\sin^{-1}x]^2$

13. $y = [4 \tan^{-1}x^2]^2$

(14-19)   Find y''.

14. $y = \sin^{-1}x$

15. $y = \cos^{-1}x$

16. $y = \tan^{-1}x$

17. $y = \cot^{-1}x$

18. $y = \sec^{-1}x$

19. $y = \csc^{-1}x$

20.   Find the slope of the tangent line to $y = \sin^{-1}x$ when $x = \frac{1}{2}$.

21.   Find the slope of the tangent line to $y = \tan^{-1}x$ when $x = \sqrt{3}$.

22.   A 6-foot high picture is placed on a wall with its lower edge 2 feet above the level of an observer's eye. How far from the wall should the observer stand so that his angle of vision will be maximum?

23.   A lighthouse is located one mile from point P on the shore. P is the nearest point on the shore to the lighthouse and the shoreline is perfectly straight. The beacon in the light house makes two revolutions per minute. It throws a beam of light that moves along the shore line as the beacon revolves. How fast is the spot of light moving on the shore line when it is 3 miles from point P?

3-10 ROLLE'S THEOREM AND THE MEAN VALUE THEOREM

Most of the topics we have considered have had some direct application. However, it is clear that the ultimate uses which most students will make of the material cannot be considered until their individual specialties have been examined in depth. There are also some topics whose ultimate application requires further study of mathematical topics. Two such concepts are Rolle's theorem and the mean value theorem. This is the logical point to introduce them, since they are associated with applications of the derivative. Their immediate application is limited at best, but they will be required for the general advancement of the theory of calculus.

Consider the behavior of the function $f(x) = x^2 - 5x + 4$ between $x = 1$ and $x = 4$. The graph of this function is shown in figure 3-26.

The interval of special interest lies between the points where the functional value is zero. That is, $f(1) = f(4) = 0$. Notice from the graph, that $f(x)$ appears to have a minimum value at $x = \frac{5}{2}$. This can be verified by using calculus.

Since
$$f(x) = x^2 - 5x + 4,$$
$$f'(x) = 2x - 5.$$

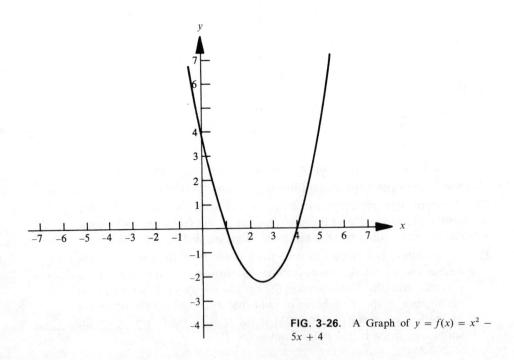

FIG. 3-26. A Graph of $y = f(x) = x^2 - 5x + 4$

Setting $f'(x)$ equal to zero.

$$2x - 5 = 0;$$

$$x = \tfrac{5}{2}.$$

Checking $f''(x)$, $f''(\tfrac{5}{2}) = 2$. The conclusion is that $f(\tfrac{5}{2}) = (\tfrac{5}{2})^2 - 5(\tfrac{5}{2}) + 4 = -\tfrac{9}{4}$ is a minimum value of the function. Rolle's theorem is concerned with a similar type of situation, namely a function defined and continuous over an interval with a zero functional value at each endpoint. Rolle's theorem draws an important conclusion about the derivative of such a function.

Theorem 3-2   Rolle's theorem. Let f be a function such that:

a) f is continuous for all x such that $a \le x \le b$;
b) f' exists for all x such that $a < x < b$;
c) $f(a) = f(b) = 0$.

Then there exists a number c such that $a < c < b$ and $f'(c) = 0$.

In words, Rolle's theorem states that if a function is continuous and differentiable over an interval and is zero at both endpoints of the interval, then at least once within the interval the derivative of the function must be zero.

Consider an unknown function which meets the conditions of Rolle's theorem. What can we deduce about the function? Suppose $f(x)$ is continuous on the interval $a \le x \le b$, $f'(x)$ exists on this interval, and $f(a) = f(b) = 0$. This case is illustrated in figure 3-27. All the curves in figure 3-27 meet the conditions of the theorem. It seems reasonable to conclude that each function illustrated must have a maximum or minimum. Since the derivative of the function must exist at maximum or minimum values, in fact, by the assumption it exists everywhere in the interval, we then know that its value must be zero at that point. Hence, Rolle's theorem seems a very reasonable one. A formal proof can be found in any standard engineering mathematics oriented calculus text.

Example.   Does $f(x) = x^{\frac{4}{3}} - 3x^{\frac{1}{3}}$ for $0 \le x \le 3$ meet the requirements of Rolle's theorem?
Solution.   First

$$f(0) = 0^{\frac{4}{3}} - 3(0)^{\frac{1}{3}} = 0 - 0 = 0.$$

$$f(3) = 3^{\frac{4}{3}} - 3(3)^{\frac{1}{3}} = 3^{\frac{4}{3}} - 3^{\frac{4}{3}} = 0.$$

$$f'(x) = \frac{4}{3}x^{\frac{1}{3}} - x^{-\frac{2}{3}}.$$

$f'(x)$ exists for $0 < x < 3$, and $f(x)$ exists and is continuous on $0 \le x \le 3$.

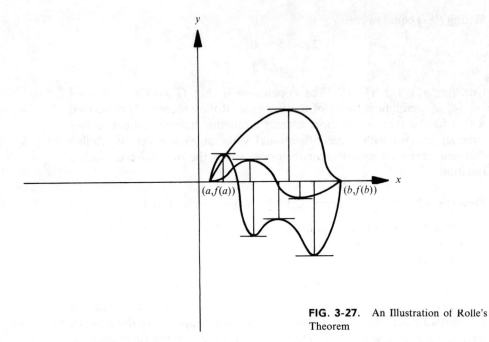

FIG. 3-27. An Illustration of Rolle's Theorem

Thus, the requirements of Rolle's theorem have been met. The conclusion is there must exist a number c such that $0 < c < 3$ and $f'(c) = 0$. Let's attempt to find c. We know that

$$f'(c) = \frac{4}{3}c^{\frac{1}{3}} - c^{-\frac{2}{3}} = 0.$$

$$\frac{4}{3}c^{\frac{1}{3}} - \frac{1}{c^{\frac{2}{3}}} = 0$$

$$\frac{4c^{\frac{1}{3}}c^{\frac{2}{3}}}{3c^{\frac{2}{3}}} - \frac{3}{3c^{\frac{2}{3}}} = 0$$

$$\frac{4c - 3}{3c^{\frac{2}{3}}} = 0.$$

This is only true if

$$4c - 3 = 0.$$

$$c = \tfrac{3}{4}.$$

Notice this value of c does meet the required condition, because

$$0 < \tfrac{3}{4} < 3.$$

This curve is shown in figure 3-28, which demonstrates that $x = \frac{3}{4}$ corresponds to a minimum value of the function.

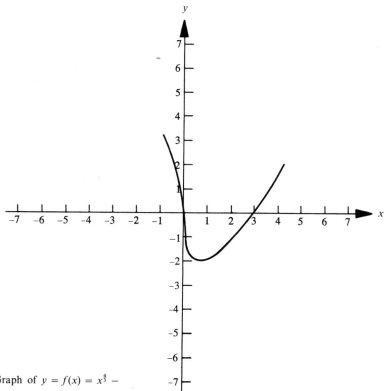

FIG. 3-28.   A Graph of $y = f(x) = x^{\frac{4}{3}} - 3x^{\frac{1}{3}}$

Example.   Consider $f(x) = x^3 - 16x$ for $-4 \leq x \leq 4$. Show that the conditions of Rolle's theorem are met, and find the required values.
Solution. $f(x) = x^3 - 16x$ is continuous everywhere and thus on the interval $-4 \leq x \leq 4$. $f'(x) = 3x^2 - 16$, also exists for $-4 < x < 4$.

$$f(4) = 4^3 - 16(4) = 64 - 64 = 0.$$

$$f(-4) = (-4)^3 - 16(-4) = -64 + 64 = 0.$$

Therefore the conditions of Rolle's theorem are met. The curve of this function is shown in figure 3-29. Now we must find the c value that Rolle's theorem tells us must exist. Setting $f'(x)$ equal to zero,

$$f'(x) = 3x^2 - 16.$$

$$3x^2 - 16 = 0.$$

$$x = \pm \frac{4}{\sqrt{3}}.$$

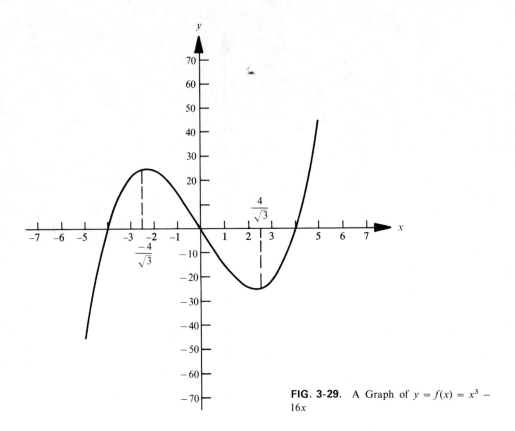

FIG. 3-29. A Graph of $y = f(x) = x^3 - 16x$

There appear to be two values, but which one is correct? Both lie in the interval: that is $-4 < -\dfrac{4}{\sqrt{3}} < 4$, and $-4 < \dfrac{4}{\sqrt{3}} < 4$. Thus either value will do. This is fine, since Rolle's theorem assures at least one value, but does not rule out more than one value.

Rolle's theorem can be applied to prove one of the most fundamental theorems of elementary calculus. This is the mean value theorem.

Theorem 3-3. The Mean Value Theorem. Let f be a function such that f is continuous for $a \leq x \leq b$, and $f'(x)$ exists for $a < x < b$. Then there exists a number d such that $a < d < b$, and

$$f'(d) = \frac{f(b) - f(a)}{b - a}.$$

The theorem is illustrated in figure 3-30. In effect, the mean value theorem states, among other things, that the slope of the tangent to the curve (as

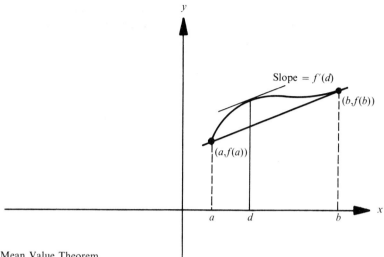

FIG. 3-30.   The Mean Value Theorem

measured by $f'(d)$) will, somewhere in the interval, equal the slope of the line connecting the endpoints of the interval.

Rolle's theorem provides an easy proof of the theorem.

Proof.   Consider a function f meeting the conditions of the mean value theorem: i.e., $f(x)$ is continuous for $a \leq x \leq b$, and $f'(x)$ exists for $a < x < b$. Consider a second function F, such that

$$F(x) = f(x) - \frac{f(b) - f(a)}{b - a}(x - a) - f(a).$$

F is also continuous for $a \leq x \leq b$.

$$F(a) = f(a) - \frac{f(b) - f(a)}{b - a}(a - a) - f(a)$$

$$= f(a) - f(a)$$

$$= 0.$$

$$F(b) = f(b) - \frac{f(b) - f(a)}{b - a}(b - a) - f(a)$$

$$= f(b) - [f(b) - f(a)] - f(a)$$

$$= f(b) - f(b) + f(a) - f(a)$$

$$= 0.$$

$$F'(x) = f'(x) - \frac{f(b) - f(a)}{b - a},$$

and $F'(x)$ exists for $a < x < b$, as $f'(x)$ exists. F meets the conditions of Rolle's theorem. Therefore, there exists a number d, such that $a < d < b$, and $F'(d) = 0$. However,

$$F'(d) = f'(d) - \frac{f(b) - f(a)}{b - a}.$$

Therefore,

$$f'(d) - \frac{f(b) - f(a)}{b - a} = 0,$$

and therefore,

$$f'(d) = \frac{f(b) - f(a)}{b - a}.$$

Thus, the d required in the mean value theorem has been found.

Example.   Find the value of d for $f(x) = x^2 - 5x + 6$ in the interval $1 \le x \le 5$, which is predicted by the mean value theorem.
Solution.   The graph of this function is shown in figure 3-31. f meets the requirements of the mean value theorem. The problem is to find the d value whose existence is assured by the theorem.

$$f(1) = 1^2 - 5 + 6 = 2.$$

$$f(5) = 25 - 25 + 6 = 6.$$

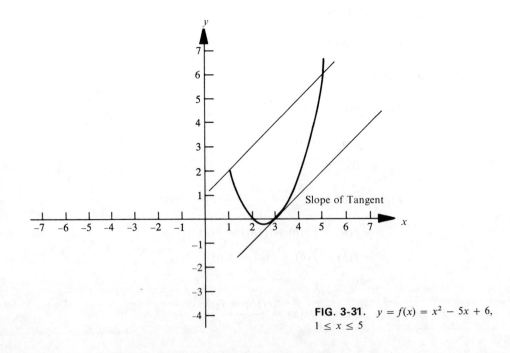

FIG. 3-31. $y = f(x) = x^2 - 5x + 6$, $1 \le x \le 5$

Therefore, $\dfrac{f(b) - f(a)}{b - a} = \dfrac{f(5) - f(1)}{5 - 1} = \dfrac{6 - 2}{5 - 1} = \dfrac{4}{4} = 1.$

$$f'(x) = 2x - 5$$

If we set $f'(x) = 1$

$$2x - 5 = 1$$
$$2x = 6$$
$$x = 3.$$

The required d is 3, $\qquad f'(3) = \dfrac{f(5) - f(1)}{5 - 1}$

and $\qquad\qquad\qquad 1 < 3 < 5.$

Example. Consider $f(x) = x^3 - 2x^2, 1 \le x \le 3$. Show that this function satisfies the conditions of the mean value theorem.

Solution. The function is continuous on $1 \le x \le 3$ and $f'(x) = 3x^2 - 4x$ exists for $1 < x < 3$.

$$f(3) = 27 - 18 = 9.$$
$$f(1) = 1 - 2 = -1.$$

Therefore,

$$\frac{f(b) - f(a)}{b - a} = \frac{f(3) - f(1)}{3 - 1} = \frac{9 - (-1)}{3 - 1} = \frac{10}{2} = 5.$$

Setting $\qquad f'(x) = \dfrac{f(b) - f(a)}{b - a},$

$$3x^2 - 4x = 5;$$
$$3x^2 - 4x - 5 = 0.$$

$$x = \frac{4 \pm \sqrt{16 - 4(-5)(3)}}{6}$$

$$= \frac{4 \pm \sqrt{16 + 60}}{6}$$

$$= \frac{4 \pm \sqrt{76}}{6} \approx \frac{4 \pm 8.7}{6} \approx \frac{12.7}{6} \quad \text{or} \quad \frac{-4.7}{6}$$

$$\approx 2.1 \text{ or } -0.78.$$

Since -0.78 is not in the interval, and 2.1 is, $\dfrac{4 + \sqrt{76}}{6}$ is the desired value.

3-10 Exercises

(1-5) For each of the following verify that the premises of Rolle's theorem have been met, and find an appropriate value of c.

1. $f(x) = x^2 - 7x + 10$ for $2 \le x \le 5$
2. $f(x) = x^3 - 5x^2 - 17x + 21$ for $-3 \le x \le 7$
3. $f(x) = \sin(2x)$ for $0 \le x \le \pi$
4. $f(x) = \cos \dfrac{x}{2}$ for $\pi \le x \le 3\pi$
5. $f(x) = 2 - \cos 4x + 2 \cos x$ for $\dfrac{3\pi}{2} \le x \le \dfrac{7\pi}{2}$

(6-10) For each of the following verify that the conditions of the mean value theorem have been met and find an appropriate value of d.

6. $f(x) = x^2 - 4x + 10$ for $0 \le x \le 3$
7. $f(x) = x^3 - 3x^2 + 3$ for $0 \le x \le 3$
8. $f(x) = \sin x$ for $0 \le x \le \dfrac{\pi}{2}$
9. $f(x) = \cos x$ for $-\dfrac{\pi}{2} \le x \le \dfrac{\pi}{2}$
10. $f(x) = x^{\frac{3}{2}} - 2x^{\frac{1}{4}}$ for $16 \le x \le 81$
11. The function $f(x) = x^3 - 2x^2$, $1 \le x \le 3$ was considered as an example related to the mean value theorem in this section. Sketch the graph of the function and plot the tangent at d when $1 \le x \le 3$.

(12-15) Determine in what way the following functions fail to meet the conditions of Rolle's theorem on the indicated interval.

12. $f(x) = 4x^2 - 8x$ for $0 \le x \le 3$
13. $f(x) = \sin 2x + \cos 2x$ for $0 \le x \le \dfrac{3\pi}{8}$
14. $f(x) = \dfrac{3x^2 - 2x + 4}{x - 2}$ for $1 \le x \le 5$
15. $f(x) = \dfrac{3x + 2}{(x - 1)^2}$ for $\tfrac{1}{2} \le x \le 2$

16. Show by supplying an example that the converse of Rolle's theorem does not hold. I.e., if $f' = 0$ for some c such that $a < c < b$ and $f(x)$ is continuous for $a \le x \le b$ and $f'(x)$ exists for $a < x < b$ that $f(b)$ or $f(a)$ or both are not necessarily equal to zero.

(17-20) Determine in what way each of the following functions fails to meet the conditions of the mean value theorem on the indicated interval.

17. $f(x) = \dfrac{x^2 - 2x}{x}$ for $-1 \le x \le 2$

18. $f(x) = \sqrt{4 - x^2}$ for $-2 \le x \le 5$

19. $f(x) = \dfrac{2}{\sin x}$ for $\dfrac{-\pi}{2} \le x \le \dfrac{\pi}{2}$

20. $f(x) = 3x + 2$ for $-1 \le x \le 2$

Chapter 3   REVIEW

1. Use Newton's method to find the real roots of $x^2 + 4x - 10 = 0$, accurate to two decimal places.

2. Find the real root of $x^3 - 6x - 2 = 0$ that is between -1 and 0, accurate to two decimal places.

3. Find the values of x for which $y = x^2 + 4x + 1$ is increasing, decreasing, concave upward, and concave downward. Also give values of x for which the function is maximum or minimum, and give points of inflection.

4. Repeat exercise 3 for $y = x^3 + 4x$.

(5-10) Find $\dfrac{dy}{dx}$.

5. $3x^2 - 4y^2 = 10$ 8. $y = x \sin^{-1} x$

6. $x^{\frac{1}{2}} + y^{\frac{1}{2}} = 4$ 9. $y = \tan^{-1}\sqrt{x + 1}$

7. $x^3 - 4xy + x^2 = 0$ 10. $y = \cos^{-1}(\sec x)$

(11-13) Find y''.

11. $x^2 - y^2 = 4$ 12. $y^2 = x^2$

13. $y = \csc^{-1} x$

14. If $y = f(x) = 2x + 5$, find $f[f^{-1}(x)]$.

15. The cost of selling x items is given by $C = 500 + 10\sqrt{x}$. What is the rate of change in the cost with respect to time at the instant that the 100th item is sold if the items are selling at the rate of 40 per hour?

16. How much metal, approximately, is used in the construction of a cubic container if the outer edges of the container are 6 inches and the sides are 0.1 inches thick?

17. Find dy and Δy for $y = 3x^2 + 8x - 4$.

18. The base of a triangle is increasing at the rate of 4 feet per minute, while the height is increasing at 2 feet per minute. How fast is the area increasing when the base and height are both 6 feet?

19. A rectangular corral is to be made inside a large barn. The corral is to be constructed in the corner of the barn, so the walls of the barn will form two of its sides. What should be the dimensions of the corral if it is to have maximum area when 250 feet of fencing is available?

20. An excursion-boat company will make its services available to any organization that will guarantee 50 passengers at $12 per passenger. For each passenger over 50 the cost per passenger is reduced $0.25. How many passengers would give the company the maximum gross income?

21. Town A is located on one side of a 100-foot wide canal and town B on the other. Town B is 1,000 feet downstream from town A. A pipeline is to be laid from town A to town B. The pipeline costs $20 per foot when laid in the soil along the canal bank and $30 per foot when laid in the canal itself. How far from town A should the pipeline enter the canal so that its cost will be minimum?

(22-23) Verify that the conditions of Rolle's theorem apply to the indicated functions and find an appropriate value of c.

22. $f(x) = x^2 - 6x - 7$ on the interval $-1 \leq x \leq 7$
23. $f(x) = x^3 + x^2 - 6x$ on the interval $0 \leq x \leq 2$

(24-25) Verify that the conditions of the mean value theorem apply to the function on the indicated interval and find an appropriate value for d.

24. $f(x) = x^3 - 2x^2 + x$ for $1 \leq x \leq 3$

25. $f(x) = \dfrac{2x - 3}{x^2 + 1}$ for $1 \leq x \leq 4$

CHAPTER FOUR **Introduction to**

the Integral

Calculus is loosely divided into two main branches. The preceding chapters have discussed differential calculus. We now introduce the second branch, *integral* calculus. The area under a curve is as basic to integral calculus as the slope of the tangent line is to differential calculus. The slope of the tangent line had numerous interpretations, which led to a number of applications for the derivative of a function. In a similar manner, the area under a curve will point to something we call the integral, which also has many applications. The integral is used in business problems of supply and demand and those of consumer and producer surpluses; in the social and behavioral sciences it is important when considering the statistical concepts of average, standard deviation, and population growth; it is also useful in economics for the analysis of a consumer's propensity to save or to consume. Its main use in the biological sciences involves problems of radioactive decay used for carbon dating and in bacterial population growth.

Integral calculus is more complicated than differential calculus. Therefore, this chapter will introduce the concept of the integral and prepare you for the next chapter which contains methods for evaluating integrals. After that, the applications of the integral will be presented. The topics of this chapter (areas, summations, and antiderivatives) might at first glance seem to be totally unrelated. However they are not. Areas can be computed using summations and, in the next chapter, we will show that the antiderivative is the key to evaluating the integral.

4-1   AREA BOUNDED BY A CURVE—APPROXIMATION BY RECTANGLES

Finding the area of a rectangle or circle presents no problem. Formulas for these areas are readily available. However, the area bounded by the curve $y = x^2 + 1$ and the lines $y = 0$, $x = 0$, and $x = 2$ is a little more difficult to find (see figure 4-1).

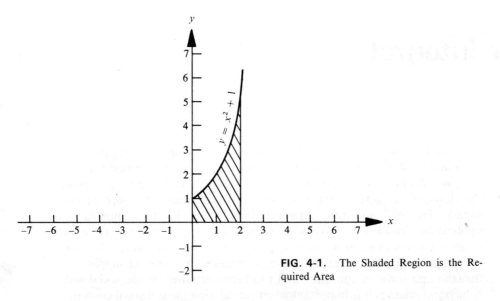

FIG. 4-1.   The Shaded Region is the Required Area

We can approximate the area by dividing it into two rectangles, as shown in figures 4-2 and 4-3. The width of each rectangle is Δx, where $\Delta x = \dfrac{2 - 0}{n}$, where n is the number of rectangles used. Since $n = 2$, $\Delta x = 1$. Figure 4-2 shows the heights of the rectangles as $f(1)$ and $f(2)$, respectively, so that the area may be approximated as the sum of the areas of the rectangles: $1(f(1)) + 1(f(2)) = 2 + 5 = 7$ square units. Figure 4-3 uses $f(0)$ and $f(1)$ as the heights of the rectangles, so that the approximation

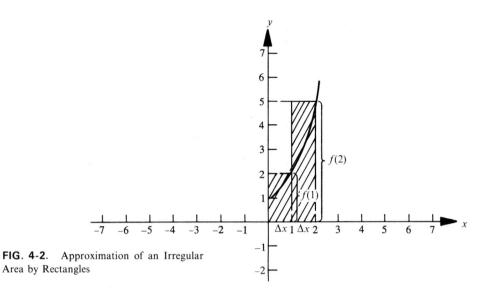

FIG. 4-2. Approximation of an Irregular
Area by Rectangles

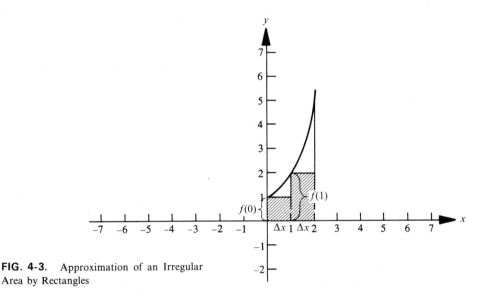

FIG. 4-3. Approximation of an Irregular
Area by Rectangles

of the area is $1(f(0)) + 1(f(1)) = 1 + 2 = 3$ square units. From the diagrams it is evident that the first approximation overestimates the area, and the second approximation underestimates it, so that the area of A is such that $3 < A < 7$. A better approximation would be obtained by partitioning the region into four rectangles ($n = 4$), as in figure 4-4. The area will again be overestimated or underestimated, depending on the values

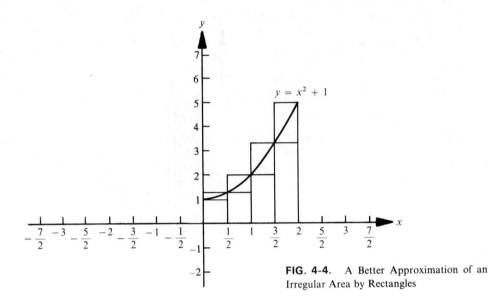

FIG. 4-4. A Better Approximation of an Irregular Area by Rectangles

selected for $f(x)$. It should be clear that, as n increases, the approximation gets closer and closer to the actual area to be found.

If the region is partitioned into n rectangles, with base $\Delta x = x_i - x_{i-1} = \dfrac{2 - 0}{n}$, where $i = 1, 2, 3, \ldots, n$, and with height $f(x_i)$, so that the area of each rectangle is $f(x_i)\Delta x$, then

$$\lim_{n \to \infty} \left[f(x_1)\Delta x + f(x_2)\Delta x + \cdots + f(x_i)\Delta x + \cdots + f(x_n)\Delta x \right]$$

is the exact area bounded by the curve $y = x^2 + 1$, $y = 0$, $x = 0$, and $x = 2$ (see figure 4-5).

In general, consider a continuous function, $f(x)$, which is on or above the x axis ($f(x) \geq 0$), and the region bounded by the curve, the x axis, and the lines $x = a$ and $x = b$, where $a < b$ (figure 4-6).

Partition the region into n rectangles with equal width, $\Delta x = \dfrac{b - a}{n}$.

As $n \to \infty$, $\Delta x \to 0$; therefore, for the ith given rectangle, $f(x_{i-1}) \to f(x_i)$; that is to say, the difference in the two function values becomes negligibly small. The required area, A, is given by the following definition.

Definition. $A = \lim\limits_{n \to \infty} \left[f(x_1)\Delta x + f(x_2)\Delta x + \cdots + f(x_i)\Delta x + \cdots + f(x_n)\Delta x \right]$. This exact area is also known as the *definite integral* of the function, $f(x)$ from $x = a$ to $x = b$, and is written

$$A = \int_a^b f(x)\,dx.$$

The function f is called the *integrand*, a and b are the *limits of integration*, and x is the *variable of integration*.

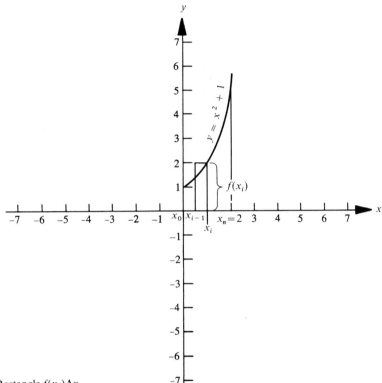

FIG. 4-5.   The Rectangle $f(x_1)\Delta x$

Example.   Find an approximation of $\displaystyle\int_2^4 (2x + 1)\,dx$ by partitioning the

required area into four rectangles of width $\Delta x = x_i - x_{i-1} = \dfrac{b - a}{n}$,

and altitude $f(x_i)$.

Solution. $\Delta x = \dfrac{b - a}{n} = \dfrac{4 - 2}{4} = \dfrac{1}{2}$

$x_0 = 2$

$x_1 = \frac{5}{2}, \; f(x_1) = 6 \qquad A_1 = f(x_1)\Delta x = 6(\tfrac{1}{2}) = 3$

$x_2 = 3, \; f(x_2) = 7 \qquad A_2 = f(x_2)\Delta x = 7(\tfrac{1}{2}) = \tfrac{7}{2}$

$x_3 = \frac{7}{2}, \; f(x_3) = 8 \qquad A_3 = f(x_3)\Delta x = 8(\tfrac{1}{2}) = 4$

$x_4 = 4, \; f(x_4) = 9 \qquad A_4 = f(x_4)\Delta x = 9(\tfrac{1}{2}) = \tfrac{9}{2}$

$A \approx 3 + \tfrac{7}{2} + 4 + \tfrac{9}{2} = 15$ sq. units.

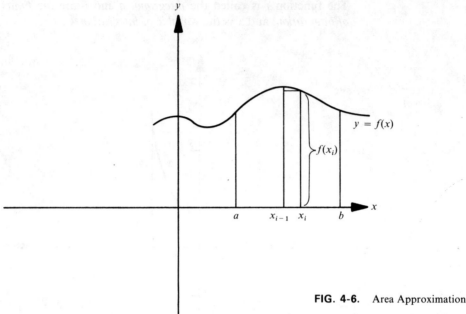

FIG. 4-6. Area Approximation

Since the required region (figure 4-7) is a trapezoid, we can compute the actual area by the formula $A = \frac{1}{2}[f(2) + f(4)]2 = 14$ sq. units.

Thus,

$$\int_2^4 (2x + 1)\, dx = 14.$$

Now we use $n = 8$ to see how much closer the approximation becomes.

When $n = 8$, $\Delta x = \dfrac{4 - 2}{8} = \dfrac{1}{4}$.

$$x_0 = 2$$

$$x_1 = \tfrac{9}{4}, \quad f(x_1) = \tfrac{11}{2} \qquad A_1 = \tfrac{11}{8}$$

$$x_2 = \tfrac{5}{2}, \quad f(x_2) = 6 \qquad A_2 = \tfrac{3}{2}$$

$$x_3 = \tfrac{11}{4}, \quad f(x_3) = \tfrac{13}{2} \qquad A_3 = \tfrac{13}{8}$$

$$x_4 = 3, \quad f(x_4) = 7 \qquad A_4 = \tfrac{7}{4}$$

$$x_5 = \tfrac{13}{4}, \quad f(x_5) = \tfrac{15}{2} \qquad A_5 = \tfrac{15}{8}$$

$$x_6 = \tfrac{7}{2}, \quad f(x_6) = 8 \qquad A_6 = 2$$

$$x_7 = \tfrac{15}{4}, \quad f(x_7) = \tfrac{17}{2} \qquad A_7 = \tfrac{17}{8}$$

$$x_8 = 4, \quad f(x_8) = 9 \qquad A_8 = \tfrac{9}{4}$$

$$A \approx \tfrac{11}{8} + \tfrac{3}{2} + \tfrac{13}{8} + \tfrac{7}{4} + \tfrac{15}{8} + 2 + \tfrac{17}{8} + \tfrac{9}{4} = 14\tfrac{1}{2} \text{ sq. units.}$$

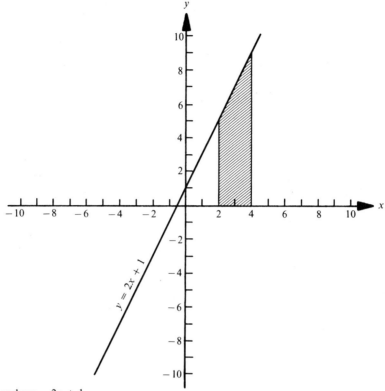

FIG. 4-7.   Area under $y = 2x + 1$

4-1   Exercises

Approximate each of the following integrals as the sum of the areas of n rectangles, using the given information.

1. $\int_0^4 x^2\, dx$, $n = 4$

2. $\int_0^4 x^2\, dx$, $n = 8$

3. $\int_1^5 (x^2 - 3x + 4)dx$, $n = 4$

4. $\int_{-2}^1 (2x^2 + x + 3)dx$, $n = 3$

5. $\int_{-2}^1 (2x^2 + x + 3)dx$, $n = 6$

6. $\int_1^4 (x^2 + 2)dx$, $n = 6$

7. $\int_3^4 \frac{x^3 + 2}{3}dx$, $n = 4$

8. $\int_1^3 (x^3 + 1)dx$, $n = 4$

9. $\int_0^2 (x^2 + 1)dx$, $n = 8$

10. $\int_0^{\pi/2} \sin x\, dx$, $n - 5$

11. $\displaystyle\int_{-\pi/4}^{\pi/4} \tan x\, dx, \; n = 4$ **12.** $\displaystyle\int_{0}^{4} 2^{-x^2}\, dx, \; n = 4$

4-2 SIGMA NOTATION

The sigma notation is a very efficient method for showing sums. We shall use it occasionally throughout this text. It should be pointed out that this is the principal notation used in statistics, that powerful tool of the social scientist.

A useful, compact notation for the sum of n terms of the sequence $\{k_1, k_2, k_3, \ldots, k_n\}$ is

$$\sum_{i=1}^{n} k_i \quad \text{(read: "The sum of } k_i \text{ as } i \text{ goes from 1 to } n.\text{")}$$

Since Σ is the Greek capital letter *sigma*, the notation is called the *sigma* or *summation notation*. Using this notation, we can write the following sums.

$$1 + 2 + 3 + 4 + 5 = \sum_{i=1}^{5} i$$

$$2 + 4 + 6 + 8 + 10 + 12 = \sum_{i=1}^{6} 2i$$

$$1 + 4 + 9 + 16 + \cdots + n^2 = \sum_{i=1}^{n} i^2$$

$$\frac{1}{2} + \frac{2}{5} + \frac{3}{10} + \frac{4}{17} = \sum_{i=1}^{4} \frac{i}{i^2 + 1}$$

We can also express the integral $\displaystyle\int_{a}^{b} f(x)\, dx$ in sigma notation.

Definition. Let $f(x)$ be a continuous function on the closed interval interval $a \leq x \leq b$; then

$$\int_{a}^{b} f(x)\, dx = \lim_{n \to \infty} \sum_{i=1}^{n} f(x_i)\Delta x,$$

where $\Delta x = \dfrac{b - a}{n}$, provided this limit exists.

The definite integral, defined as an area in the preceding section, restricted $f(x)$ to be a nonnegative function. This restriction is not necessary for our new definition, and, as a result, it is not always meaningful to regard the integral as an area. The following theorems, which are proved in section 4-3, show that an integral can be a negative number or zero.

Theorem 4-1. $\displaystyle\int_a^b f(x)\,dx = -\int_b^a f(x)\,dx.$

Theorem 4-2. $\displaystyle\int_a^a f(x)\,dx = 0.$

Example.   Evaluate each of the following sums:

$$\sum_{i=2}^4 (i^2 + 1),\ \sum_{i=3}^5 \frac{4i^2}{i-1},\ \text{and}\ \sum_{i=1}^4 f(i)\Delta x.$$

Solution. $\displaystyle\sum_{i=2}^4 (i^2 + 1) = (2^2 + 1) + (3^2 + 1) + (4^2 + 1)$

$$= 5 + 10 + 17 = 32$$

$$\sum_{i=3}^5 \frac{4i^2}{i-1} = \frac{4(3^2)}{3-1} + \frac{4(4^2)}{4-1} + \frac{4(5^2)}{5-1} = 18 + \frac{64}{3} + 25 = 64\tfrac{1}{3}$$

$\displaystyle\sum_{i=1}^4 f(i)\Delta x,$ where $f(x) = x^2 + 1,\ \Delta x = 3$

$$= (1^2 + 1)3 + (2^2 + 1)3 + (3^2 + 1)3 + (4^2 + 1)3$$

$$= 6 + 15 + 30 + 51$$

$$= 102.$$

The following theorems can easily be proved.

Theorem 4-3. $\displaystyle\sum_{i=1}^n k_i = nk,$ if $k_i = k$, a constant for every i.

Theorem 4-4. $\displaystyle\sum_{i=1}^n (k_i \pm g_i) = \sum_{i=1}^n k_i \pm \sum_{i=1}^n g_i.$

Theorem 4-5. $\displaystyle\sum_{i=1}^n ak_i = a \sum_{i=1}^n k_i,$ if a is constant.

Proofs.

Theorem 4-3. $\displaystyle\sum_{i=1}^n k_i = k + k + k + \cdots + k = nk$

Theorem 4-4.

$$\sum_{i=1}^{n} (k_i + g_i) = (k_1 + g_1) + (k_2 + g_2) + (k_3 + g_3) + \cdots + (k_n + g_n)$$

$$= (k_1 + k_2 + k_3 + \cdots + k_n) + (g_1 + g_2 + g_3 + \cdots + g_n)$$

$$= \sum_{i=1}^{n} k_i + \sum_{i=1}^{n} g_i.$$

Theorem 4-5. $\displaystyle\sum_{i=1}^{n} ak_i = ak_1 + ak_2 + ak_3 + \cdots + ak_n$

$$= a(k_1 + k_2 + k_3 + \cdots + k_n)$$

$$= a \sum_{i=1}^{n} k_i.$$

The above theorems, in addition to the following formulas (which can be proved by mathematical induction), enable us to compute many integrals.

Theorem 4-6. $\displaystyle\sum_{i=1}^{n} i = \frac{n(n+1)}{2}.$

Theorem 4-7. $\displaystyle\sum_{i=1}^{n} i^2 = \frac{n(n+1)(2n+1)}{6}.$

Theorem 4-8. $\displaystyle\sum_{i=1}^{n} i^3 = \left[\frac{n(n+1)}{2} \right]^2.$

Example. Let $f(x) = x^2 + x + 1$. Find $\displaystyle\int_{2}^{4} (x^2 + x + 1)\, dx.$

By definition, $\displaystyle\int_{2}^{4} (x^2 + x + 1)\, dx = \lim_{n \to \infty} \sum_{i=1}^{n} f(x_i)\Delta x$

$$\Delta x = \frac{b - a}{n} = \frac{4 - 2}{n} = \frac{2}{n},$$

x_i is the right endpoint of the width of the ith rectangle, and $f(x_i)$ is the height of the ith rectangle (figure 4-8).

$$x_0 = 2,\ x_1 = 2 + \Delta x,\ x_2 = 2 + 2\Delta x,\ x_3 = 2 + 3\Delta x,\ \text{and}\ x_i = 2 + i\Delta x.$$

$$f(x_i) = f(2 + i\Delta x) = (2 + i\Delta x)^2 + (2 + i\Delta x) + 1$$

$$= 4 + 4i\Delta x + i^2(\Delta x)^2 + 2 + i\Delta x + 1$$

$$= i^2(\Delta x)^2 + 5i\Delta x + 7.$$

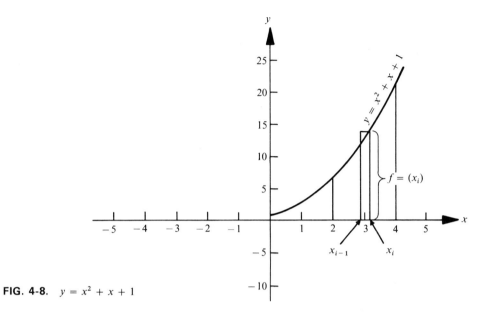

FIG. 4-8. $y = x^2 + x + 1$

$$\sum_{i=1}^{n} f(x_i)\Delta x = \sum_{i=1}^{n} \left[i^2(\Delta x)^2 + 5i(\Delta x) + 7 \right]\Delta x.$$

Applying the theorems for sigma notation, and remembering that Δx is constant, we can write

$$\sum_{i=1}^{n} \left[i^2(\Delta x)^2 + 5i(\Delta x) + 7 \right]\Delta x = (\Delta x)^3 \sum_{i=1}^{n} i^2 + 5(\Delta x)^2 \sum_{i=1}^{n} i + 7n\Delta x.$$

By theorem 4-7,

$$(\Delta x)^3 \sum_{i=1}^{n} i^2 = (\Delta x)^3 \frac{n(n + 1)(2n + 1)}{6}$$

By theorem 4-6,

$$5(\Delta x)^2 \sum_{i=1}^{n} i = 5(\Delta x)^2 \frac{n(n + 1)}{2}$$

$$\sum_{i=1}^{n} f(x_i)\Delta x = (\Delta x)^3 \frac{n(n + 1)(2n + 1)}{6} + 5(\Delta x)^2 \frac{n(n + 1)}{2} + 7n\Delta x$$

But

$$\Delta x = \frac{b - a}{n} = \frac{2}{n};$$

therefore,

$$\lim_{n \to \infty} \sum_{i=1}^{n} f(x_i) \Delta x = \lim_{n \to \infty} \left[\frac{8}{n^3} \frac{n(n+1)(2n+1)}{6} + \frac{20}{n^2} \frac{n(n+1)}{2} + 7n \cdot \frac{2}{n} \right]$$

$$= \lim_{n \to \infty} \left(\frac{80n^2 + 42n + 4}{3n^2} \right)$$

$$= \frac{80}{3}.$$

Thus, $$\int_{2}^{4} (x^2 + x + 1) \, dx = \frac{80}{3}.$$

It should be pointed out that the letter i in the symbol $\sum_{i=1}^{n}$ stands for the *index* of the summation but the letters j or k are also frequently used. For example, $\sum_{j=2}^{4} (2j + j^2)$.

4-2   Exercises

(1-5)   Write each of the indicated sums in expanded notation, and compute the sums.

1. $\sum_{i=1}^{5} (2i - 3)$

4. $\sum_{i=1}^{3} \frac{i^2 - 2}{i}$

2. $\sum_{j=2}^{4} (j^2 + 3j + 1)$

5. $\sum_{k=1}^{4} \left[\frac{1}{k} - \frac{1}{k+1} \right]$

3. $\sum_{k=1}^{6} \frac{1}{k}$

(6-10)   Use the theorems and formulas given in this section to compute the indicated sums.

6. $\sum_{i=1}^{n} (2i - 3)$

9. $\sum_{i=1}^{n} (i + 2)(2i + 3)$

7. $\sum_{i=1}^{n} (i^2 + 3i + 1)$

10. $\sum_{i=1}^{n} (i - 2)(3i^2)$

8. $\sum_{i=1}^{n} i(2i + 1)$

(11-16)   Find the exact value of each of the following integrals by the method outlined in this section. Compare these values with the approximations obtained in exercise 4-1.

11. $\displaystyle\int_0^4 x^2 \, dx$ 14. $\displaystyle\int_1^3 (x^3 + 1) \, dx$

12. $\displaystyle\int_1^4 (x^2 + 2) \, dx$ 15. $\displaystyle\int_{-2}^1 (2x^2 + x + 3) \, dx$

13. $\displaystyle\int_0^2 (x^2 + 1) \, dx$ 16. $\displaystyle\int_2^5 (x^3 - 3x + 4) \, dx$

17.   The Little Profit Manufacturing Company has a policy of increasing each employee's salary by $200 per year. If Miss Rapidtype's starting salary is $5,000, how much money will she have earned at the end of 12 years?

18.   If $600 is invested at 5% simple interest, what will the investment amount to after 10 years?

4-3   PROPERTIES OF THE INTEGRAL

In section 4-2, the integral of a continuous function, $f(x)$, from $x = a$ to $x = b$ was defined as

$$\int_a^b f(x) \, dx = \lim_{n \to \infty} \sum_{i=1}^n f(x_i) \, \Delta x, \text{ where } \Delta x = \frac{b - a}{n},$$

provided this limit exists.

If f is a continuous function for all x such that $a \leq x \leq b$, then $\displaystyle\int_a^b f(x) \, dx$ exists, and $f(x)$ is said to be *integrable* on the interval $a \leq x \leq b$.

The following theorems on the definite integral are useful in all applications of integrals and follow directly from the definition of the integral and the properties of the summation notation. (Assume $f(x)$ is integrable over the interval $a \leq x \leq b$.)

Theorem 4-9. $\displaystyle\int_a^b k f(x) \, dx = k \int_a^b f(x) \, dx$, where k is any constant.

Theorem 4-1. $\displaystyle\int_a^b f(x)\,dx = -\int_b^a f(x)\,dx$. (This theorem was introduced in the preceding section.)

Proof. Since $\displaystyle\Delta x = \frac{b-a}{n}$, $\displaystyle\frac{a-b}{n} = -\Delta x$.

Therefore,

$$\sum_{i=1}^n f(x_i)(-\Delta x) = -\sum_{i=1}^n f(x_i)\,\Delta x,$$

and theorem 4-1 follows.

Theorem 4-2. $\displaystyle\int_a^a f(x)\,dx = 0$. (This theorem was also introduced in the preceding section.)

Proof. Let $b = a$ in theorem 4-1. Then

$$\int_a^a f(x)\,dx = -\int_a^a f(x)\,dx$$

from which it follows that

$$\int_a^a f(x)\,dx = 0.$$

Theorem 4-10. Let $a \le c \le b$; then

$$\int_a^c f(x)\,dx + \int_c^b f(x)\,dx = \int_a^b f(x)\,dx.$$

The student can easily verify this theorem.

Theorem 4-11. If f and g are continuous functions on the interval from $x = a$ to $x = b$, then

$$\int_a^b (f(x) + g(x))\,dx = \int_a^b f(x)\,dx + \int_a^b g(x)\,dx.$$

This theorem is derived from the fact that the limit of a sum is the sum of the limits, provided these limits exist.

Another theorem which shall be stated without proof is the mean-value theorem for integrals.

Theorem 4-12. Mean-Value Theorem for Integrals. Let $f(x)$ be a non-negative continuous function on the interval $a \le x \le b$, then there exists a number c, $a \leq c \leq b$ such that

$$\int_a^b f(x)\,dx = f(c)(b - a).$$

Among other things, this theorem states that for every area bounded by a curve, $f(x)$, the x axis, and the lines $x = a$ and $x = b$, there exists a rectangle of equal area, with length $(b - a)$ and height $f(c)$ for some c such that $a \leq c \leq b$. (Figure 4-9.)

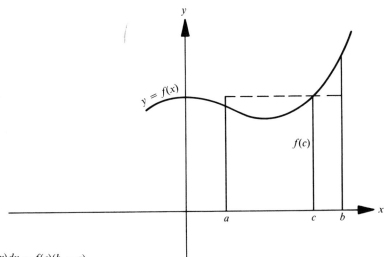

FIG. 4-9. $\int_a^b f(x)\,dx = f(c)(b - a)$

The mean-value theorem for integrals guarantees the existence of the number c such that the required area, $A = f(c)(b - a)$, but this number is usually not easy to find, unless the value of the integral is known. Thus, if

$$\int_3^6 x^2\,dx = 63, \text{ then}$$

$$A = f(c)(b - a) = 63,\ b - a = 6 - 3 = 3;\ f(c) = 21, \text{ and } c = \sqrt{21}.$$

4-3   Exercises

(1-5)   Use the results of the indicated exercise from section 4-2 to find the number c guaranteed by the mean-value theorem for integrals. Sketch each curve and the corresponding rectangle $f(c)(b - a)$.

1. $\displaystyle\int_0^4 x^2\,dx$, (Exercise 11)

2. $\displaystyle\int_1^4 (x^2 + 2)\,dx$, (Exercise 12)

3. $\displaystyle\int_0^2 (x^2 + 1)\,dx$, (Exercise 13)

4. $\displaystyle\int_1^3 (x^3 + 1)\,dx$, (Exercise 14)

5. $\displaystyle\int_{-2}^1 (2x^2 + x + 3)\,dx$, (Exercise 15)

6. If $f(x) = x^2 - 2x + 1$, and $\displaystyle\int_{-1}^3 f(x)\,dx = \frac{16}{3}$, find two values of c, such that

$$\int_{-1}^3 f(x)\,dx = f(c)(3 + 1).$$

(7-12) If $\displaystyle\int_0^1 x^3\,dx = \frac{1}{4}$, $\displaystyle\int_0^1 x^2\,dx = \frac{1}{3}$, and $\displaystyle\int_1^2 x^2\,dx = \frac{7}{3}$, evaluate each of the following.

7. $\displaystyle\int_0^2 x^2\,dx$ 10. $\displaystyle\int_0^1 4x^3\,dx$

8. $\displaystyle\int_0^1 (x^3 + x^2)\,dx$ 11. $\displaystyle\int_0^1 (3x^3 + 2x^2)\,dx$

9. $\displaystyle\int_2^1 x^2\,dx$ 12. $\displaystyle\int_0^2 6x^2\,dx$

(13-16) State if the mean-value theorem for integrals applies. If it does not apply, say why not.

13. $\displaystyle\int_0^3 \frac{x}{x - 1}\,dx$ 16. $\displaystyle\int_2^5 \sqrt{16 - x^2}\,dx$

14. $\displaystyle\int_1^5 \frac{x - 1}{x + 1}\,dx$ 17. If $f(x) = \begin{cases} x & ,\text{ when } -1 \le x < 1 \\ 2 - x, & \text{ when } 1 \le x < 10 \end{cases}$

15. $\displaystyle\int_{-10}^{20} (x^9 + x^2 + 3)\,dx$

does the mean-value theorem for integrals apply to $\int_0^4 f(x)\,dx$? Justify your answer by sketching $f(x)$ and shading the desired area.

4-4   AREA BOUNDED BY A CURVE— APPROXIMATION BY TRAPEZOIDS

The use of rectangles to estimate the area under a curve is important to our development of the basic theory and properties of the integral. However, using trapezoids to estimate the area under a curve is a valuable practical device. In any area of application of the integral, such as those presented in subsequent chapters, it is often necessary to evaluate integrals that cannot be evaluated using the elementary methods of the next chapter. In these cases, the integral can be estimated to any degree of accuracy by using the trapezoidal rule. The trapezoidal rule is very well suited to computer use. When computer time is available, even integrals that can be evaluated analytically are often estimated by the trapezoidal rule.

In section 4-1 we found that an approximation of an area bounded by a curve can be made by partitioning the region into rectangles and summing their areas. Figures 4-2 and 4-3 illustrate how this sum overestimates or underestimates the desired area. A better approximation can sometimes be achieved by partitioning the area into trapezoids (figure 4-10).

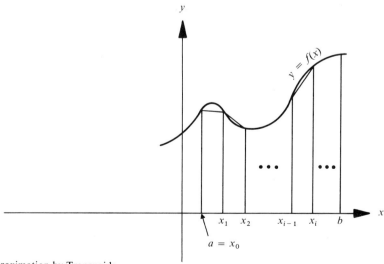

FIG. 4-10. Approximation by Trapezoids

Partition the interval $a \leq x \leq b$ into n equal intervals, and construct trapezoids with parallel sides $f(x_{i-1})$ and $f(x_i)$ (where $i = 1, 2, 3, \ldots, n$), and altitude $\Delta x = x_i - x_{i-1}$. Since the area of a trapezoid, A_T, is equal to one half the product of the altitude and the sum of the lengths of the parallel sides, the area of the ith trapezoid,

$$A_{T_i} = \tfrac{1}{2}\Delta x[f(x_{i-1}) + f(x_i)].$$

The total area of all trapezoids in the region is

$$A_{T_1} + A_{T_2} + A_{T_3} + \cdots + A_{T_n}, \text{ where}$$
$$A_{T_1} = \tfrac{1}{2}\Delta x[f(x_0) + f(x_1)]$$
$$A_{T_2} = \tfrac{1}{2}\Delta x[f(x_1) + f(x_2)]$$
$$A_{T_3} = \tfrac{1}{2}\Delta x[f(x_2) + f(x_3)]$$
$$\vdots$$
$$A_{T_{n-1}} = \tfrac{1}{2}\Delta x[f(x_{n-2}) + f(x_{n-1})]$$
$$A_{T_n} = \tfrac{1}{2}\Delta x[f(x_{n-1}) + f(x_n)]$$

Using the associative, commutative, and distributive properties of the real numbers, we combine these areas to obtain the sum of the areas of these trapezoids,

$$S_T = \tfrac{1}{2}\Delta x[f(x_0) + 2f(x_1) + 2f(x_2) + \cdots + 2f(x_i) + \cdots$$
$$+ 2f(x_{n-1}) + f(x_n)]$$

Since $\Delta x = \dfrac{b - a}{n}$, this yields the formula

$$\text{Total Area} \approx S_T = \dfrac{b - a}{2n}[f(x_0) + 2f(x_1) + \cdots + 2f(x_i) + \cdots$$
$$+ 2f(x_{n-1}) + f(x_n)]$$

It is again obvious that as $n \to \infty$, and $\Delta x \to 0$,

$$S_T \to \int_a^b f(x)\,dx$$

Example. Use the approximation by trapezoids to find $\int_0^2 (x^2 + 1)dx$, when $n = 4$.

Solution. $\Delta x = \dfrac{b - a}{n} = \dfrac{2 - 0}{4} = \dfrac{1}{2}; \dfrac{b - a}{2n} = \dfrac{1}{4}.$

$x_0 = 0$ implies $f(x_0) = 1$.

$x_1 = \tfrac{1}{2}$ implies $f(x_1) = \tfrac{5}{4}$ and $2f(x_1) = \tfrac{5}{2}$.

$x_2 = 1$ implies $f(x_2) = 2$ and $2f(x_2) = 4$.

$x_3 = \frac{3}{2}$ implies $f(x_3) = \frac{13}{4}$ and $2f(x_3) = \frac{13}{2}$.

$x_4 = 2$ implies $f(x_4) = 5$.

$$A \approx S_T = \frac{b-a}{2n}[f(x_0) + 2f(x_1) + 2f(x_2) + 2f(x_3) + f(x_4)]$$

$$= \tfrac{1}{4}[1 + \tfrac{5}{2} + 4 + \tfrac{13}{2} + 5]$$

$$= \tfrac{19}{4} \text{ sq. units} = 4.75 \text{ sq. units.}$$

From section 4-2, exercise 13, we know that the exact value of $\displaystyle\int_0^2 (x^2 + 1)\,dx =$ $\frac{14}{3} \approx 4.67$, so the approximation by use of four trapezoids is not far off.

4-4   Exercises

Approximate each of the following integrals by the trapezoidal method for the given number n. Compare these results with the appropriate exercises from sections 4-1 and 4-2 whenever possible.

1. $\displaystyle\int_0^4 x^2\,dx, \; n = 4$
         7. $\displaystyle\int_0^{\pi/2} \sin x\,dx, \; n = 5$

2. $\displaystyle\int_2^5 (x^3 - 3x + 4)\,dx, \; n = 3$
      8. $\displaystyle\int_1^4 x(x^2 - 1)\,dx, \; n = 3$

3. $\displaystyle\int_{-2}^1 (2x^2 + x + 3)\,dx, \; n = 3$
      9. $\displaystyle\int_0^{\pi/2} \cos x\,dx, \; n = 5$

4. $\displaystyle\int_1^4 (x^2 + 2)\,dx, \; n = 6$
      10. $\displaystyle\int_0^{\pi/4} \tan x\,dx, \; n = 3$

5. $\displaystyle\int_3^4 \frac{x^3 + 2}{3}\,dx, \; n = 4$
      11. $\displaystyle\int_{-2}^2 2^{-x^2}\,dx, \; n = 4$

6. $\displaystyle\int_1^3 (x^3 + 1)\,dx, \; n = 4$
      12. $\displaystyle\int_{-10}^{10} 2^{-x^2}\,dx, \; n = 10$

4-5   THE INDEFINITE INTEGRAL—ANTIDERIVATIVE

In section 4-1, the definite integral $\displaystyle\int_a^b f(x)\,dx$ was defined as the limit of a sum, $\displaystyle\sum_{i=1}^n f(x_i)\Delta x$, as $n \to \infty$. This sum is usually called a *Riemann sum*, and the integral it defines is called a *Riemann integral* in honor of the German mathematician G. F. B. Riemann (1826–1866).

We shall now define the *indefinite integral* of a function, f. In chapter 5 we will relate the indefinite and the definite integrals.

Definition.   If $f(x)$ is a function, then any function $F(x)$ such that $F'(x) = f(x)$ is an *indefinite integral* of $f(x)$.

The notation for the indefinite integral is $\int f(x)\,dx$. (Note that the limits of integration are omitted.) $\int f(x)\,dx$ is also called an *antiderivative* of f. Suppose $f(x) = 2x + 3$. Then a function $F(x)$ such that $F'(x) = 2x + 3$ is $x^2 + 3x$. If $F(x) = x^2 + 3x$, then $F'(x) = 2x + 3$, or

$$d(F(x)) = (2x + 3)\,dx,$$

and

$$\int (2x + 3)\,dx = x^2 + 3x.$$

But we know that the derivative of any constant is zero; therefore, $F(x) = x^2 + 3x + 2$ also yields $F'(x) = 2x + 3$, and so does $F(x) = x^2 + 3x - 5$, $F(x) = x^2 + 3x + 99$, and $F(x) = x^2 + 3x + C$, where C is any constant. We can say that the most general antiderivative of $2x + 3$ is

$$\int (2x + 3)\,dx = x^2 + 3x + C.$$

It can be shown that if $F(x)$ and $G(x)$ are functions such that $F'(x) = G'(x)$ over an interval $a \le x \le b$, then $F(x)$ and $G(x)$ differ by at most a constant; that is $F(x) + C = G(x)$ where C is constant. Thus,

$$\int f(x)\,dx = F(x) + C.$$

It should be evident from the definition and the example that integration is the inverse process of differentiation; that is to say, it poses the problem of finding a function whose derivative (or differential) is given.

The following integration formulas are given for the solution of simple problems. Their proofs are based upon the theorems on the derivative and the differential. Further techniques of integration are given in chapter 5, and tables of integrals have been compiled to facilitate the integration of many problems.

$$\int dx = x + C.$$

$$\int du = u + C,$$

(where u is a function of some other variable.)

$$\int a \, du = a \int du, \ a \text{ is a constant}$$

$$\int [f(x) + g(x)] \, dx = \int f(x) \, dx + \int g(x) \, dx$$

$$\int u^n \, du = \frac{u^{n+1}}{n+1} + C,$$

(if n is a rational number, and $n \neq -1$.)

The last formula can easily be verified. Let u be a function of x such that $F(x) = \dfrac{u^{n+1}}{n+1} + C$, then $F'(x) \, dx = (n+1) \dfrac{u^{n+1-1}}{n+1} du = u^n \, du$. This formula is called the *power formula*, since it involves a function raised to a power. Notice the restriction, $n \neq -1$. If $n = -1$ the denominator would be zero and division by zero has no meaning. The integral $\int u^{-1} \, du$ involves a logarithmic function and will be discussed later.

Example. Find $\displaystyle\int 3 \, dx$.

Solution. $\displaystyle\int 3 \, dx = 3 \int dx = 3x + C.$

Example. Find $\displaystyle\int (x^2 + 5x + 1) \, dx$.

Solution. $\displaystyle\int (x^2 + 5x + 1) \, dx = \int x^2 \, dx + 5 \int x \, dx + \int dx.$

$$= \frac{x^3}{3} + \frac{5x^2}{2} + x + C.$$

Example. Find $\displaystyle\int (x^2 + 2)^3 (2x) \, dx$.

Solution. A substitution, let $u = x^2 + 2$, makes this seemingly complicated problem quite simple. If $u = x^2 + 2$, then $du = 2x \, dx$, and the expression $u^3 \, du$ has an antiderivative, $\dfrac{u^{3+1}}{4} = \dfrac{u^4}{4}$.

$$\int u^3 \, du = \tfrac{1}{4} u^4 + C. \text{ Since } u = x^2 + 2,$$

$$\int \overbrace{(x^2 + 2)^3}^{u} \overbrace{(2x) \, dx}^{du} = \tfrac{1}{4}(x^2 + 2)^4 + C.$$

To check the solution recall that the integral is an antiderivative, and if $F = \int f\,dx$, then $F' = f$.

$$F(x) = \tfrac{1}{4}(x^2 + 2)^4 + C \to F'(x) = (x^2 + 2)^3(2x) = f(x).$$

Example. Find $\displaystyle\int x^3 \sqrt{x^4 + 2}\,dx$.

Solution. Again a substitution simplifies the problem.

Let $$u = x^4 + 2; \text{ then } du = 4x^3\,dx.$$

We can rewrite $x^3 \sqrt{x^4 + 2}\,dx$ as $\tfrac{1}{4}\sqrt{x^4 + 2}\,(4x^3)\,dx$ (Multiply and divide by 4). Thus,

$$\int x^3 \sqrt{x^4 + 2}\,dx = \int \tfrac{1}{4} u^{\frac{1}{2}}\,du = \tfrac{1}{4}\int u^{\frac{1}{2}}\,du$$

$$= \tfrac{1}{4}\frac{u^{\frac{3}{2}}}{\frac{3}{2}} + C = \tfrac{1}{6}u^{\frac{3}{2}} + C$$

$$= \tfrac{1}{6}(x^4 + 2)^{\frac{3}{2}} + C.$$

To check this result, take the derivative of $\tfrac{1}{6}(x^4 + 2)^{\frac{3}{2}} + C$ and obtain $\tfrac{1}{4}(x^4 + 2)^{\frac{1}{2}}(4x^3)$ which simplifies to $x^3\sqrt{x^4 + 2}$.

Example. Find $\displaystyle\int \frac{x\,dx}{\sqrt{a^2 + x^2}}$ (a is constant).

Solution. The substitution $u = a^2 + x^2$ is advisable; then $du = 2x\,dx$. Proceed as in the preceding example and multiply and divide by 2.

$$\int \frac{x\,dx}{\sqrt{a^2 + x^2}} = \tfrac{1}{2}\int \frac{2x\,dx}{\sqrt{a^2 + x^2}}$$

$$= \tfrac{1}{2}\int \frac{du}{\sqrt{u}}$$

$$= \tfrac{1}{2}\int u^{-\frac{1}{2}}\,du$$

$$= \tfrac{1}{2}\frac{u^{\frac{1}{2}}}{\frac{1}{2}} + C$$

$$= u^{\frac{1}{2}} + C$$

$$= \sqrt{a^2 + x^2} + C.$$

Therefore, $$\int \frac{x\,dx}{\sqrt{a^2 + x^2}} = \sqrt{a^2 + x^2} + C.$$

CHECK: If $$F(x) = \sqrt{a^2 + x^2} + C$$

then $$F'(x) = \tfrac{1}{2}(a^2 + x^2)^{-\frac{1}{2}}(2x) = \frac{x}{\sqrt{a^2 + x^2}} = f(x).$$

It should be pointed out that the variable of integration need not be called x, but can be any other letter, such as θ, t, or y.

$$\int 2t\,dt = t^2 + C.$$

$$\int \theta\,d\theta = \frac{\theta^2}{2} + C.$$

4-5 Exercises

Integrate the following. Check your answers by differentiation.

1. $\displaystyle\int 3x\,dx$

2. $\displaystyle\int (5x^2 + 3x + 2)\,dx$

3. $\displaystyle\int (x^{10} - 2x^6 + x^3)\,dx$

4. $\displaystyle\int \sqrt{x}\,dx$

5. $\displaystyle\int \frac{dx}{\sqrt{x}}$

6. $\displaystyle\int (x + 2)^2\,dx$

7. $\displaystyle\int x\sqrt{x^2 + 5}\,dx$

8. $\displaystyle\int \frac{x}{\sqrt{1 - x^2}}\,dx$

9. $\displaystyle\int \left(\frac{2}{x^2} + \frac{3}{x^3}\right)dx$

10. $\displaystyle\int (x^2 - 1)(4 - x^2)\,dx$

11. $\displaystyle\int (4x^2 + 2x + 1)^3\,(8x + 2)\,dx$

12. $\displaystyle\int (2x + 5)(x^2 + 5x + 3)^{10}\,dx$

13. $\displaystyle\int 3(6x + 9)^4\,dx$

14. $\displaystyle\int \frac{2\,dx}{(x + 5)^5}$

15. $\displaystyle\int x^{2a}\,dx$ (a is a positive constant)

16. $\displaystyle\int \frac{4x - 3}{(2x^2 - 3x + 1)^3}\,dx$

17. $\displaystyle\int \frac{(1 + \sqrt{x})}{x^2}\,dx$

18. $\displaystyle\int \frac{dx}{\sqrt[3]{(2x + 1)^2}}$

19. $\int (x^2 - 2x + 1)^{\frac{5}{3}} \, dx$

20. $\int \sqrt{3 - x} \, dx$

21. $\int \dfrac{3x^4 + x^3 + x - 3}{x^2 + 1} \, dx$ (*Hint*: use long division to simplify the expression first.)

22. $\int \dfrac{3x^3 + 6x^2 + 3x + 1}{x^2 + 2x + 1} \, dx$

23. $\int \dfrac{x^3}{\sqrt{x^4 - 1}} \, dx$

24. $\int (x - 3)^{\frac{3}{2}} \, dx$

4-6 INDEFINITE INTEGRALS—TRIGONOMETRIC FUNCTIONS

Integrals of trigonometric functions are important for the nonengineering oriented student chiefly as a tool for integrating other functions. These applications will be considered in chapter 5. The following formulas can easily be verified by differentiation.

$$\int \sin x \, dx = -\cos x + C.$$

$$\int \cos x \, dx = \sin x + C.$$

$$\int \sec^2 x \, dx = \tan x + C.$$

$$\int \sec x \tan x \, dx = \sec x + C.$$

$$\int \csc^2 x \, dx = -\cot x + C.$$

$$\int \csc x \cot x \, dx = -\csc x + C.$$

From previous experience, it is evident, for example, that if u is a function of x, then

$$\int \sin u \, du = -\cos u + C.$$

Example. Find $\int \sin 3x \, dx$.

Solution. $\int \sin 3x \, dx = \frac{1}{3} \int \sin 3x \, (3) \, dx = -\frac{1}{3} \cos 3x + C.$

Example. Find $\int \sec^2 5\theta \, d\theta$.

Solution. $\int \sec^2 5\theta \, d\theta = \frac{1}{5} \int \sec^2 5\theta \, (5) \, d\theta = \frac{1}{5} \tan 5\theta + C.$

The following integrals result in inverse trigonometric functions.

$$\int \frac{dx}{\sqrt{1 - x^2}} = \sin^{-1} x + C.$$

$$\int \frac{-dx}{\sqrt{1 - x^2}} = \cos^{-1} x + C.$$

$$\int \frac{dx}{1 + x^2} = \tan^{-1} x + C.$$

$$\int \frac{-dx}{1 + x^2} = \cot^{-1} x + C.$$

$$\int \frac{dx}{|x|\sqrt{x^2 - 1}} = \sec^{-1} x + C.$$

$$\int \frac{-dx}{|x|\sqrt{x^2 - 1}} = \csc^{-1} x + C.$$

Example. Find $\int \frac{dx}{\sqrt{1 - 9x^2}}$.

Solution. $\int \frac{dx}{\sqrt{1 - 9x^2}} = \frac{1}{3} \int \frac{du}{\sqrt{1 - u^2}}$ where $u = 3x$ and $du = 3 \, dx$.

We multiply and divide the first integral by 3, placing the $\frac{1}{3}$ outside the integral.

Then, $\dfrac{1}{3} \displaystyle\int \dfrac{du}{\sqrt{1 - u^2}} = \dfrac{1}{3} \sin^{-1} u + C = \dfrac{1}{3} \sin^{-1} 3x + C.$

Example.   Find $\displaystyle\int \dfrac{dx}{9 + x^2}.$

Solution. $\displaystyle\int \dfrac{dx}{9 + x^2} = \int \dfrac{dx}{9\left(1 + \dfrac{x^2}{9}\right)} = \dfrac{1}{9} \int \dfrac{dx}{1 + \left(\dfrac{x}{3}\right)^2}.$

Let $u = \dfrac{x}{3}$; then $du = \frac{1}{3}dx$. Multiply and divide by $\frac{1}{3}$, and obtain

$$\dfrac{1}{3} \int \dfrac{du}{1 + u^2} = \dfrac{1}{3} \tan^{-1} u + C$$

$$= \dfrac{1}{3} \tan^{-1}\left(\dfrac{x}{3}\right) + C.$$

Example.   Find $\displaystyle\int \dfrac{dx}{x\sqrt{4x^2 - 1}}, x > \dfrac{1}{2}.$

Solution. $\displaystyle\int \dfrac{dx}{x\sqrt{4x^2 - 1}} = \int \dfrac{dx}{x\sqrt{(2x)^2 - 1}}.$

Let $u = 2x$; then $du = 2\,dx$.

$$\int \dfrac{2\,dx}{2x\sqrt{(2x)^2 - 1}} = \int \dfrac{du}{u\sqrt{u^2 - 1}}$$

$$= \sec^{-1} u + C$$

$$= \sec^{-1}(2x) + C.$$

As a direct consequence of the integral

$$\int \dfrac{du}{\sqrt{1 - u^2}}$$

the student may verify that:

$$\int \dfrac{du}{\sqrt{a^2 - u^2}} = \sin^{-1}\left(\dfrac{u}{a}\right) + C,$$

and $\displaystyle\int \dfrac{-du}{\sqrt{a^2 - u^2}} = \cos^{-1}\left(\dfrac{u}{a}\right) + C.$

Example.   Find $\displaystyle\int \frac{dx}{\sqrt{2 + x - x^2}}$.

Solution.   This situation usually calls for completing the square under the radical.

$$2 + x - x^2 = 2 - (x^2 - x + \tfrac{1}{4} - \tfrac{1}{4})$$
$$= \tfrac{9}{4} - (x - \tfrac{1}{2})^2.$$

Thus, $\displaystyle\int \frac{dx}{\sqrt{2 + x - x^2}} = \int \frac{dx}{\sqrt{\tfrac{9}{4} - (x - \tfrac{1}{2})^2}}$

Now let $u = (x - \tfrac{1}{2})$; then $du \doteq dx$, and the integral becomes

$$\int \frac{du}{\sqrt{a^2 - u^2}}, \text{ where } a = \frac{3}{2}.$$

$$\int \frac{du}{\sqrt{a^2 - u^2}} = \sin^{-1}\left(\frac{u}{a}\right) + C$$

$$= \sin^{-1}\left(\frac{x - \tfrac{1}{2}}{\tfrac{3}{2}}\right) + C$$

$$= \sin^{-1}\left[\frac{2(x - \tfrac{1}{2})}{3}\right] + C.$$

4-6   Exercises

Perform the indicated integrations.

1. $\displaystyle\int \cos 2x \, dx$

2. $\displaystyle\int \sin 3\theta \, d\theta$

3. $\displaystyle\int \sec^2\left(\frac{\theta}{2}\right) d\theta$

4. $\displaystyle\int \sin x \cos x \, dx$

5. $\displaystyle\int \tan^3 x \sec^2 x \, dx$

6. $\displaystyle\int \tan \theta \sec \theta \, d\theta$

7. $\displaystyle\int \frac{1}{\sin^2 x} \, dx$

8. $\displaystyle\int \frac{\sin 3t}{\sec^3 3t} \, dt$

9. $\displaystyle\int \frac{\cos \theta}{\csc^2 \theta} \, d\theta$

10. $\displaystyle\int \frac{\sin 2x}{\sin x \cos x} \, dx$

11. $\displaystyle\int \frac{dx}{\sqrt{1-3x^2}}$

12. $\displaystyle\int \frac{dx}{2+x^2}$

13. $\displaystyle\int \frac{dx}{-1-x^2}$

14. $\displaystyle\int \frac{dx}{x\sqrt{x^2-4}}, \; x > 2$

15. $\displaystyle\int \frac{dx}{4+9x^2}$

16. $\displaystyle\int \frac{dx}{x\sqrt{2x^2-1}}, \; x > \frac{1}{\sqrt{2}}$

17. $\displaystyle\int \frac{dx}{\sqrt{1+2x-x^2}}$

18. $\displaystyle\int \frac{dx}{\sqrt{2-2x^2+x}}$

19. $\displaystyle\int \frac{\cos x}{1+\sin^2 x}\,dx$

20. $\displaystyle\int \frac{\sin x}{\sqrt{1-\cos^2 x}}\,dx$

21. $\displaystyle\int \frac{1}{x^2}\sec\left(\frac{1}{x}\right)\tan\left(\frac{1}{x}\right)dx$

Chapter 4   REVIEW

(1-5)   For each of the following integrals,

a)   approximate as a sum of the areas of n rectangles,

b)   approximate as a sum of the areas of n trapezoids, and

c)   use the definition $\displaystyle\int_a^b f(x)\,dx = \lim_{n\to\infty}\sum_{i=1}^n f(x_i)\Delta x$

to find the exact numerical answer.

1. $\displaystyle\int_0^2 x^2\,dx, \; n = 4$

2. $\displaystyle\int_1^4 (2x+1)\,dx, \; n = 6$

3. $\displaystyle\int_0^2 (2x^3 + 3x + 4)\,dx, \; n = 4$

4. $\displaystyle\int_2^4 (x^2 + x - 3)\,dx, \; n = 4$

5. $\displaystyle\int_0^{\pi/2} \cos x\,dx, \; n = 3$. Find parts (a) and (b) only. The answer to part (c) is 1.

6.   Use the definition of $\displaystyle\int_a^b f(x)\,dx$ to find the area between the curve $y = 4 - x^2$ and the x axis.

7.   Use the method of exercise 6 to find the area bounded by the curve $y = x^2 + 1$, the x axis, and the lines $x = 0$ and $x = 3$.

8. If $\displaystyle\int_0^{\pi/3} \sin x\, dx = \frac{1}{2}$, find the number c guaranteed by the mean-value

theorem for integrals such that $\displaystyle\int_0^{\pi/3} \sin x\, dx = f(c)(b - a)$.

(9-25) Find the following antiderivatives.

9. $\displaystyle\int (3x^5 + 2x^3 - x^2 + 1)\, dx$

10. $\displaystyle\int (x + 3)^{\frac{3}{2}}\, dx$

11. $\displaystyle\int (x\sqrt{x} + \sqrt{x} - 3)\, dx$

12. $\displaystyle\int \frac{dx}{\sqrt{2x + 1}}$

13. $\displaystyle\int \frac{x}{\sqrt{1 + 2x^2}}\, dx$

14. $\displaystyle\int \frac{dx}{\sqrt{2 - x^2}}$

15. $\displaystyle\int \sqrt{x - 2}\, dx$

16. $\displaystyle\int \frac{dx}{1 + 2x^2}$

17. $\displaystyle\int (x^3 + 3x + 4)^4 (x^2 + 1)\, dx$

18. $\displaystyle\int (\sqrt{x} + 1)^2\, dx$

19. $\displaystyle\int \sin^2 3x \cos 3x\, dx$

20. $\displaystyle\int \frac{\sin x}{\cos^3 x}\, dx$

21. $\displaystyle\int 2 \sin(2x + 3)\, dx$

22. $\displaystyle\int \frac{\tan^3 x}{\cos^2 x}\, dx$

23. $\displaystyle\int x \cos(x^2)\, dx$

24. $\displaystyle\int 3x \sin^2(x^2) \cos(x^2)\, dx$

25. $\displaystyle\int \sec^2 x \tan^2 x\, dx$

CHAPTER FIVE

Integration

In the last chapter, the integral and its properties were introduced. Certain definite integrals were evaluated using Riemann sums; others could only be estimated. In either case the work involved was tedious and time consuming. Before we can present applications of the integral in the next chapter better techniques are needed for its calculation. The objective of this chapter is to develop these techniques.

5-1 THE FUNDAMENTAL THEOREM OF CALCULUS

In chapter 4 the indefinite integral, $\int f(x)dx$, was introduced, and integration was studied as antidifferentiation. We looked at the integrand, $f(x)$, and went through a mental process of discovering a function, $F(x)$, such that $F'(x) = f(x)$. The following theorem, which links antidifferentiation and the definite integral, is fundamental to the study of calculus, and is, therefore, called the fundamental theorem of calculus.

Theorem. The Fundamental Theorem of Calculus. If $f(x)$ is defined and continuous for all $a \le x \le b$, and if $F(x)$ is any indefinite integral (antiderivative) of $f(x)$, then

$$\int_a^b f(x)\,dx = F(b) - F(a).$$

Proof. The general proof of this theorem may be found in any engineering calculus text. It relies on the mean-value theorem for integrals, and the properties of integrals stated in chapter 4. We shall prove the fundamental theorem under the special conditions that $\int_a^b f(x)\,dx$ represents the area above the x axis and under the graph of $y = f(x)$ between $x = a$ and $x = b$ and $y = f(x)$ is a positive, continuous, increasing function over the interval $a \le x \le b$, as shown in figure 5-1.

Let $F(x)$ be any antiderivative of $f(x)$. That is, $F'(x) = f(x)$. Let $A(x)$ be a new function that represents the area above the x axis and below the graph of $y = f(x)$ between the vertical lines at a and x. Thus $A(a) = 0$, since the area below $f(x)$ between a and a is 0. $A(b)$ is the area under $f(x)$ between a and b, which means $A(b) = \int_a^b f(x)\,dx$. A positive change in

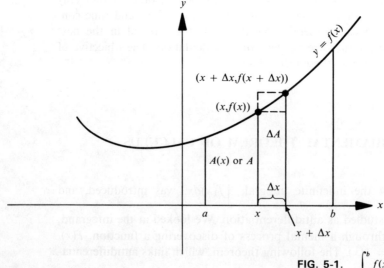

FIG. 5-1. $\int_a^b f(x)dx = F(b) - F(a)$

x of Δx would cause a change in $A(x)$ of ΔA as shown in figure 5-1. The area ΔA is greater than that of the rectangle whose base is Δx and whose height is $f(x)$, and the area ΔA is less than that of the rectangle with base Δx and height $f(x + \Delta x)$. That is,

$$f(x)\,\Delta x \le \Delta A \le f(x + \Delta x)\,\Delta x.$$

Dividing by Δx gives,

$$f(x) \le \frac{\Delta A}{\Delta x} \le f(x + \Delta x).$$

Since $\lim_{\Delta x \to 0} f(x + \Delta x) = f(x)$, taking the limit of the above inequality as Δx approaches 0 implies that

$$\lim_{\Delta x \to 0} \frac{\Delta A}{\Delta x} = f(x).$$

But,

$$\lim_{\Delta x \to 0} \frac{\Delta A}{\Delta x} = A'(x).$$

So, $A'(x) = f(x).$

By hypothesis, $F'(x) = f(x)$. Therefore, $F(x)$ and $A(x)$ are both antiderivatives of $f(x)$, which means they can differ, at most, by a constant. Let c be the constant such that

$$A(x) = F(x) + c.$$

Since $A(a) = 0$,

$$A(a) = F(a) + c$$

$$0 = F(a) + c$$

$$c = -F(a).$$

Therefore by replacing c with $-F(a)$,

$$A(x) = F(x) - F(a).$$

Replacing x with b gives

$$A(b) = F(b) - F(a).$$

As stated earlier,

$$A(b) = \int_a^b f(x)\,dx.$$

So

$$\int_a^b f(x)\,dx = F(b) - F(a).$$

This proves the fundamental theorem of calculus for the conditions stated; that is, $\int_a^b f(x)\,dx$ represents an area above the x axis, under the graph of $y = f(x)$, between $x = a$ and $x = b$, and $y = f(x)$ is a positive, continuous, increasing function over the interval $a \leq x \leq b$.

In order to appreciate this theorem, let us refer to the method of chapter 4,

$\lim\limits_{n\to\infty} \sum\limits_{i=1}^{n} f(x_i)\,\Delta x$, to evaluate

$$\int_2^4 (x^2 + x + 1)\,dx.$$

Now note that the fundamental theorem of calculus applies, since $x^2 + x + 1$ is defined and continuous on the closed interval $2 \leq x \leq 4$. To find $F(x)$, we take the indefinite integral

$$\int (x^2 + x + 1)\,dx = \frac{x^3}{3} + \frac{x^2}{2} + x + C.$$

Thus, $F(x) = \dfrac{x^3}{3} + \dfrac{x^2}{2} + x + C,$

$$F(4) = \frac{4^3}{3} + \frac{4^2}{2} + 4 + C = \frac{64}{3} + 8 + 4 + C = \frac{100}{3} + C, \text{ and}$$

$$F(2) = \frac{2^3}{3} + \frac{2^2}{2} + 2 + C = \frac{8}{3} + 2 + 2 + C = \frac{20}{3} + C$$

$$F(4) - F(2) = \left(\frac{100}{3} + C\right) - \left(\frac{20}{3} + C\right) = \frac{80}{3}$$

NOTE: The constant C will always cancel when computing the definite integral, $\int_a^b f(x)\,dx$, so it may be omitted. Having discussed the method of applying the fundamental theorem in this example, let us write the problem in a more compact form.

$$\int_2^4 (x^2 + x + 1)\,dx = \frac{x^3}{3} + \frac{x^2}{2} + x \Big]_2^4$$

The right-hand side of the statement is the indefinite integral of $(x^2 + x + 1)$, and the symbol $\Big]_2^4$ indicates that we are to evaluate the integral, $F(x)$, for $F(4) - F(2)$.

Example. Evaluate $\displaystyle\int_{-1}^{3} (x^3 + 1)\,dx$.

Solution. An antiderivative of $x^3 + 1$ is $\dfrac{x^4}{4} + x$.

$$\int_{-1}^{3} (x^3 + 1)\,dx = \left. \frac{x^4}{4} + x \right]_{-1}^{3} = \left(\frac{3^4}{4} + 3 \right) - \left(\frac{(-1)^4}{4} + (-1) \right)$$

$$= \frac{93}{4} - \left(-\frac{3}{4} \right) = 24.$$

Example. Evaluate $\displaystyle\int_{0}^{\pi} \sin\theta\,d\theta$.

Solution. An antiderivative of $\sin\theta$ is $-\cos\theta$.

$$\int_{0}^{\pi} \sin\theta\,d\theta = \left. -\cos\theta \right]_{0}^{\pi} = (-\cos\pi) - (-\cos 0) = 2.$$

Example. Evaluate $\displaystyle\int_{0}^{3} \sqrt{x - 2}\,dx$.

Solution. An indefinite integral, $\displaystyle\int \sqrt{x - 2}\,dx$ is readily found by letting $u = x - 2$, then $du = dx$. Thus,

$$\int \sqrt{x - 2}\,dx = \int u^{\frac{1}{2}}\,du = \frac{u^{\frac{3}{2}}}{\frac{3}{2}} + C$$

$$= \frac{2}{3}(x - 2)^{\frac{3}{2}} + C.$$

An antiderivative of $\sqrt{x - 2}$ is, therefore, $\frac{2}{3}(x - 2)^{\frac{3}{2}}$. However, before we fall into the trap of evaluating the expression $\left. \frac{2}{3}(x - 2)^{\frac{3}{2}} \right]_{0}^{3}$, we should realize that $\sqrt{x - 2}$ is not defined for all $0 \le x \le 3$, and the fundamental theorem does not apply. The integral, $\displaystyle\int_{2}^{3} \sqrt{x - 2}\,dx$, can be evaluated by the fundamental theorem, and

$$\int_{2}^{3} \sqrt{x - 2}\,dx = \left. \tfrac{2}{3}(x - 2)^{\frac{3}{2}} \right]_{2}^{3} = \tfrac{2}{3}[(1)^{\frac{3}{2}} - (0)^{\frac{3}{2}}] = \tfrac{2}{3}.$$

Example. Evaluate $\displaystyle\int_{0}^{5} \frac{dx}{(x + 2)^2}$.

Solution.   Here the fundamental theorem of calculus applies, since $\dfrac{1}{(x+2)^2}$ is continuous and defined for all x in the interval $0 \le x \le 5$. An indefinite integral is found by substituting $u = x + 2$, whence $du = dx$ and

$$\int u^{-2}\, du = -u^{-1} + C = \frac{-1}{x+2} + C.$$

$$\int_0^5 \frac{dx}{(x+2)^2} = \frac{-1}{x+2} \Big]_0^5 = \frac{-1}{7} - \left(-\frac{1}{2}\right) = \frac{5}{14}.$$

5-1   Exercises

(1-5)   For each of the following integrals, $\displaystyle\int_a^b f(x)\, dx$, find values for a and b for which the integral may be evaluated by the fundamental theorem of calculus.

1. $\displaystyle\int_a^b \frac{dx}{x^2}$

2. $\displaystyle\int_a^b \sqrt{3x - 2}\, dx$

3. $\displaystyle\int_a^b \tan x\, dx$

4. $\displaystyle\int_a^b \frac{x\, dx}{(4 - x^2)^{\frac{3}{2}}}$

5. $\displaystyle\int_a^b \frac{dx}{x^2 + x - 2}$

(6-20)   Evaluate each of the following integrals.

6. $\displaystyle\int_1^5 (x^2 + x)\, dx$

7. $\displaystyle\int_{-3}^{-1} (x^2 + x + 3)\, dx$

8. $\displaystyle\int_0^3 x(x^2 + 1)^4\, dx$

9. $\displaystyle\int_1^3 \left(2x^3 - \frac{4}{x^2}\right) dx$

10. $\displaystyle\int_0^1 (x^9 + 1)\, dx$

11. $\displaystyle\int_0^1 x^8(x^9 + 1)^2\, dx$

12. $\displaystyle\int_{-1}^1 \frac{dx}{x^2 + 1}$

13. $\displaystyle\int_{-\pi/4}^{\pi/4} \sec^2 x\, dx$

14. $\displaystyle\int_0^{\pi/2} \sin x\, dx$

15. $\displaystyle\int_{\pi/2}^{\pi} \cos x\, dx$

16. $\displaystyle\int_1^2 x^2 \sqrt{1 + x^3}\, dx$

17. $\displaystyle\int_0^a x\sqrt{a - x}\, dx$ (a is a positive constant)

18. $\displaystyle\int_0^a \frac{dx}{\sqrt{x+a}}$ (*a* is a positive constant)

19. $\displaystyle\int_{-1}^0 (1-x)(2+x^2)\,dx$

20. $\displaystyle\int_0^{1/2} \frac{dx}{\sqrt{1-x^2}}$

21. Discuss the following statement:

$$\int_0^2 \frac{dx}{(1-x)^2} = \frac{1}{1-x}\Bigg]_0^2 = \frac{1}{1-2} - \frac{1}{1-0} = -2.$$

22. Graph the function $f(x) = \sin x$ from $0 \le x \le 2\pi$. Notice that the curve lies above the x axis in the interval $0 < x < \pi$ and below the x axis in the interval $\pi < x < 2\pi$. Evaluate $\displaystyle\int_0^{2\pi} \sin x\,dx$. If the integral is interpreted as an area, what problems are encountered?

23. Apply the results of exercise 22 to evaluate and discuss $\displaystyle\int_{-2}^6 (2x-2)\,dx$.

5-2   THE NATURAL LOGARITHM

When the $\displaystyle\int x^n\,dx$ was discussed, it was emphasized that $\displaystyle\int x^n\,dx = \frac{x^{n+1}}{n+1} + C$ as long as $n \ne -1$, since $n = -1$ would cause division by 0. Thus $\displaystyle\int \frac{1}{x}\,dx$ has not been defined. However, figure 5-2 is a graph of $f(t) = \dfrac{1}{t}$, and, as this graph illustrates, $\displaystyle\int_1^x \frac{1}{t}\,dt$ does have a real measurable value. Since the indefinite integral is an antiderivative, it is necessary to know a function whose derivative is $\dfrac{1}{x}$, but no such function has, as yet, been encountered or discussed. We can, therefore, simply define the function and then discuss some of its remarkable properties and applications.

> **Definition.** $\ln x = \displaystyle\int_1^x \frac{1}{t}\,dt$, where $x > 0$.

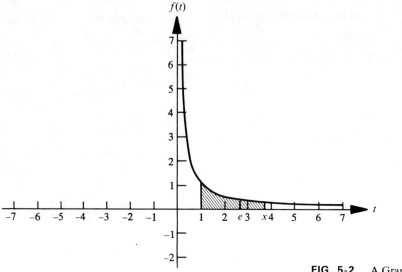

FIG. 5-2.   A Graph of $f(t) = \dfrac{1}{t}$

To see if this definition is reasonable, let us consider the graph of $f(t) = \dfrac{1}{t}$.

The shaded region in figure 5-2 represents $\ln x$.

When $x = 1$, $$\ln 1 = \int_1^1 \frac{1}{t}\,dt = 0$$

If $x < 1$, then $$\ln x = \int_1^x \frac{1}{t}\,dt = -\int_x^1 \frac{1}{t}\,dt$$

It is obvious from the graph that t can never equal zero, since $\dfrac{1}{t}$ is not defined at $t = 0$. Furthermore, from the definition

$$\ln x = \int_1^x \frac{1}{t}\,dt, \; x > 0$$

it is clear that if $\ln x$ is to fulfill our definition of a function t must be positive.

The expression "$\ln x$" is read "$\log x$" and is defined as the *natural logarithm of x*. The properties of logarithms, which are developed in courses in algebra, also hold for natural logarithms. The natural logarithm is so important in mathematics that many books use the abbreviation "log" to mean natural logarithm.

1. $\ln ax = \ln a + \ln x$,

2. $\ln \dfrac{x}{a} = \ln x - \ln a$, and

3. $\ln x^r = r \ln x,$

provided a and x are positive, and r is a rational number.

To show $\ln ax = \ln a + \ln x$, let a be constant, and define $f(x) = \ln ax.$

Then by the chain rule, $f'(x) = \dfrac{1}{ax} \cdot a = \dfrac{1}{x},$ since $\displaystyle\int \dfrac{1}{x}\, dx = \ln x$, by

definition.

Thus $\ln ax$ and $\ln x$ have the same derivative for all positive a and x, which means that $\ln ax$ and $\ln x$ must differ by, at most, a constant.

$$\ln ax - \ln x = C.$$

When $x = 1$, $\ln x = \ln 1 = 0$, and $\ln a = C$. Thus, $\ln ax - \ln x = \ln a$

implies $\ln ax = \ln a + \ln x$. To show that $\ln \dfrac{x}{a} = \ln x - \ln a$, substitute

$x = \dfrac{1}{a}$ in the statement

$$\ln ax = \ln x + \ln a.$$

Then,
$$\ln a\left(\frac{1}{a}\right) = \ln\left(\frac{1}{a}\right) + \ln a.$$

But,
$$\ln a\left(\frac{1}{a}\right) = \ln 1 = 0;\ \text{thus}$$

$$0 = \ln\left(\frac{1}{a}\right) + \ln a,$$

and
$$\ln\left(\frac{1}{a}\right) = -\ln a.$$

Thus, $\ln\left(\dfrac{x}{a}\right) = \ln x\left(\dfrac{1}{a}\right) = \ln x + \ln\left(\dfrac{1}{a}\right) = \ln x - \ln a.$

The proof for the third statement, $\ln x^r = r \ln x$, is similar to the proof for the first two statements, and should be attempted by the student.

Finally, if $\ln x$ is a logarithm like those studied in algebra, it must have a base. Recall that $\log_b b^r = r$, for any logarithm of base b. Let e be the number such that $\ln e^r = r$. By equation 3, $\ln e^r = r \ln e$. Therefore,

$$\ln e^r = r, \text{ and } \ln e^r = r \ln e,$$

which implies that

$$r \ln e = r$$

or
$$\ln e = 1.$$

By the definition of ln x,

$$\ln e = \int_1^e \frac{1}{t}\,dt = 1.$$

This means that e is a number on the t axis of figure 5-2, such that the area above the t axis and below the graph of $f(t) = \dfrac{1}{t}$ between 1 and e is 1. It is easy to show that e must be between 2 and 3. Using the trapezoidal rule, the area under $f(t) = \dfrac{1}{t}$ between 1 and 2 is about 0.69. The area under $f(t) = \dfrac{1}{t}$ between 1 and 3 is about 1.1. Therefore e, the number such that the area under $f(t) = \dfrac{1}{t}$ and between 1 and e is 1, is between 2 and 3. In fact, e is approximately 2.71828 . . . and is irrational, as is π.

This discussion shows that $\ln x = \log_e x$. The appendix contains a table of logarithms for $\ln x$ and a table of powers of e.

From the discussion so far, you might wonder why we bother with the natural logarithm and its base, e. The reason is that they occur often in nature. The number e is the prime constant in equations that describe the curves formed by suspended cables such as those used in bridge construction. Hence engineers use e and natural logarithms. We will use these concepts in problems of population growth, radioactive decay, and carbon 14 dating.

Example.   If $f(x) = \ln(2x + 1)$ find $f'(x)$.

Solution.   Let $u = 2x + 1$; then $\dfrac{du}{dx} = 2$, and if $f(x) = \ln u$,

$$f'(x) = \frac{1}{u} \cdot \frac{du}{dx} = \frac{1}{2x + 1}\,(2) = \frac{2}{2x + 1}.$$

Example.   If $f(x) = \ln(3x^2 + 4)^{\frac{2}{3}}$, find $f'(x)$.

Solution.   Recall that $\ln(3x^2 + 4)^{\frac{2}{3}} = \frac{2}{3}\ln(3x^2 + 4)$.

Let

$$u = 3x^2 + 4,$$

then

$$\frac{du}{dx} = 6x$$

$$f(x) = \frac{2}{3}\ln u$$

and

$$f'(x) = \frac{2}{3}\left(\frac{1}{u}\right)\frac{du}{dx}$$

$$= \frac{2}{3}\left(\frac{1}{3x^2 + 4}\right)(6x)$$

$$= \frac{4x}{(3x^2 + 4)}.$$

Example.   If $f(x) = \ln[(x^2 + 3)(x - 2)]$, find $f'(x)$.

Solution. $\ln[(x^2 + 3)(x - 2)] = \ln(x^2 + 3) + \ln(x - 2)$.

$$f(x) = \ln(x^2 + 3) + \ln(x - 2).$$

$$f'(x) = \frac{1}{x^2 + 3}(2x) + \frac{1}{x - 2}$$

$$= \frac{2x}{x^2 + 3} + \frac{1}{x - 2}$$

$$= \frac{3x^2 - 4x + 3}{(x^2 + 3)(x - 2)}.$$

Example.   Find $\displaystyle\int \frac{dx}{3x + 1}$.

Solution.   Let $u = 3x + 1$, then $du = 3\,dx$.

$$\int \frac{dx}{3x + 1} = \frac{1}{3}\int \frac{3\,dx}{3x + 1} = \frac{1}{3}\int \frac{du}{u}$$

$$= \frac{1}{3}\ln u + C = \frac{1}{3}\ln|3x + 1| + C.$$

Note the use of absolute values. Since $\ln u$ is only defined when $u > 0$, the use of absolute values insures a defined term.

Example.   Find $\displaystyle\int \tan x\,dx$.

Solution.   There is no function which immediately comes to mind, such that its derivative is the tangent. However,

$$\int \tan x\,dx = \int \frac{\sin x}{\cos x}\,dx.$$

Now if we let $u = \cos x$, then $du = -\sin x \, dx$, and the integral becomes

$$-\int \frac{1}{u} \, du = -\ln|u| + C$$

$$= -\ln|\cos x| + C$$

It is sometimes convenient to recognize that

$$-\ln u = \ln \frac{1}{u}, \text{ and therefore,}$$

$$-\ln|\cos x| + C = \ln\left|\frac{1}{\cos x}\right| + C = \ln|\sec x| + C.$$

It is often necessary to integrate the expressions $\int \sec x \, dx$ and $\int \csc x \, dx$.

If we write $\int \csc x \, dx = \int \frac{dx}{\sin x}$, and let $u = \sin x$, then we cannot find a ready expression for du, since $u = \sin x$ implies $du = \cos x \, dx$ and there is no $\cos x$ in the integrand. The following identities are useful for integrating $\int \sec x \, dx$ and $\int \csc x \, dx$.

$$\sec x = \sec x \, \frac{(\sec x + \tan x)}{\sec x + \tan x}.$$

$$\csc x = \csc x \, \frac{(\csc x - \cot x)}{\csc x - \cot x}.$$

Using these identities, it is easy to perform the required integrations.

$$\int \sec x \, dx = \int \frac{\sec x(\sec x + \tan x)}{\sec x + \tan x} \, dx.$$

Now let $u = \sec x + \tan x$, then

$$du = (\sec x \tan x + \sec^2 x) \, dx = \sec x(\sec x + \tan x) \, dx,$$

and

$$\int \sec x \, dx = \int \frac{du}{u} = \ln|u| + C$$

$$= \ln|\sec x + \tan x| + C.$$

$\int \csc x \, dx$ can be found by using the second identity. These integrals are listed below as a useful aid.

$$\int \sec x \, dx = \ln|\sec x + \tan x| + C.$$

$$\int \csc x \, dx = \ln|\csc x - \cot x| + C.$$

Example.   Evaluate $\displaystyle\int_1^3 \frac{dx}{x}$.

Solution. $\displaystyle\int_1^3 \frac{dx}{x} = \ln x \bigg]_1^3 = \ln 3 - \ln 1 = \ln 3.$

Example.   Find $\displaystyle\int \frac{6x^2 + 5}{x - 1} \, dx.$

Solution.   Since the numerator is of higher degree than the denominator, simplify the integrand first by division.

$$\frac{6x^2 + 5}{x - 1} = 6x + 6 + \frac{11}{x - 1}. \text{ Therefore,}$$

$$\int \frac{6x^2 + 5}{x - 1} \, dx = \int \left(6x + 6 + \frac{11}{x - 1}\right) dx$$

$$= \int 6x \, dx + \int 6 \, dx + 11 \int \frac{dx}{x - 1}$$

$$= 3x^2 + 6x + 11 \ln|x - 1| + C.$$

A number of formulas from economics can be stated in terms of natural logarithms. One of these is the coefficient of price elasticity. It measures the effect lowering or raising the price of an item has on the total revenue from the sales of the item. A commodity like salt is said to be price in-elastic since any reasonable change in price has no effect on the amount of salt consumed, whereas a small decrease in the price of a certain brand of Scotch may greatly increase its total revenue (which is to say that the demand for Scotch is price elastic).

Let $y = f(x)$ be a function that relates the number of items sold, y, to the price of a single item, x. One measure of the change in demand with respect to change in price is, of course, $\dfrac{dy}{dx}$. Economists do not use this measure because it involves absolute units of y and x that may not be comparable for different commodities. For instance, a 5¢ change in the price of one candy bar does not mean the same thing as a 5¢ change in the price of one refrigerator. Therefore the coefficient of price elasticity com-pares a percentage change in y with a percentage change in x. If y changes

Δy then Δy is the $\dfrac{\Delta y}{y}$ part of y. In the same manner, a change of Δx is the

$\dfrac{\Delta x}{x}$ part of x. The coefficient of price elasticity at a point of $y = f(x)$,

denoted by the Greek letter eta, η, is;

$$\eta = -\lim_{\Delta x \to 0} \frac{\Delta y}{y} \div \frac{\Delta x}{x}$$

$$= -\lim_{\Delta x \to 0} \frac{x}{y} \cdot \frac{\Delta y}{\Delta x}$$

$$= -\frac{x}{y} \cdot \frac{dy}{dx}$$

The minus sign is inserted in the formula to make the answer positive. When the price is reduced (Δx is negative) the demand increases (Δy is positive). Thus the ratio $\dfrac{\Delta y}{\Delta x}$ would be negative. In other words, η compares a percentage change in price with a percentage change in demand. The easiest way to remember η is not by the formula above but by this one:

$$\eta = -\frac{x\,dy}{y\,dx}$$

$$= -\frac{1}{y} \cdot \frac{dy}{dx} \cdot x$$

$$= -\frac{1}{y} \cdot \frac{dy}{dx} \div \frac{1}{x}$$

But $D_x(\ln y) = \dfrac{1}{y} \cdot \dfrac{dy}{dx}$ and $D_x(\ln x) = \dfrac{1}{x}$, so

$$\eta = -\frac{D_x \ln y}{D_x \ln x}$$

Example. If the number of items sold, y, is related to price, x, for a certain item by $y = -10x + 50$, find the coefficient of price elasticity when the price is $x = 3$.

Solution.

$$\eta = -\frac{D_x(\ln y)}{D_x(\ln x)} = -\frac{D_x[\ln(-10x + 50)]}{D_x \ln(x)}$$

$$= -\frac{\dfrac{-10}{-10x + 50}}{\dfrac{1}{x}}$$

$$= \frac{+10x}{-10x + 50}.$$

When $x = 3$,

$$\eta = \frac{10(3)}{-10(3) + 50}$$

$$= \frac{30}{-30 + 50}$$

$$= \frac{30}{20}$$

$$= 1.5.$$

An η greater than 1, as in this example, means that any percentage change in price will result in a greater percentage change in demand, and the demand is elastic. If $\eta = 1$, then any percentage change in price results in the same percentage change as demand, and the demand has "unit elasticity." If $\eta < 1$, then demand is said to be inelastic.

5-2   Exercises

(1-15)   Differentiate each of the following functions.

1. $y = \ln(3x + 2)$

2. $y = \ln(x^2 + 2x)$

3. $y = \ln(x^2 + 3)^2$

4. $y = \ln\left(\dfrac{x + 2}{x - 3}\right)$

5. $y = \ln\left(\dfrac{x^2 + 3}{2x^2 - 1}\right)$

6. $y = \ln\left(\dfrac{\sqrt{x + 3}}{x^2 + 1}\right)$

7. $y = x \ln x$

8. $y = \ln(2x - x^3)$

9. $y = \ln(\sec x + \tan x)$

10. $y = \ln(\csc x)$

11. $y = \ln(x + \sqrt{x^2 + 1})$

12. $y = \dfrac{x}{\ln x}$

13. $y = \ln(x^3 + 3x)^{\frac{1}{3}}$

14. $y = [\ln(x^3 + 3x)]^{\frac{1}{3}}$

15. $y = \ln\sqrt{\dfrac{2x + 1}{2x - 1}}$

(16-30) Integrate each of the following and evaluate where indicated.

16. $\displaystyle\int \frac{dx}{x+2}$

17. $\displaystyle\int_{-1}^{3} \frac{dx}{x+2}$

18. $\displaystyle\int \frac{6x}{3x^2-1}\,dx$

19. $\displaystyle\int \frac{\cos x}{\sin x}\,dx$

20. $\displaystyle\int \frac{\sec^2 x\,dx}{1+2\tan x}$

21. $\displaystyle\int \frac{4x^2+2}{2x+1}\,dx$

22. $\displaystyle\int \frac{x^3+4x^2}{x+3}\,dx$

23. $\displaystyle\int \frac{(4x+1)}{2x^2+x+5}\,dx$

24. $\displaystyle\int \frac{x^2}{1-5x^3}\,dx$

25. $\displaystyle\int_{2}^{5} \frac{x}{x^2-1}\,dx$

26. $\displaystyle\int \frac{x\,dx}{x^2-a^2}$, a is constant, $a^2 \neq x^2$

27. $\displaystyle\int_{1}^{3} \frac{3x^2}{3x-1}\,dx$

28. $\displaystyle\int_{0}^{3} \frac{x}{2x^2+3}\,dx$

29. $\displaystyle\int \frac{2+\sin x}{2x-\cos x}\,dx$

30. $\displaystyle\int \frac{1}{x\ln x}\,dx$

31. $\displaystyle\int \frac{dx}{\cos x}$

32. $\displaystyle\int \frac{dx}{\sin x}$

(33-35) The given function relates the quantity, $y = f(x)$, to the price, x, of a commodity. Determine if the demand is elastic, unit elastic, or inelastic at the given price.

33. $f(x) = -100x + 1,000$, $x = 4$.

34. $f(x) = \dfrac{1}{x}$, $x = 75$.

35. $f(x) = \dfrac{1}{x^2}$, $x = 8,000$.

5-3 THE EXPONENTIAL FUNCTION

We know the algebraic definition of a logarithm requires

$$x = \log_b y \text{ if and only if } y = b^x,$$

where b is a positive number not equal to 1, and $y > 0$. The function $y = b^x$, or $f(x) = b^x$, with the stated restrictions, is called an *exponential function*.

The exponential function is the *inverse* of the logarithmic function. If $f(x) = \log_b x$, then $f^{-1}(x) = b^x$, and

$$f(f^{-1}(x)) = \log_b b^x = x \log_b b = x.$$

Also
$$f^{-1}(f(x)) = b^{\log_b x} = x.$$

We have now learned the base of the natural logarithm, ln x, is the number e (named for the Swiss mathematician Euler), so that

$$y = \ln x \text{ if and only if } x = e^y.$$

or,   if $f(x) = \ln x$, then $f^{-1}(x) = e^x$.

Also, since $\log_b b = 1$ for all $b > 0$ and $b \neq 1$, ln $e = 1$. Since the natural logarithm function and its inverse, the exponential function to the base e, are so important in calculus, this function is often written exp x, which means e^x.

Let us examine exp x further, and find its derivative.

$$y = e^x \text{ if and only if } \ln y = x.$$

By implicit differentiation,

$$\frac{1}{y} \frac{dy}{dx} = 1$$

$$\frac{dy}{dx} = y = e^x$$

Thus, if $y = e^x$, $\dfrac{dy}{dx} = e^x$, and $\dfrac{d^2y}{dx^2} = e^x$. In fact, $\dfrac{d^n(e^x)}{dx^n} = e^x$. If $u = f(x)$,

then $\dfrac{d(e^u)}{dx} = e^u \dfrac{du}{dx}$.

Example.   Find the derivative of e^{3x+2}.

Solution. $f(x) = e^{3x+2} = e^u$, where $u = 3x + 2$ and $\dfrac{du}{dx} = 3$.

$$f'(x) = e^{3x+2}(3) = 3e^{3x+2}.$$

Similarly, since $\dfrac{d(e^u)}{du} = e^u$, $\displaystyle\int e^u \, du = e^u + C$.

Example.   Find $\displaystyle\int e^{3x} \, dx$.

Solution. $\displaystyle\int e^{3x} \, dx = \tfrac{1}{3} \int e^{3x}(3)dx = \tfrac{1}{3}e^{3x} + C$.

Example.   Find $\dfrac{dy}{dx}$ if $y = e^{\sin^{-1}x}$.

Solution.   Let $u = \sin^{-1}x$,

then
$$\frac{du}{dx} = \frac{1}{\sqrt{1 - x^2}},$$

And
$$\frac{dy}{dx} = e^u \frac{du}{dx}$$

$$= \frac{e^{\sin^{-1}x}}{\sqrt{1 - x^2}}.$$

It is often necessary to find the derivative of an expression of the form

$$y = a^x, \text{ where } a > 0, a \neq 1, a \neq e.$$

If $y = a^x$, then $\ln y = \ln a^x$, and $\ln y = x \ln a$ if x is a rational number. By implicit differentiation,

$$\frac{1}{y} \frac{dy}{dx} = \ln a.$$

Therefore,
$$\frac{dy}{dx} = y \ln a = a^x \ln a.$$

It can be shown that this statement is true for all real numbers, x, but the proof for this statement is beyond the scope of this text. Thus, in general, for all x and for $a > 0, a \neq 1$,

$$\frac{d(a^x)}{dx} = a^x \ln a,$$

and if $u = f(x)$, then

$$\frac{d(a^u)}{dx} = a^u \ln a \frac{du}{dx}.$$

Clearly this formula is true if $a = e$, since $\ln e = 1$.

Example.   If $y = 2^{3x^2+1}$, find $\dfrac{dy}{dx}$.

Solution. $\dfrac{dy}{dx} = 2^{3x^2+1} (\ln 2)(6x)$

$$= 6x2^{3x^2+1} \ln 2.$$

Example.   Find $\int 2^{4x}\, dx$.

Solution.   This integral involves a general solution for $\int a^u\, du$.

Since
$$\frac{d(a^u)}{du} = a^u \ln a,$$

$$d(a^u) = a^u \ln a\, du.$$

If we multiply and divide by $\ln a$, we obtain

$$\frac{1}{\ln a} \int a^u \ln a\, du = \frac{1}{\ln a}\, (a^u) + C.$$

Therefore,

$$\int 2^{4x}\, dx = \frac{1}{\ln 2} \int 2^{4x} \ln 2\, dx.$$

But $u = 4x \rightarrow du = 4\, dx$, therefore

$$\int 2^{4x}\, dx = \frac{1}{4 \ln 2} \int 2^{4x}\, 4 \ln 2\, dx$$

$$= \frac{1}{4 \ln 2}\, (2^{4x}) + C.$$

Example.   If $y = \log_b x$, find $\dfrac{dy}{dx}$.

Solution.   This problem can be solved by several different methods. If $b = e$, then the solution is trivial, so assume $b \ne e$.

$$y = \log_b x \text{ if and only if } x = b^y.$$

Taking the natural logarithm of each side of the exponential equation, we obtain

$$\ln x = y \ln b.$$

Differentiating both sides with respect to x,

$$\frac{1}{x} = \ln b\, \frac{dy}{dx}.$$

$$\frac{dy}{dx} = \frac{1}{x \ln b}.$$

Therefore, $D_x(\log_b x) = \dfrac{1}{x \ln b}$.

Another approach would have been to use the formula

$$D_x(a^u) = a^u \ln a \frac{du}{dx}.$$

$$x = b^y \rightarrow 1 = b^y \ln b \frac{dy}{dx}.$$

$$\rightarrow \frac{dy}{dx} = \frac{1}{b^y \ln b}.$$

To reconcile these two apparently different answers, it is only necessary to note that $x = b^y$, and make the substitution.

$$\frac{dy}{dx} = \frac{1}{b^y \ln b} = \frac{1}{x \ln b}.$$

5-3   Exercises

(1-17)   For each of the following functions, find $\dfrac{dy}{dx}$.

1. $y = e^{x^2}$

2. $y = 3xe^{2x}$

3. $y = \frac{1}{2}(e^x - e^{-x})$

4. $y = \dfrac{e^x - e^{-x}}{e^x + e^{-x}}$

5. $y = e^{-x^2}$

6. $y = \ln e^{ax+b}$, where a and b are constants

7. $y = x^e$

8. $y = x^x$

9. $y = \ln e^x$

10. $\ln y + e^{\sqrt{x}} = 2$

11. $x = e^y$

12. $y = e^{\sin x} + x \sin x$

13. $y = 3^{x^2}$

14. $y = \log_3 4x$

15. $y = \log_{10} x^2$

16. $y = \ln 3^x$

17. $e^x + x^e = y$

(18-32)   Integrate.

18. $\displaystyle\int e^{3x}\, dx$

19. $\displaystyle\int x\, e^{x^2}\, dx$

20. $\displaystyle\int e^x \sin e^x\, dx$

21. $\displaystyle\int 2^{3x+2}\, dx$

22. $\displaystyle\int \dfrac{e^x}{1 + e^{2x}}\, dx$

23. $\displaystyle\int \dfrac{e^x}{1 + e^x}\, dx$

24. $\displaystyle\int \cos x\, e^{\sin x}\, dx$

25. $\displaystyle\int \dfrac{dx}{e^x}$

26. $\int \dfrac{x}{2^{x^2}} \, dx$

30. $\int x^4 \, e^{x^5} \, dx$

27. $\int \dfrac{e^x + e^{-x}}{2} \, dx$

31. $\int e^{\ln x} \, dx$

28. $\int \dfrac{e^x - e^{-x}}{2} \, dx$

32. $\int x^e \, dx$

29. $\int \dfrac{e^{\tan^{-1} x}}{1 + x^2} \, dx$

5-4   INTEGRATION BY PARTS

Frequently, a problem in integration does not lend itself to a substitution of the form $u \, du$. For example, $\int \ln x \, dx$. If we let $u = \ln x$, then $du = \dfrac{1}{x} dx$, and since there is no way of introducing a factor of $\dfrac{1}{x}$ to the integrand without further complicating matters, this substitution is not practical.

Another way of looking at the integral $\int \ln x \, dx$ is to recognize that there is no simple function, $F(x)$ such that $F'(x) = \ln x$.

Before offering a solution to this problem, let us examine the following. Let u and v be functions of x. Then

$$d(u \cdot v) = u \, dv + v \, du,$$

and $$\int d(u \cdot v) = u \cdot v = \int u \, dv + \int v \, du + C.$$

(1)   So that, $\int u \, dv = u \cdot v - \int v \, du + C.$

The integral on the left, $\int u \, dv$, offers a solution for an integrand which is the product of a function, u, and the derivative of a function, v. For example, in the problem $\int \ln x \, dx$,

$$\text{let } u = \ln x \text{ and } dv = dx,$$

$$\text{then } du = \dfrac{1}{x} dx \text{ and } v = x + C_1.$$

By equation (1),

$$\int \ln x \, dx = uv - \int v \, du + C$$

$$= \ln x (x + C_1) - \int (x + C_1) \frac{1}{x} \, dx$$

$$= \ln x (x + C_1) - x - C_1 \ln x + C$$

$$= x \ln x + C_1 \ln x - x - C_1 \ln x + C$$

$$= x \ln x - x + C.$$

When using this method of integration, the constant, C_1, associated with v always cancels, so it is not necessary to include it when finding v.

Example.   Find $\int x e^x \, dx$.

Solution.   Again no immediate solution is available unless the integrand is expressed in the form $u \, dv$.

$$\text{Let } u = x \text{ and } dv = e^x \, dx,$$

$$\text{then } du = dx \text{ and } v = e^x.$$

$$\int x \, e^x \, dx = x \, e^x - \int e^x \, dx + C$$

$$= x \, e^x - e^x + C$$

$$= e^x (x - 1) + C.$$

The student may ask how to select u and dv, and whether the choice makes any difference. The answers to these questions are not easy, since each problem must be analyzed individually. If an integrand is a product of an algebraic function (a polynomial, or x^p, where p is a real number) and a logarithmic function or an inverse trigonometric function, then the algebraic function is selected as the dv part, since these functions have simple antiderivatives, whereas this cannot be said for logarithmic or inverse trigonometric functions. For example, there was only one way to find $\int \ln x \, dx$. In the example $\int x \, e^x \, dx$, if we had let $u = e^x$ and $dv = x \, dx$, then $du = e^x \, dx$ and $v = \dfrac{x^2}{2}$, and the resulting expression would have been more complicated than the original, since

$$\int x \, e^x \, dx = \frac{x^2}{2} e^x - \int \frac{x^2}{2} e^x \, dx + C.$$

There are times, however, when the selection is entirely arbitrary.

Example.   Find $\int e^x \cos x \, dx$.

Solution.   Let $u = \cos x$ and $dv = e^x \, dx$, then

$$du = -\sin x \, dx \quad \text{and} \quad v = e^x.$$

$$\int e^x \cos x \, dx = e^x \cos x - \int e^x(-\sin x) \, dx + C.$$

The new integrand presents the same difficulties as the original integral, so parts are once again used. In the new integral, let $u = -\sin x$ and $dv = e^x \, dx$, then

$$du = -\cos x \, dx \quad \text{and} \quad v = e^x.$$

$$\int e^x \cos x \, dx = e^x \cos x - \left[e^x(-\sin x) - \int e^x(-\cos x) \, dx \right] + C$$

$$= e^x \cos x + e^x \sin x - \int e^x \cos x \, dx + C.$$

Thus,

$$2 \int e^x \cos x \, dx = e^x \cos x + e^x \sin x + C.$$

$$\int e^x \cos x \, dx = \tfrac{1}{2}(e^x \cos x + e^x \sin x + C).$$

Note that after integration by parts was used twice, the original integral appeared on the right side (preceded by a minus sign) and when it was added to both sides we had the solution. In this problem, the selection of u and dv was arbitrary and could have been reversed. However, when the second application of parts was necessitated, the pattern of the first selection had to be repeated. The student should check what would happen if the second application had been changed to let $u = e^x$ and $dv = -\sin x \, dx$.

Example.   Find $\int x \tan^{-1} x \, dx$.

Solution.   Since integration by parts is indicated here, we must select $u = \tan^{-1} x$, since we don't know an antiderivative for this function.

Let

$$u = \tan^{-1} x \quad \text{and} \quad dv = x \, dx,$$

then

$$du = \frac{dx}{1 + x^2} \quad \text{and} \quad v = \frac{x^2}{2}.$$

$$\int x \tan^{-1} x \, dx = \frac{x^2}{2} \tan^{-1} x - \frac{1}{2} \int \frac{x^2}{1+x^2} \, dx + C$$

$$= \frac{x^2}{2} \tan^{-1} x - \frac{1}{2} \int \left(1 - \frac{1}{x^2+1}\right) dx + C$$

$$= \frac{x^2}{2} \tan^{-1} x - \frac{1}{2} [x - \tan^{-1} x] + C$$

$$= \frac{x^2}{2} \tan^{-1} x - \frac{x}{2} + \frac{\tan^{-1} x}{2} + C.$$

For the definite integral,

$$\int_a^b u \, dv = uv \Big]_a^b - \int_a^b v \, du.$$

Example. Evaluate $\int_1^3 x^2 \ln x \, dx$.

Solution. Let $u = \ln x$ and $dv = x^2 \, dx$, then

$$du = \frac{1}{x} dx \text{ and } v = \frac{x^3}{3}.$$

$$\int_1^3 x^2 \ln x \, dx = \frac{x^3}{3} \ln x \Big]_1^3 - \frac{1}{3} \int_1^3 x^2 \, dx$$

$$= \frac{x^3}{3} \ln x \Big]_1^3 - \frac{1}{3} \left(\frac{x^3}{3}\right) \Big]_1^3$$

$$= 9 \ln 3 - \tfrac{1}{3} \ln 1 - \tfrac{1}{3}(9) + \tfrac{1}{3}(\tfrac{1}{3})$$

$$= 9 \ln 3 - \tfrac{26}{9}.$$

5-4   Exercises

Integrate.

1. $\int x e^{-ax} \, dx$ (a is a constant)

2. $\int x \cos x \, dx$

3. $\int x \sec^2 x \, dx$

4. $\int x a^x \, dx$ (a is a constant, $a > 0$, and $a \neq 1$)

5. $\int x^2 \ln x \, dx$

6. $\int x \tan^{-1} x \, dx$

7. $\displaystyle\int x^2 e^x \, dx$

14. $\displaystyle\int \sec^3 x \, dx$ (Hint:
$\sec^3 x = \sec x \sec^2 x$)

8. $\displaystyle\int x^2 \sin x \, dx$

15. $\displaystyle\int x^3 e^{-x^2} \, dx$

9. $\displaystyle\int \sin^{-1}(2x) \, dx$

16. $\displaystyle\int_0^{\pi/2} x \sin^2 x \, dx$

10. $\displaystyle\int x^2 e^{-x} \, dx$

17. $\displaystyle\int_{\pi/4}^{\pi/2} x^2 \cos x \, dx$

11. $\displaystyle\int e^{ax} \sin bx \, dx$ (a and b constant)

18. $\displaystyle\int_1^e x^e \ln x \, dx$

12. $\displaystyle\int x \cos^2 x \, dx$ $\left(\text{Hint: } \cos^2 x = \dfrac{1 + \cos 2x}{2}\right)$

19. $\displaystyle\int_1^4 x e^{-x} \, dx$

13. $\displaystyle\int \ln(x + 1) \, dx$

20. $\displaystyle\int_0^2 x^3 e^{x^2} \, dx$

5-5   TRIGONOMETRIC SUBSTITUTIONS

Integrals containing terms $\sqrt{a^2 - u^2}, \sqrt{a^2 + u^2}, \sqrt{u^2 - a^2}, a^2 + u^2,$ $a^2 - u^2$ can often be simplified and interpreted by means of a trigonometric substitution. In chapter 4 some of these integrals were introduced. In this section we shall explore these problems in more depth.

Let us recall the following identities.

$$\sin^2 x + \cos^2 x = 1; \cos x = \sqrt{1 - \sin^2 x}.$$

$$\tan^2 x + 1 = \sec^2 x; \sec x = \sqrt{\tan^2 x + 1}; \tan x = \sqrt{\sec^2 x - 1}.$$

Example.   Find $\displaystyle\int \sqrt{4 + x^2} \, dx$.

Solution.   If we let $u = 4 + x^2$, then $du = 2x \, dx$, so this approach is impractical.

Let $\qquad\qquad\qquad\qquad x = 2 \tan \theta,$

then $\qquad\qquad\qquad\qquad x^2 = 4 \tan^2 \theta,$

$$4 + x^2 = 4 + 4\tan^2 \theta = 4(1 + \tan^2 \theta) = 4 \sec^2 \theta$$

$$\sqrt{4 + x^2} = 2\sqrt{1 + \tan^2 \theta} = 2 \sec \theta.$$

Also if
$$x = 2 \tan \theta,$$
$$dx = 2 \sec^2 \theta \, d\theta.$$

$$\int \sqrt{4 + x^2} \, dx = \int 2 \sec \theta (2 \sec^2 \theta) \, d\theta$$

$$= 4 \int \sec^3 \theta \, d\theta.$$

From exercise 14, section 5-4, recall that $\int \sec^3 \theta \, d\theta$ can be solved by integration by parts.

$$4 \int \sec^3 \theta \, d\theta = 4 \int \sec \theta \sec^2 \theta \, d\theta.$$

Let $u = \sec \theta$ and $dv = \sec^2 \theta \, d\theta$, then

$$du = \sec \theta \tan \theta \, d\theta \text{ and } v = \tan \theta$$

$$\int \sec^3 \theta \, d\theta = \sec \theta \tan \theta - \int \sec \theta \tan^2 \theta \, d\theta + C$$

$$= \sec \theta \tan \theta - \int \sec \theta (\sec^2 \theta - 1) \, d\theta + C$$

$$= \sec \theta \tan \theta - \int \sec^3 \theta + \int \sec \theta \, d\theta + C$$

$$= \sec \theta \tan \theta - \int \sec^3 \theta + \ln |\sec \theta + \tan \theta| + C.$$

$$2 \int \sec^3 \theta \, d\theta = \sec \theta \tan \theta + \ln |\sec \theta + \tan \theta| + C.$$

$$4 \int \sec^3 \theta \, d\theta = 2 \sec \theta \tan \theta + 2 \ln |\sec \theta + \tan \theta| + C.$$

(Note that $2C$ is still a constant, so it may be written as C.)

Figure 5-3 illustrates the assumption $x = 2 \tan \theta$, or $\tan \theta = \dfrac{x}{2}$. Using

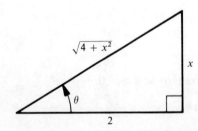

FIG. 5-3

the theorem of Pythagoras and the basic definitions of the trigonometric functions, we can label the sides of the right triangle. Then, from the diagram we read

$$\sec \theta = \frac{\sqrt{4 + x^2}}{2}, \ \tan \theta = \frac{x}{2}.$$

Therefore, $2 \sec \theta \tan \theta + 2 \ln |\sec \theta + \tan \theta|$

$$= 2 \frac{\sqrt{4 + x^2}}{2} \left(\frac{x}{2} \right) + 2 \ln \left| \frac{\sqrt{4 + x^2}}{2} + \frac{x}{2} \right|$$

$$= \frac{x \sqrt{4 + x^2}}{2} + 2 \ln \left| \frac{x + \sqrt{4 + x^2}}{2} \right|.$$

So that,

$$\int \sqrt{4 + x^2} \, dx = \frac{x \sqrt{4 + x^2}}{2} + 2 \ln \left| \frac{x + \sqrt{4 + x^2}}{2} \right| + C.$$

Example.   Determine $\displaystyle \int \frac{dx}{9 - 4x^2}$

Solution. $9 - 4x^2$ is of the form $a^2 - u^2$, where $a = 3$ and $u = 2x$. Let $2x = 3 \sin \theta$, then $4x^2 = 9 \sin^2 \theta$, and

$$9 - 4x^2 = 9 - 9 \sin^2 \theta = 9(1 - \sin^2 \theta) = 9 \cos^2 \theta.$$

If $2x = 3 \sin \theta$, $x = \frac{3}{2} \sin \theta$, and $dx = \frac{3}{2} \cos \theta \, d\theta$.

Therefore

$$\int \frac{dx}{9 - 4x^2} = \int \frac{\frac{3}{2} \cos \theta \, d\theta}{9 \cos^2 \theta}$$

$$= \frac{1}{6} \int \frac{d\theta}{\cos \theta} = \frac{1}{6} \int \sec \theta \, d\theta$$

$$= \frac{1}{6} \ln |\sec \theta + \tan \theta| + C.$$

Figure 5-4 illustrates the assumption $2x = 3 \sin \theta$, which implies $\sin \theta = \frac{2x}{3}$. Thus, $\sec \theta = \dfrac{3}{\sqrt{9 - 4x^2}}$, and $\tan \theta = \dfrac{2x}{\sqrt{9 - 4x^2}}$.

$$\int \frac{dx}{9 - 4x^2} = \frac{1}{6} \ln \left| \frac{3 + 2x}{\sqrt{9 - 4x^2}} \right| + C.$$

Example.   Find $\displaystyle \int \frac{x^2}{\sqrt{1 - x^2}} \, dx.$

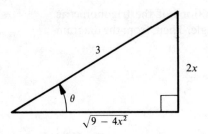

FIG. 5-4

Solution. This problem could be solved by using parts.

$$\int \frac{x^2}{\sqrt{1-x^2}}dx = \int x \cdot \frac{x}{\sqrt{1-x^2}}dx$$

$$= -\frac{1}{2}\int x \cdot \frac{-2x}{\sqrt{1-x^2}}dx.$$

If we let $$u = x \quad \text{and} \quad dv = \frac{-2x}{\sqrt{1-x^2}}dx,$$

then $$du = dx \quad \text{and} \quad v = 2\sqrt{1-x^2}$$

$$\int \frac{x^2}{\sqrt{1-x^2}}dx = -\frac{1}{2}\int x \cdot \frac{-2x}{\sqrt{1-x^2}}dx$$

$$= -\frac{1}{2}\left[2x\sqrt{1-x^2} - \int 2\sqrt{1-x^2}\,dx\right] + C.$$

The integral $\int \sqrt{1-x^2}\,dx$ now requires a trigonometric substitution. It seems, therefore, that a substitution in the first place would have been a better approach to this problem. Let $x = \sin\theta$, then $x^2 = \sin^2\theta$,

and $$\sqrt{1-x^2} = \sqrt{\cos^2\theta} = \cos\theta.$$

Therefore, $$dx = \cos\theta\,d\theta.$$

$$\int \frac{x^2}{\sqrt{1-x^2}}dx = \int \frac{\sin^2\theta}{\cos\theta}(\cos\theta)\,d\theta$$

$$= \int \sin^2\theta\,d\theta$$

$$= \frac{1}{2}\int (1 - \cos 2\theta)\,d\theta$$

$$= \frac{1}{2}(\theta - \frac{1}{2}\sin 2\theta) + C.$$

If $x = \sin\theta$, then $\theta = \sin^{-1}x$. Also, $\sin 2\theta = 2\sin\theta\cos\theta$, which, the information from figure 5-5 shows to be $\sin 2\theta = 2x\sqrt{1 - x^2}$.

$$\int \frac{x^2}{\sqrt{1 - x^2}}\,dx = \tfrac{1}{2}(\theta - \tfrac{1}{2}\sin 2\theta) + C$$

$$= \tfrac{1}{2}\sin^{-1}x - (\tfrac{1}{4})2x\sqrt{1 - x^2} + C$$

$$= \tfrac{1}{2}(\sin^{-1}x - x\sqrt{1 - x^2}) + C.$$

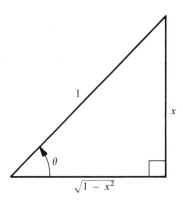

FIG. 5-5

Example. Evaluate $\displaystyle\int_0^1 \sqrt{3 + x^2}\,dx$.

Solution. Let $x = \sqrt{3}\tan\theta$, then

$$3 + x^2 = 3(1 + \tan^2\theta) = 3\sec^2\theta,$$

and

$$\sqrt{3 + x^2} = \sqrt{3}\sec\theta\,d\theta$$

$$dx = \sqrt{3}\sec^2\theta\,d\theta$$

It is important to note here that the original definite integral had its limits stated in terms of x, that is, from $x = 0$ to $x = 1$. The substitution, $x = \sqrt{3}\tan\theta$, requires either that the limits now be changed to correspond to θ, or that the integral in terms of θ be interpreted as an indefinite integral, then expressed in terms of x and evaluated for the original limits.

METHOD 1. Change of limits.

If $x = 0$, then $x = \sqrt{3}\tan\theta$

implies that $0 = \sqrt{3}\tan\theta,$

and $\theta = 0.$

If $x = 1$, then
$$1 = \sqrt{3} \tan \theta.$$

$$\tan \theta = \frac{1}{\sqrt{3}}.$$

$$\theta = \frac{\pi}{6}.$$

$$\int_0^1 \sqrt{3 + x^2}\, dx = 3 \int_0^{\pi/6} \sec^3 \theta\, d\theta$$

From the first example of this section, we know that $\int \sec^3 \theta\, d\theta = \frac{1}{2}(\sec \theta \cdot \tan \theta + \ln|\sec \theta + \tan \theta|)$. Thus,

$$3 \int_0^{\pi/6} \sec^3 \theta\, d\theta = \frac{3}{2}(\sec \theta \tan \theta + \ln|\sec \theta + \tan \theta|)\Big]_0^{\pi/6}$$

$$= \frac{3}{2}\left(\frac{2}{\sqrt{3}} \cdot \frac{1}{\sqrt{3}} + \ln\left|\frac{2}{\sqrt{3}} + \frac{1}{\sqrt{3}}\right|\right) - \frac{3}{2}(0 + \ln 1)$$

$$= \frac{3}{2}\left[\frac{2}{3} + \ln\left(\frac{3}{\sqrt{3}}\right)\right]$$

$$= 1 + \frac{3}{2}\ln(\sqrt{3}) = 1 + \frac{3}{4}\ln 3.$$

METHOD 2.   Instead of changing limits, express $3 \int \sec^3 \theta\, d\theta$ in terms of x from figure 5-6.

$$3 \int \sec^3 \theta\, d\theta = \frac{3}{2}(\sec \theta \tan \theta + \ln|\sec \theta + \tan \theta|)$$

$$= \frac{3}{2}\left(\frac{\sqrt{3 + x^2}}{\sqrt{3}} \cdot \frac{x}{\sqrt{3}} + \ln\left|\frac{\sqrt{3 + x^2}}{\sqrt{3}} + \frac{x}{\sqrt{3}}\right|\right)$$

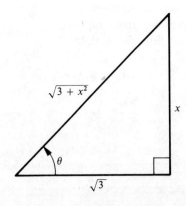

FIG. 5-6

and evaluate this expression $\Big]_0^1$

$$= \frac{3}{2}\left(\frac{2}{3} + \ln\left|\frac{2}{\sqrt{3}} + \frac{1}{\sqrt{3}}\right|\right) - \frac{3}{2}(0 + \ln 1)$$

$$= 1 + \frac{3}{2}\ln(\sqrt{3}) = 1 + \frac{3}{4}\ln 3.$$

It is evident that method one is faster, and that a change of limits will often facilitate a given problem. It is sometimes convenient to write $\displaystyle\int_{x=a}^{x=b} u\,du,$ which reminds us that a and b are limits for x.

Example.   Evaluate $\displaystyle\int_2^4 \frac{x\,dx}{2 + x^2}.$

Solution.   Let $u = 2 + x^2$, then $du = 2x\,dx$. Changing the limits to evaluate the integral for u, when $x = 2$, $u = 6$ and when $x = 4$, $u = 18$.

Then
$$\int_2^4 \frac{x\,dx}{2 + x^2} = \frac{1}{2}\int_6^{18} \frac{du}{u} = \frac{1}{2}\ln(u)\Big]_6^{18}$$

$$= \tfrac{1}{2}[\ln(18) - \ln(6)]$$

$$= \tfrac{1}{2}\ln\left(\tfrac{18}{6}\right)$$

$$= \tfrac{1}{2}\ln(3).$$

5-5   Exercises

(1-15)   Integrate

1. $\displaystyle\int \sqrt{1 + x^2}\,dx$ (*Hint:* $\displaystyle\int \sec^3\theta\,d\theta$ is given in the first example of this

section.)

2. $\displaystyle\int \frac{1}{\sqrt{1 + x^2}}\,dx$

3. $\displaystyle\int \sqrt{4 - x^2}\,dx$

4. $\displaystyle\int \sqrt{4x^2 - 1}\,dx$

5. $\displaystyle\int \frac{x + 1}{\sqrt{9 - x^2}}\,dx$

6. $\displaystyle\int \frac{\cos\theta}{\sqrt{3 - \sin^2\theta}}\,d\theta$

7. $\displaystyle\int \frac{\sin^2\theta}{1 + \cos 2\theta}\,d\theta$

8. $\displaystyle\int \frac{dx}{x\sqrt{x^2 + 1}}$

9. $\displaystyle\int \frac{\sqrt{x^2 + 1}}{x}\,dx$

10. $\displaystyle\int \frac{dx}{3x^2 + 2x + 4}$ (*Hint*: Complete the square.)

11. $\displaystyle\int \frac{dx}{3 - 2x - x^2}$ **14.** $\displaystyle\int (x^2 - 1)\, dx$

12. $\displaystyle\int \frac{x^2}{x^2 - 1}\, dx$ **15.** $\displaystyle\int \sqrt{x^2 - 1}\, dx$

13. $\displaystyle\int \frac{x^2}{x^2 + 1}\, dx$

(16-24)   Evaluate each of the following by using an appropriate change of limits.

16. $\displaystyle\int_1^2 \frac{dx}{\sqrt{2x - x^2}}$ **21.** $\displaystyle\int_0^2 x^2 \sqrt{1 + x^3}\, dx$

17. $\displaystyle\int_0^1 \frac{dx}{\sqrt{2 - x^2}}$ **22.** $\displaystyle\int_2^4 \frac{dx}{\sqrt{x}(\sqrt{x} - 1)}$

18. $\displaystyle\int_{-1}^{\sqrt{3}} \frac{x^2\, dx}{(4 - x^2)^{\frac{3}{2}}}$ **23.** $\displaystyle\int_0^1 \frac{dx}{4 - x^2}$

19. $\displaystyle\int_0^1 \frac{dx}{(x^2 + 1)^2}$ **24.** $\displaystyle\int_0^2 \frac{dx}{x^2 + 4}$

20. $\displaystyle\int_2^4 \frac{x\, dx}{x^2 + 3}$

5-6   INTEGRATION BY USE OF TABLES

Most of the basic techniques for finding elementary integrals have been discussed in chapter 4 and the preceding sections of chapter 5. Often an integral requires much manipulation with these techniques and cumbersome arithmetic and algebra $\left(\text{for example, } \displaystyle\int \sec^7 x\, dx\right)$.

Tables of integrals are useful for such problems. These tables are generally organized according to the different integrands. For instance, the first integrals are usually the elementary forms, followed by basic trigonometric or logarithmic forms, and then by different combinations of $ax + b, ax^2 + b, ax^n + b$, and so forth. To return to the integral, $\int \sec^7 x \, dx$, turn to the table of integrals in the appendix of this text. Formula 38 states:

$$\int \sec^n u \, du = \frac{\tan u \sec^{n-2} u}{(n-1)} + \frac{n-2}{n-1} \int \sec^{n-2} u \, du \qquad n \neq 1.$$

Applying this formula, where $u = x$ and $n = 7$,

$$\int \sec^7 x \, dx = \frac{\tan x \sec^5 x}{6} + \frac{5}{6} \int \sec^5 x \, dx.$$

Applying formula 38 again with $n = 5$.

$$\int \sec^7 x \, dx = \frac{\tan x \sec^5 x}{6} + \frac{5}{6} \left[\frac{\tan x \sec^3 x}{4} + \frac{3}{4} \int \sec^3 x \, dx \right].$$

Applying formula 38 for the third time gives with $n = 3$

$$\int \sec^7 x \, dx = \frac{\tan x \sec^5 x}{6} + \frac{5 \tan x \sec^3 x}{24}$$

$$+ \frac{15}{24} \left[\frac{\tan x \sec x}{2} + \frac{1}{2} \int \sec x \, dx \right]$$

$$= \frac{\tan x \sec^5 x}{6} + \frac{5 \tan x \sec^3 x}{24} + \frac{15 \tan x \sec x}{48}$$

$$+ \frac{15}{48} \ln|\sec x + \tan x| + C.$$

The last integral, $\int \sec x \, dx$, represented the case $n = 1$, so that the formula did not apply, but we already know an antiderivative of $\sec x$.

The table of integrals in this text is an abbreviated list to acquaint the student with the use of tables for integration. The student is advised to look at the *Mathematical Handbook of Formulas and Tables* by Murray R. Spiegel, Schaum's Outline Series, McGraw-Hill Book Company.

Example.   Use the table of integrals to find $\int x^3 e^{2x} \, dx$.

Solution.   Formula 43 applies, where $n = 3$, $a = 2$.

$$\int x^3 e^{2x} \, dx = \tfrac{1}{2} x^3 e^{2x} - \tfrac{3}{2} \int x^2 e^{2x} \, dx.$$

Apply formula 43 with $n = 2$, $a = 2$

$$\int x^3 e^{2x} \, dx = \tfrac{1}{2}x^3 e^{2x} - \tfrac{3}{2}(\tfrac{1}{2}x^2 e^{2x} - \tfrac{2}{2} \int x e^{2x} \, dx)$$

$$= \tfrac{1}{2}x^3 e^{2x} - \tfrac{3}{4}x^2 e^{2x} + \tfrac{3}{2} \int x e^{2x} \, dx$$

Now let $n = 1$ and $a = 2$

$$\int x^3 e^{3x} \, dx = \tfrac{1}{2}x^3 e^{2x} - \tfrac{3}{4}x^2 e^{2x} + \tfrac{3}{2}(\tfrac{1}{2}x e^{2x} - \tfrac{1}{2} \int e^{2x} \, dx).$$

We can apply formula 42 to find the final answer.

$$\int x^3 e^{2x} \, dx = \tfrac{1}{2}x^3 e^{2x} - \tfrac{3}{4}x^3 e^{2x} + \tfrac{3}{4}x e^{2x} - \tfrac{3}{8}e^{2x} + C.$$

Example.   Use the table of integrals to find $\displaystyle\int \frac{dx}{3x^2 + 2x - 4}$.

Solution.   This calls for formula 22, 23, or 24, depending on the relationship between b^2 and $4ac$. $b = 2$, $b^2 = 4$, $a = 3$, $c = -4$, $4ac = -48$. $4 > -48$; therefore, formula 23 applies.

$$\int \frac{dx}{3x^2 + 2x - 4} = \frac{1}{\sqrt{52}} \ln \left| \frac{6x + 2 - \sqrt{52}}{6x + 2 + \sqrt{52}} \right| + C$$

$$= \frac{1}{2\sqrt{13}} \ln \left| \frac{3x + 1 - \sqrt{13}}{3x + 1 + \sqrt{13}} \right| + C.$$

Example.   Use the table of integrals to find $\displaystyle\int \cos 3x \sin 5x \, dx$.

Solution.   Formula 32 applies, with $a = 5$ and $b = 3$.

$$\int \cos 3x \sin 5x \, dx = -\frac{1}{2} \left[\frac{\cos 2x}{2} + \frac{\cos 8x}{8} \right] + C.$$

5-6   Exercises

Use the table of integrals to find each of the following.

1. $\displaystyle\int \tan^5 x \, dx$ 2. $\displaystyle\int \sin 2x \sin 3x \, dx$

3. $\displaystyle\int \frac{dx}{3x\sqrt{2x+5}}$

14. $\displaystyle\int x\, e^{4x}\, dx$

4. $\displaystyle\int \frac{dx}{x\sqrt{9-4x^2}}$

15. $\displaystyle\int \frac{(1+2x)\, dx}{x\sqrt{4x^2+1}}$

5. $\displaystyle\int x(2x+5)^5\, dx$

16. $\displaystyle\int \sqrt{4x-x^2}\, dx$

6. $\displaystyle\int \frac{\sqrt{4x^2-7}}{2x}\, dx$

17. $\displaystyle\int e^{-x}\cos(2x)\, dx$

7. $\displaystyle\int \frac{dx}{x^2+4x+5}$

18. $\displaystyle\int e^{3x}\sin x\, dx$

8. $\displaystyle\int \frac{dx}{x^2+5x+5}$

19. $\displaystyle\int \cos^2(3x)\, dx$

9. $\displaystyle\int \tan^5(3x)\, dx$

20. $\displaystyle\int x^2 \sin(2x)\, dx$

10. $\displaystyle\int x^2\, e^{4x}\, dx$

21. $\displaystyle\int x^2\,(\ln 2x)^3\, dx$

11. $\displaystyle\int x^3\, a^{2x}\, dx$ (a is constant)

22. $\displaystyle\int_0^{\infty} e^{-2x^2}\, dx$

12. $\displaystyle\int \frac{dx}{3x\ln(2x)}$

23. $\displaystyle\int_0^{\infty} x^3\, e^{-x}\, dx$

13. $\displaystyle\int x^4 \ln x\, dx$

24. $\displaystyle\int_0^{\infty} e^{-5x^2}\, dx$

25. To find $\displaystyle\int \frac{dx}{\sin x + \cos x}$, make the following substitution:

$$\text{let } z = \tan \frac{x}{2}$$

Use the identity that $\tan \dfrac{x}{2} = \sqrt{\dfrac{1 - \cos x}{1 + \cos x}}$ to find $\cos x$, $\sin x$, and dx in terms of z. Then integrate by use of the tables.

26. Use the substitution and data from exercise 25 to find

$$\int \sqrt{1 + \sin x}\, dx.$$

5-7 IMPROPER INTEGRALS

The fundamental theorem of calculus states that if $f(x)$ is defined and continuous for all $a \leq x \leq b$, and if $F(x)$ is any indefinite integral of $f(x)$, then

$$\int_a^b f(x)\,dx = F(b) - F(a).$$

What happens if the hypotheses of the fundamental theorem are not satisfied? For instance, what about $\int_0^2 \dfrac{dx}{x^2}$? This integral is not defined at $x = 0$.

Or $\int_1^\infty \dfrac{dx}{x^2}$? $1 \leq x < \infty$ does not represent a closed interval, since ∞ is not a real number, but a symbol indicating that x gets larger and larger without bound.

Integrals of the types illustrated above are called *improper integrals*, and they may or may not exist. Let us first examine $\int_1^\infty \dfrac{dx}{x^2}$. If $\int_1^\infty \dfrac{dx}{x^2}$ is viewed as the area under $y = \dfrac{1}{x^2}$ which is to the right of $x = 1$, this may be tested by considering the definite integral $\int_1^b \dfrac{dx}{x^2}$, and then the limit (if it exists) as $b \to \infty$.

$$\int_1^b \frac{dx}{x^2} = -\frac{1}{x}\bigg]_1^b = -\frac{1}{b} + 1.$$

$$\lim_{b \to \infty} -\frac{1}{b} + 1 = 1.$$

This limit exists; therefore, $\int_1^\infty \dfrac{dx}{x^2} = 1$. The graph of this function (figure 5-7) shows that the area under the curve where $1 \leq x < \infty$ is actually unbounded, yet the definite integral exists, and thus the area is measurable.

The other example, $\int_0^2 \dfrac{dx}{x^2}$ can be treated in a similar manner, by writing

$$\lim_{b \to 0^+} \int_b^2 \frac{dx}{x^2}.$$

Note that $b \to 0^+$, that is, b approaches zero from the right side, and a one-sided limit is desired.

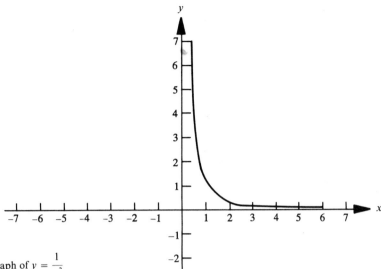

FIG. 5-7.   A Graph of $y = \dfrac{1}{x^2}$

$$\lim_{b \to 0^+} \int_b^2 \frac{dx}{x^2} = \lim_{b \to 0^+} \left[-\frac{1}{x} \right]_b^2 = \lim_{b \to 0^+} \left(-\frac{1}{2} + \frac{1}{b} \right) = \infty.$$

Since this limit does not exist, we cannot evaluate $\displaystyle\int_0^2 \frac{dx}{x^2}$.

Example.   Find the area under the curve $y = \dfrac{1}{x^2 + 1}$ from $-\infty < x$ $< +\infty$, if it exists.

Solution.   The graph of the curve is represented in Figure 5-8.

Clearly, the curve is symmetric about the y axis, and is always above the x axis. We can, therefore, attempt to compute $\displaystyle\lim_{b \to \infty} \int_0^b \frac{dx}{x^2 + 1}$ and if the integral exists, double it.

$$\int_0^b \frac{dx}{x^2 + 1} = \tan^{-1} x \Big]_0^b = \tan^{-1} b - \tan^{-1} 0 = \tan^{-1} b.$$

$$\lim_{b \to \infty} \tan^{-1} b = \frac{\pi}{2}.$$

The area is twice this limit, $2\left(\dfrac{\pi}{2}\right) = \pi$.

Example.   Find $\displaystyle\int_{-\pi/4}^{\pi/4} \cot \theta \, d\theta$.

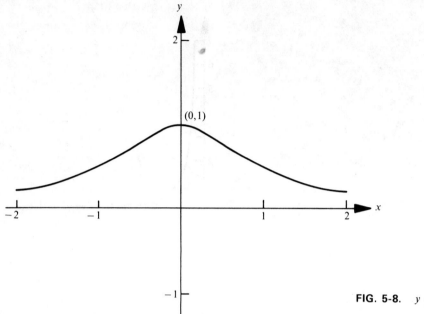

FIG. 5-8. $y = \dfrac{1}{x^2 + 1}$

Solution.   This integrand is undefined for a value of θ in the interval $-\dfrac{\pi}{4} \le \theta \le \dfrac{\pi}{4}$ rather than at an endpoint. Specifically, $\cot \theta$ is undefined for $\theta = 0$. Recall that $\displaystyle\int_a^b f(x)\,dx = \int_a^c f(x)\,dx + \int_c^b f(x)\,dx$.

We can write

$$\int_{-\pi/4}^{\pi/4} \cot \theta \, d\theta = \int_{-\pi/4}^{0} \cot \theta \, d\theta + \int_{0}^{\pi/4} \cot \theta \, d\theta$$

and consider

$$\lim_{b \to 0^-} \int_{-\pi/4}^{b} \cot \theta \, d\theta + \lim_{b \to 0^+} \int_{b}^{\pi/4} \cot \theta \, d\theta$$

$$= \lim_{b \to 0^-} \ln|\sin \theta| \Big]_{-\pi/4}^{b} + \lim_{b \to 0^+} \ln|\sin \theta| \Big]_{b}^{\pi/4}$$

$$= \lim_{b \to 0^-} \ln \frac{\sin b}{\dfrac{-\sqrt{2}}{2}} + \lim_{b \to 0^+} \ln \frac{\dfrac{\sqrt{2}}{2}}{\sin b}$$

$$= (-\infty) + \infty.$$

Neither limit exists, and the integral cannot be evaluated. Actually, the nonexistence of either limit is a sufficient condition for the divergence (nonexistence) of the integral.

5-7   Exercises

Evaluate each of the following integrals, if they exist.

1. $\displaystyle\int_1^\infty \frac{2\,dx}{x^2}$

2. $\displaystyle\int_0^1 \frac{2\,dx}{x^2}$

3. $\displaystyle\int_1^\infty \frac{dx}{x}$

4. $\displaystyle\int_2^\infty \frac{3\,dx}{x^3}$

5. $\displaystyle\int_0^2 \frac{dx}{x^2 - 4}$ (use table)

6. $\displaystyle\int_{-2}^0 \frac{dx}{x + 2}$

7. $\displaystyle\int_0^\infty e^x\,dx$

8. $\displaystyle\int_0^\infty e^{-x}\,dx$

9. $\displaystyle\int_1^\infty \frac{dx}{x^{\frac{3}{2}}}$

10. $\displaystyle\int_3^\infty \frac{dx}{(1 + x)^{\frac{3}{2}}}$

11. Show that $\displaystyle\int_0^\infty e^{-ax}\,dx = \frac{1}{a}, \quad a > 0$

12. Show that $\displaystyle\int_0^\infty x\,e^{-ax}\,dx = \frac{1}{a^2}, \quad a > 0$

13. Consider $\displaystyle\int_0^1 x^n\,dx$. Is this integral improper for any values of n? If so, state these values.

(14-20)   Evaluate the following integrals if they exist.

14. $\displaystyle\int_{\pi/4}^{\pi/2} \tan\theta\,d\theta$

15. $\displaystyle\int_0^\pi \frac{d\theta}{1 - \sin\theta}$ (Hint: Multiply numerator and denominator by $(1 + \sin\theta)$.)

16. $\displaystyle\int_{\pi/2}^\pi \frac{d\theta}{1 + \cos\theta}$ (See hint in problem 15.)

17. $\displaystyle\int_1^2 \frac{dx}{\sqrt{x - 1}}$

18. $\displaystyle\int_{1}^{\infty} \frac{x \, dx}{(1 + x^2)^2}$

19. $\displaystyle\int_{-1}^{2} \frac{dx}{\sqrt[3]{x}}$ $\left(Hint: \displaystyle\int_{a}^{b} f(x) \, dx = \int_{a}^{c} f(x) \, dx + \int_{c}^{b} f(x) \, dx.\right)$

20. $\displaystyle\int_{-1}^{1} \frac{dx}{x^2}$

Chapter 5   REVIEW

(1-10) Evaluate each of the following integrals by the fundamental theorem.

1. $\displaystyle\int_{1}^{5} (x^3 + 2x + 1) \, dx$

2. $\displaystyle\int_{0}^{3} x^2 \sqrt{x^3 + 9} \, dx$

3. $\displaystyle\int_{-2}^{2} x^2 e^x \, dx$

4. $\displaystyle\int_{1}^{4} x \ln x \, dx$

5. $\displaystyle\int_{1}^{2} x \, 2^{x^2} \, dx$

6. $\displaystyle\int_{0}^{\pi/2} \sin^2 \theta \, d\theta$

7. $\displaystyle\int_{1}^{0} \tan^{-1} x \, dx$

8. $\displaystyle\int_{0}^{1} \frac{dx}{1 + x^2}$

9. $\displaystyle\int_{2}^{5} \frac{dx}{x + 1}$

10. $\displaystyle\int_{-\pi/2}^{0} (1 - \sin x) \, dx$

(11-20)   Integrate each of the following.

11. $\displaystyle\int \frac{d\theta}{1 - \sin \theta}$

12. $\displaystyle\int \sqrt{x^2 + 1} \, dx$

13. $\displaystyle\int x \sin^{-1} x \, dx$

14. $\displaystyle\int \frac{\ln x}{x} \, dx$

15. $\displaystyle\int \frac{e^x}{e^{2x} + 1} \, dx$

16. $\displaystyle\int x \, e^{x^2} \, dx$

17. $\displaystyle\int \frac{\sin \sqrt{x}}{\sqrt{x}} \, dx$

18. $\displaystyle\int x^2 \cos x \, dx$

19. $\displaystyle\int x \cos^2 x \, dx$

20. $\displaystyle\int e^{-2x} \, dx$

(21-25)   Evaluate each of the following improper integrals, if they exist.

21. $\displaystyle\int_0^4 \frac{2\,dx}{\sqrt{x}}$

22. $\displaystyle\int_1^\infty \frac{2\,dx}{\sqrt{x}}$

23. $\displaystyle\int_1^\infty \frac{dx}{x^2 + 1}$

24. $\displaystyle\int_1^\infty \frac{dx}{x^3}$

25. $\displaystyle\int_1^\infty \frac{dx}{x}$

CHAPTER SIX **Applications**

# of Integration

The concepts and methods related to integration that have been developed to this point have a very extensive set of applications. Traditionally, these applications lie in the areas of physics, chemistry, and engineering, and as a consequence applications to these fields are usually considered in elementary calculus texts. Many readers will find these of interest and are directed to any standard calculus text for engineers for examples. In the last few years, a number of applications outside the physical sciences have been developed. These applications are in the fields of probability and statistics, economics, biology, and the social sciences, and it is for this reason that the nonmathematics, nonengineering major is advised to become familiar with the fundamentals of calculus.

A large number of problems that can be solved with the aid of calculus can be interpreted in terms of areas bounded by plane curves; therefore, this most fundamental application of integration will be developed as the basis for the further applications.

6-1   AREAS

Finding the areas bounded by plane curves has already been considered in the previous chapter. Specifically, if $y = f(x)$ defines a function such that $f(x) \geq 0$ for all x, and $a \leq x \leq b$, then

$$\int_a^b f(x)\,dx$$

equals the area bounded by the graphs of $y = f(x)$, $x = a$, $x = b$, and $y = 0$ (the x axis), provided the integral in question exists.

Example.   Find the area bounded by $y = \sin(x)$, $x = 0$, $x = \dfrac{\pi}{2}$ and $y = 0$.

Solution.   Area $= \displaystyle\int_0^{\pi/2} \sin x\,dx = -\cos x \Big]_0^{\pi/2}$

$$= -\cos\left(\frac{\pi}{2}\right) - (-\cos 0)$$

$$= 0 - (-1)$$

$$= 1.$$

The area in this example is illustrated in figure 6-1. There are any number of variations of this basic result.

VARIATION: Consider a function given by $y = f(x)$ where $f(x) \leq 0$ for all x such that $a \leq x \leq b$. Associated with this function there is a second function given by $y = -f(x)$, which is always non-negative over the interval $a \leq x \leq b$. This situation is illustrated in figure 6-2.

It is reasonable to conclude that the two shaded areas of figure 6-2 are equal. Since $-f(x)$ is a positive valued function on the interval, the area of figure 6-2a and 6-2b is given by

$$\int_a^b -f(x)\,dx = -\int_a^b f(x)\,dx$$

Thus the area below the x axis bounded by $y = f(x)$, $x = a$, and $x = b$ is given by

$$-\int_a^b f(x)\,dx.$$

Example.   Find the area bounded by $y = -x^2$, $x = 2$, $x = 4$, and the x axis.

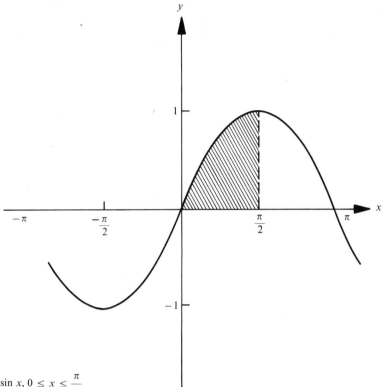

FIG. 6-1. $y = \sin x, 0 \le x \le \dfrac{\pi}{2}$

Solution.   The area is shown in figure 6-3.
This area is given by

$$-\int_2^4 (-x^2)\, dx = -\left(-\frac{x^3}{3}\right)\Bigg]_2^4$$

$$= -\left[-\frac{4^3}{3} - \left(-\frac{2^3}{3}\right)\right]$$

$$= -\left[-\frac{64}{3} + \frac{8}{3}\right]$$

$$= -\left[-\frac{56}{3}\right]$$

$$= \frac{56}{3}.$$

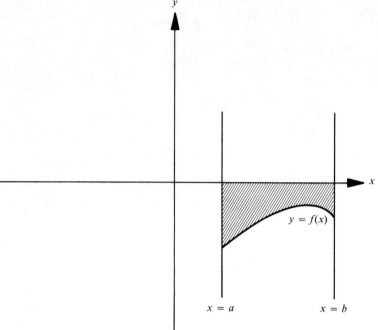

FIG. 6-2. (a) $y = f(x) \leq 0, a \leq x \leq b$

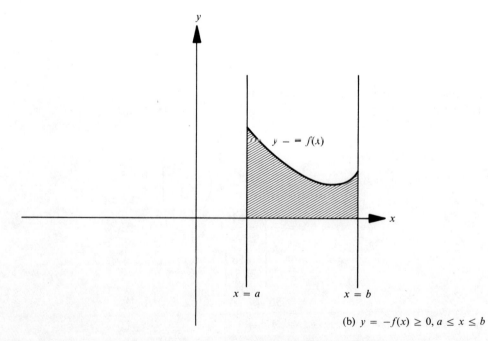

(b) $y = -f(x) \geq 0, a \leq x \leq b$

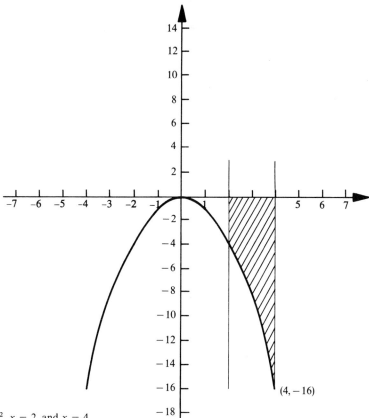

FIG. 6-3. $y = -x^2, x = 2,$ and $x = 4$

VARIATION: Consider a function that is sometimes positive valued and sometimes negative valued on an interval $a \leq x \leq b$. The graph of such a function is shown in figure 6-4. Assume that the zeros of this function are known, for example, in the figure: $f(c_1) = f(c_2) = f(c_3) = f(c_4) = 0$. Further suppose that

$$f(x) \geq 0 \text{ for } a \leq x \leq c_1,$$

$$f(x) \leq 0 \text{ for } c_1 \leq x \leq c_2,$$

$$f(x) \geq 0 \text{ for } c_2 \leq x \leq c_3,$$

$$f(x) \leq 0 \text{ for } c_3 \leq x \leq c_4, \text{ and}$$

$$f(x) \geq 0 \text{ for } c_4 \leq x \leq b.$$

The total area in this type of problem can be found by breaking down the

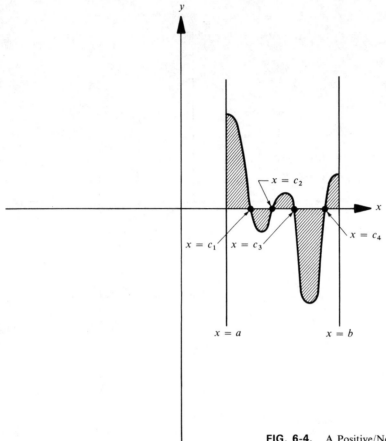

FIG. 6-4.   A Positive/Negative Valued
Function with Zeros at $x = c_1, c_2, c_3,$ and c_4

problem into a number of parts, evaluating the individual areas in turn, and finding the sum of the partial areas. For the above problem, the shaded area of figure 6-4 is

$$\int_a^{c_1} f(x)\,dx + \left[-\int_{c_1}^{c_2} f(x)\,dx\right] + \int_{c_2}^{c_3} f(x)\,dx +$$

$$\left[-\int_{c_3}^{c_4} f(x)\,dx\right] + \int_{c_4}^{b} f(x)\,dx.$$

Example.   Find the area bounded by the sine curve between $x = 0$, $x = 4\pi$, and the x axis.

Solution.   The area in question is shown in figure 6-5.

Then the area is given by

$$\int_0^\pi \sin x\, dx - \int_\pi^{2\pi} \sin x\, dx + \int_{2\pi}^{3\pi} \sin x\, dx - \int_{3\pi}^{4\pi} \sin x\, dx$$

$$= -\cos x \Big]_0^\pi + \cos x \Big]_\pi^{2\pi} - \cos x \Big]_{2\pi}^{3\pi} + \cos x \Big]_{3\pi}^{4\pi}$$

$$= -(\cos \pi) + \cos 0 + \cos 2\pi - (\cos \pi) - \cos(3\pi)$$

$$\qquad\qquad + \cos(2\pi) + \cos(4\pi) - \cos(3\pi)$$

$$= -(-1) + 1 + 1 - (-1) - (-1) + 1 + 1 - (-1)$$

$$= 1 + 1 + 1 + 1 + 1 + 1 + 1 + 1$$

$$= 8.$$

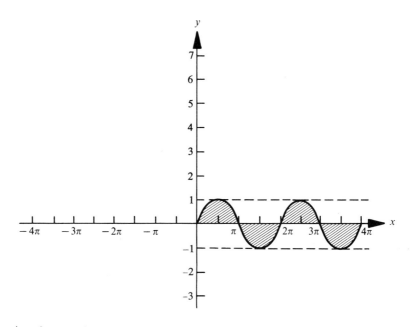

FIG. 6-5. $y = \sin x,\ 0 \le x \le 4\pi$

Example.   Find the area bounded by the x axis, $y = (x - 3)(x - 2)(x + 1)$, $x = 0$, and $x = 4$.

Solution.   The graph of this function is shown in figure 6-6.

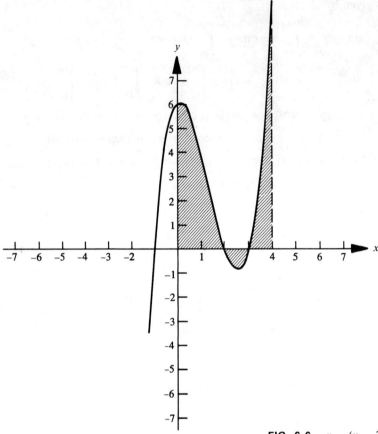

FIG. 6-6. $y = (x - 3)(x - 2)(x + 1) =$
$x^3 - 4x^2 + x + 6$

The area is given by

$$\int_0^4 (x - 3)(x - 2)(x + 1)\,dx = \int_0^2 (x^3 - 4x^2 + x + 6)\,dx$$

$$- \int_2^3 (x^3 - 4x^2 + x + 6)\,dx + \int_3^4 (x^3 - 4x^2 + x + 6)\,dx$$

$$= \frac{x^4}{4} - \frac{4x^3}{3} + \frac{x^2}{2} + 6x\bigg]_0^2 - \left[\frac{x^4}{4} - \frac{4x^3}{3} + \frac{x^2}{2} + 6x\right]_2^3$$

$$+ \left[\frac{x^4}{4} - \frac{4x^3}{3} + \frac{x^2}{2} + 6x\right]_3^4$$

$$= \frac{22}{3} - \left(-\frac{7}{12}\right) + \frac{47}{12} = \frac{88 + 7 + 47}{12} = \frac{142}{12} = \frac{71}{6}.$$

VARIATION: Consider the area bounded by the graphs of $y = f(x), y = g(x)$, $x = a$, and $x = b$ where $0 \leq g(x) \leq f(x)$ for all $x, a \leq x \leq b$. The situation is illustrated in figure 6-7.

The required area is the difference between the two shaded areas, that is

$$\text{Area} = \int_a^b f(x)\,dx - \int_a^b g(x)\,dx = \int_a^b (f(x) - g(x))\,dx.$$

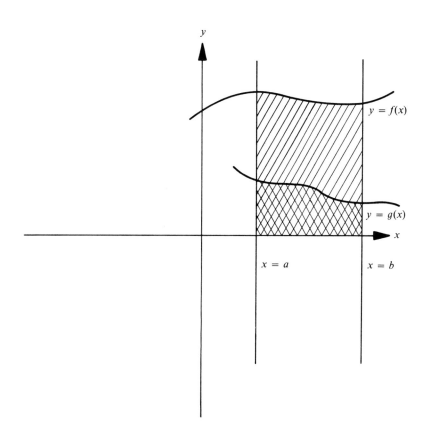

FIG. 6-7. $y = f(x), y = g(x)$ with $f(x) \geq g(x) \geq 0$ for all $x, a \leq x \leq b$

Example.   Find the area bounded by $y = x^2 + 2, y = x, x = 1$, and $x = 2$ as shown in figure 6-8.

Solution.   The area is given by

$$\int_1^2 (x^2 + 2)\,dx - \int_1^2 x\,dx = \int_1^2 (x^2 + 2 - x)\,dx = \left. \frac{x^3}{3} + 2x - \frac{x^2}{2} \right]_1^2$$

$$= \frac{8}{3} + 4 - 2 - \left(\frac{1}{3} + 2 - \frac{1}{2} \right)$$

$$= \frac{8}{3} + 2 - \frac{1}{3} - 2 + \frac{1}{2}$$

$$= \frac{7}{3} + \frac{1}{2}$$

$$= \frac{17}{6}.$$

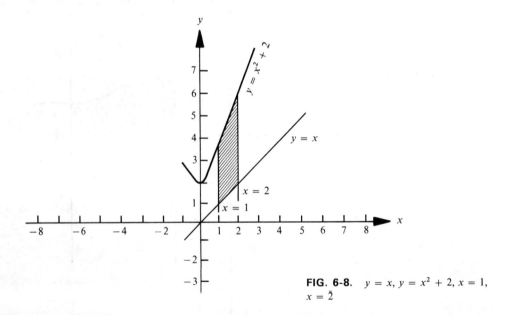

FIG. 6-8. $y = x$, $y = x^2 + 2$, $x = 1$, $x = 2$

Example.   Find the area bounded by $y = \cos(x) + 1$, $y = \frac{3}{2}$, $x = 0$, and $x = \pi$ as shown in figure 6-9.

Solution.   The two curves intersect where

$$\cos(x) + 1 = \tfrac{3}{2}$$

or

$$\cos(x) = \tfrac{1}{2}$$

$$x = \frac{\pi}{3} \text{ and } y = \tfrac{3}{2}.$$

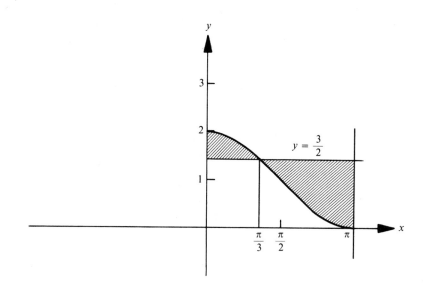

FIG. 6-9. $y = \cos(x) + 1$, $y = \frac{3}{2}$, $x = 0$,
and $x = \pi$

The area can be found by breaking the problem into two parts. For

$$0 \le x \le \frac{\pi}{3}, \quad \cos(x) + 1 \ge \tfrac{3}{2},$$

and for $\dfrac{\pi}{3} \le x \le \pi, \quad \dfrac{3}{2} \ge \cos(x) + 1.$

Thus the area is

$$\int_0^{\pi/3} \left(\cos(x) + 1 - \frac{3}{2} \right) dx + \int_{\pi/3}^{\pi} \left(\frac{3}{2} - [\cos(x) + 1] \right) dx$$

$$= \int_0^{\pi/3} \left(\cos x - \frac{1}{2} \right) dx + \int_{\pi/3}^{\pi} \left(\frac{1}{2} - \cos x \right) dx$$

$$= \sin x - \frac{x}{2} \Bigg]_0^{\pi/3} + \left(\frac{x}{2} - \sin x \right) \Bigg]_{\pi/3}^{\pi}$$

$$= \sin \frac{\pi}{3} - \frac{\pi}{6} + \left(\frac{\pi}{2} - \left[\frac{\pi}{6} - \sin \frac{\pi}{3} \right] \right)$$

$$= \frac{\sqrt{3}}{2} - \frac{\pi}{6} + \left(\frac{\pi}{2} - \frac{\pi}{6} + \frac{\sqrt{3}}{2} \right) = \sqrt{3} + \frac{\pi}{6}.$$

In this example one of the two functions is a constant function.

VARIATION: Sometimes a problem can be set up and solved with respect to an inverse function more easily than with respect to the given function. This is best illustrated with an example.

Example.   Find the area bounded by the graph of $y = \ln(x)$, $y = \ln(2)$, and $x = 4$. This area is shown in figure 6-10.
Solution.   The area is given by

$$\int_2^4 (\ln x - \ln 2)\, dx.$$

This integral is complicated. The problem can be simplified by viewing x as a function of y rather than y as a function of x.

   Since $y = \ln x$, it follows that $x = e^y$. This result comes from the definition of the log/exponent inverse pair of functions. Now suppose that we partition the *interval* from $y = \ln 2$ to $y = \ln 4$. This follows from the fact that $(4, \ln 4)$ is the point of intersection of $y = \ln x$ and $x = 4$.

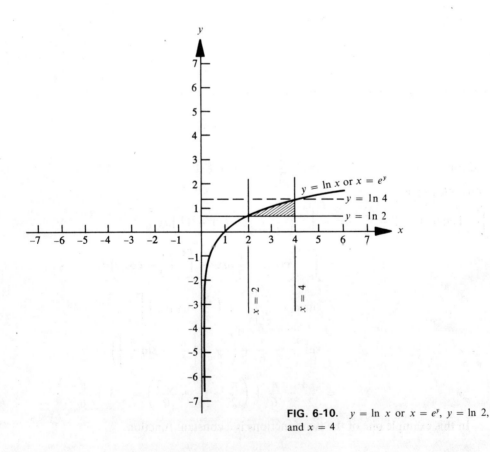

FIG. 6-10. $y = \ln x$ or $x = e^y$, $y = \ln 2$, and $x = 4$

By turning the picture we can see that the area is given by

$$\int_{\ln 2}^{\ln 4} 4\, dy - \int_{\ln 2}^{\ln 4} e^y\, dy,$$

which is the difference between the area bounded by $x = 0$, $x = 4$, $y = \ln 2$, and $y = \ln 4$, and the area bounded by $x = e^y$, $x = 0$, $y = \ln 2$, and $y = \ln 4$. Then,

$$\int_{\ln 2}^{\ln 4} 4\, dy - \int_{\ln 2}^{\ln 4} e^y\, dy = \int_{\ln 2}^{\ln 4} (4 - e^y)\, dy$$

$$= 4y - e^y \Big]_{\ln 2}^{\ln 4}$$

$$= 4 \ln 4 - 4 - (4 \ln 2 - 2)$$

$$= 4 \ln 2 - 2.$$

The variations and examples considered above make it clear that the key to solution is determining the exact integrand and limits of integration. Therefore, the sketch of the problem is invaluable. Once a sketch has been made it is usually a simple matter to find the required integral or integrals. It should be observed that in many problems the determination of the nature of the graph of the functions involved may require the applications of the graphing methods using calculus developed earlier in this text.

6-1   Exercises

(1-16)   In each case find the area bounded by the given functions. Make a sketch.

1. $y = x^3$, $x = -3$, $x = -2$, $y = 0$
2. $y = \sqrt{x} - 4$, $x = 1$, $x = 4$, $y = 0$
3. $y = \tan x$, $x = \dfrac{2\pi}{3}$, $x = \pi$, $y = 0$
4. $y = -e^{-x}$, $x = \ln 2$, $x = \ln 5$, $y = 0$
5. $y = 0$, $y = 2 \sin x \cos x$, $x = 0$, $x = 3\pi$
6. $y = 0$, $y = (x - 3)(x - 1)(x - 5)$
7. $y = 0$, $y = \sin x - 1$, $x = \pi$, $x = 4\pi$
8. $y = 0$, $y = x$, $y = -x + 2$, $y = x - 4$
9. $y = \sqrt{x}$, $y = x$

10. $y = \sin 4x, y = -4, x = 0, x = \dfrac{\pi}{2}$

11. $y = \tan^2 x, y = 0, x = \dfrac{\pi}{3}$

12. $y = \dfrac{e^x + e^{-x}}{2}, y = \dfrac{e^x - e^{-x}}{2}, x = 0, x = 1$

13. $y = \ln x, y = \ln 3, x = 10, x = 100$

14. $y = \ln x^2, y = \ln 4, x = e$

15. $y = \sin^{-1} x, x = \frac{1}{2}, x = 1, y = 0$

16. $y = \tan^{-1} x, x = 1, x = \sqrt{3}, y = 0$

(17-20) Set up integrals only to find the area bounded by the indicated curves.

17. $x = 0, y = 0, x = 3, y = e^{-x^2}$

18. $y = 0, y = \sqrt{(x - 2)(x - 3)}$

19. $x^2 + y^2 = 4, y = 0,$ and $y \geq 0$

20. $x^{\frac{2}{3}} + y^{\frac{2}{3}} = 8^{\frac{2}{3}}, y = 0, x = 0,$ and $y \geq 0$

6-2 PROBABILITY

Many applications of integration are made by giving a suitable interpretation to the area under a curve. A very useful application involves viewing such areas as the probability of an outcome of an experiment.

Definition. The probability of a specific outcome of an experiment is the fraction of the time that outcome can be expected to take place if the experiment is repeated a very large number of times.

Example. Consider the experiment "tossing a coin." The probability of a head is $\frac{1}{2}$ (assuming an honest coin), since half of the time one would expect to get a head.

Example. In the experiment "rolling a pair of dice" $\frac{1}{6}$ of the time 7 will come up, thus the probability of a 7 is $\frac{1}{6}$.

An analysis of a given experiment can be achieved by specifying a complete set of "mutually exclusive" outcomes for the experiment together with the probability of each outcome. To require the outcomes to be mutually exclusive is to insist that the occurrence of one outcome precludes the occurrence of any other outcome of the set. The set of outcomes must be extensive enough so that any possible outcome of the experiment falls into one of the outcomes in the set.

Example. Consider the pair of dice experiment. This experiment can be analyzed with the following table showing a set of mutually exclusive outcomes together with the corresponding distribution of probabilities.

outcome total spots	probability
2	$\frac{1}{36}$
3	$\frac{2}{36} = \frac{1}{18}$
4	$\frac{3}{36} = \frac{1}{12}$
5	$\frac{4}{36} = \frac{1}{9}$
6	$\frac{5}{36}$
7	$\frac{6}{36} = \frac{1}{6}$
8	$\frac{5}{36}$
9	$\frac{4}{36} = \frac{1}{9}$
10	$\frac{3}{36} = \frac{1}{12}$
11	$\frac{2}{36} = \frac{1}{18}$
12	$\frac{1}{36}$

These probabilities were calculated by thinking of a pair of dice, one red and one green. Then there are 36 possible outcomes as listed below:

red	green	red	green	red	green
1	1	3	1	5	1
1	2	3	2	5	2
1	3	3	3	5	3
1	4	3	4	5	4
1	5	3	5	5	5
1	6	3	6	5	6
2	1	4	1	6	1
2	2	4	2	6	2
2	3	4	3	6	3
2	4	4	4	6	4
2	5	4	5	6	5
2	6	4	6	6	6

The question is how many of these outcomes result in a total of 2 spots, how many in 3, and so forth? For 2 spots there is only 1 outcome. Thus the probability of a 2 is $\frac{1}{36}$. There are 2 ways to get 3 spots, therefore the probability of 3 spots is $\frac{2}{36}$, and so on.

Notice that the sum of the probabilities is 1. Figure 6-11 illustrates a probability diagram for this experiment.

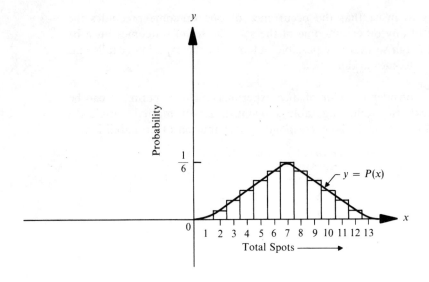

FIG. 6-11. Dice Probability Diagram

In figure 6-11 each possible outcome is indicated by its total number of spots represented as a number on a number line. A series of equal-width columns have then been drawn. The height of each column was then adjusted so that the area in each column represents the same fraction of the total area of all of the columns as the probability of the outcome.

This approach is fine in cases like the above where the number of possible outcomes of the experiment is small. However, when the number of outcomes being considered becomes large, it is usually simpler to replace discrete columns with a continuous function that yields corresponding areas when integrated between the bounding values of a given column. For example if $y = P(x)$ is the smooth curve shown in figure 6-11,

$$\int_{1.5}^{2.5} P(x)dx = \tfrac{1}{36}$$

so that the area corresponding to the outcome "2" will be correct. Similarly,

$$\int_{2.5}^{3.5} P(x)dx = \tfrac{2}{36},$$

$$\int_{3.5}^{4.5} P(x)dx = \tfrac{3}{36},$$

etc.

$P(x)$ is called the *probability density function* for the experiment. In other words, a probability density function is a continuous function that can be used to replace the discrete descriptions of probability. Then the probabilities can be calculated by integration.

While in many real-life cases the actual nature of such probability density functions is complex, the basic properties of such a function are relatively simple. First, we will be talking about experiments whose outcomes correspond to some set of real numbers. That is, the set of outcomes for the experiment will be represented by a number x, where x is within some interval $a \leq x \leq b$. Second, $P(x) \geq 0$ for all $a \leq x \leq b$. Third,

$\int_a^b P(x)dx = 1$; that is, the total area bounded by the probability density

function and the x axis must be 1, because the probability that a given result will be one of the possible answers is, of course, 1. In practice almost any nonnegative valued function $f(x)$ whose integral is finite on a specific interval might represent a probability density function. The factor

$$c = \frac{1}{\int_a^b f(x)dx}$$

can be used to adjust the area involved to 1 square unit. That is, if

$$c = \frac{1}{\int_a^b f(x)dx},$$

and

$$P(x) = cf(x),$$

then $P(x)$ will be a probability density function, because

$$\int_a^b P(x)dx = \int_a^b cf(x)dx = c\int_a^b f(x)dx$$

$$= \frac{1}{\int_a^b f(x)dx} \cdot \int_a^b f(x)dx = 1.$$

Example.   Consider the function $f(x) = \dfrac{\sin x}{2}$ on $0 \leq x \leq \pi$. Within this interval $\sin x \geq 0$, and

$$\int_0^\pi \frac{\sin x}{2}dx = \frac{1}{2}\left[-\cos x\right]_0^\pi$$

$$= \frac{1}{2}[-\cos \pi - (-\cos 0)]$$

$$= \frac{1}{2}(+1 + 1) = 1.$$

Thus, $f(x) = \dfrac{\sin x}{2}$ meets the basic requirements of a probability density function. The area is shown in figure 6-12.

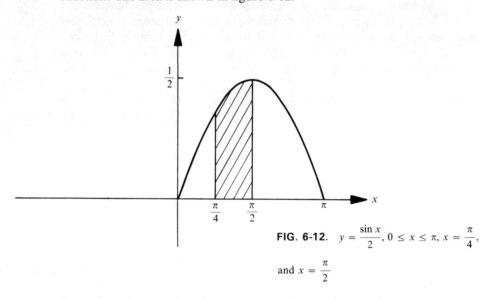

FIG. 6-12. $y = \dfrac{\sin x}{2}, 0 \leq x \leq \pi, x = \dfrac{\pi}{4},$

and $x = \dfrac{\pi}{2}$

Example. Assume that the outcomes of a certain experiment correspond to real-number values between 0 and π and that the probability density function for the outcomes is known to be $P(x) = \frac{1}{2}\sin x$. What is the probability that when the experiment is performed an outcome between $\dfrac{\pi}{4}$ and $\dfrac{\pi}{2}$ will occur?

Solution. The area is the shaded portion of figure 6-12. The probability will correspond to the area bounded by the x axis and the probability density function. Specifically the probability of an outcome between $\dfrac{\pi}{4}$ and $\dfrac{\pi}{2}$ is

$$\int_{\pi/4}^{\pi/2} \frac{1}{2}\sin x\, dx = \frac{1}{2}(-\cos x)\Big]_{\pi/4}^{\pi/2}$$

$$= \frac{1}{2}\left[-\cos\frac{\pi}{2} - \left(-\cos\frac{\pi}{4}\right)\right]$$

$$= \frac{1}{2}\left[\cos\frac{\pi}{4}\right]$$

$$= \frac{1}{2}\cdot\frac{\sqrt{2}}{2} = \frac{\sqrt{2}}{4} \approx \frac{1.414}{4} = 0.3535.$$

Thus approximately 35.35% of the time one would expect an experimental outcome between $\dfrac{\pi}{4}$ and $\dfrac{\pi}{2}$ for this experiment.

It is often the case that the experimental values in question will correspond to infinite integrals. This will require the use of improper integrals.

Example.   Assume that the outcomes of a certain experiment correspond to the positive real numbers, and that the corresponding probability density function is

$$P(x) = \frac{1}{(x + 1)^2} \quad \text{where } 0 \leq x < \infty.$$

What is the probability of an experimental outcome greater than or equal to 3?

Solution.   First we should check that

$$\int_0^\infty \frac{1}{(x + 1)^2}\, dx = 1.$$

$$\int_0^\infty \frac{1}{(x + 1)^2}\, dx = \lim_{b \to \infty} \int_0^b \frac{1}{(x + 1)^2}\, dx$$

$$= \lim_{b \to \infty} \left[\frac{-1}{(x + 1)} \right]_0^b$$

$$= \lim_{b \to \infty} \left[\frac{-1}{b + 1} + \frac{1}{1} \right] = 1.$$

Then the probability of an experimental outcome greater than or equal to 3 will be given by

$$\int_3^\infty \frac{1}{(x + 1)^2}\, dx = \lim_{b \to \infty} \int_3^b \frac{1}{(x + 1)^2}\, dx$$

$$= \lim_{b \to \infty} \left[\frac{-1}{(x + 1)} \right]_3^b$$

$$= \lim_{b \to \infty} \left[\frac{-1}{b + 1} + \frac{1}{3 + 1} \right]$$

$$= \frac{1}{4}.$$

This area is shown in figure 6-13. Thus for this experiment $\frac{1}{4}$ of the time an outcome greater than or equal to 3 can be expected.

Sometimes the interval of outcomes can extend from $-\infty$ to $+\infty$.

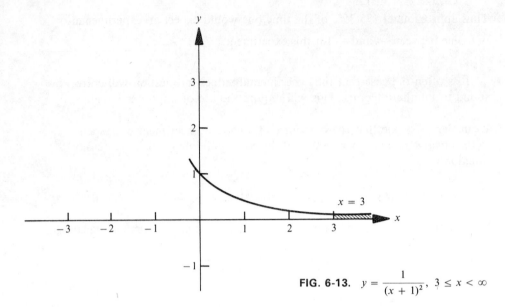

FIG. 6-13. $y = \dfrac{1}{(x+1)^2}, \; 3 \le x < \infty$

Example. Consider an experiment whose outcomes range from $-\infty$ to $+\infty$ and whose probability density function is given by

$$P(x) = \frac{1}{\pi} \frac{1}{x^2 + 1}$$

What is the probability that an outcome corresponding to values between $x = 1$ and $x = \sqrt{3}$ will occur?

Solution. Checking that this function meets the requirements of a probability density function,

$$\int_{-\infty}^{\infty} \frac{1}{\pi} \frac{1}{x^2 + 1} \, dx = \frac{1}{\pi} \lim_{b \to \infty} \int_{-b}^{b} \frac{1}{x^2 + 1} \, dx$$

$$= \frac{1}{\pi} \lim_{b \to \infty} \tan^{-1} x \Big]_{-b}^{b}$$

$$= \frac{1}{\pi} \left[\lim_{b \to \infty} \{ \tan^{-1}(b) - \tan^{-1}(-b) \} \right]$$

$$= \frac{1}{\pi} \left[\frac{\pi}{2} - \left(-\frac{\pi}{2} \right) \right] = 1$$

Then the probability of an outcome between 1 and $\sqrt{3}$ is given by

$$\frac{1}{\pi} \int_{1}^{\sqrt{3}} \frac{1}{x^2 + 1} \, dx,$$

and is shown in figure 6-14.

$$\frac{1}{\pi} \int_1^{\sqrt{3}} \frac{1}{x^2 + 1} \, dx = \frac{1}{\pi} \tan^{-1} x \Big]_1^{\sqrt{3}}$$

$$= \frac{1}{\pi} \left[\tan^{-1} \sqrt{3} - \tan^{-1} 1 \right]$$

$$= \frac{1}{\pi} \left[\frac{\pi}{3} - \frac{\pi}{4} \right] = \frac{1}{12}.$$

Thus, $\frac{1}{12}$ of a time the described experiment will have an outcome between 1 and $\sqrt{3}$.

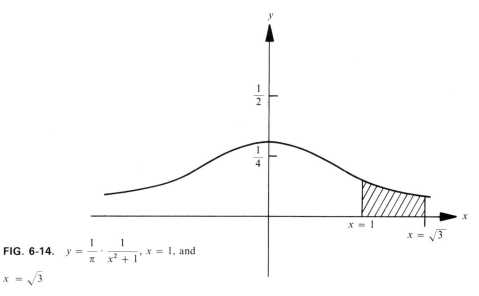

FIG. 6-14. $y = \dfrac{1}{\pi} \cdot \dfrac{1}{x^2 + 1}$, $x = 1$, and

$x = \sqrt{3}$

The practical applications of probability often involve calculations similar to those considered here. Usually the problem involves the comparison of an observed experimental outcome with the theoretical probability of its occurrence. For example, it might be known that 95% of all patients with a certain medical problem die. Based on this, one can construct a mathematical probability model of what might be expected in a group of 20 patients. Then such a group is given a new treatment. Suppose that all but 2 recover. By assuming that the treatment *was not* effective and then using the mathematical model one can calculate the probability that only 2 of the 20 would die. Suppose that this probability comes out 0.00002%. That is, 99.99998% of the time *more* than 2 patients would be expected to die. It then would appear reasonable to conclude that the treatment was effective.

Naturally we have oversimplified our example to illustrate one possible direction of application of the theory of probability. However, a modern course in probability theory and its application makes use of the calculus tools we have considered here. A very elementary discussion of such applications can be found in *Introduction to Mathematical Ideas* by D. Crowdis and B. Wheeler, McGraw-Hill, 1969.

6-2   Exercises

1. A life insurance table states that the probability of a 70-year-old man living to be 80 is $\frac{4}{9}$. Interpret this according to the definition of probability.

2. A gambler observes that on the average he wins a certain game 60 times out of every 110 times he plays. What is his probability of winning? What is his probability of losing?

3. A single card is drawn from a deck of playing cards. Two possible outcomes are that the card is a red card, or it is an ace. Are these outcomes mutually exclusive? If not, why not?

4. Give an example of three mutually exclusive outcomes of an experiment involving tossing five coins and counting the number of heads.

(5-8)   An experiment has outcomes corresponding to real number values between 0 and π with a probability density function given by $P(x) = \frac{1}{2} \sin x$. Determine the probability of outcomes of this experiment in the domain indicated. Sketch the curve and shade the appropriate area.

5. An outcome x such that $\dfrac{\pi}{4} \le x \le \dfrac{3\pi}{4}$.

6. An outcome x such that $0 \le x \le \dfrac{\pi}{2}$.

7. An outcome x such that $\left| x - \dfrac{\pi}{2} \right| \le \dfrac{\pi}{6}$.

8. An outcome x such that $\left| x - \dfrac{\pi}{2} \right| \ge \dfrac{\pi}{3}$.

(9-12)   An experiment has outcomes corresponding to the positive real numbers with a probability density function given by

$$P(x) = \frac{1}{(x + 1)^2}.$$

In each case, determine the probability of an outcome in the domain indicated. Sketch the curve and shade the appropriate area.

9.   An outcome x such that $1 \le x \le 6$.
10.   An outcome x such that $x \ge 4$.
11.   An outcome x such that $x \le 1$.
12.   An outcome x such that $|x - 3| \le 2$.

(13-16)   An experiment has outcomes corresponding to the real numbers with a probability density function given by

$$P(x) = \frac{1}{\pi} \frac{1}{x^2 + 1}.$$

In each case determine the probability of an outcome in the domain indicated. Make use of the trigonometric function tables in the appendix. Sketch the curve and shade the appropriate area.

13.   An outcome such that $0 \le x \le \dfrac{1}{\sqrt{3}}$.

14.   An outcome such that $-1 \le x \le 1$.
15.   An outcome such that $-3 \le x \le 1$.
16.   An outcome such that $|x| \le 2$.

17.   For the probability density function $P(x) = \dfrac{1}{(x + 1)^2}$, $x \ge 0$, determine a value for a such that there is 80% probability that $0 \le x \le a$.

18.   For the probability density function $P(x) = \dfrac{1}{\pi} \dfrac{1}{x^2 + 1}$, $-\infty < x < \infty$, determine a value for a such that there is a 95% chance that $|x| \le a$.

19.   For the probability density function $P(x) = \frac{1}{2} \sin x$, $0 \le x \le \pi$, determine a value for a such that there is a 50% probability that

$$\left| x - \frac{\pi}{2} \right| \le a.$$

(20-28)   Many functions $f(x)$ are nonnegative valued over a specific interval and have integrals that are finite, but not equal to 1. That is, for $a \le x \le b$, $f(x) \ge 0$, and $\displaystyle\int_a^b f(x)\,dx = A$, a positive finite value. To find a related function $P(x)$ that does have a unit integral it is only necessary to multiply the original function by the factor

$$\frac{1}{A} = \frac{1}{\displaystyle\int_a^b f(x)\,dx}$$

then $P(x) = \dfrac{1}{A} f(x)$ will be such that

$$\int_a^b P(x)dx = \int_a^b \frac{1}{A} f(x)dx = \frac{1}{A} \int_a^b f(x)dx = \frac{1}{A}(A) = 1.$$

For each of the functions and intervals indicated find that related $P(x)$ expression; then find the probability of an outcome assuming the $P(x)$ determined within the second range of values indicated.

20. $f(x) = \cos x$ on $-\dfrac{\pi}{2} \le x \le \dfrac{\pi}{2}$, an outcome such that $0 \le x \le \dfrac{\pi}{4}$

21. $f(x) = x^2$ on $0 \le x \le 2$, an outcome such that $1 \le x \le 2$

22. $f(x) = x(x^2 + 1)^2$ on $1 \le x \le 2$, an outcome such that $\left| x - \frac{1}{2} \right| \le \frac{1}{4}$

23. $f(x) = \dfrac{x^2}{(x^3 + 1)^2}$ on $0 \le x < \infty$, an outcome such that $x \ge \sqrt[3]{3}$

24. $f(x) = xe^{-x^2}$ on $0 \le x < \infty$, an outcome such that $x \le 1$

25. $f(x) = \dfrac{1}{x^{\frac{3}{2}}}$ on $1 \le x < \infty$, an outcome such that $x \le 9$

26. $f(x) = \dfrac{1}{(2x)^2 + 1}$ on $-\infty < x < \infty$, an outcome such that $|x| \le \frac{1}{2}$

27. $f(x) = \dfrac{1}{x^2 + 2x + 1} + 1$ on $-\infty < x < \infty$, an outcome such that

$|x + 1| \le 1$

28. $f(x) = \dfrac{1}{e^x + e^{-x}}$ $\left(\text{Hint}: \dfrac{1}{e^x + e^{-x}} = \dfrac{e^x}{e^x(e^x + e^{-x})} = \dfrac{e^x}{e^{2x} + 1} \right)$

on $-\infty < x < \infty$, an outcome such that $\ln 2 \le x \le \ln 10$

(29-32) For each of the functions and intervals given, determine a value for c such that $x = c$ divides the area involved into two equal size areas.

29. $f(x) = \cos x$ on the interval $0 \le x \le \dfrac{\pi}{2}$.

30. $f(x) = x^2$ on the interval $0 \le x \le 4$

31. $f(x) = \dfrac{1}{\pi} \dfrac{1}{x^2 + 1}$ on the interval $0 \le x < \infty$

32. $f(x) = \dfrac{1}{e^x + e^{-x}}$ on the interval $-\infty < x < \infty$

(33-34)   For each of the following functions and intervals determine values for a, b, and c such that $x = a$, $x = b$, and $x = c$ divide the area under the curve into four areas of equal size. The numbers a, b, and c are called the quartiles of the distribution.

33. $y = \frac{1}{2} \sin x$ on $0 \leq x \leq \pi$

34. $y = \dfrac{1}{\pi} \dfrac{1}{x^2 + 1}$ on $-\infty < x < \infty$

6-3   FAMILIES OF CURVES, PARAMETERS, MOMENTS

A large group of real-life probability problems have probability density functions of the same type. That is, they belong to the same family of curves. A *family of curves* is a set of curves having a common characteristic.

Example.   The curves whose equations can be written in the form $y = Ax + B$ are members of the family of straight lines. By assigning specific values to A and B, a specific member of the family can be found.

Example.   The curves whose equations are of the form $y = A(x - B)^2$, where $A > 0$ are all members of a family of parabolas which open upward and have vertices lying on the x axis.

The constants in the examples are called *parameters*. By giving specific values to parameters like A and B in these examples, an individual member of a family of curves is specified. There is usually some physical or intuitive reason to guess which family of curves describes a specific problem. To make use of a density function in solving a problem one must first determine the actual values of the parameters needed to identify the one individual member of the family of curves which best describes the distribution of outcomes. The three most common parameters used in identifying individual members of a family of probability distributions are the "first moment of the distribution about zero," the "second moment of the distribution about the mean," and the square root of this latter quantity.

> **Definition.**   Let $P(x)$ be a probability density function defined over an interval $a \leq x \leq b$. The first moment of the distribution, μ, is defined as
>
> $$\mu = \int_a^b x P(x)\, dx,$$

provided this integral exists. μ is also called *the average value of the distribution, the expectation of the distribution, the mean of the distribution,* or *the mean of the density function.*

At first glance, μ does not appear to be the usual kind of average: a sum divided by the number of addends. But an example will show that it is just that. Suppose that $y = P(x)$ is a probability distribution for an intelligence test. The test scores range from 40 to 195. That is, the domain of x is from $a = 40$ to $b = 195$. Further, suppose that the standardizing population, the number of people who have taken the test, is 7,000 and that test scores are whole numbers only; therefore, scores such as $105\frac{1}{2}$ cannot happen. A diagram such as figure 6-11 could be made for $y = P(x)$. The width of any rectangle is one unit, and its height is found by substituting the value indicated at the base of the rectangle into $P(x)$. By definition, the area of the ith rectangle is the probability of x_i occurring. In other words, the area of the ith rectangle is the fraction of time that x_i will occur. But the area of the ith rectangle is the product of its width and height; $1 \cdot P(x_i)$ $= P(x_i)$. Therefore, in this example $y_i = P(x_i)$ gives the probability of score x_i occurring. For instance, $P(120)$ would give the probability of an intelligence score of 120. If $P(120) = 0.1$ then one tenth of the people taking the test would have a score of 120. Since 7,000 have taken the test, 0.1 of 7,000, or 700, would score 120. If $K = 7,000$, the total number taking the test, then $f(x) = KP(x)$ is a function that gives the actual number of people receiving each test score. If we apply this information for a score of 120, $f(120) = 7,000\, P(120) = 7,000(0.1) = 700$. That is, $f(120) = 700$, the number of times the score 120 happened. The expression $f(x_i) \cdot x_i$ is the number of x_i scores times the actual score, x_i. Referring again to the 120 score, $f(x_i) \cdot x_i = (700)(120) = 84,000$, which is the total number of points accumulated by the 700 people who scored 120. Thus, $f(x_i) \cdot x_i$ is the total number of points accumulated by all the people who had an intelligence score of x_i. Therefore, the following expresses the total number of points scored by all 7,000 people taking the test.

$$\sum_{i=1}^{n} x_i \cdot f(x_i).$$

The average test score can now be found by dividing the above expression by the number who took the test, 7,000. Another way of writing 7,000 is

$$\sum_{i=1}^{n} f(x_i),$$

since $f(x_i)$ is the number receiving each score, and the sum of those receiving each individual score must equal the number who took the test. The average test score is the total number of test points divided by the number who took the test:

$$\frac{\sum\limits_{i=1}^{n} x_i f(x_i)}{\sum\limits_{i=1}^{n} f(x_i)}.$$

Multiplying numerator and denominator by $\dfrac{\Delta x}{K}$ gives

$$\frac{\sum\limits_{i=1}^{n} x_i \cdot \dfrac{f(x_i)}{K} \Delta x}{\sum\limits_{i=1}^{n} \dfrac{f(x_i)}{K} \Delta x}.$$

By definition,

$$f(x_i) = KP(x_i).$$

Solving for $P(x_i)$ gives

$$P(x_i) = \frac{f(x_i)}{K}.$$

Substituting in the last expression for the average gives

$$\frac{\sum\limits_{i=1}^{n} x_i \cdot P(x_i)\Delta x}{\sum\limits_{i=1}^{n} P(x_i)\Delta x}.$$

The limit of the average as n becomes infinite is

$$\lim_{n \to \infty} \frac{\sum\limits_{i=1}^{n} x_i \cdot P(x_i)\Delta x}{\sum\limits_{i=1}^{n} P(x_i)\Delta x} = \frac{\int_a^b xP(x)\,dx}{\int_a^b P(x)\,dx}.$$

But $\int_a^b P(x)\,dx = 1$. So the average x score is

$$\frac{\int_a^b xP(x)\,dx}{1} = \int_a^b xP(x)\,dx.$$

Example.   Let $P(x) = \frac{1}{2} \sin x$ on the interval $0 \le x \le \pi$ (figure 6-15).

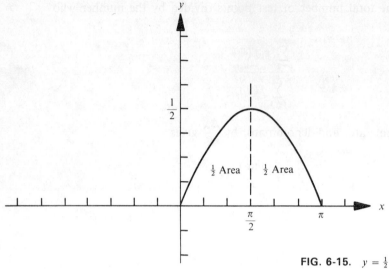

FIG. 6-15. $y = \tfrac{1}{2}\sin x, \ 0 \le x \le \pi$

Then,

$$\mu = \int_0^\pi \frac{x \sin x}{2}\, dx$$

$$= \frac{1}{2}\int_0^\pi x \sin x\, dx.$$

Using the integral tables,

$$\frac{1}{2}\int_0^\pi x \sin x\, dx = \frac{1}{2}\left[\sin x - x \cos x\right]_0^\pi$$

$$= \frac{\sin \pi - \pi(\cos \pi) - (\sin 0 - 0 \cos 0)}{2}$$

$$= \frac{-\pi(-1)}{2} = \frac{\pi}{2}.$$

This result agrees with the usual intuitive concept of an average, with the symmetric area bounded by $y = \tfrac{1}{2}\sin x$.

Example.   Find the first moment of the probability density function

$$P(x) = \frac{1}{\pi}\, \frac{1}{x^2 + 1} \quad \text{on } -\infty < x < \infty.$$

Solution. $\mu = \dfrac{1}{\pi}\displaystyle\int_{-\infty}^{\infty} \dfrac{x}{x^2 + 1}\, dx$

$$= \lim_{b \to \infty} \frac{1}{\pi} \int_{-b}^{b} \frac{x}{x^2 + 1} \, dx$$

$$= \lim_{b \to \infty} \frac{1}{\pi} \left[\tfrac{1}{2} \ln(x^2 + 1) \right]_{-b}^{b}$$

$$= \lim_{b \to \infty} \frac{1}{2\pi} \{ \ln(b^2 + 1) - \ln(b^2 + 1) \}$$

$$= \lim_{b \to \infty} \frac{1}{2\pi} (0) = 0.$$

Definition. Let $P(x)$ be a probability density function defined on an interval $a \leq x \leq b$. Then the second moment of $P(x)$ around the mean, σ^2, is defined by

$$\sigma^2 = \int_{a}^{b} (x - \mu)^2 P(x) \, dx,$$

where μ is the mean of the density function, provided such an integral exists. σ^2 (read "sigma squared") is also called *the variance of the distribution.* $\sigma = \sqrt{\sigma^2}$ is called the *standard deviation,* or *root mean squared deviation* of the distribution.

μ can be thought of as describing where the distribution is located, while σ^2 measures the variability, or the spread of the distribution. Figure 6-16a shows several different distributions, each exactly the same shape, with the same σ^2 but with different means. Figure 6-16b shows several

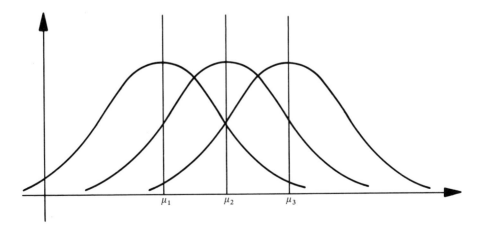

FIG. 6-16. (a) Normal Curves with $\sigma^2 = 1$ and Various Values for μ

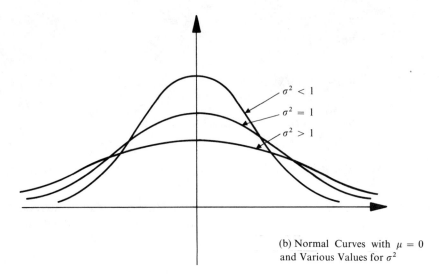

(b) Normal Curves with $\mu = 0$
and Various Values for σ^2

different distributions, each with the same mean but with different variances. Notice that, as the value of σ^2 decreases, the distribution gets tighter.

As in the case of μ, the mean of the distribution, the definition of σ^2, the variance of the distribution, differs in formula from the usual expression found in statistics; however, it can be shown in similar manner that the formulas are equivalent, $i.e.$,

$$\sigma^2 = \lim_{n \to \infty} \frac{\sum_{i=1}^{n} (x_i - \mu)^2}{n} = \int_a^b (x - \mu)^2 P(x)\, dx.$$

Example.   Let $P(x) = \frac{1}{2} \sin x$ on $0 \le x \le \pi$, with $\mu = \dfrac{\pi}{2}$. Find σ.

Solution. $\sigma^2 = \displaystyle\int_0^\pi \left(x - \frac{\pi}{2}\right)^2 \frac{\sin x}{2}\, dx.$

Let $u = x - \dfrac{\pi}{2}$, thus $du = dx$.

If $x = 0$ then $u = -\dfrac{\pi}{2}$, and

if $x = \pi$ then $u = \dfrac{\pi}{2}$,

thus $\sigma^2 = \displaystyle\int_{-\pi/2}^{\pi/2} u^2 \frac{\sin\left(u + \dfrac{\pi}{2}\right)}{2}\, du.$

However, $\sin\left(u + \dfrac{\pi}{2}\right) = \cos u$, thus

$$\sigma^2 = \frac{1}{2}\int_{-\pi/2}^{\pi/2} u^2 \cos u\, du.$$

$$= \frac{1}{2}\left[2u\cos u + (u^2 - 2)\sin u\right]_{-\pi/2}^{\pi/2}$$

$$= \frac{1}{2}\left\{\left[(2)\frac{\pi}{2}\cos\frac{\pi}{2} + \left(\left(\frac{\pi}{2}\right)^2 - 2\right)\sin\frac{\pi}{2}\right] - \left[2\left(-\frac{\pi}{2}\right)\cos\left(-\frac{\pi}{2}\right)\right.\right.$$
$$\left.\left. + \left[\left(-\frac{\pi}{2}\right)^2 - 2\right]\sin\left(-\frac{\pi}{2}\right)\right]\right\}$$

$$= \left[\left(\frac{\pi}{2}\right)^2 - 2\right] = \frac{\pi^2}{4} - 2 = \frac{\pi^2 - 8}{4}$$

$$\approx \frac{9.8696 - 8}{4} = \frac{1.8696}{4} = 0.4674.$$

Therefore,

$$\sigma = \sqrt{0.4674} \approx 0.6837.$$

As one can see from the examples, the calculations of μ, σ^2, and σ are often very complex. In most cases, these parameters are estimated from observed data rather than calculated directly. However, the concepts of first and second moments have analogies in physical applications which do require direct theoretical calculation.

Example.   Find the first and second moments of the probability density function $P(x) = \frac{3}{8}x^2$ on the interval $0 \le x \le 2$.

Solution. $\mu = \displaystyle\int_0^2 \frac{3}{8}x^2 \cdot x\, dx$

$$= \frac{3}{8}\frac{x^4}{4}\bigg]_0^2$$

$$= \left(\frac{3}{8}\right)\left(\frac{16}{4}\right) = \frac{3}{2}.$$

$$\sigma^2 = \int_0^2 \frac{3}{8}x^2\left(x - \frac{3}{2}\right)^2 dx$$

$$= \frac{3}{8}\int_0^2 x^2\left(x^2 - 3x + \frac{9}{4}\right)dx$$

$$= \frac{3}{8} \int_0^2 \left(x^4 - 3x^3 + \frac{9x^2}{4} \right) dx$$

$$= \frac{3}{8} \left[\frac{x^5}{5} - \frac{3x^4}{4} + \frac{3x^3}{4} \right]_0^2$$

$$= \frac{3}{8} \left[\frac{32}{5} - \frac{48}{4} + \frac{24}{4} \right]$$

$$= \frac{3}{8} \left[\frac{32}{5} - 12 + 6 \right]$$

$$= \frac{3}{8} \left[\frac{32}{5} - 6 \right] = \frac{3}{8} \left[\frac{32 - 30}{5} \right]$$

$$= \frac{3}{8} \left(\frac{2}{5} \right) = \frac{6}{40} = \frac{3}{20}.$$

6-3   Exercises

(1-10)   Find μ in each case for the given probability density function.

1. $P(x) = \dfrac{3x^2}{56}$ on the interval $2 \le x \le 4$

2. $P(x) = \dfrac{3(8x - 2x^2)}{64}$ on the interval $0 \le x \le 4$

3. $P(x) = \dfrac{\cos x}{2}$ on the interval $-\dfrac{\pi}{2} \le x \le \dfrac{\pi}{2}$

4. $P(x) = \dfrac{3(x^3 - 4x^2 + x + 6)}{22}$ on the interval $0 \le x \le 2$

5. $P(x) = \dfrac{6}{17}(x^2 - x + 2)$ on the interval $1 \le x \le 2$

6. $P(x) = \dfrac{6x^2 - 3x^3}{4}$ on the interval $-1 \le x \le 1$

7. $P(x) = ce^{-\frac{x}{2}}$ on the interval $-2 \le x \le 3$, where $c = \dfrac{-e^{\frac{3}{2}}}{2(1 - e^{\frac{5}{2}})}$

8. $P(x) = \sqrt{2}\sin x$ on the interval $\dfrac{\pi}{2} \le x \le \dfrac{3\pi}{4}$

9. $P(x) = \dfrac{4}{\pi(x^2 + 4)}$ on the interval $-2 \le x \le 2$

10. $P(x) = \ln x$ on the interval $1 \le x \le e$

(11-15)   Find μ and σ^2 for the indicated probability density functions.

11. $P(x) = 2\sqrt{x}$ for $0 \le x \le 1$

12. $P(x) = \dfrac{5x^4}{2}$ for $-1 \le x \le 1$

13. $P(x) = \dfrac{6}{27}(3x - x^2)$ for $0 \le x \le 3$

14. $P(x) = \dfrac{3}{2}(x + 1)^2$ for $-2 \le x \le 0$

15. $P(x) = \dfrac{1}{18}(x - 5)^2,\ 2 \le x \le 8$

(16-20)   Calculate μ in each case.

16. $P(x) = \dfrac{4x^{\frac{1}{3}}}{3}$ for $1 \le x \le 3$

17. $P(x) = |x|$ for $-1 \le x \le 1$

18. $P(x) = \frac{1}{6}$ for $0 \le x \le 6$

19. $P(x) = \dfrac{e^{-x^2}}{\sqrt{2\pi}}$ for $1 \le x < \infty$

20. $P(x) = \dfrac{e^x}{9}$ for $1 \le x \le \ln 10$

6-4   NORMAL CURVE AREAS, AREAS WITH TABLES

The one probability density function that has the widest application is the "normal," "Gaussian," or "bell" distribution. The formula for this density is

$$P(x) = \frac{1}{\sigma\sqrt{2\pi}} e^{-\frac{1}{2}\left(\frac{x - \mu}{\sigma}\right)^2}$$

over the range of values $-\infty < x < \infty$. Figure 6-17 shows the graph of one

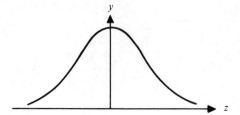

FIG. 6-17. $y = \dfrac{1}{\sqrt{2\pi}}\, e^{-\frac{1}{2}z^2}$

member of this family of densities for the specific values $\mu = 0$ and $\sigma = 1$. μ and σ are the first and second moments as considered in the last section, and are the identifying parameters for this family. When an experiment has outcomes known to follow this distribution the outcomes are said to be normally distributed. The density is symmetric about the value $x = \mu$.

Nature is, of course, responsible for the widespread use of this family; if man had any say he would have chosen a less complex one. The problem in using a density this complex is easy to see. Suppose that the values for μ and σ were known, and one wished to calculate the probability of an experimental outcome between two values, say x_1 and x_2. In theory this probability is given by

$$\int_{x_1}^{x_2} \frac{1}{\sigma\sqrt{2\pi}}\, e^{-\frac{1}{2}\left(\frac{x-\mu}{\sigma}\right)^2}\, dx$$

but how does one go about evaluating this integral? One hope would be to use some numerical scheme like the trapezoidal rule and a computer. The limitations of such an approach are obvious. Instead, an approach similar to the one we used to evaluate trigonometric functional images or logarithms has been developed. In finding values for images, a table of selected values has been computed. A procedure for relating nontabulated values to tabulated values has been worked out. In the case of the trigonometric images, the table covers arguments between 0 and $\dfrac{\pi}{2}$ radians. For arguments outside this range, a system of reference "angles" is used. For logarithms, the tabulated values range from 1 to 10, while the logarithms of numbers outside this range make use of the ideas of characteristics and mantissa. For normal curve integrals, a suitable change in the variable of integration will solve the problem.

To evaluate

$$I = \int_{x_1}^{x_2} \frac{1}{\sigma\sqrt{2\pi}}\, e^{-\frac{1}{2}\left(\frac{x-\mu}{\sigma}\right)^2}\, dx$$

Let
$$z = \frac{x - \mu}{\sigma}.$$

Then
$$dz = \frac{dx}{\sigma} \text{ or } \sigma dz = dx.$$

When
$$x = x_1, z = \frac{x_1 - \mu}{\sigma} = z_1,$$

and, when
$$x = x_2, z = \frac{x_2 - \mu}{\sigma} = z_2.$$

Then,

$$I = \int_{z_1}^{z_2} \frac{1}{\sigma \sqrt{2\pi}} e^{-\frac{1}{2}z^2} \sigma \, dz$$

$$= \frac{1}{\sqrt{2\pi}} \int_{z_1}^{z_2} e^{-\frac{1}{2}z^2} \, dz.$$

Notice that in the transformed integral the parameters μ and σ no longer appear in the integrand but have been incorporated into the new limits of integration. Now suppose we had a table of values for

$$\frac{1}{\sqrt{2\pi}} \int_0^{z_1} e^{-\frac{1}{2}z^2} \, dz.$$

Such a table could be used to evaluate integrals like I by breaking them down into combinations of integrals of this latter type, with 0 as the lower limit of integration. The examples will illustrate this procedure.

Such a table is called a *normal curve area table* or a *normal curve of error table*. The latter name comes from the historical fact that some of the first quantities found to be normally distributed were the errors in the repeated measurement of the physical characteristics of some object. Table I, found in the appendix of this text, is one of these tables.

Example.   The results of an experiment are known to be normally distributed with $\mu = 3$ and $\sigma = 2$. What is the probability of an experimental outcome between 3 and 5?
Solution.   Since the experimental results are normally distributed

$$P(x) = \frac{1}{\sigma \sqrt{2\pi}} e^{-\frac{1}{2}\left(\frac{x - \mu}{\sigma}\right)^2}$$

$$= \frac{1}{2 \sqrt{2\pi}} e^{-\frac{1}{2}\left(\frac{x - 3}{2}\right)^2}$$

The probability of an outcome between 3 and 5 will be given by

$$P = \int_3^5 P(x)\,dx$$

$$= \frac{1}{2\sqrt{2\pi}} \int_3^5 e^{-\frac{1}{2}\left(\frac{x-3}{2}\right)^2} dx.$$

Letting

$$z = \frac{x-3}{2},$$

$$P = \frac{1}{\sqrt{2\pi}} \int_0^1 e^{-\frac{1}{2}z^2}\,dz,$$

where when

$$x = 3,\ z = \frac{3-3}{2} = 0,$$

and when

$$x = 5,\ z = \frac{5-3}{2} = 1.$$

According to table I

$$\frac{1}{\sqrt{2\pi}} \int_0^1 e^{-\frac{1}{2}z^2}\,dz = 0.3413.$$

The curve and area in question are shown in figure 6-18a. Thus 34.13% of the time, a result between 3 and 5 can be expected.

This example was of course set up so that the lower limit of the transformed integral was 0. If this is not the case, no difficulty is encountered but a few more calculations arise. Table I yields the shaded area corresponding to a specific z_1 value, as illustrated in figure 6-18a. Notice that the graph of

$$y = \frac{1}{\sqrt{2\pi}} e^{-\frac{1}{2}z^2}$$ is symmetrical about $z = 0$. This means that for any positive

value z_1,

$$\frac{1}{\sqrt{2\pi}} \int_{-z_1}^0 e^{-\frac{1}{2}z^2}\,dz = \frac{1}{\sqrt{2\pi}} \int_0^{z_1} e^{-\frac{1}{2}z^2}\,dz.$$

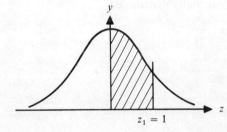

FIG. 6-18. (a) Normal Curve Area

Using this, together with the usual properties of integrals and a sketch of the specific z values involved, the table can be made to yield almost any desired integral of the type being considered.

Example.   Suppose that the results of an experiment are normally distributed with $\mu = 3$ and $\sigma = 2$. What is the probability of a result between 1 and 4?

Solution. $P = \displaystyle\int_{1}^{4} P(x)\,dx = \frac{1}{\sqrt{2\pi}} \int_{-1}^{1/2} e^{-\frac{1}{2}z^2}\,dz,$

using $\qquad\qquad\qquad z = \dfrac{x - \mu}{\sigma} = \dfrac{x - 3}{2}.$

When $\qquad\qquad x = 1, z = \dfrac{1 - 3}{2} = \dfrac{-2}{2} = -1,$ and

when $\qquad\qquad x = 4, z = \dfrac{4 - 3}{2} = \dfrac{1}{2}.$

The area corresponding to P is shown in figure 6-18b. However,

$$\frac{1}{\sqrt{2\pi}} \int_{-1}^{1/2} e^{-\frac{1}{2}z^2}\,dz = \frac{1}{\sqrt{2\pi}} \int_{-1}^{0} e^{-\frac{1}{2}z^2}\,dz + \frac{1}{\sqrt{2\pi}} \int_{0}^{1/2} e^{-\frac{1}{2}z^2}\,dz,$$

$$\frac{1}{\sqrt{2\pi}} \int_{-1}^{0} e^{-\frac{1}{2}z^2}\,dz = \frac{1}{\sqrt{2\pi}} \int_{0}^{+1} e^{-\frac{1}{2}z^2}\,dz = 0.3413,$$

and

$$\frac{1}{\sqrt{2\pi}} \int_{0}^{1/2} e^{-\frac{1}{2}z^2}\,dz = 0.1915.$$

these values are from table I. Thus,

$$P = 0.3413 + 0.1915 = 0.5328,$$

indicating a 53.28% chance of an outcome between 1 and 4.

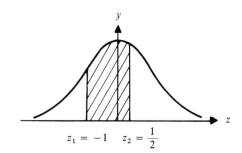

(b) Normal Curve Area

Example. Suppose that the results of an experiment are known to be normally distributed with $\mu = 3$ and $\sigma = 2$. What is the probability of an outcome between 4 and 7?

Solution. $P = \int_4^7 P(x)\,dx$ where $P(x) = \dfrac{1}{2\sqrt{2\pi}} e^{-\frac{1}{2}\left(\frac{x-3}{2}\right)^2}$

letting $\qquad\qquad\qquad z = \dfrac{x-3}{2},$

$$P = \frac{1}{\sqrt{2\pi}} \int_{1/2}^{2} e^{-\frac{1}{2}z^2}\,dz.$$

This area is shown in figure 6-18c. To use the table to evaluate the integral we need only observe that

$$\frac{1}{\sqrt{2\pi}} \int_0^2 e^{-\frac{1}{2}z^2}\,dz = \frac{1}{\sqrt{2\pi}} \int_0^{1/2} e^{-\frac{1}{2}z^2}\,dz + \frac{1}{\sqrt{2\pi}} \int_{1/2}^2 e^{-\frac{1}{2}z^2}\,dz.$$

Thus,

$$\frac{1}{\sqrt{2\pi}} \int_{1/2}^2 e^{-\frac{1}{2}z^2}\,dz = \frac{1}{\sqrt{2\pi}} \int_0^2 e^{-\frac{1}{2}z^2}\,dz - \frac{1}{\sqrt{2\pi}} \int_0^{1/2} e^{-\frac{1}{2}z^2}\,dz$$

$$= 0.4772 - 0.1915$$

$$= 0.2857.$$

Thus, there is a 0.2857 probability of a result between 4 and 7.

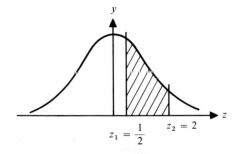

(c) Normal Curve Area

Example. An experimental result is known to be normally distributed with $\mu = 3$ and $\sigma = 2$. Find a value for a such that 95% of the time results between $\mu - a$ and $\mu + a$ can be expected.

Solution.   We know that

$$\frac{1}{2\sqrt{2\pi}} \int_{3-a}^{3+a} e^{-\frac{1}{2}\left(\frac{x-3}{2}\right)^2} dx = 0.9500.$$

Using the usual transformation $z = \dfrac{x-3}{2}$, this becomes

$$\frac{1}{\sqrt{2\pi}} \int_{-a/2}^{a/2} e^{-\frac{1}{2}z^2} dz = 0.9500.$$

If $\qquad\qquad x = 3 + a, z = \dfrac{3+a-3}{2} = \dfrac{a}{2},$

and if $\qquad\quad x = 3 - a, z = \dfrac{3-a-3}{2} = -\dfrac{a}{2}.$

The area corresponding to this integral is shown in figure 6-19. Since the function is symmetrical

$$\frac{1}{\sqrt{2\pi}} \int_{0}^{a/2} e^{-\frac{1}{2}z^2} dz = \tfrac{1}{2}(0.9500) = 0.475.$$

According to table I a z_1 value such that

$$\frac{1}{\sqrt{2\pi}} \int_{0}^{z_1} e^{-\frac{1}{2}z^2} dz = 0.475$$

is $\qquad\qquad\qquad\qquad z_1 = 1.96.$

Thus, $\qquad\qquad\quad \dfrac{a}{2} = 1.96,$ and $a = 3.92.$

Thus 95% of the time an experimental result between $3 - 3.92$ and $3 + 3.92$

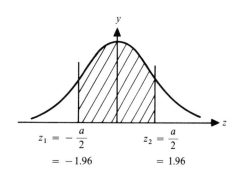

FIG. 6-19.   Normal Curve Area Enclosing
95% of the Total Area

or between -0.92 and 6.92 can be expected. We note that approximately 95% of all outcomes occur between $\mu - 2\sigma$ and $\mu + 2\sigma$.

6-4   Exercises

(1-10)   Using the normal curve area tables evaluate each of the following integrals.

1. $\dfrac{1}{\sigma\sqrt{2\pi}} \displaystyle\int_3^7 e^{-\frac{1}{2}\left(\frac{x-\mu}{\sigma}\right)^2} dx$, if $\mu = 3$ and $\sigma = 2$

2. $\dfrac{1}{2\sqrt{2\pi}} \displaystyle\int_{-2}^3 e^{-\frac{1}{2}\left(\frac{x-3}{2}\right)^2} dx$

3. $\dfrac{1}{\sqrt{2\pi}} \displaystyle\int_{-3}^{-1} e^{-\frac{1}{2}\left(\frac{x+1}{1}\right)^2} dx$

4. $\dfrac{1}{\sqrt{2\pi}} \displaystyle\int_{-1}^{3.2} e^{\frac{-(x+1)^2}{2}} dx$

5. $\dfrac{1}{2\sqrt{2\pi}} \displaystyle\int_1^4 e^{-\frac{1}{2}\left(1-\frac{x}{2}\right)^2} dx$

6. $\dfrac{1}{4\sqrt{2\pi}} \displaystyle\int_2^{5.1} e^{-\frac{x^2}{16}\left(\frac{1}{2}\right)} dx$

7. $\dfrac{1}{\sigma\sqrt{2\pi}} \displaystyle\int_{-1.1}^{2.2} e^{-\frac{x^2}{2\sigma^2}} dx$ if $\sigma = 1.1$

8. $\dfrac{1}{(2.1)\sqrt{2\pi}} \displaystyle\int_{-2}^{2.1} e^{-\frac{x^2}{2(2.1)^2}} dx$

9. $\dfrac{1}{\sqrt{2\pi}} \displaystyle\int_1^\infty e^{-\frac{1}{2}\left(\frac{x+1}{1}\right)^2} dx$

10. $\dfrac{1}{\sqrt{2\pi}} \displaystyle\int_2^\infty e^{\frac{-(x-1)^2}{2}} dx$

(11-15)   Normal curve probabilities can be used to approximately evaluate probabilities that are not normally distributed. For example if n honest coins are tossed the resulting distribution of heads is approximately normally distributed with $\mu = n(\frac{1}{2}) = \dfrac{n}{2}$ and $\sigma = \sqrt{n(\frac{1}{4})} = \dfrac{\sqrt{n}}{2}$. Assume that in an experiment 400 coins are tossed. Then the probability of getting between

190 and 210 heads is approximately

$$\frac{1}{\sigma\sqrt{2\pi}} \int_{189.5}^{210.5} e^{-\frac{1}{2}\left(\frac{x-\mu}{\sigma}\right)^2} dx,$$

but $\dfrac{n}{2} = 200$ and $\dfrac{\sqrt{n}}{2} = \dfrac{20}{2} = 10.$

Therefore, $P = \dfrac{1}{10\sqrt{2\pi}} \displaystyle\int_{189.5}^{210.5} e^{-\frac{1}{2}\left(\frac{x-200}{10}\right)^2} dx,$

which can be evaluated using a normal curve numerical table.

11.   Evaluate this integral. Why were the limits 189.5 and 210.5 used?

(12-15)   Using the normal integral find, relative to the described experiment:

12.   The probability of more than 210 heads.

13.   The probability of fewer than 205 heads.

14.   The probability of between 205 and 210 heads.

15.   The probability of not fewer than 180 heads and not more than 201 heads.

(16-21)   Using the normal curve values determine a value of x_1 so that each of the integrals has the value indicated if possible.

16.   a) $\dfrac{1}{\sqrt{2\pi}} \displaystyle\int_{0}^{x_1} e^{-\frac{1}{2}x^2} dx = 0.37$

b) $\dfrac{1}{\sqrt{2\pi}} \displaystyle\int_{x_1}^{0} e^{-\frac{1}{2}x^2} dx = 0.46$

17.   a) $\dfrac{1}{\sqrt{2\pi}} \displaystyle\int_{0}^{x_1} e^{-\frac{1}{2}x^2} dx = 0.425$

b) $\dfrac{1}{\sqrt{2\pi}} \displaystyle\int_{x_1}^{0} e^{-\frac{1}{2}x^2} dx = 0.321$

18.   a) $\dfrac{1}{\sqrt{2\pi}} \displaystyle\int_{-\infty}^{x_1} e^{-\frac{1}{2}x^2} dx = 0.75$

b) $\dfrac{1}{\sqrt{2\pi}} \displaystyle\int_{x_1}^{\infty} e^{-\frac{1}{2}x^2} dx = 0.60$

19.   a) $\dfrac{1}{\sqrt{2\pi}} \displaystyle\int_{-x_1}^{x_1} e^{-\frac{1}{2}x^2} dx = 0.60$

b) $\dfrac{1}{\sqrt{2\pi}} \displaystyle\int_{-x_1}^{x_1} e^{-\frac{1}{2}x^2}\, dx = 0.50$

20. a) $\dfrac{1}{3\sqrt{2\pi}} \displaystyle\int_{2}^{x_1} e^{-\frac{1}{2}\left(\frac{x-2}{3}\right)^2}\, dx = 0.40$

b) $\dfrac{1}{3\sqrt{2\pi}} \displaystyle\int_{-1}^{x_1} e^{-\frac{1}{2}\left(\frac{x+1}{3}\right)^2}\, dx = 0.25$

21. a) $\dfrac{1}{\sqrt{2\pi}} \displaystyle\int_{0}^{x_1} e^{-\frac{1}{2}x^2}\, dx = 0.61$

b) $\dfrac{1}{\sqrt{2\pi}} \displaystyle\int_{-x_1}^{\infty} e^{-\frac{1}{2}x^2}\, dx = 1.2$

6-5   APPLICATIONS TO CAPITAL AND PRESENT VALUE

Many models of economic problems can be constructed using the concepts of calculus. For example, suppose that one wishes to determine the total amount of revenue or profit from a certain source over a period of time. Further, suppose that a function, $f(t)$, gives the flow of revenue as a function of time, t, in years.

That is, $f(t)$ gives the amount of revenue which is being received at any specified time. Normally, $f(t)$ would be expected to be a discontinuous function, since income usually comes in lump sums, for example on payday, rather than a steady continuous stream. For the purpose of analysis let us assume that $f(t)$ is continuous.

Now, if the period of time involved is t' years the total revenue would be approximated by

$$R \approx \sum_{i=1}^{n} f(t_i)\Delta t_i,$$

where $0 \le t_1 \le t_2 \le t_3 \ldots \le t_n = t'.$

$\Delta t_i = t_i - t_{i-1}$ and the revenue on each subinterval is approximated by $f(t_i)\Delta t_i$. If we take a limiting case, as n tends to ∞ and $|\Delta t_i|$ tends to zero for each subinterval

$$R = \lim_{\substack{n \to \infty \\ |\Delta t_i| \to 0}} \sum_{i=1}^{n} f(t_i)\Delta t_i.$$

The total revenue, R, fits the limit definition of an integral. Thus,

$$R = \int_0^{t'} f(t)\,dt.$$

Example.   Suppose that the revenue in dollars from a certain source is known to be given by

$$f(t) = (t + 1)^{-\frac{3}{2}}(3{,}000),$$

where t is given in years. What is the total revenue expected from this source over the next 18 months?

Solution.   The revenue is given by

$$\int_0^{3/2} 3{,}000(t + 1)^{-\frac{3}{2}}\,dt = 3{,}000(-2)(t + 1)^{-\frac{1}{2}}\Big]_0^{3/2}$$

$$= -6{,}000\left[\left(\frac{3}{2} + 1\right)^{-\frac{1}{2}} - (1)^{-\frac{1}{2}}\right]$$

$$= -6{,}000\left[\left(\frac{5}{2}\right)^{-\frac{1}{2}} - 1\right]$$

$$= -6{,}000\left[\left(\frac{2}{5}\right)^{+\frac{1}{2}} - 1\right]$$

$$= 6{,}000\left[1 - \sqrt{\frac{2}{5}}\right] \text{ dollars.}$$

This type of problem leads in turn to a problem of a more complex nature. Suppose that a businessman knows that he will need a certain sum of money at some later point in time. He then might ask how much he would have to invest today at a fixed interest rate in order to have this required amount at the later date. We need not consider the actual amount, but rather ask how much he would have to invest now to have $1 at the later point in time. Suppose he invested $1 at a rate r per year. We need only consider the $1 figure, as any other dollar amount can be found by multiplying the $1 figure by the actual amount. For example, if $1 yields $1.05 then $7,300 yields $7,300(1.05) = $7,525.

At the end of one year he would have $(1 + r)$ dollars. In two years he would have

$$(1 + r) + (1 + r)r = (1 + r)(1 + r) = (1 + r)^2$$

dollars, and so forth. In general he would have $(1 + r)^t$ dollars if his interest were compounded yearly.

If the amount were compounded n times per year the one dollar would become

$$\left(1 + \frac{r}{n}\right)^{tn} \text{ dollars} = \left(1 + \frac{r}{n}\right)^{(n/r)(tr)} = \left\{\left[1 + \frac{r}{n}\right]^{n/r}\right\}^{tr}$$

Now consider what happens as n tends to infinity, $i.e.$, the number of times interest is compounded becomes large.

$$\lim_{n \to \infty} \left(1 + \frac{r}{n}\right)^{n/r} = \lim_{x \to 0} (1 + x)^{1/x} = e,$$

where $\dfrac{r}{n} = x$.

(This limit is sometimes used as a definition of e.) Thus,

$$\lim_{n \to \infty} \left(\left[1 + \frac{r}{n}\right]^{n/r}\right)^{tr} = e^{tr}.$$

One dollar today becomes e^{tr} dollars in t years at an interest rate r when interest is compounded continuously. However, the original problem was what amount a becomes 1 dollar in t years. Using the result for one dollar,

$$ae^{tr} = 1$$

$$\text{or } a = e^{-tr}.$$

In other words, the *present value* of 1 dollar, t years in the future is e^{-tr} dollars.

Example. How much would one have to invest at 6% interest in order to have 5,000 dollars in 30 months?

Solution. $t = \frac{5}{2}$ years

$$r = 0.06$$

Thus, $$5,000e^{-\frac{5}{2}(0.06)} = 5,000e^{-0.15}$$

$$= \frac{5,000}{e^{0.15}}$$

Using table III in the appendix to evaluate $e^{0.15}$,

$$\frac{5,000}{e^{0.15}} = \frac{5,000}{1.1618} = 4,303.67.$$

The ideas of present value and future revenue can be combined. That is, we can formulate an expression for the total present value or worth of future revenue. Consider the actual amount of a future revenue. Assuming that the amount of revenue is given by a function $f(t)$, the actual amount of revenue over a short period of time, Δt, would be $f(t)\Delta t$. The present value of this is $e^{-rt} f(t)\Delta t$ if the interest rate is r.

The total present value of this revenue over an interval of time from 0 to t' would be given by

$$\int_0^{t'} e^{-rt} f(t)dt.$$

This integral is called the *capital value* of the future income.

Example.   Consider a constant income of \$100 per month over a period covering the next 5 years. What is the capital value of this income if the interest rate is 5%?

Solution.   The capital value is given by

$$\int_0^{t'} e^{-rt} f(t)dt,$$

where $t' = 5, f(t) = $ \$100 per month or \$1,200 per year,

$$r = 0.05.$$

Therefore, we have

$$\int_0^5 e^{-0.05t} 1{,}200 \, dt = 1{,}200 \int_0^5 e^{-0.05t} \, dt$$

$$= 1{,}200 \left(\frac{e^{-0.05t}}{-0.05} \right) \Big]_0^5$$

$$= \frac{-1{,}200}{0.05} \left[e^{-0.25} - e^0 \right]$$

$$= 24{,}000 \left[1 - \frac{1}{e^{0.25}} \right]$$

$$= 24{,}000 \left[1 - \frac{1}{1.2840} \right]$$

$$= 24{,}000 \left[1 - 0.7788 \right]$$

$$= 24{,}000 \left[0.2212 \right]$$

$$= 5{,}308.80$$

Example.   Assuming a constant income of a dollars per year and an interest rate of r per year, what is the capital value of this income in the future?

Solution.   The capital value would be given by

$$\int_0^\infty e^{-rt} a \, dt,$$

∞ as an upper limit indicating on into the unlimited future.

$$\int_0^\infty e^{-rt} a \, dt = \lim_{b \to \infty} \int_0^b e^{-rt} a \, dt$$

$$= \lim_{b \to \infty} \frac{ae^{-rt}}{-r} \Big]_0^b$$

$$= \lim_{b \to \infty} \frac{a}{r} [1 - e^{-rb}]$$

$$= \lim_{b \to \infty} \frac{a}{r} \left[1 - \frac{1}{e^{rb}}\right] = \frac{a}{r}.$$

This result indicates that the present value of a constant income is inversely proportional to the interest rate.

6-5   Exercises

(1-6) For the given revenue function and the indicated number of years, find the expected total revenue.

1. $f(t) = (t + 1)^{-\frac{2}{3}}(2,000)$ for 3 years
2. $f(t) = (t^2 + 1)^{\frac{1}{2}}t(1,000)$ for 4 years
3. $f(t) = (t + 2)^2(500)$ for 2 years

4. $f(t) = \dfrac{1}{t + 1}(250)$ for 2.5 years

5. $f(t) = \dfrac{1}{t^2 + 5t + 6}(500)$ for 10 years

6. $f(t) = |\sin[(t + 2)\pi](1,000)|$ for 3 years

(7-10)   Assume interest is compounded continuously.

7. How much would one have to invest at 6% to have $4,000 in 24 months?
8. How much would one have to have invested at 3% 4 years ago to have $9,500 today?
9. How much would one have to have invested at 7% 3.5 years ago to have $102,000 today?
10. How much would one have to invest at 12.5% to have 1.5 million dollars in 3 years?

(11-20)   In each case a revenue function is given. Find the capital value of the indicated income at the time in the future with the given interest rate.

11. $f(t) = \$150/\text{month}$ for 3 years, the interest rate is 5%.

12. $f(t) = \$200/\text{month}$ for 4 years, the interest rate is 4%.

13. $f(t) = \$250/\text{month}$ for 5 years, the interest rate is 8%.

14. $f(t) = \$500/\text{year}$ for 10 years, the interest rate is 7%.

15. $f(t) = \$400t/\text{year}$ for 8 years, the interest rate is 4.5%.

16. $f(t) = e^{rt}(t^2 + 2)1,000$ dollars/year, the interest rate r is 2%, for 4 years.

17. $f(t) = e^{rt}(t^3)500$ dollars/year, the interest rate r is 5%, for 4 years.

18. $f(t) = e^{rt}(\ln(t + 1))1,500$ dollars/year, for 5 years if the interest rate r is 3.5%.

19. $f(t) = e^{rt}(\sin^2(\pi t))1,200$ dollars/year, for 6 years if the interest rate r is 6%.

20. $f(t) = e^{rt}\dfrac{1}{t + 1}\,2,000$ dollars/year, for 10 years if the interest rate r is 6%.

6-6 MARGINAL ANALYSIS

In one form, integration may be regarded as the recovery of a function when the derivative of the function is known. In many applications of calculus to business and economics this is the type of problem encountered. When considering the behavior of an economic function through its derivative, one is performing marginal analysis. For example, let $p = f(x)$ describe the price at which each unit of a commodity can be sold if x represents the number of units sold. p is called a demand function. The total revenue, R, produced by such sales would be $R = px = xf(x)$.

If R is the total revenue produced by the sale of x number of units, then the revenue from the sale of the ith unit sold is said to be the *marginal revenue*, and is defined as $\dfrac{dR}{dx}$, the first derivative of R with respect to x, evaluated at $x = i$.

Example.   If the revenue from the sale of some automotive parts is computed according to

$$R = \tfrac{1}{10}x^2 - 8x$$

then the total revenue from the sale of 100 units is $200, and the total revenue from the sale of 200 units is $2,400. The marginal revenue from the sale of the 120th unit is computed by

$$\frac{dR}{dx} = \frac{1}{5}x - 8, \text{ and } \frac{dR}{dx} = \$16 \text{ when } x = 120$$

whereas the marginal revenue of the 200th unit is $\frac{1}{5}(200) - 8 = \$32$, and the marginal revenue from the sale of the 5th unit is $\frac{1}{5}(5) - 8 = -\$7$, or a *loss* of seven dollars.

Example. Let the marginal revenue relative to the sales of a certain object be given by

$$\frac{dR}{dx} = 4x^2 - 3x + 2.$$

What is the total revenue produced by the sale of 5 of these items?

Solution. Since $\frac{dR}{dx} = 4x^2 - 3x + 2$,

$$dR = (4x^2 - 3x + 2)dx.$$

$$R = \int (4x^2 - 3x + 2)dx$$

$$= \frac{4x^3}{3} - \frac{3x^2}{2} + 2x + C.$$

However, clearly $R = 0$ if $x = 0$, thus

$$0 = \frac{4}{3}(0)^3 - \frac{3}{2}(0)^2 + 2(0) + C, \text{ and}$$

$$C = 0.$$

Then,

$$R - \frac{4x^3}{3} - \frac{3x^2}{2} \mid 2x.$$

If $x = 5$,

$$R = \frac{4}{3}(125) - \frac{3}{2}(25) + 2(5)$$

$$= \frac{500}{3} - \frac{75}{2} + 10$$

$$= \frac{1,000 - 225 + 60}{6}$$

$$= \frac{835}{6}.$$

Definition.   Let $y = f(x)$ describe the total cost of producing and selling x items of some commodity. Then $\dfrac{dy}{dx}$ or y' is the *marginal cost of producing* an item.

Example.   If the marginal cost of producing a certain item is

$$y' = 3 + x + \frac{e^{-x}}{4}$$

what is the cost of producing 1 item if there is a fixed cost of $4?

Solution.
$$y = \int y' \, dx = \int \left(3 + x + \frac{e^{-x}}{4} \right) dx$$

$$= 3x + \frac{x^2}{2} - \frac{e^{-x}}{4} + C.$$

Since the fixed cost is 4, when

$$x = 0, \; y = 4, \text{ hence}$$

$$y = 4 = 0 + \frac{0^2}{2} - \frac{1}{4} + C.$$

Thus
$$C = 4 + \frac{1}{4} = \frac{17}{4},$$

and

$$y = 3x + \frac{x^2}{2} - \frac{e^{-x}}{4} + \frac{17}{4}.$$

when $x = 1$,

$$y = 3 + \frac{1}{2} - \frac{1}{4e} + \frac{17}{4}$$

$$= \frac{12 + 2 + 17}{4} - \frac{1}{4e}$$

$$= \frac{31}{4} - \frac{1}{4e}$$

$$= \frac{31e - 1}{4e}.$$

Definition.   In a certain mathematical model of the economy, the total consumption, c, is described as a function of the total national income x. That is, $c = f(x)$. $\dfrac{dc}{dx}$ is called the *marginal propensity* *to consume.* If s stands for the total national amount in savings, then $s = g(x)$, *i.e.*, the total amount in savings is a function of total income. $\dfrac{ds}{dx}$ is called the *marginal propensity to save.*

If we assume that $x = c + s$, *i.e.*, that total income equals the income consumed plus the income saved, then

$$1 = \frac{dc}{dx} + \frac{ds}{dx}$$

or

$$\frac{dc}{dx} = 1 - \frac{ds}{dx}.$$

The total physical output of a number of workers or machines is a function of the number of workers or machines. If P is a measure of the output of x workers or machines, then

$$P = f(x).$$

Definition. $\dfrac{dP}{dx}$ is called the *marginal physical productivity.*

Example. Suppose that the marginal physical productivity for lumberjacks is given by

$$P' = (100 - 0.08x),$$

where P is in thousands of board feet per day. How many lumberjacks would be required to cut 1,000,000 board feet of lumber per day?

Solution. Since $\dfrac{dP}{dx} = (100 - 0.08x),$

$$dP = (100 - 0.08x)dx.$$

$$P = \int (100 - 0.08x)dx = 100x - 0.04x^2 + C.$$

However if $x = 0$, $P = 0$ (no workers, no production).

Thus, $$P = 100x - 0.04x^2.$$

The problem is to determine x when $P = 1,000$.

$$1,000 = 100x - 0.04x^2.$$

$$4x^2 - 10,000x + 100,000 = 0$$

$$x = \frac{10,000 \pm \sqrt{100,000,000 - 4(4)(100,000)}}{8}$$

$$= \frac{10,000 \pm \sqrt{98,400,000}}{8}$$

$$= \frac{10,000 \pm 9,919.6}{8}$$

$$= \frac{80.4}{8} \text{ or } \frac{19,919.6}{8}$$

$$= 10.05 \text{ or } 2,489.95.$$

Hence 11 lumberjacks would be required to assure 1,000,000 board feet of production; the 2,489.9 solution is valid, but, you must admit not practical.

In addition to the above examples, economists also consider such concepts as *marginal demand* for commodities, the *marginal rate of substitution*, the *marginal efficiency of investment*, and so forth. The basic approach in each case follows the pattern considered here. The marginal rate is the derivative in each case, and as such, has interpretations as indicated in earlier chapters. Perhaps the most important one relates to a single item. This means, for instance, that if $c = f(x)$ represents the total cost of producing and selling x items then $c' = \dfrac{df}{dx}$, the marginal cost, when evaluated for $x = 15$ represents the cost of producing and selling the 15th item.

6-6   Exercises

1. How does the analysis of marginal revenue relate to the total revenue found by integration in section 6-5?

(2-5)   For the given marginal revenue find the total revenue produced by the sales of the indicated number of items.

2. $R'(x) = 3x^2 - 6x + 8$, with $R = 0$ when $x = 0$. Find the total income from the sale of 10 items.

3. $R'(x) = \sin(\pi x) + 2$ with $R = 2$ when $x = 0$. Find the total income from the sale of 4 items.

4. $R'(x) = x\sqrt{x^2 + 2}$ with $R = 2$ when $x = 0$. Find the total income from the sale of 4 items.

5. $R'(x) = \dfrac{e^{-x}}{2} + 8x$ with $R = 1$ when $x = 0$. Find the total income from the sale of 8 items.

6. If the marginal propensity to consume as a function of income is given

    by $\dfrac{dc}{dx} = 4e^x + 2x$ find the analytic expression for consumption and

    savings as a function of income.

(7-10)   In each case below the marginal cost of producing an item is given, together with the fixed cost. Find the cost of producing the indicated number of items.

7. $y' = x + \dfrac{e^{-x}}{2}$, with a fixed cost of 7. The cost of producing 6 items.

8. $y' = x\sqrt{4 + 2x^2}$, with a fixed cost of 10. The cost of producing 4 items.

9. $y' = x^{\frac{1}{3}} - \dfrac{x^{\frac{1}{2}}}{2}$, with a fixed cost of 3. The cost of producing 10 items.

10. $y' = 4x^3 - 2x^2 + 2$, with a fixed cost of 10. The cost of producing 3 items.

(11-12)   If $C(x)$ defines the cost of producing x items, and $R(x)$ the revenue from the sale of the same x items, $R(x) - C(x)$ is an expression estimating the profit produced by the items. Under the indicated conditions find the profit generated by the indicated number of items.

11. $C'(x) = x^2 + 2$, $R'(x) = 2x + 4$ with $R(0) = 0$ and $C(0) = 4$. Find the profit in 2 items.

12. $R'(x) = -\frac{1}{2}x$ with $R(0) = 225$, $C'(x) = 4x$ with $C(0) = 0$. Find the profit in 10 items.

13. The marginal physical productivity for x lumberjacks is given by $P' = (23 - 0.06x)$, where P is in thousands of board feet per day. How many lumberjacks would be required to cut 2,000,000 board feet per day?

14. The marginal physical productivity for x used car salesmen is given by $P' = (2 - 0.1x)$ where P is in cars per day. A company wishes to sell 15 cars per day. How many salesmen should be used?

15. The marginal efficiency of investment is the derivative of the yield of investment with respect to the amount of investment. If the investment in farm equipment in thousands of dollars is given by x, and the yield

    in tons of sugar beets is y, with $y = f(x)$, then if $y' = \dfrac{4x^2}{100}$ find the

    yield for an investment of $75,000, if there is a yield of 2 tons with no actual cash investment.

6-7 SUPPLY AND DEMAND FUNCTIONS

One straightforward application of integration to find areas is related to the economic concepts of supply and demand, and the related concepts of a consumers' or producers' surplus. In a certain economic model, the price, y, at which a commodity sells is functionally related to the quantity, x, which can be sold at a given price. A sample of the type of relationship being considered is illustrated in the graph of figure 6-20. Notice that as smaller and smaller amounts of the items are demanded a higher and higher price can be expected, while as more and more of the item can be sold one would expect a lower price. The function involved is called the *demand function*.

In this model let us suppose that in actuality an amount $x = a$ is being sold at a price $b = f(a)$. Then on paper any consumer who would have been willing to pay a higher price for the item "saves" funds or has a surplus. The total surplus involved, considering the whole range of possible values involved, is called the *consumers' surplus*, and corresponds to the shaded area of figure 6-20. Here integration can be used to evaluate the surplus. The total area beneath the graph of $y = f(x)$, and above $y = 0$, between $x = 0$ and $x = a$ is given by

$$\int_0^a f(x)\,dx.$$

The shaded area, which corresponds to the consumers' surplus, is this area

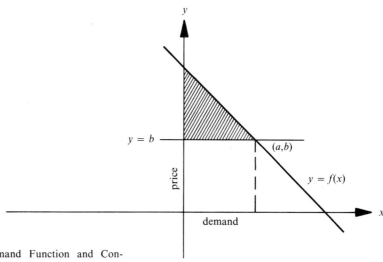

FIG. 6-20. Demand Function and Consumers' Surplus

minus the rectangular area bounded by $x = 0$, $x = a$, $y = 0$, and $y = b$. Hence the consumers' surplus, C, is given by

$$C = \int_0^a f(x)\,dx - ab.$$

Example. If the demand function is $y = 4 - x^2$ and there is 1 unit actually sold find the consumers' surplus C.

Solution. The problem is illustrated in figure 6-21. C is given by

$$C = \int_0^1 (4 - x^2)\,dx - 1(3)$$

$$= 4x - \frac{x^3}{3}\Big]_0^1 - 3$$

$$= 4 - \frac{1}{3} - 3 = \frac{2}{3}.$$

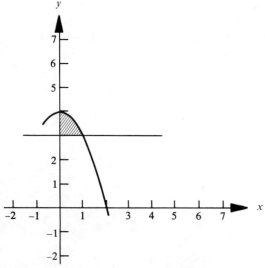

FIG. 6-21. Demand Function $y = 4 - x^2$

Example. If the demand function is given by $y = \sqrt{25 - x^2}$ find the consumers' surplus, C, if the actual selling price is $y = 3$.

Solution. If $y = 3$, then the corresponding number of items sold is given by

$$3 = \sqrt{25 - x^2}$$

$$9 = 25 - x^2$$

$$x^2 = 16$$

$$x = 4.$$

The problem is illustrated in figure 6-22.

$$C = \int_0^4 \sqrt{25 - x^2}\, dx - 4(3).$$

Using the integral tables,

$$\int_0^4 \sqrt{25 - x^2}\, dx = \frac{x}{2}\sqrt{25 - x^2} + \frac{25}{2}\sin^{-1}\left(\frac{x}{5}\right)\Big]_0^4$$

$$= 2\sqrt{25 - 16} + \frac{25}{2}\sin^{-1}\frac{4}{5}$$

$$= 6 + 12.5\sin^{-1}0.8$$

$$= 6 + 12.5(0.925) = 6 + 11.6 = 17.6.$$

Therefore,

$$C = 17.6 - 12 = 5.6.$$

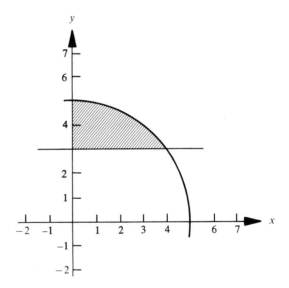

FIG. 6-22.   Demand Function
$y = \sqrt{25 - x^2}$

If we consider the producer of goods rather than the consumer we can develop the idea of a producers' surplus. Again, our two variables are price and quantity. This time, however, the quantity involved is the number of items that would be produced if they could be sold at a certain price. Here y represents price and x the number of items produced. The problem is illustrated in figure 6-23.

Notice that there is a minimum price which would be required before any items are produced, and as the price paid for items increases, so does the supply. A function used in this manner is called a *supply function*. Suppose that the actual price at which an item is being sold is b, with $b = f(a)$,

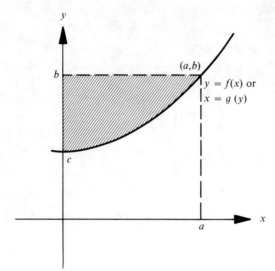

FIG. 6-23. Supply Function $y = f(x)$, Indicating Producers' Surplus

a the amount being sold. Then any manufacturer or supplier who had expected to supply the item at a lower price has, on paper, made a gain. Figure 6-23 demonstrates this gain by the shaded area below $y = b$ but above $y = f(x)$. The total of this gain is called the *producers' surplus*, and can be evaluated analytically by integration. P, the producers' surplus, is given by

$$P = a \cdot b - \int_0^a f(x)\,dx.$$

Example. Suppose that in figure 6-23 $y = f(x) = 4 + x^2$ with $a = 5$ and hence $b = 29$. Find the producers' surplus.

Solution. The producers' surplus P is given by

$$P = (29)(5) - \int_0^5 (4 + x^2)\,dx$$

$$= 145 - \left[\left(4x + \frac{x^3}{3} \right) \right]_0^5$$

$$= 145 - \left(20 + \frac{125}{3} \right)$$

$$= 125 - \frac{125}{3} = \frac{2(125)}{3} = \frac{250}{3}.$$

The functional relation being considered, the producers' surplus, can be evaluated by using integration with respect to y rather than x. If $y = f(x)$ can be solved for x as a function of y as in $x = g(y)$, then the producers' surplus is given by

$$P = \int_c^b g(y)\,dy, \text{ where } 0 = g(c).$$

Example.   Using $f(x) = 4 + x^2$, with $x = 5$ and $y = 29$ as the actual number of items involved and price as above evaluate the producers' surplus by finding $x = g(y)$.

Solution. $y = f(x) = 4 + x^2$, with the further restriction that $y \geq 4$. Hence,

$$y - 4 = x^2,$$

$$x = \sqrt{y - 4}, \text{ with } y \geq 4.$$

When $x = 0$, $y = 4$, hence the producers' surplus P is given by

$$P = \int_4^{29} \sqrt{y - 4}\,dy = \frac{2(y - 4)^{\frac{3}{2}}}{3} \Bigg]_4^{29}$$

$$= \frac{2(29 - 4)^{\frac{3}{2}}}{3} = \frac{2(25)^{\frac{3}{2}}}{3}$$

$$= \frac{2(5)^3}{3}$$

$$= \frac{2(125)}{3}$$

$$= \frac{250}{3}.$$

Under the assumption that the marketplace acts under pure competition, the actual price an item would reach would be determined when supply equals demand. If supply and demand were characterized by supply and demand functions, this would occur when these two functions yielded the same price.

Example.   Assume that in a market under pure competition the supply function for a certain item is given by $f(x) = 3x + 3$, while the demand function for the same item is given by $g(x) = 13 - x^2$. Determine the price at which the item would be sold and the consumers' and producers' surplus.

Solution.   The graphs of these supply and demand functions are shown in figure 6-24. The point of intersection, (a, b), can be found by setting $f(x)$ equal to $g(x)$.

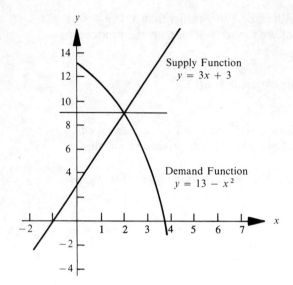

FIG. 6-24

$$3x + 3 = 13 - x^2$$

$$x^2 + 3x - 10 = 0$$

$$x = \frac{-3 \pm \sqrt{9 - 4(-10)(1)}}{2}$$

$$= \frac{-3 \pm \sqrt{49}}{2}$$

$$= \frac{-3 \pm 7}{2}$$

$$= -5 \text{ or } +2.$$

Realistically, $x = 2$ is the number of items sold, since it is hard to sell -5 items. The corresponding y value of price is $3(2) + 3 = 9$ units. Hence, the point (a,b) is $(2,9)$. The surpluses can then be found by integration. The producers' surplus P is given by

$$P = (2)(9) - \int_0^2 (3x + 3)\,dx$$

$$= 18 - \left[\frac{3x^2}{2} + 3x\right]_0^2$$

$$= 18 - [6 + 6]$$

$$= 18 - 12 = 6.$$

The consumers' surplus C is given by

$$C = \int_0^2 (13 - x^2)\,dx - (2)(9)$$

$$= 13x - \frac{x^3}{3}\Big]_0^2 - 18$$

$$= 26 - \frac{8}{3} - 18$$

$$= 8 - \frac{8}{3}$$

$$= \frac{16}{3}.$$

6-7   Exercises

1. Two integrals were given for finding the producers' surplus. One involved the supply function $y = f(x)$, and the other a function $x = g(y)$. Only one integral for the consumers' surplus was given in the first example. Find an integral for the consumers' surplus involving x as a function of y.

(2-7)   For the given demand functions find the consumers' surplus for the number of items or price given. Make a sketch in each case.

2. $f(x) = 9 - x^2$, number of items $= 2$
3. $f(x) = 64 - x^3$, number of items $= 3$
4. $f(x) = \sqrt{16 - x^2}$, number of items $= 2$
5. $f(x) = \sqrt{25 - x^2}$, number of items $= 4$
6. $f(x) = 10 - \frac{1}{2}x$, price $= 5$
7. $f(x) = 3e^{-x}$, number of items $= \ln 6$

(8-13)   For each of the given supply functions find the producers' surplus if the actual number of items is as given. Make a sketch in each case.

8. $f(x) = 1 + x^3$, number of items $= 4$
9. $f(x) = 2 + \ln(x + 1)$, number of items $= 4$
10. $f(x) = 3 + \sin x$, number of items $= \dfrac{\pi}{2}$
11. $f(x) = xe^x + 1$, number of items $= 3$
12. $f(x) = x^2 - 6x + 9$, number of items $= 6$
13. $f(x) = 4x + \cos x$, number of items $= 3$

(14-15) Evaluate the producers' surplus for each of the following by finding x as a function of y and integrating with respect to y.

14. $f(x) = \sin x$, number of items $= \dfrac{\pi}{4}$

15. $f(x) = e^x$, number of items $= \ln 3$

(16-20) In each case $f(x)$ gives the demand function and $g(x)$ gives the supply function. Assume that the market functions under pure competition and find the producers' and consumers' surplus and the price at which the items would be sold.

16. $f(x) = 14 - x^2$
    $g(x) = 4x + 2$
17. $f(x) = 10 - x^2$
    $g(x) = 8x + 1$
18. $f(x) = 27 - x^{\frac{3}{2}}$
    $g(x) = 2x + 7$
19. $f(x) = 4 - \sqrt{x}$
    $g(x) = \sqrt{x} + 2$
20. $f(x) = 8e^{-x}$
    $g(x) = 2e^x$

6-8 NATURAL GROWTH AND DECAY

Many real-world problems involving population density or mathematically similar ideas lead to problems involving integration.

Example. By definition radioactive substances are those elements that naturally break down into other elements, releasing energy as they do. The rate at which such a substance decays is proportional to the mass of the material present. If A is the amount present then $\dfrac{dA}{dt} = -kA$, where k is positive and constant. Hence,

$$\frac{dA}{A} = -kdt.$$

$$\int \frac{dA}{A} = \int -kdt.$$

$$\ln A = -kt + C.$$

$$A = e^{-kt+C} = e^C e^{-kt}.$$

Letting
$$e^C = A_0,$$

$$A = A_0 e^{-kt}.$$

Notice that when $t = 0$, $A = A_0$, hence A_0 is the amount of substance present when $t = 0$.

> **Definition.**   The *half-life*, t_h, of a radioactive substance is the time necessary for a given amount of the substance to decay to one-half of the original amount.

Example.   Since $A = A_0 e^{-kt}$ what is the relationship between the half-life t_h of a substance and the constant k?

Solution.   By definition when $t = t_h$, $A = \frac{1}{2}A_0$. Thus,

$$\tfrac{1}{2}A_0 = A_0 e^{-kt_h}$$

$$\tfrac{1}{2} = e^{-kt_h}$$

$$\ln\left(\tfrac{1}{2}\right) = -kt_h$$

$$-\ln 2 = -kt_h$$

$$kt_h = \ln 2$$

or

$$t_h = \frac{\ln 2}{k}$$

or

$$k = \frac{\ln 2}{t_h}.$$

Example.   The half-life of radium is 1,590 years. Find the equation describing the amount of radium present as a function of time. Then determine how long it would take a given sample of radium to decay to $\frac{1}{6}$ of its present amount.

Solution. $t_h = 1,590$, hence

$$k = \frac{\ln 2}{1,590}.$$

Thus,

$$A = A_0 e^{\frac{-\ln 2}{1,590} t}.$$

Find the time necessary for A to equal $\dfrac{A_0}{6}$.

$$\frac{A_0}{6} = A_0 e^{\frac{-\ln 2}{1,590}t}$$

$$\frac{1}{6} = e^{\left(\frac{-\ln 2}{1,590}\right)t}$$

$$\ln \frac{1}{6} = \frac{-\ln 2}{1,590}t$$

$$-\ln 6 = \frac{-\ln 2}{1,590}t$$

$$t = \frac{1,590(\ln 6)}{\ln 2} = \frac{1,590(1.792)}{0.693}$$

$$= 4,110 \text{ years.}$$

One of the most useful applications for the social or biological scientist of the equations describing radioactive decay is the application of these equations to radioactive dating of materials. While many radioactive substances are used in this process, the most common is C^{14}, carbon 14, a radioactive isotope of carbon. C^{14} is produced through the action of cosmic rays striking the nitrogen in the earth's upper atmosphere. For many centuries, thousands in fact, the amount of C^{14} manufactured has exactly balanced the amount lost through radioactive decay, so that the amount present in the atmosphere remains constant. Living things—plants and animals—constantly replace the carbon in their bodies, so that the amount of C^{14} present in a living organism matches that normally found in the atmosphere. When a living organism dies this replacement process stops, and no new C^{14} is introduced into the cell structure of the organism. By measuring the amount of C^{14} remaining in an organic specimen, the date of its death can be determined.

Example.   Since the half-life of C^{14} is 5,570 years, how old is an organic object if it has $\frac{1}{10}$ of the normal amount of C^{14} present?

Solution.   Since C^{14} is a radioactive substance it obeys the radioactive decay principle described by the equation

$$A = A_0 e^{-kt} \text{ where}$$

$$k = \frac{\ln 2}{t_h} = \frac{\ln 2}{5,570}.$$

The problem is to find t such that

$$A = \frac{1}{10} A_0$$

$$\frac{A_0}{10} = A_0 e^{\frac{-\ln 2}{5,570} t}$$

$$\frac{1}{10} = e^{\frac{-\ln 2}{5,570} t}$$

$$\ln \frac{1}{10} = \frac{-\ln 2}{5,570} t$$

$$-\ln(10) = \frac{-\ln 2}{5,570} t$$

$$t = \frac{5,570 \ln 10}{\ln 2} = \frac{5,570(2.303)}{0.693}$$

$$= 18,510 \text{ years.}$$

The same mathematical model used in radioactive decay applies to unlimited population growth.

Example.   If the population of the earth was 3.5 billion in 1970, and is increasing at a rate of 2% per year, when will a population of 50 billion be reached?

Solution.   If P is the population, then

$$\frac{dP}{dt} = kP = 0.02P$$

$$\frac{dP}{P} = 0.02 \, dt$$

$$\int \frac{dP}{P} = \int 0.02 \, dt$$

$$\ln P = 0.02t + C$$

$$P = e^{0.02t + C} = e^C e^{0.02t}$$

$$P = P_0 e^{0.02t} \quad (P_0 \text{ is the population when } t = 0).$$

Since we are measuring time from 1970, $P_0 = 3.5$ (in billions). Hence,

$$P = 3.5 e^{0.02t}.$$

Setting $P = 50$ billion,

$$50 = 3.5e^{0.02t}$$

$$e^{0.02t} = \frac{50}{3.5}$$

$$0.02t = \ln\frac{50}{3.5}$$

$$t = \frac{\ln\dfrac{50}{3.5}}{0.02}$$

$$= \frac{\ln 50 - \ln(3.5)}{0.02}$$

$$= \frac{3.91 - 1.25}{0.02}$$

$$= 133 \text{ years.}$$

Hence the population will reach 50 billion in 1970 + 133 years or 2103 A.D.

More complex models of growth and decay assume that the rate of growth also depends on a limiting factor. For example, in a closed growth system the rate of growth slows down as the total population reaches some limiting factor.

Example. Assume that the earth cannot support a population greater than 20 billion persons, and that the rate of population growth is proportional to how close the world population is to this limiting value. What is the mathematical expression describing the world population as a function of time?
Solution. If P is the world population then according to the described model $\frac{dP}{dt} = k(P - 20)$, where k is negative to make $\frac{dP}{dt}$ positive, since P must be less than 20 billion.
Then,

$$\frac{dP}{P - 20} = kdt$$

$$\int \frac{dP}{P - 20} = \int kdt$$

$$\ln|P - 20| = kt + C$$

$$|P - 20| = e^{kt + C} = e^C e^{kt}.$$

Let $e^C = B$, then

$$|P - 20| = Be^{kt}.$$

However, $|P - 20| = -(P - 20)$, since P is assumed less than 20 billion. Thus,

$$-(P - 20) = Be^{kt}$$

$$P - 20 = -Be^{kt}$$

$$P = 20 - Be^{kt},$$

where B is positive and k is negative.

What does B represent? Let us assume that $P = 3.5$ billion in 1970. If we call $t = 0$ in 1970,

$$3.5 = 20 - Be^{k \cdot 0}$$

$$3.5 = 20 - B$$

$$B = 16.5$$

B is the difference between the world population at $t = 0$ and the 20-billion limit.

The equations developed in this section have many interpretations other than those given. For example, the same equations describe radioactive decay and unlimited population growth. The equation developed above for limited population growth describes investment amounts when a company wishes to invest toward a certain total investment and the rate of investment is proportional to how close the total investment is to the desired limit. Several other similar mathematical models are considered in the exercises.

6-8   Exercises

1. A 20-gram sample of radium with a half-life of 1,590 years is refined and stored for future use. How much radium will remain at the end of 15.9 years? How much will remain at the end of 15,900 years? How much will remain at the end of 159,000 years?

2. An organic sample is found to have $\frac{1}{5}$ of the normal amount of C^{14}. How old is it? The half-life of C^{14} is 5,570 years.

3. An organic sample is found to have 0.01% of the normal amount of C^{14}. How old is it?

4. Carbon 14 dating is said to be accurate only over a period of about 70,000 years. What factors contribute to this limitation?

5. A radioactive isotope of potassium is also used for dating. This isotope

of potassium has a half-life of approximately 1,300,000,000. If a sample containing this isotope is found to have $\frac{2}{3}$ of the original amount of radioactive potassium, how old is it?

6. Referring to the potassium isotope of exercise 5, a sample is found to have $\frac{1}{5}$ of the original amount of radioactive potassium. How old is the sample?

(7-9)   Assume that the population of the earth was 3.5 billion in 1970 and population growth is unlimited.

7. If the earth's population is growing at the rate of 2% per year, when will a population of 60 billion be reached?

8. If the earth's population has been growing at a rate of 2% per year, estimate the world population in 1900, 1800, and 1500.

9. If India's population was 600 million in 1970 and was growing at a 5% annual rate, and China's population was 750 million and growing at an annual rate of 4%, when will the population of the two be equal? Why is this model of population unrealistic?

(10-12)   Assume, as in the example, the world cannot support a population of more than 20 billion. If in the analysis $k = -0.02$ and in 1970 the world's population was 3.5 billion then:

10. When will the world population reach 10 billion?

11. When will the world population reach 19 billion?

12. Show that after suitable values of P_0 and k have been found that $\lim_{t \to \infty} P = 20$.

13. Suppose that the rate of bacteria growth in a culture is proportional to the bacteria present. If in the first hour of growth the culture grows to $1\frac{1}{2}$ times its original amount, how long will it take to double the original amount?

14. If the culture in problem 13 grows at a rate such that it doubles the original amount in 2 days, how long would it take to triple the original amount?

15. Assume a bacteria culture growing in such a way that it doubles the original amount in t days. Discuss the parallels between this number t and the half-life of a radioactive substance.

16. Some scientists discover a new radioactive substance. They discover that their 1 gram sample is decaying at a rate of 0.004 grams per day. What is the half-life of this substance?

(17-19)   Assume that the world population follows a pattern of inhibited growth where the population P is such that

$$\frac{dP}{dt} = kP(20 - P) \text{ where } P \text{ is in billions.}$$

17. Show that $P = \dfrac{20P_0}{P_0 + (20 - P_0)e^{-20kt}}$ satisfies this equation if P_0 is the population when $t = 0$.

18. Using the result of problem 17 and $k = 0.02$, determine when the world population will reach 15 billion if the population in 1970 is 3.5 billion.

19. According to the results of problem 17, $k = 0.02$, and $P_0 = 3.5$ billion, when will the world's population reach 20 billion?

6-9   VOLUMES

Integration can be used to find volumes as well as areas. Consider a solid as shown in figure 6-25. Assume that along an axis through the solid the cross-section area perpendicular to the axis at each point on the axis is known. The volume can be estimated by dividing up the portion of the axis within the solid. Let the points along the axis be identified by values of x, and $A(x)$ give the cross-section area perpendicular to the axis at each point on the axis from $x = a$ through $x = b$, the limiting values of x within the solid. Let ΔV represent the volume between $x = x_1$ and $x = x_1 + \Delta x$. Then ΔV is approximately $A(x_1)\Delta x$. V, the total volume, is then estimated by

$$V = \sum_{i=1}^{n} A(x_i)\Delta x.$$

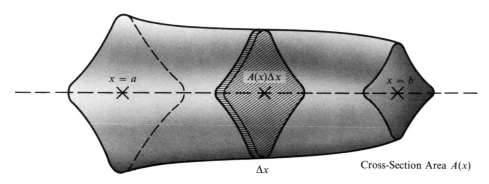

FIG. 6-25.   Volume by Slicing

Letting the divisions becomes finer and finer, *i.e.*, finding the limit of the indicated sum as the values of Δx tend toward zero,

$$V = \lim_{\Delta x \to 0} \sum_{\substack{\text{over} \\ \text{division}}} A(x_i)\Delta x = \int_a^b A(x)dx.$$

Example. Find the volume of a solid formed by connecting one corner of a cube to the four opposite corners of the cube. Assume that the cube is 8 inches on an edge. The volume is shown in figure 6-26(a).

Solution. As a first step it will be necessary to find an expression for the cross-sectional area as a function of position. The cross-sectional area is a square whose side can be determined by using similar triangles. Figure 6-26(b) illustrates the triangles, and

$$\frac{x}{8} = \frac{y}{8}.$$

Hence, $x = y.$

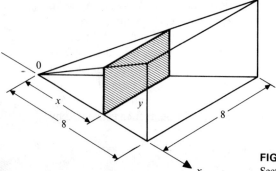

FIG. 6-26. (a) Volume of Known Cross Section Area

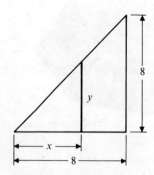

(b) Similar Triangles

The cross-sectional area is given by $A(x) = x^2$. The volume is

$$\int_0^8 x^2 \, dx = \frac{x^3}{3}\Bigg]_0^8$$

$$= \frac{8^3}{3} = \frac{512}{3}.$$

A large family of problems applying this idea can be solved relative to the concept of a solid of revolution. Consider the area bounded by $y = f(x)$, $x = a$, $x = b$, and $y = 0$ where $f(x) \geq 0$ for all x such that $a \leq x \leq b$. Such an area is shown in figure 6-27. If this area is revolved about the x axis the resulting solid is called a *solid of revolution*. Due to the manner in which the solid has been generated, cross-sectional areas taken perpendicular to the x axis are clearly circles of radius $f(x)$. Hence the cross-sectional area as a function of x is given by

$$A(x) = \pi[f(x)]^2.$$

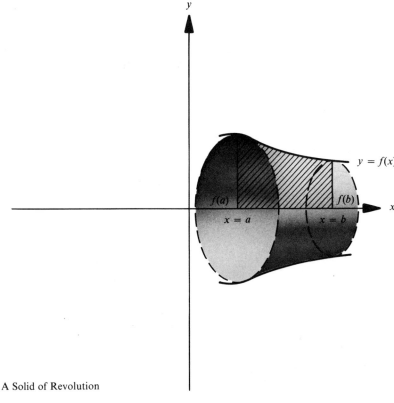

FIG. 6-27.   A Solid of Revolution

The volume is

$$V = \int_a^b A(x)dx = \int_a^b \pi[f(x)]^2 \, dx.$$

Example. Find the volume generated when the graph of $y = \sin x$ between $x = 0$ and $x = \dfrac{\pi}{2}$ is revolved around the x axis.

Solution.

$$V = \int_0^{\pi/2} \pi[\sin x]^2 \, dx$$

$$= \pi \int_0^{\pi/2} \frac{1 - \cos 2x}{2} \, dx$$

$$= \pi \left[\frac{x}{2} - \frac{\sin 2x}{4} \right]_0^{\pi/2}$$

$$= \pi \left[\frac{\pi}{4} - \frac{\sin \pi}{4} - \left(0 - \frac{\sin 0}{4} \right) \right]$$

$$= \frac{\pi^2}{4} \text{ cubic units.}$$

Sometimes the volume integral involves an improper integral. This in turn can lead to paradoxes involving infinity.

Example. The area bounded by $y = 0$, $y = \dfrac{1}{x^{\frac{2}{3}}}$, and $x = 1$ is revolved about the x axis, figure 6-28. Find the volume thus generated.

Solution. From above

$$V = \int_1^\infty \pi \left(\frac{1}{x^{\frac{2}{3}}} \right)^2 \, dx$$

$$= \pi \lim_{b \to \infty} \int_1^b \frac{1}{[x^{\frac{4}{3}}]} \, dx$$

$$= \pi \lim_{b \to \infty} \left. -3x^{-\frac{1}{3}} \right]_1^b$$

$$= \pi \lim_{b \to \infty} \left[\frac{-3}{b^{\frac{1}{3}}} + 3 \right]$$

$$= 3\pi.$$

The volume is 3π cubic units.

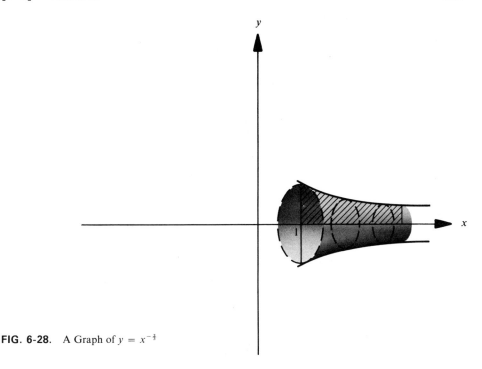

FIG. 6-28.   A Graph of $y = x^{-\frac{2}{3}}$

The paradox arises when we consider the size of the area that was revolved. The area in question is shown in figure 6-28. Integrating to find the area one gets

$$A = \int_1^\infty \frac{1}{x^{\frac{2}{3}}} \, dx.$$

$$= \lim_{b \to \infty} \int_1^b \frac{1}{x^{\frac{2}{3}}} \, dx$$

$$= \lim_{b \to \infty} \left[3x^{\frac{1}{3}} \right]_1^b$$

$$= \lim_{b \to \infty} \left[3b^{\frac{1}{3}} - 3 \right]$$

$$= \infty, \; i.e., \text{ is undefined.}$$

In short, the volume is finite, but the cross-sectional area is infinite!

Example.   The region bounded by $y = x^2$ and $y = \sqrt{x}$ between $x = 1$ and $x = 2$ is revolved around the x axis. Find the volume generated. The region is shown in figure 6-29.
Solution.   The volume in question can be found by taking the difference in

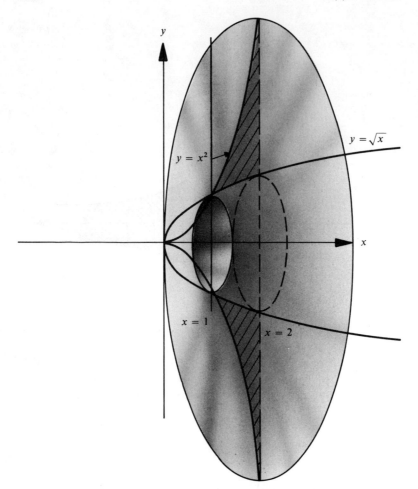

FIG. 6-29. Volume Formed by Revolving the Shaded Region Bounded by $y = \sqrt{x}$, $y = x^2$, $x = 1$, and $x = 2$ Around the x Axis

volumes generated when $y = x^2$ and $y = \sqrt{x}$ are revolved separately.

$$V = \int_1^2 \pi [x^2]^2 \, dx - \int_1^2 \pi [\sqrt{x}]^2 \, dx$$

$$= \pi \left\{ \int_1^2 x^4 \, dx - \int_1^2 x \, dx \right\}$$

$$= \pi \left\{ \frac{x^5}{5} \right]_1^2 - \frac{x^2}{2} \right]_1^2 \right\}$$

$$= \pi \left[\frac{32}{5} - \frac{1}{5} - 2 + \frac{1}{2} \right]$$

$$= \pi \left[\frac{31}{5} - \frac{3}{2} \right]$$

$$= \pi \left[\frac{62 - 15}{10} \right]$$

$$= \frac{47\pi}{10} \text{ cubic units.}$$

6-9   Exercises

(1-10)   In each case a function $A(x)$ giving the cross-sectional area of a solid perpendicular to the x axis over the indicated interval has been given. Find the volume.

1. $x = 0$ to $x = 1$, $A(x) = 3x^2$

2. $x = 0$ to $x = 1$, $A(x) = \dfrac{x^3}{(x^4 + 1)^3}$

3. $x = 2$ to $x = 5$, $A(x) = \dfrac{x - 1}{x + 1}$

4. $x = 1$ to $x = 3$, $A(x) = \left(2x - \dfrac{1}{2x} \right)^2$

5. $x = 1$ to ∞, $A(x) = \dfrac{1}{x\sqrt{x}}$

6. $x = 1$ to $x = e^3$, $A(x) = \dfrac{\ln x}{x}$

7. $x = \dfrac{\pi}{2}$ to $x = \dfrac{2\pi}{3}$, $A(x) = \dfrac{\sin x}{1 - \cos x}$

8. $x = 0$ to $x = \sqrt{\dfrac{\pi}{2}}$, $A(x) = x \sin 3x^2$

9. $x = 0$ to $x = \ln \dfrac{\pi}{4}$, $A(x) = e^x \sin e^x$

10. $x = 2\pi$ to $x = 4\pi$, $A(x) = |\sin x|$

(11-21) In each case the indicated area is to be revolved around the x axis. Find the volume generated. Sketch the area involved.

11. $y = \sqrt{x}$, $x = 0$, $x = 4$, $y = 0$

12. $y = \dfrac{1}{x + 1}$, $x = 0$, $x = 8$, $y = 0$

13. $x = 3$, $y = 0$, $y = x + 2$, $x = 0$

14. $x = y^2$, $x = 0$, $y = 2$

15. $x = 4y - y^2$, $x = 0$

16. $y^2 = x^3$, $x = 4$, $y = 0$

17. $y = 0$, $y = \cos x$ between $x = -\dfrac{\pi}{2}$ and $x = \dfrac{\pi}{2}$

18. $y = 0$, $x = 0$, $y = \dfrac{1}{(x + 1)^{\frac{3}{2}}}$ (*Hint*: graph extends to ∞.)

19. $y = 0$, $y = e^{-x}$, $x = 0$, $x = \ln 2$

20. $y = 0$, $y = \dfrac{1}{x}$, $x = 1$ (*Hint*: graph extends to ∞.)

21. $y = 0$, $y = e^{-x}$, $x = 0$

22. Find the area of the region described in exercise 18.

23. Find the area of the region described in exercise 20.

24. Find the area of the region described in exercise 21.

25. If, instead of y being a function of x, x was given as a function of y, find an integral which would be used to find the volume generated when the region bounded by $x = f(y)$, $x = 0$, $y = c$, and $y = d$ is revolved around the y axis.

(26-30) The method we have used can be generalized to find the volume generated when regions are revolved around lines other than the x axis. In these problems find the volume generated when the area is revolved about the specified line.

26. The region bounded by $y = 0$, $x = 4$, and $y = \sqrt{x}$ is revolved around the line $y = -1$.

27. The region bounded by $y = 0$, $x = 4$, and $y = \sqrt{x}$ is revolved around the line $y = 2$.

28. The region bounded by $y = 0$, $x = 1$, $x = 4$, and $y = \sqrt{x}$ is revolved around the line $y = 1$.

29. The region bounded by $y = 0$, $y = \sqrt{x}$, and $x = 4$ is revolved around the line $x = 4$.

30. The region bounded by $y = 0$, $y = \sqrt{x}$, $x = 1$, and $x = 4$ is revolved around the line $x = 0$.

Chapter 6 REVIEW

(1-8) In each case find the area bounded by the given graphs. Sketch the curves.

1. $y = x^2 + 4x + 4$, $x = 0$, $x = 3$, $y = 0$

2. $y = (\sqrt{x} - 4)^2$, $x = 1$, $x = 0$, $y = 0$

3. $y = -xe^{-x^2}$, $x = 0$, $x = \sqrt{\ln 3}$, $y = 0$

4. $y = \dfrac{1}{x} \ln x$, $x = 1$, $x = 2$, $y = 0$

5. $y = x + \sin x$, $y = x$, $x = 0$, $x = \dfrac{\pi}{6}$

6. $y = (x^2 + 3)$, $y = 2$, $x = 0$, $x = 1$

7. $y = \sin x$, $y = -x - 1$, $x = \dfrac{\pi}{4}$, $x = \dfrac{\pi}{2}$

8. $y = \tan^{-1}x$, $y = -e^x$, $x = 0$, $x = 1$

9. State the definition of a probability.

10. An alternate definition of the probability of an outcome of an experiment that can turn out in n ways, all of which are considered equally likely, is defined as the ratio of the number of these ways favorable to the outcome over n. Compare this definition with the fraction of the time definition used in the text.

11. Why is the area under a probability distribution curve chosen to be equal to 1?

(12-13) An experiment has outcomes which fall between -1 and 1 with a probability density function

$$P(x) = \frac{\pi}{4} \cos\left(\frac{\pi x}{2}\right).$$

12. Sketch the curve described by the $P(x)$ function and find the probability of an experimental outcome between 0 and $\frac{1}{2}$.

13. Find the probability of an experimental outcome between $-\frac{1}{3}$ and $+\frac{1}{6}$.

(14-15) An experiment has outcomes corresponding to the real numbers, with a probability density function given by

$$P(x) = \frac{1}{\pi} \frac{1}{x^2 + 1}.$$

14. What is the probability of an outcome corresponding to a real number greater than 1?

15. What is the probability of an outcome corresponding to a real number between $-\frac{1}{2}$ and $\frac{1}{3}$?

16. Consider the function $f(x) = \dfrac{2x^2}{(x^3 + 1)^2}$ on the interval from $0 \le x < \infty$. Find a related $P(x)$, probability distribution.

(17-18)   For the given probability density functions find μ and σ^2.

17. $P(x) = \frac{4}{3}x^{\frac{1}{3}}$ on the interval $0 \le x \le 1$.
18. $P(x) = \frac{3}{16}(x + 1)^2$ on the interval $-3 \le x \le 1$.

(19-22)   Find the indicated normal curve areas using the normal curve area tables.

19. $\dfrac{1}{3\sqrt{2\pi}} \displaystyle\int_{-4}^{4} e^{-\frac{1}{2}\left(\frac{x-1}{3}\right)^2} \, dx$

20. $\dfrac{1}{5\sqrt{2\pi}} \displaystyle\int_{0}^{3} e^{-\frac{1}{2}\left(\frac{x}{5}\right)^2} \, dx$

21. $\dfrac{1}{2\sqrt{2\pi}} \displaystyle\int_{0}^{3} e^{-\frac{1}{2}\left(\frac{x-1.5}{2}\right)^2} \, dx$

22. $\dfrac{1}{3\sqrt{2\pi}} \displaystyle\int_{3}^{\infty} e^{-\frac{1}{2}\left(\frac{x-3}{3}\right)^2} \, dx$

23. In an experiment involving tossing 10,000 coins what is the normal curve approximation of the probability of tossing more than 5,025 heads?

(24-25)   Determine a value for x_1 so that the given integral has the value indicated.

24. $\dfrac{1}{\sqrt{2\pi}} \displaystyle\int_{0}^{x_1} e^{-\frac{1}{2}x^2} \, dx = 0.41$

25. $\dfrac{1}{\sqrt{2\pi}} \displaystyle\int_{-x_1}^{x_1} e^{-\frac{1}{2}x^2} \, dx = 0.28$

(26-29)   For the given revenue function and the indicated number of years, find the expected total revenue.

26. $f(t) = \dfrac{1}{(t + 2)^2} (500)$ for 3 years

27. $f(t) = \dfrac{1}{t + 1} (1{,}000)$ for 4 years

28. $f(t) = \dfrac{1}{t^2 + 1} (1{,}500)$ for 6 years

29. $f(t) = \left[\dfrac{\sin(\pi t)}{\pi} + t \right] 100$ for 10 years

30. How much would one have to invest at 5.5% to have $120,000 five years in the future?

31. How much would have had to be invested at 2.5% four years ago to have $15,000 today?

(32-35)   In each case a revenue function is given. Find the capital value of the indicated income at the time in the future indicated at the given interest rate.

32. $f(t) = \$225$ per month, the interest rate is 6%, 4 years in the future.

33. $f(t) = \$400$ per month, the interest rate is 5%, 3 years in the future.

34. $f(t) = \$100t/\text{month}$, the interest rate is 3%, 10 years in the future.

35. $f(t) = e^{rt} \dfrac{1}{t + 1} (1{,}000)$ dollars/year for 5 years with an interest rate $r = 2\%$.

(36-39)   In each case below $f(x)$ gives a demand function and $g(x)$ gives a supply function for a certain item. Assume that the market for this item functions under pure competition and find the producers' and consumers' surplus and the price of the item.

36. $f(x) = 7 - x^2$
      $g(x) = x + 1$

37. $f(x) = 10e^{-x}$
      $g(x) = x + 5 - \ln 2$

38. $f(x) = \cos x + 2$
      $g(x) = \dfrac{2x}{\pi} + 1$

39. $f(x) = 100 - x^2$
      $g(x) = (x - 2)^2$

40. If the marginal revenue $R'(x) = x^2 + 2x$ for a certain item, with $R = 0$ when $x = 0$, find the total revenue produced from the sale of four items.

41. If the marginal revenue $R'(x) = \dfrac{e^{-x}}{4} + 8x$ with $R = 6$ when $x = 0$, find the total revenue from the sale of six items.

42. If the marginal cost of a certain item is $c'(x) = x + \dfrac{e^{-x}}{2}$, with a fixed cost of 3, find the cost of producing four items.

43. If the marginal cost of a certain item is $c'(x) = x^{\frac{1}{4}} - \dfrac{x^{\frac{1}{3}}}{2}$, with a fixed cost of 3, what is the cost of producing ten items?

44. The marginal physical productivity of pretzel makers is given by $P' = (102 - 0.4x)$, where P is in thousands of pretzels per day. How many workers would be required to produce 1,000,000 pretzels per day?

45. A 10-gram sample of radium with a half-life of 1,590 years is refined and stored. At some later time the sample is opened and found to contain 8 grams of radium. How long has the sample been stored?

46. The half-life of uranium, U_{235}, is 7.1×10^8 years. If 30 pounds of pure U_{235} are stored, how long would it require for this to decay to 22.8 pounds of U_{235}?

47. Assume that a population is unlimited and is growing at a rate of $k\%$ per year. If the population is 205 million in 1970 what value of k will lead to a population of 250 million by 2000?

(48-51) In each case a cross-sectional area function $A(x)$ is given for a certain volume. Find the volume over the indicated interval.

48. $A(x) = \dfrac{1}{x} - \dfrac{1}{x^2}$, $x = 1$ to $x = 4$

49. $A(x) = \ln x$, $x = e^2$ to $x = e^3$

50. $A(x) = x \sin(2x^2)$, $x = \sqrt{\dfrac{\pi}{2}}$ to $x = \sqrt{\dfrac{2\pi}{3}}$

51. $A(x) = \tan x$, $x = 0$ to $x = 1$

(52-55) In each case below the area bounded by the given graphs is revolved about the indicated line. Find the volume generated.

52. $x = 1, x = 4, y = 0$ and $y = \left(\sqrt{x} - \dfrac{1}{\sqrt{x}}\right)$ about the x axis.

53. $x = 1, x = 4, y = 0$ and $y = \left(\sqrt{x} - \dfrac{1}{\sqrt{x}} \right)$ about the line $y = -2$.

54. $x = 1, x = 2, y = e^x, y = 0$ about the x axis.

55. $x = 1, x = 2, y = e^x, y = 0$ about the y axis.

CHAPTER SEVEN Functions of

Several Variables

311

The mathematical models of real-life situations examined to this point have, of necessity, been of a very simple nature. When we have considered functional models, the dependent quantities involved have been viewed as functions of a single independent variable. In real life, any dependent quantity can be expected to depend on a number of independent factors. For example, the outcome of a partisan election in a certain precinct may depend on the party preference of the voters of the precinct, on the popularity of the candidate, and on the weather on election day. In business, the productivity of an individual worker is affected by his rate of work, the availability of the most effective tools for his use, and the availability of capital and land. The purpose of this chapter and the next is to extend the functional concept to such cases and to extend the ideas of a derivative and integral appropriately.

7-1 FUNCTIONS OF SEVERAL VARIABLES, LIMITS

The extension of the function concept to functions of several variables is straightforward enough. The three basic ingredients of a function—the domain, the range, and the function rule—remain, but the domain must be modified to allow two or more independent variables to be involved.

The actual details of such an extension can be carried out in steps: first, a specific extension to functions of two independent variables, and then a generalized extension to functions of n independent variables.

Definition. Let D be a set of ordered pairs of real numbers. Let f be a rule which pairs with each element of D a unique real number, and let S be the set of real numbers thus specified. Then D, S, and f form a function of two variables with D the domain of the function, S the range, and f the functional rule.

$f:(x,y) \to z$ will indicate that the image under the functional rule of the pair (x,y) is z. Usually, in place of z there will be the specific form of the association.

Example. Let $D = \{(x,y)|x^2 + y^2 \le 1\}$, and
$$f:(x,y) \to x^2 + y^2.$$
Calculate values of $f(x,y)$.
Solution. $S = \{z|0 \le z \le 1\}$.

Specifically,
$$f: (\tfrac{1}{2},\tfrac{1}{4}) \to (\tfrac{1}{2})^2 + (\tfrac{1}{4})^2 = \tfrac{1}{4} + \tfrac{1}{16} = \tfrac{5}{16},$$
$$f: (0, (-\tfrac{1}{3})) \to 0^2 + (-\tfrac{1}{3})^2 = \tfrac{1}{9},$$
$$f: (0,0) \to 0, \text{ etc.}$$

$f:(3,-2)$ is meaningless, since $(3,-2)$ is not in the domain of the function.

Example. Does $D = \{(x,y)|0 \le x \le 1, 0 \le y \le 1\}$, $f:(x,y) \to z$ such that $z^2 + x^2 + y^2 = 1$, and $S = \{z||z| \le 1\}$ define a function?
Solution. D, S, and f fail to define a function. Consider $f:(0,0) \to z$. $z^2 + 0^2 + 0^2 = 1$. Thus, z could be ± 1, and the images under f are not unique; hence no function has been defined.

As with a function of a single variable, the definition of a function is applied by convention to a more compact notational form. $z = f(x,y)$ will be used to indicate that the variable z is a real-valued function of two independent variables, x and y. The domain of the function is assumed to be the set of all ordered pairs (x,y) for which the expression is defined. The range of the function is the appropriate set of image values.

Example. $z = f(x,y) = \dfrac{\sqrt{4 - x^2}}{y + 2}$. Find the values of z for a few values of x and y.

Solution.   The domain of the function is

$$\{(x,y)|-2 \le x \le 2 \text{ and } y \ne -2\}.$$

The restriction on x is needed to ensure that $\sqrt{4 - x^2}$ is a real number, and that on y is necessary to exclude division by zero. The functional notation applies in the usual way.

$$f(1,3) = \frac{\sqrt{4 - 1^2}}{3 + 2} = \frac{\sqrt{3}}{5},$$

$$f(0,8) = \frac{\sqrt{4 - 0^2}}{8 + 2} = \frac{\sqrt{4}}{10} = \frac{2}{10} = \frac{1}{5},$$

$$f(2,7) = \frac{\sqrt{4 - 4}}{7 + 2} = 0,$$

$$f(2,12) = \frac{\sqrt{4 - 4}}{12 + 2} = 0, \text{ etc.}$$

$$f(w,r) = \frac{\sqrt{4 - w^2}}{r + 2},$$

$$f(x^2,y^3) = \frac{\sqrt{4 - (x^2)^2}}{y^3 + 2}, \text{ etc.}$$

Example. $z = f(x,y) = \sin\left(\dfrac{1}{x + y}\right)$. Find the values of z for particular

values of x and y.

Solution.   The domain of this function is $\{(x,y)|x \ne -y\}$. The range of this function is the range of the sine function, *i.e.*, $\{z|-1 \le z \le 1\}$.

$$f(0,1) = \sin\left(\frac{1}{0 + 1}\right) = \sin(1), \text{ approx. } 0.84$$

$$f\left(\frac{2}{\pi},0\right) = \sin\left(\frac{1}{\dfrac{2}{\pi} + 0}\right) = \sin\left(\frac{\pi}{2}\right) = 1$$

$$f(w,y) = \sin\left(\frac{1}{w + y}\right)$$

$$f(w^2 + 1,k) = \sin\left(\frac{1}{(w^2 + 1) + k}\right)$$

etc.

Since the domains of the functions being considered are sets of ordered pairs, it is natural to visualize these domains by finding their graphs in an xy plane.

Example. Graph the domain of the function

$$D = \{(x,y)|x^2 + y^2 \le 1\};$$
$$f:(x,y) \rightarrow x^2 + y^2.$$

Solution. This function becomes $z = f(x,y) = x^2 + y^2$ with $D = \{(x,y)|x^2 + y^2 \le 1\}$. The graph of D is shown in figure 7-1.

Example. Graph the domain of

$$z = f(x,y) = \frac{\sqrt{4 - x^2}}{y + 2}.$$

Solution. It is shown in figure 7-2.

Example. Graph the domain of

$$z = f(x,y) = \sin\left(\frac{1}{x + y}\right).$$

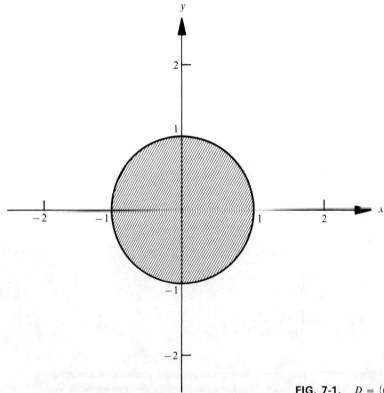

FIG. 7-1. $D = \{(x,y)|x^2 + y^2 \le 1\}$

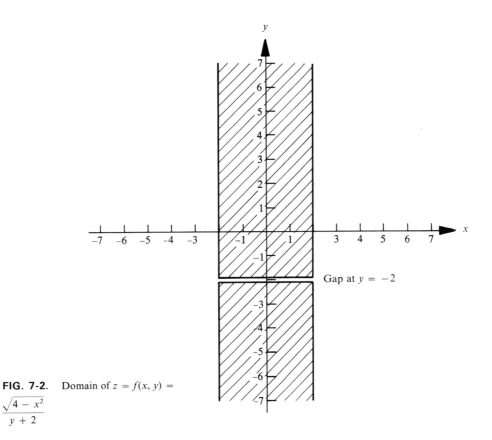

FIG. 7-2.   Domain of $z = f(x, y) =$
$$\frac{\sqrt{4 - x^2}}{y + 2}$$

Solution.   It is shown in figure 7-3.

Example.   Determine the domain and construct its graph for the function defined by $z = f(x, y) = \ln x$.
Solution.   Here, z is a function of two variables, yet the defining expression for z omits reference to y. In this case, the domain would be $\{(x, y) | 0 < x\}$, which does not restrict the value of y. Thus,

$$f(1, 7) = \ln 1 = 0$$
$$f(1, 3) = \ln 1 = 0$$
$$f(e, e) = \ln e = 1$$
$$f(e, 7) = \ln e = 1$$
$$f(e, y) = \ln e = 1$$

Still, it can be thought of as a function of y in the same way the constant

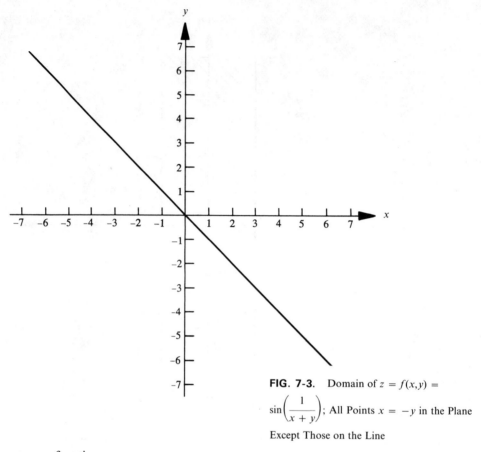

FIG. 7-3. Domain of $z = f(x,y) = \sin\left(\dfrac{1}{x+y}\right)$; All Points $x = -y$ in the Plane Except Those on the Line

function

$$f(x) = 3$$

is viewed as a function of x with

$$f(2) = 3$$
$$f(0) = 3$$

etc.

The graph of the domain of this function is the right half of an xy plane, and is shown in figure 7-4.

The concept of a limit extends to a function of two variables.

$$\lim_{(x,y) \to (x_0,y_0)} f(x,y) = L \text{ indicates}$$

that the value of $f(x,y)$ approaches (or is at) L as the point corresponding to (x,y) is taken nearer and nearer to (x_0,y_0).

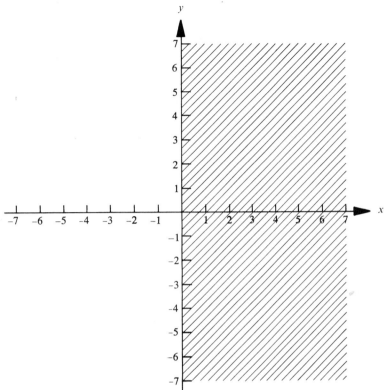

FIG. 7-4.   Domain of $f(x, y) = \ln x$, *i.e.*, $\{(x, y)|x > 0\}$

Example. $\displaystyle \lim_{(x,y) \to (0,0)} \frac{\sqrt{4 - x^2}}{y + 2} = 1.$

Example. $\displaystyle \lim_{(x,y) \to \left(\frac{4}{\pi},0\right)} \sin\left(\frac{1}{x + y}\right) = \frac{1}{\sqrt{2}} \left(i.e., \sin\left(\frac{\pi}{4}\right)\right)$

Example. $\displaystyle \lim_{(x,y) \to (0,0)} \sin\left(\frac{1}{x + y}\right)$ is not defined.

The examples above were found in an informal manner. In order to provide a formal definition for such limits it is necessary to assign a specific meaning to the terms "approaches" and "nearer" as used above. The quantity $|f(x,y) - L|$ would provide a measure of how close $f(x,y)$ is to L for a specific pair (x,y) but the question of how near (x,y) is to (x_0,y_0) and how this is to be measured is a more complex one. The distance formula would provide one measure of this. That is $\sqrt{(x - x_0)^2 + (y - y_0)^2}$ could be used. One could then say that $\lim\limits_{(x,y)\to(x_0,y_0)} f(x,y) = L$ provided that we can guarantee that $|f(x,y) - L|$ is as small as we want whenever $\sqrt{(x - x_0)^2 + (y - y_0)^2}$ is small enough, depending on exactly how small we want $|f(x,y) - L|$. However, while $\sqrt{(x - x_0)^2 + (y - y_0)^2}$ is a natural measure of how close (x,y) is to (x_0,y_0), it is mathematically easier to measure the closeness of (x,y) to (x_0,y_0) with two quantities, $|x - x_0|$ and $|y - y_0|$. The advantage of these measures lies in the fact that they can be considered separately. That is, the behavior of the function when x is fixed and $|y - y_0|$ becomes small, or y is fixed, and $|x - x_0|$ becomes small can be examined. Geometrically $\sqrt{(x - x_0)^2 + (y - y_0)^2}$ involves a circular area about the point (x_0,y_0) while $|x - x_0|$, $|y - y_0|$ relates to a rectangular region about (x_0,y_0).

Figure 7-5 illustrates the geometry. In terms of ϵ and δ from Chapter 1 the definition might take on two forms.

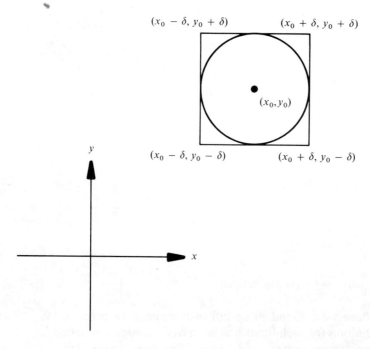

$(x_0 - \delta, y_0 + \delta)$ $(x_0 + \delta, y_0 + \delta)$

(x_0, y_0)

$(x_0 - \delta, y_0 - \delta)$ $(x_0 + \delta, y_0 - \delta)$

y

x

FIG. 7-5. $\lim\limits_{(x,y)\to(x_0,y_0)} f(x,y) = L$

CIRCULAR: $\lim\limits_{(x,y)\to(x_0,y_0)} f(x,y) = L$ if and only if given a positive number ϵ

there exists a δ such that $|f(x,y) - L| < \epsilon$ whenever $\sqrt{(x - x_0)^2 + (y - y_0)^2} < \delta$.

RECTANGULAR: $\lim_{(x,y) \to (x_0,y_0)} f(x,y) = L$ if and only if given a positive number ϵ there exists a δ such that $|f(x,y) - L| < \epsilon$ whenever $0 < |x - x_0| < \delta$ and $0 < |y - y_0| < \delta$.

Because of the complex nature of the formal application of limits in these cases we will restrict our study to an informal application such as the examples above.

7-1 Exercises

1. Give three examples of real-life quantities whose value depends on two or more independent quantities.

(2-6) For each D and f given find, if possible, the functional images of $(0,0)$, $(1,1)$, $(2,2)$, $(4,1)$, $(2x,3)$, (u,v), and $(x^2 + y^2, x)$. Graph D in each case.

2. $D = \{(x,y)\,|\,x^2 + y^2 \le 25\}$

$$f:(x,y) \to \frac{x^2 + y^2}{25}$$

3. $D = \{(x,y)\,|\,|x - 2| \le 2, |y - 3| \le 3\}$

$$f:(x,y) \to \frac{\sqrt{x^2 + 4}}{\sqrt{y + 1}}$$

4. $D = \{(x,y)\,|\,x = 2, y^2 \le 1\}$

$$f:(x,y) \to \cos\left(\pi x - \frac{\pi}{2}y\right)$$

5. $D = \{(x,y)\,|\,xy = 1\}$

$$f:(x,y) \to \frac{1}{x^2 y^2}$$

6. $D = \{(x,y)\,|\,xy = 0\}$

$$f:(x,y) \to \frac{1}{x^2 y^2}$$

(7-16) For each functional expression determine the domain of the function and graph the domain.

7. $f(x,y) = \cos\left(\dfrac{x+y}{2}\right)$

8. $f(x,y) = \dfrac{y^2 + 2}{x^2 - 5x + 6}$

9. $f(x,y) = e^{\ln x} \cdot e^{\ln y}$

10. $f(x,y) = \dfrac{(x^2 + 4)(y^2 - 9)}{\sin(xy)}$

11. $f(x,y) = \dfrac{\sqrt{e^x + e^y}}{\sqrt{1 - e}}$

12. $f(x,y) = \sqrt[3]{-x^2 - y^2}$

13. $f(x,y) = \sqrt{25 - x^2 - y^2}$

14. $f(x,y)$ such that $[f(x,y)] + x^2 + y^2 = 9$ (greatest integer function)

15. $f(x,y)$ such that $f(x,y) + x - 2y^2 = 4$

16. $f(x,y)$ such that $f(x,y)(x^2 + y^2) = 0$

(17-26) Evaluate the following limits.

17. $\displaystyle\lim_{(x,y) \to (0,0)} \left\{ \cos\left(\dfrac{x+y}{2}\right) \right\}$

18. $\displaystyle\lim_{(x,y) \to (4,4)} \left\{ \dfrac{y^2 + 2}{x^2 - 5x + 8} \right\}$

19. $\displaystyle\lim_{(x,y) \to (-1,4)} \left(\dfrac{|x - 3|}{|y + 2|} \right)^2$

20. $\displaystyle\lim_{(x,y) \to (4,3)} \dfrac{\sqrt{x^2 + y^2}}{2}$

21. $\displaystyle\lim_{(x,y) \to (-1,-1)} e^{x^2 + y^2}$

22. $\displaystyle\lim_{(x,y) \to (1,-1)} e^{\ln x} e^{\ln(-y)}$

23. $\displaystyle\lim_{(x,y) \to (0,5)} \dfrac{\sin x}{x} y^2$

24. $\displaystyle\lim_{(x,y) \to \left(\frac{\pi}{2}, \frac{\pi}{4}\right)} \dfrac{\sin x \sin y}{\sqrt{2}}$

25. $\displaystyle\lim_{(x,y) \to (e,e)} \dfrac{\ln x}{\ln y + 1}(x^2 + y^2)$

26. $\displaystyle\lim_{(x,y)\to(0,0)} y\sin\left(\frac{1}{x}\right)$

27. Construct a definition for an ordered triple of numbers as the extension of the concept of an ordered pair.

28. Provide an informal definition for $w = f(x,y,z)$ and
$$\lim_{(x,y,z)\to(x_0,y_0,z_0)} f(x,y,z) = L.$$

29. Find $\displaystyle\lim_{(x,y,z)\to(1,0,1)}\left\{\frac{x^2 + y^2 + z^2}{\sqrt{3}}\right\}.$

30. Find $f\left(7,4,-\dfrac{2}{\pi}\right)$ if $f(x,y,z) = \dfrac{x^2 - 2xy + \sin z}{\sqrt{x^2 + y^2 + (\pi z)^2}}.$

(31-36)   Consider
$$\lim_{(x,y)\to(1,1)} \frac{x^2(x^2 + 1)}{y^2} = 2.$$

Now consider taking this limit along some "path" or curve passing through $(1,1)$, for example, $x = y$ or $y = \sin\dfrac{\pi x}{2}$.

$$\lim_{\substack{(x,y)\to(1,1)\\ \text{along the path}\\ x = y}} \frac{x^2(x^2 + 1)}{y^2} = \lim_{x\to1} \frac{x^2(x^2 + 1)}{x^2} = 2.$$

$$\lim_{\substack{(x,y)\to(1,1)\\ \text{along the path}\\ y = \sin\frac{\pi x}{2}}} \frac{x^2(x^2 + 1)}{y^2} = \lim_{x\to1} \frac{x^2(x^2 + 1)}{\sin^2\left(\frac{\pi x}{2}\right)} = 2.$$

However,
$$\lim_{(x,y)\to(0,0)} \frac{y(x^2 + 1)}{x} \text{ is undefined. Consider,}$$

then
$$\lim_{\substack{(x,y)\to(0,0)\\ \text{along the path}\\ y = x^2}} \frac{y(x^2 + 1)}{x} = \lim_{x\to0} \frac{x^2(x^2 + 1)}{x}$$
$$= \lim_{x\to0} x(x^2 + 1) = 0,$$

whereas
$$\lim_{\substack{(x,y)\to(0,0)\\ \text{along the path}\\ y = \sin x}} \frac{y(x^2 + 1)}{x} = \lim_{x\to0} \frac{\sin x(x^2 + 1)}{x} = 1.$$

Thus, one gets different values along different paths. In each case below find the limit along the given path.

31. $\displaystyle\lim_{(x,y)\to(0,0)} \frac{y(x^2 + 1)}{x}$

along the path

$x = y$

32. $\displaystyle\lim_{(x,y)\to(2,2)} \frac{x - 2}{y^2 - 4}$

along the path

$x = y$

33. $\displaystyle\lim_{(x,y)\to(0,0)} \frac{x^2(x + 2)}{y^2}$

along the path

$y = \sin x$

34. $\displaystyle\lim_{(x,y)\to(2,2)} \frac{x^2 - 4}{2y - 4}$

along the path

$x = y$

35. $\displaystyle\lim_{(x,y)\to(2,2)} \frac{x^2 - 4}{2y - 4}$

along the path

$y = \dfrac{x^2}{2}$

36. $\displaystyle\lim_{(x,y)\to(2,2)} \frac{x^2 - 4}{2y - 4}$

along the path

$y = \dfrac{2}{x^2}$

(37-40) Consider the $\displaystyle\lim_{(x,y)\to(4,4)}\left\{\frac{y^2 + 2}{x^2 - 5x + 8}\right\} = \frac{18}{4} = \frac{9}{2}.$

For the conditions indicated, estimate how close $\left\{\dfrac{y^2 + 2}{x^2 - 5x + 8}\right\}$ is to $\dfrac{9}{2}$.

37. $|x - 4| < 1$ and $|y - 4| < 1$

38. $|x - 4| < 0.5$ and $|y - 4| < 1$

39. $\sqrt{(x - 4)^2 + (y - 4)^2} < 1$

40. $|x - 4| < 0.01$ and $|y - 4| < 0.5$

7-2 THREE-DIMENSIONAL COORDINATE GEOMETRY

If two-dimensional coordinate geometry provides a useful tool for visualizing the domains of functions of two independent variables, it is reasonable to assume that a three-dimensional coordinate geometry could provide a visualization of such functions as a whole. While there are many schemes which could be used to construct such a three-dimensional system, the most straightforward one makes use of a standard rectangular Cartesian coordinate system in a plane, with the third coordinate measuring perpendicular distances to the plane. Such a system is illustrated in figure 7-6. By constructing the third or z axis perpendicular to the original or xy plane at the origin of the xy system, each point in space can be assigned an identifying tag or set of coordinates. An ordered triple then can serve as the actual coordinates of the point.

The coordinate system shown in figure 7-6 is considered "right-handed" because of the positive direction assigned to the z axis relative to the x axis and the y axis. Consider a standard right-handed screw (a normal wood screw for example) placed along the z axis, as illustrated in figure 7-6. Assume the slot of the screw is parallel to the x axis. Now visualize the direction this screw would advance if the slot were rotated 90° to be parallel

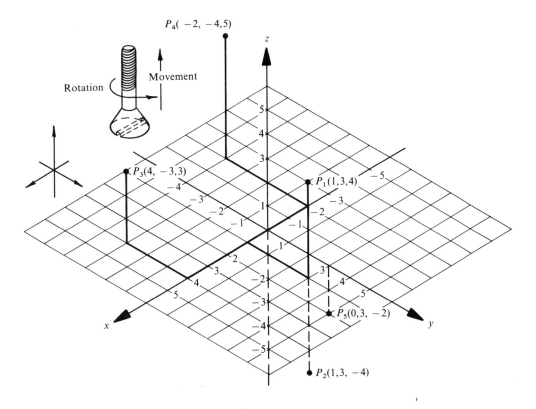

FIG. 7-6. Three-Dimensional Coordinate System

to the y axis. The direction the screw moves determines the positive direction to be assigned to the z axis. Points identified by $P;(x,y,z)$ are located by using the x and y values to identify the location of the point relative to the xy plane and then using the value of z to tell how far above or below the xy plane the point lies.

Example. Consider the points $P_1;(1,3,4)$, $P_2;(1,3,-4)$, $P_3;(4,-3,3)$, $P_4;(-2,-4,5)$, and $P_5;(0,3,-2)$. Each of these points has been plotted in figure 7-6.

Defining the three coordinate axes, in turn, defines three coordinate planes. These are the original xy plane, or the $z = 0$ plane, the xz plane where $y = 0$, and the yz plane where $x = 0$. The coordinates of a point (x,y,z) can be thought of as the perpendicular distances to the three coordinate planes. The three coordinate planes divide space into eight octants. The octant where all three coordinates of a point are positive is known as the first octant. There is no set pattern used in identifying the other seven octants.

The formula used to calculate the distance between two points in a plane when their coordinates are known has its counterpart for two points in space. If $P_1;(x_1,y_1,z_1)$ and $P_2;(x_2,y_2,z_2)$ are two points, whose coordinates are given relative to a three-dimensional coordinate system, and P_1P_2 denotes the distance between P_1 and P_2 then:

$$P_1P_2 = \sqrt{(x_2 - x_1)^2 + (y_2 - y_1)^2 + (z_2 - z_1)^2}.$$

Example. Find the distance between $P_1;(2,3,1)$ and $P_2;(4,1,5)$.
Solution. $P_1;(2,3,1)$ and $P_2;(4,1,5)$ are shown in figure 7-7,

$$P_1P_2 = \sqrt{(4 - 2)^2 + (1 - 3)^2 + (5 - 1)^2}$$

$$= \sqrt{2^2 + (-2)^2 + 4^2}$$

$$= \sqrt{4 + 4 + 16}$$

$$= \sqrt{24}$$

$$= 2\sqrt{6}.$$

Example. Find the distance from $P_1;(2,3,1)$ to $(0,0,0)$.
Solution. The distance is shown in figure 7-7.

$$P_1 0 = \sqrt{(2 - 0)^2 + (3 - 0)^2 + (1 - 0)^2}$$

$$= \sqrt{4 + 9 + 1}$$

$$= \sqrt{14}.$$

The distance from P_2; $(4,1,5)$ to $(0,0,0)$ is

$$P_2 0 = \sqrt{(4 - 0)^2 + (1 - 0)^2 + (5 - 0)^2}$$

$$= \sqrt{16 + 1 + 25}$$

$$= \sqrt{42}.$$

The definition of the graph of a function of two variables defined by $z = f(x,y)$ follows the same form as the definition of the graph of a function of a single variable in a two-dimensional coordinate system.

Definition.   The graph of a function defined by $z = f(x,y)$ is the set of points P; (x,y,z) whose coordinates satisfy the defining functional equation.

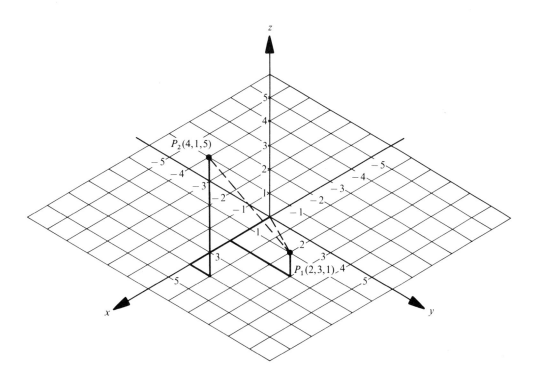

FIG. 7-7.   The Distance Formula for
$P_1(2, 3, 1)$ and $P_2(4, 1, 5)$

Example.   Consider $z = f(x,y) = \sqrt{9 - x^2 - y^2}$. The domain of this function is the set of all values of x and y such that $x^2 + y^2 \le 9$. This condition is necessary to assure that the value of z will be real. In the xy plane of a three-dimensional coordinate system this corresponds to a circular region bounded by the circle $x^2 + y^2 = 9$, *i.e.*, a circle of radius 3 with its center at the origin. This region is shown in figure 7-8.

Now examine the defining equation

$$z = \sqrt{9 - x^2 - y^2}.$$

This is equivalent to

$$z^2 = 9 - x^2 - y^2$$

with the further condition that z must be nonnegative. This in turn is equivalent to

$$x^2 + y^2 + z^2 = 9.$$

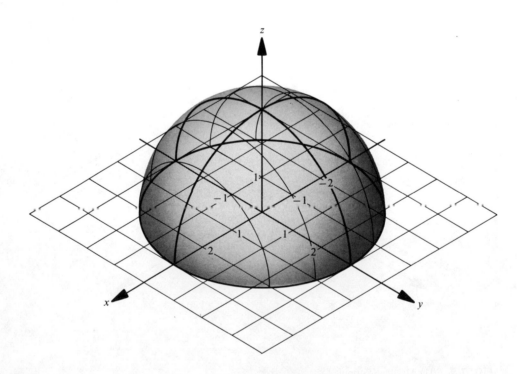

FIG. 7-8.   A Graph of $z = \sqrt{9 - x^2 - y^2}$

Therefore, $\sqrt{x^2 + y^2 + z^2} = 3.$

A comparison of this result with the distance formula indicates that a point $P;(x,y,z)$, where x, y, and z satisfy the original equation, must lie three units from the origin and above the xy plane. Thus, $z = \sqrt{9 - x^2 - y^2}$ represents a hemisphere of radius 3 with center at the origin.

In the example we were lucky (or rather the example was the result of calculated cheating on the part of the authors) to have a function which generated a graph with a recognizable geometric form. In order to analyze more complex, less prearranged problems, more graphing tools are needed. This can be done with the aid of the idea of the trace of a graph. This concept is the three-dimensional extension of the idea of the points of intersection of two graphs in two dimensions.

> **Definition.**   The graph of an equation in three dimensions is called a *surface*.

> **Definition.**   The curve formed when two surfaces intersect is called the *trace* of one surface on the other.

Consider all of the points satisfying an equation like $z = 3$. All of these points would lie in a plane parallel to the xy plane and 3 units above it. In general $z = c$, a constant, represents the equation of a plane parallel to the xy plane and c units above or below it. Similarly $x = c$ or $y = c$ represent planes parallel to the yz or xz planes. In order to visualize the nature of the graph of an equation like $z = f(x,y)$ it is usually useful to examine the traces the graph makes with the planes $x = $ a constant, $y = $ a constant, or $z = $ a constant.

Example.   Draw the traces of the surface corresponding to $z = \sqrt{9 - x^2 - y^2}$ and $z = c$, a constant plane.
Solution.   If $z = 1$, then

$$1 = \sqrt{9 - x^2 - y^2}, \text{ or}$$

$$1 = 9 - x^2 - y^2, \text{ or}$$

$$x^2 + y^2 = 8.$$

Thus the trace of the surface defined by $z = \sqrt{9 - x^2 - y^2}$ in the plane $z = 1$ is a circle with radius $\sqrt{8}$ and center on the z axis. The circle is shown in figure 7-8. Similarly the trace of the surface with the plane $z = 2$ is given by $2 = \sqrt{9 - x^2 - y^2}$ which reduces to $x^2 + y^2 = 5$, a circle with radius $\sqrt{5}$ also centered on the z axis. In fact, all of the traces, which exist, with planes whose equations are of the form $z = c$, a constant, are circles centered along the z axis. Now consider traces of the surface with planes parallel to the yz plane, *i.e.*, those planes whose equations are of the type $x = c$, a constant. With the plane $x = 2$ the trace is given by

$$z = \sqrt{9 - 4 - y^2}$$

$$z = \sqrt{5 - y^2}$$

This is a semicircle of radius $\sqrt{5}$, and it is shown in figure 7-8. All of the traces with $x = c$, a constant plane, will be semicircles. In a like manner, all of the traces with y equal to a constant plane will be semicircles. The overall conclusion from examination of the traces is that the surface is a hemispherical dome of radius 3 centered at the origin.

Example.   Using traces sketch the graph of the first octant of the surface defined by $z = 4 - x - y$.
Solution.   Consider the traces this surface makes with each of the co-ordinate planes in turn. With $z = 0$, *i.e.*, the xy plane, the trace is given by $0 = 4 - x - y$, which is equivalent to $y = 4 - x$, a straight line. With $y = 0$, the xz plane, the trace is given by $z = 4 - x$. With $x = 0$, the yz plane, the trace is described by $z = 4 - y$.

These traces are shown in figure 7-9. The traces with the planes $z = 1$, $z = 2$, $z = 3$, $x = 1$, $x = 2$, $x = 3$, $y = 1$, $y = 2$, and $y = 3$ are also shown in figure 7-9. It appears that the surface $z = 4 - x - y$ is a plane.

Example.   Using traces sketch the graph of the surface $z = x^2 + y^2$.
Solution.   In this case the trace of the surface with the xy plane is a point; *i.e.*, $0 = x^2 + y^2$, whose only solution is $x = 0$ and $y = 0$. Thus the point $(0,0,0)$ is on the surface. The surface does not have a trace with any $z = c$ planes where c is negative; $x^2 + y^2$ is always positive. With the plane $z = 1$ the trace is given by $1 = x^2 + y^2$. This is a circle with radius 1 centered on the z axis. The planes $z = 2$, $z = 3$, etc., each yield traces that are circles centered on the z axis. In the plane $x = 0$ the trace is the parabola $z = y^2$. The trace in the $x - 1$ plane is the raised parabola $z = y^2 + 1$. These trace curves are shown in figure 7-10. The graph appears to be bowl shaped. This surface is called a paraboloid because of the parabolic traces it produces.

This section represents only a very limited introduction to the develop-ment and use of three-dimensional coordinates. If the reader is interested he is directed to one of several modern books on the subject, such as *Analytic Geometry* by Middlemiss, Marks, and Smart, McGraw-Hill, 1968, or to a traditional calculus book with analytic geometry such as *Modern Calculus with Analytic Geometry* by Goodman, Macmillan, 1967. In the present context, three-dimensional geometry will only serve to aid our visualization of the behavior of functions of two variables.

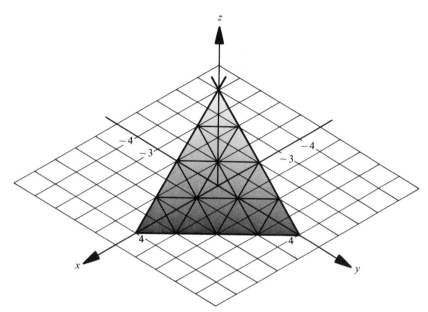

FIG. 7-9.   The First Octant Graph of $z = 4 - x - y$

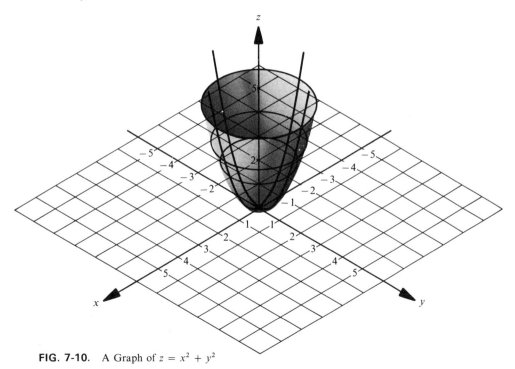

FIG. 7-10.   A Graph of $z = x^2 + y^2$

7-2 Exercises

(1-5) Plot each of the pairs of points indicated in a three-dimensional coordinate system and calculate the distance between them.

1. $A;(0,1,3)$, $B;(6,-1,2)$

2. $A;(1,-1,4)$, $B;(3,2,7)$

3. $A;(-1,-1,4)$, $B;(1,1,4)$

4. $A;(3,2,7)$, $B;(-3,1,-6)$

5. $A;(-4,-5,-4)$, $B;(-4,-5,-2)$

(6-10) Each of the following equations describes a plane in three dimensions. Graph the traces each plane forms with the coordinate planes.

6. $z = x + y + 2$

7. $z = 4 + 3x - 2y$

8. $z = -x - y + 3$

9. $12z = -2x - 3y + 24$

10. $x + y = 3$

(11-19) Using traces sketch each of the following surfaces.

11. $z = \sqrt{25 - x^2 - y^2}$

12. $z = 25 - \dfrac{x^2}{9} - \dfrac{y^2}{16}$

13. $x^2 + y^2 + z^2 = 16$

14. $z = x^2 - y$

15. $z = y^2 - x + 2$

16. $z = y^2$

17. $z = \sin y$

18. $z = \sqrt{9 - (x - 3)^2 - (y - 2)^2}$

19. $z = e^{x+y}$

20. Consider the paraboloid described by $4z = x^2 + y^2$. Show, using the distance formula, that any point on this surface is the same distance from the point $(0,0,1)$ as it is from the plane $z = -1$.

21. Find all of the points on the z axis that are exactly 5 units from the point $(1,2\sqrt{2},0)$.

(22-24) Assuming that the description of a left-handed coordinate system follows in form that of a right-handed coordinate system. Plot each of the points indicated in a left-handed system.

22. Plot $A;(1,2,-3),\ B;(0,1,3),\ C;(-3,1,5)$

23. Plot $A;(-1,-1,4),\ B;(-4,-5,3),\ C;(-2,-6,8)$

24. Sketch $z = \sqrt{9 - x^2 - y^2}$

7-3 PARTIAL DERIVATIVES

Since the concepts of function and limit both extend to functions of several variables, the next step is to extend the concept of a derivative to several variables. Two equally reasonable approaches seem to present themselves. One is to attempt to extend the definition of a derivative to the more complex case, and the second approach would attempt to extend the application of the regular derivative to functions dependent on more than one variable. The more basic approach, that of extending the idea of the derivative as the limit of a rate of change, involves defining an appropriate incremental change and limit.

Consider $z = f(x,y)$ with a specific point, (x_0,y_0), in the domain of the function. Then one can define the derivative of z at (x_0,y_0) as

$$\lim_{(\Delta x, \Delta y)\to(0,0)} \left\{ \frac{f(x_0 + \Delta x, y_0 + \Delta y) - f(x_0,y_0)}{\sqrt{\Delta x^2 + \Delta y^2}} \right\},$$

where $\sqrt{\Delta x^2 + \Delta y^2}$ measures the change in the independent variables from (x_0,y_0) to $(x_0 + \Delta x, y_0 + \Delta y)$. At first glance this approach seems reasonable enough. In reality, it is the more complex of the two proposed. A more practical approach is to apply the methods of ordinary differentiation to the new case.

Definition.   Let $z = f(x,y)$ be a function of x and y. Then

$$\frac{\partial z}{\partial x} = f_x(x,y) = \lim_{\Delta x \to 0} \frac{f(x + \Delta x, y) - f(x,y)}{\Delta x}$$

provided such a limit exists at the point (x,y) in the domain of the function. $\dfrac{\partial z}{\partial x}$ is called the *partial derivative* of z with respect to x.

This definition of the partial derivative in effect creates a derivative of a function of two variables by treating one of the variables as a constant. To partially differentiate with respect to x, one need only treat y as a constant and apply the usual differentiation rules.

Example.   If $z = x^2y$, find $\dfrac{\partial z}{\partial x}$.

Solution.
$$\frac{\partial z}{\partial x} = \lim_{\Delta x \to 0} \frac{(x + \Delta x)^2 y - x^2 y}{\Delta x}$$
$$= \lim_{\Delta x \to 0} y \left\{ \frac{(x + \Delta x)^2 - x^2}{\Delta x} \right\}$$
$$= y \lim_{\Delta x \to 0} \left\{ \frac{(x + \Delta x)^2 - x^2}{\Delta x} \right\}.$$

However,

$$\lim_{\Delta x \to 0} \left\{ \frac{(x + \Delta x)^2 - x^2}{\Delta x} \right\}$$

is $\dfrac{d}{dx}(x^2)$ by definition, or $2x$.

Thus,

$$\frac{\partial z}{\partial x} = y\, 2x = 2xy.$$

Example.   If $z = \sin(x + y)$, find $\dfrac{\partial z}{\partial x}$.

Solution. $\dfrac{\partial z}{\partial x} = \lim_{\Delta x \to 0} \dfrac{\sin[(x + \Delta x) + y] - \sin(x + y)}{\Delta x}$

$$= \lim_{\Delta x \to 0} \left\{ \frac{\sin(x + \Delta x)\cos y + \cos(x + \Delta x)\sin y}{\Delta x} \right.$$

$$\left. \frac{- \sin x \cos y - \cos x \sin y}{\Delta x} \right\}$$

$$= \lim_{\Delta x \to 0} \left\{ \left[\frac{\sin(x + \Delta x) - \sin x}{\Delta x} \right] \cos y \right.$$

$$\left. + \left[\frac{\cos(x + \Delta x) - \cos x}{\Delta x} \right] \sin y \right\}$$

However,

$$\lim_{\Delta x \to 0} \left[\frac{\sin(x + \Delta x) - \sin x}{\Delta x} \right] = \frac{d}{dx}(\sin x)$$

$$= \cos x,$$

and

$$\lim_{\Delta x \to 0} \left[\frac{\cos(x + \Delta x) - \cos x}{\Delta x} \right] = \frac{d}{dx}(\cos x)$$

$$= - \sin x.$$

Thus,

$$\frac{\partial z}{\partial x} = \cos x \cos y - \sin x \sin y$$

$$= \cos(x + y).$$

Without supplying a formal proof, it is reasonable to conclude that the mechanics of partial differentiation follow the usual differentiation rules, treating other independent variables as constants.

Example. $\dfrac{\partial}{\partial x}(x^2 + y^2) = 2x.$

Example. $\dfrac{\partial}{\partial x}\{\sin(x^2 + y^2)\} = \cos(x^2 + y^2)(2x).$

Example. $\dfrac{\partial}{\partial x}(xy^3) = y^3.$

Example. $\dfrac{\partial}{\partial x}(e^{x^2 y^3}) = e^{x^2 y^3} \cdot 2xy^3$

Example. $\dfrac{\partial}{\partial x}\sqrt{x^2 + y^2} = \dfrac{1}{2\sqrt{x^2 + y^2}}(2x)$

$$= \frac{x}{\sqrt{x^2 + y^2}}.$$

Example. $\dfrac{\partial}{\partial x}(x^3 + 3xy + y^3) = 3x^2 + 3y.$

The obvious parallel exists in definition and application for partial differentiation with respect to y or any other variable.

Example. $\dfrac{\partial}{\partial y}(x^2 + y^2) = 2y.$

Example. $\dfrac{\partial}{\partial y}\sin(x^2 + y^2) = \cos(x^2 + y^2)(2y).$

Example. $\dfrac{\partial}{\partial y}(x^2y) = x^2.$

Example. $\dfrac{\partial}{\partial y}(xy^3) = 3xy^2.$

Example. $\dfrac{\partial}{\partial y}\sqrt{x^2 - y^2} = \dfrac{1}{2\sqrt{x^2 - y^2}}(-2y) = \dfrac{-y}{\sqrt{x^2 - y^2}}.$

Example. $\dfrac{\partial}{\partial y}(x^3 + 3xy + y^4) = 3x + 4y^3.$

An alternative notation is,

$$\frac{\partial}{\partial y}f(x,y) = f_y(x,y).$$

Just as the regular differentiation process can be repeated any number of times, so can the process of partial differentiation.

Example. Let $z = x^5y^6 = f(x,y)$. Find the third partial derivative of z with respect to x and y.

$$\frac{\partial z}{\partial x} = f_x(x,y) = 5x^4y^6.$$

$$\frac{\partial^2 z}{\partial x^2} = f_{xx}(x,y) = \frac{\partial}{\partial x}\left(\frac{\partial z}{\partial x}\right) = \frac{\partial}{\partial x}[5x^4y^6]$$

$$= 20x^3y^6.$$

$$\frac{\partial^3 z}{\partial x^3} = f_{xxx}(x,y) = 60x^2 y^6.$$

$$\frac{\partial z}{\partial y} = f_y(x,y) = 6x^5 y^5.$$

$$\frac{\partial^2 z}{\partial y^2} = f_{yy}(x,y) = \frac{\partial}{\partial y}\left(\frac{\partial z}{\partial y}\right) = \frac{\partial}{\partial y}(6x^5 y^5)$$

$$= 30x^5 y^4.$$

$$\frac{\partial^3 z}{\partial y^3} = f_{yyy}(x,y) = 120x^5 y^3.$$

With partial differentiation, a new type of higher order derivative can be introduced. Since any partial derivative is usually still a function of both of the original variables, the second or higher derivative can be found with respect to a variable other than the first one used.

Example. If $z = f(x,y) = x^5 y^6$, find $f_{yyx}(x,y)$.

Solution.
$$\frac{\partial z}{\partial x} = 5x^4 y^6.$$

$$\frac{\partial}{\partial y}\left(\frac{\partial z}{\partial x}\right) = \frac{\partial}{\partial y}(5x^4 y^6)$$

$$= 30x^4 y^5.$$

$$\frac{\partial}{\partial y}\left(\frac{\partial}{\partial y}\left(\frac{\partial z}{\partial x}\right)\right) = 150x^4 y^4 = f_{yyx}(x,y).$$

These types of partial derivatives are called *mixed partial derivatives*. A more compact notation for mixed partial derivatives can be developed.

If
$$z = f(x,y),$$

$$\frac{\partial^2 z}{\partial y \partial x} = \frac{\partial}{\partial y}\left(\frac{\partial z}{\partial x}\right) = f_{yx}(x,y), \text{ and}$$

$$\frac{\partial^2 z}{\partial x \partial y} = \frac{\partial}{\partial x}\left(\frac{\partial z}{\partial y}\right) = f_{xy}(x,y).$$

Thus, there are two mixed second-order partial derivatives. The concept extends to six third-order partial derivatives.

$$\frac{\partial^3 z}{\partial x \partial y^2} = f_{xyy}(x,y) = \frac{\partial}{\partial x}\left(\frac{\partial^2 z}{\partial y^2}\right).$$

$$\frac{\partial^3 z}{\partial y \partial x \partial y} = \frac{\partial}{\partial y}\left(\frac{\partial^2 z}{\partial x \partial y}\right) = f_{yxy}(x,y).$$

$$\frac{\partial^3 z}{\partial y^2 \partial x} = \frac{\partial^2}{\partial y^2}\left(\frac{\partial z}{\partial x}\right) = f_{yyx}(x,y).$$

$$\frac{\partial^3 z}{\partial y \partial x^2} = \frac{\partial}{\partial y}\left(\frac{\partial^2 z}{\partial x^2}\right) = f_{yxx}(x,y).$$

$$\frac{\partial^3 z}{\partial x \partial y \partial x} = \frac{\partial}{\partial x}\left(\frac{\partial^2 z}{\partial y \partial x}\right) = f_{xyx}(x,y).$$

$$\frac{\partial^3 z}{\partial x^2 \partial y} = \frac{\partial^2}{\partial x^2}\left(\frac{\partial z}{\partial y}\right) = f_{xxy}(x,y).$$

Example.   If $z = x^7 y^{\frac{7}{2}}$, find the third-order partial derivatives of z.

Solution. $\dfrac{\partial z}{\partial x} = 7x^6 y^{\frac{7}{2}}.$

$$\frac{\partial z}{\partial y} = \frac{7}{2} x^7 y^{\frac{5}{2}}.$$

$$\frac{\partial^2 z}{\partial x^2} = 42x^5 y^{\frac{7}{2}}.$$

$$\frac{\partial^2 z}{\partial y^2} = \frac{35}{4} x^7 y^{\frac{3}{2}}.$$

$$\frac{\partial^2 z}{\partial y \partial x} = \frac{\partial}{\partial y}\left(\frac{\partial z}{\partial x}\right) = \frac{\partial}{\partial y}(7x^6 y^{\frac{7}{2}}) = \frac{49}{2} x^6 y^{\frac{5}{2}}.$$

$$\frac{\partial^2 z}{\partial x \partial y} = \frac{\partial}{\partial x}\left(\frac{\partial z}{\partial y}\right) = \frac{\partial}{\partial x}\left(\frac{7}{2} x^7 y^{\frac{5}{2}}\right) = \frac{49}{2} x^6 y^{\frac{5}{2}}.$$

$$\frac{\partial^3 z}{\partial y \partial x^2} = \frac{\partial}{\partial y}\left(\frac{\partial^2 z}{\partial x^2}\right) - \frac{\partial}{\partial y}(42x^5 y^{\frac{7}{2}}) - \frac{294}{2} x^5 y^{\frac{5}{2}}.$$

$$\frac{\partial^3 z}{\partial x \partial y \partial x} = \frac{\partial}{\partial x}\left(\frac{\partial^2 z}{\partial y \partial x}\right) = \frac{\partial}{\partial x}\left(\frac{49}{2} x^6 y^{\frac{5}{2}}\right) = \frac{294}{2} x^5 y^{\frac{5}{2}}.$$

$$\frac{\partial^3 z}{\partial x^2 \partial y} = \frac{\partial^2}{\partial x^2}\left(\frac{\partial z}{\partial y}\right) = \frac{\partial}{\partial x}\left(\frac{\partial}{\partial x}\left(\frac{7}{2} x^7 y^{\frac{5}{2}}\right)\right)$$

$$= \frac{\partial}{\partial x}\left(\frac{49}{2} x^6 y^{\frac{5}{2}}\right) = \frac{294}{2} x^5 y^{\frac{5}{2}}.$$

$$\frac{\partial^3 z}{\partial x \partial y^2} = \frac{\partial}{\partial x}\left(\frac{\partial^2 z}{\partial y^2}\right) = \frac{\partial}{\partial x}\left(\frac{35}{4} x^7 y^{\frac{3}{2}}\right) = \frac{245}{4} x^6 y^{\frac{3}{2}}.$$

$$\frac{\partial^3 z}{\partial y \partial x \partial y} = \frac{\partial}{\partial y}\left(\frac{\partial^2 z}{\partial x \partial y}\right) = \frac{\partial}{\partial y}\left(\frac{49}{2}x^6 y^{\frac{5}{2}}\right) = \frac{245}{4}x^6 y^{\frac{3}{2}}.$$

$$\frac{\partial^3 z}{\partial y^2 \partial x} = \frac{\partial}{\partial y}\left(\frac{\partial^2 z}{\partial y \partial z}\right) = \frac{\partial}{\partial y}\left(\frac{49}{2}x^6 y^{\frac{5}{2}}\right) = \frac{245}{4}x^6 y^{\frac{3}{2}}.$$

From this example, it appears that

$$\frac{\partial^2 z}{\partial x \partial y} = \frac{\partial^2 z}{\partial y \partial x},$$

$$\frac{\partial^3 z}{\partial x^2 \partial y} = \frac{\partial^3 z}{\partial x \partial y \partial x} = \frac{\partial^3 z}{\partial y \partial x^2}, \text{ and}$$

$$\frac{\partial^3 z}{\partial y^2 \partial x} = \frac{\partial^3 z}{\partial y \partial x \partial y} = \frac{\partial^3 z}{\partial x \partial y^2}$$

This result is, in fact, always true, provided the partial derivatives are continuous. However, a proof of this must be delayed until a more formal development of the topic is encountered. In general, the order of differentiation does not affect the result in finding a mixed partial derivative.

Example.   Find $\dfrac{\partial^3}{\partial x^2 \partial y}\left\{x^2 y^3 - \sin\sqrt{y^{\frac{3}{2}} - \ln y}\right\}.$

Solution.   Rather than following the indicated order of differentiation, it is easier to proceed as follows.

$$\frac{\partial}{\partial x}\left\{x^2 y^3 - \sin\sqrt{y^{\frac{3}{2}} - \ln y}\right\} = 2xy^3.$$

$$\frac{\partial^2}{\partial x^2}\left\{x^2 y^3 - \sin\sqrt{y^{\frac{3}{2}} - \ln y}\right\} = 2y^3.$$

$$\frac{\partial^3}{\partial x^2 \partial y}\left\{x^2 y^3 - \sin\sqrt{y^{\frac{3}{2}} - \ln y}\right\} = 6y^2.$$

Example.   If $z = \ln(x^2 + y)$, find $\dfrac{\partial^2 z}{\partial x \partial y}.$

Solution.

$$\frac{\partial z}{\partial x} = \frac{1}{x^2 + y}(2x).$$

$$\frac{\partial^2 z}{\partial y \partial x} = \frac{-2x}{(x^2 + y)^2}.$$

An alternate solution is:

$$\frac{\partial z}{\partial y} = \frac{1}{x^2 + y}.$$

$$\frac{\partial^2 z}{\partial x \partial y} = \frac{\partial^2 z}{\partial y \partial x} = \frac{-1}{(x^2 + y)^2}(+2x)$$

$$= \frac{-2x}{(x^2 + y)^2}.$$

7-3 Exercises

(1-10) Find $\dfrac{\partial z}{\partial x}$, $\dfrac{\partial z}{\partial y}$ in each case.

1. $z = \dfrac{1}{x^2 y^2}$

2. $z = \cos\left(\dfrac{x + y}{2}\right)$

3. $z = \ln(x^2 y)$

4. $z = e^{x^2 + 2xy}$

5. $z = \sin(x^2 + 2\cos y)$

6. $z = \dfrac{y^2 + 2}{x^2 - 5x + 8}$

7. $z = \dfrac{\sqrt{x^2 - y^2}}{2xy}$

8. $z = 25 - (x - y)^4 + (y - 1)^4$

9. $z = 2xy - 5y^2 - 2x^2 + 4x + 4y - 4$

10. $z = 2x + xy + y^2 + 3y + 5$

(11-15) Find the four second partial derivatives for each of the following.

11. $z = \dfrac{1}{x^2 y^2}$

12. $z = 25 - (x - y)^4 + (y - 1)^4$

13. $z = \dfrac{y^2 + 2}{x^2 - 5x + 8}$

14. $z = 2x + 2y + y^2 + 3x^2 + 5$

15. $z = x^2 + xy + y^2 + 3x - 3y + 4$

(16-20)   Find the indicated third partial derivatives for each of the following functions.

16. $f(x,y) = x^9 y^{\frac{1}{3}}$, find f_{xxx}, f_{xyy}

17. $f(x,y) = \ln(x^2 y^2)$, find f_{yyy}, f_{xyx}

18. $f(x,y) = \sin(x^2 + y^2)$, find f_{yyx}, f_{xxy}

19. $f(x,y) = e^{xy}$, find $f_{xxy}, f_{xyx}, f_{yxx}$

20. $f(x,y) = 2x^3 + 2y^3$, find $f_{xyy}, f_{yxy}, f_{yyx}$

21. By first differentiating with respect to y find

$$\frac{\partial^3}{\partial x^2 \partial y} \{x^2 y^2 - \sin(\sqrt{y^{\frac{3}{2}}} - \ln y)\}.$$

(22-23)   For a given function of two variables, z, the Laplacian operator, ∇^2, (read "del" squared) is defined

$$\nabla^2 z = \frac{\partial^2 z}{\partial x^2} + \frac{\partial^2 z}{\partial y^2}.$$

A function $z = f(x,y)$ is called harmonic if it satisfies Laplace's equation $\nabla^2 z = 0$. Show that the functions indicated are harmonic.

22. $z = x^2 - y^2$

23. $z = \ln\sqrt{x^2 + y^2}$

(24-25)   For each of the following find all values (x,y) that satisfy the simultaneous conditions

$$\frac{\partial z}{\partial x} = 0, \text{ and } \frac{\partial z}{\partial y} = 0.$$

24. $z = 2x + 2y + y^2 + 3x^2 + 5$

25. $z = 2xy - 5y^2 - 2x^2 + 4x + 4y - 4$

(26-30)   In each of the following $\dfrac{\partial z}{\partial x}$ and $\dfrac{\partial z}{\partial y}$ are given. Use antidifferentia-

tion with respect to x holding y constant and the antidifferentiation with respect to y holding x constant and find z. *Hint*: $\dfrac{\partial}{\partial x} f(y) = 0$, and $\dfrac{\partial}{\partial y} f(x) = 0$.

Thus $\dfrac{\partial}{\partial x}(f(x,y) + g(y)) = \dfrac{\partial}{\partial x} f(x,y)$, and $\dfrac{\partial}{\partial y}(f(x,y) + h(x)) = \dfrac{\partial}{\partial y} f(x,y)$.

26. $\dfrac{\partial z}{\partial x} = 12x^2 y^2$

$\dfrac{\partial z}{\partial y} = 8x^3 y$

27. $\dfrac{\partial z}{\partial x} = y\cos(xy) - 5x^4$

$\dfrac{\partial z}{\partial y} = x\cos(xy) + 3y^2$

28. $\dfrac{\partial z}{\partial x} = \dfrac{1}{x}$

$\dfrac{\partial z}{\partial y} = \dfrac{1}{y}$

29. $\dfrac{\partial z}{\partial x} = y + \dfrac{y}{x}$

$\dfrac{\partial z}{\partial y} = x + \ln xy + 1$

30. $\dfrac{\partial z}{\partial x} = \dfrac{1}{2\sqrt{x - y^2}}$

$\dfrac{\partial z}{\partial y} = \dfrac{-y}{\sqrt{x - y^2}}$

7-4 EXTREMA FOR FUNCTIONS OF TWO VARIABLES— MAXIMUM AND MINIMUM

One of the most useful applications of differentiation was finding the extrema (maximum and minimum) values of a function. Naturally, one wonders about a similar application involving partial differentiation and a function of two variables. The trace of a graph in three dimensions can assist in visualizing the role of the partial derivative in such a problem.

Consider the trace of a surface $z = f(x,y)$ in the plane $y = c$, a constant. The trace is a plane curve in the $y = c$ plane. In this plane, z is a function

of x only. Now $\dfrac{\partial z}{\partial x}$ is found by treating y as a constant, which is true in the

$y = c$ plane, and $\dfrac{\partial z}{\partial x}$ acts like the ordinary derivative of z with respect to x

in the $y = c$ plane. It is reasonable to conclude that at any value of x,

$\dfrac{\partial z}{\partial x}$, yields the slope of the line in the $y = c$ plane tangent to the trace curve

in the $y = c$ plane. Now suppose (x_0, y_0) corresponds to an extremum of

$z = f(x, y)$, and $\dfrac{\partial z}{\partial y}\bigg|_{(x_0, y_0)}$ (read, "$\dfrac{\partial z}{\partial y}$ evaluated at (x_0, y_0)") and $\dfrac{\partial z}{\partial y}\bigg|_{(x_0, y_0)}$ (read,

"$\dfrac{\partial z}{\partial y}$ evaluated at (x_0, y_0)") both exist. Since $f(x_0, y_0)$ is an extremum of z, it

must also be an extremum for the trace $z = f(x, y)$ in the $y = y_0$ plane. This is illustrated in figure 7-11.

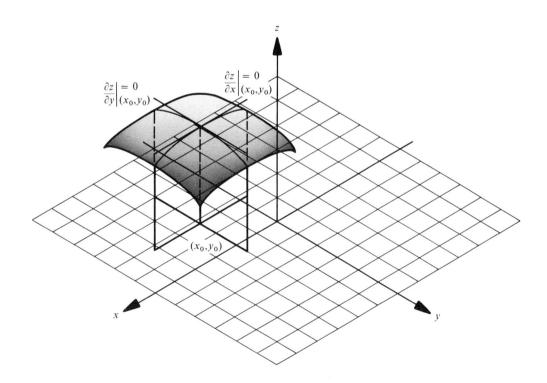

FIG. 7-11.   A Graph of $z = f(x, y)$, with (x_0, y_0) an Extremum (Maximum)

Thus $\dfrac{\partial z}{\partial x}\bigg|_{(x_0,y_0)}$ must equal zero. If the roles of x and y are changed in the preceding discussion, one can conclude that if $f(x_0,y_0)$ is an extremum, $\dfrac{\partial z}{\partial x}\bigg|_{(x_0,y_0)} = 0$ and $\dfrac{\partial z}{\partial y}\bigg|_{(x_0,y_0)} = 0$. These are necessary, but not sufficient, conditions for $f(x_0,y_0)$ to be an extremum of z, for, as we know in the ordinary regular derivative case, the fact the derivative of a function is zero at a specific value of the independent variables does not assure a maximum or minimum function value. This happens when the curve only flattens and does not change direction, as $f(x) = x^3$ does at $x = 0$. A later example will demonstrate a second way in which a zero for both first partials can fail to be an extremum of the function.

Example.   Find the extrema of the function

$$z = 2xy - 5y^2 - 2x^2 + 4x + 4y - 4.$$

Solution. $\dfrac{\partial z}{\partial x} = 2y - 4x + 4,$

and $\dfrac{\partial z}{\partial y} = 2x - 10y + 4.$

Setting these equal to zero one can find the only possibilities for extrema.

$$2x - 10y + 4 = 0.$$
$$-4x + 2y + 4 = 0.$$

Thus,

$$2x - 10y + 4 = 0$$
$$\underline{-20x + 10y + 20 = 0}$$
$$-18x + 24 \qquad = 0,$$

or $x = \dfrac{4}{3}.$

And,

$$4x - 20y + 8 = 0$$
$$\underline{-4x + 2y + 4 = 0}$$
$$-18y + 12 = 0,$$

or $y = \dfrac{2}{3}.$

Conclusion: If an extremum for z exists it must occur at $(\frac{4}{3}, \frac{2}{3})$.

Does $(\frac{4}{3}, \frac{2}{3})$ in the example correspond to a maximum or minimum value of z? Perhaps the second partial derivatives can test the result.

$$\frac{\partial^2 z}{\partial x^2} = -4,$$

$$\frac{\partial^2 z}{\partial y^2} = -10,$$

and

$$\frac{\partial^2 z}{\partial x \partial y} = 2.$$

The fact that $\dfrac{\partial^2 z}{\partial x^2} = -4$ would indicate that the point $(\frac{4}{3}, \frac{2}{3}, z)$ corresponds to a maximum of the trace curve in the $y = \frac{2}{3}$ plane, and because $\dfrac{\partial^2 z}{\partial y^2} = -10$, one can conclude that $(\frac{4}{3}, \frac{2}{3}, z)$ is also a maximum of the trace of the surface in the $x = \frac{4}{3}$ plane. However, $\dfrac{\partial^2 z}{\partial x \partial y} = 2$, a positive value. What effect does this fact have on the nature of z at $(\frac{4}{3}, \frac{2}{3})$? For the moment, let us assume that we do have a maximum. The value of the maximum is

$$f\left(\frac{4}{3}, \frac{2}{3}\right) = 2\left(\frac{4}{3}\right)\left(\frac{2}{3}\right) - 5\left(\frac{2}{3}\right)^2 - 2\left(\frac{4}{3}\right)^2 + 4\left(\frac{4}{3}\right) + 4\left(\frac{2}{3}\right) - 4$$

$$= \frac{16}{9} - \frac{20}{9} - \frac{32}{9} + \frac{16}{3} + \frac{8}{3} - 4$$

$$= \frac{16 - 20 - 32 + 48 + 24 - 36}{9}$$

$$= \frac{88 - 88}{9}$$

$$= 0.$$

Is 0 actually the largest value of z? We will have to develop a test. Before examining a test for maximum and minimum let us consider an example of a function with neither.

Example. Find the extrema of

$$z = (x - 1)^2 - (y - 2)^2.$$

Solution. $$\frac{\partial z}{\partial x} = 2(x - 1).$$

$$\frac{\partial z}{\partial y} = -2(y - 2).$$

Clearly the only possibility for an extremum occurs at (1,2).
Checking second partials,

$$\left.\frac{\partial^2 z}{\partial x^2}\right|_{(1,2)} = 2, \text{ and}$$

$$\left.\frac{\partial^2 z}{\partial y^2}\right|_{(1,2)} = -2.$$

Our conclusion is that the trace of z in the $y = +2$ plane has a maximum
at (1,2) while the trace of the surface in the $x = 1$ plane has a minimum
at (1,2). Thus, (1,2) cannot correspond to either a maximum or minimum
value of z. This point is called a saddle point, and is illustrated in figure 7-12.

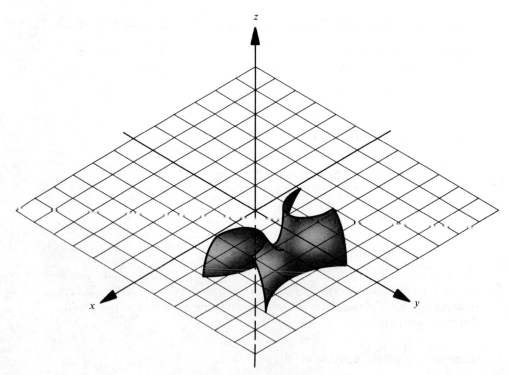

FIG. 7-12. A Graph of $z = (x - 1)^2 - (y - 2)^2$

To make the application of extrema of functions of two variables useful, a simple test is required which will indicate whether a pair of values (x_0, y_0), which produce simultaneous zeros of the first partial derivatives, are maxima or minima of $f(x, y)$. Advanced calculus supplies just such a test, which we will use without proof.

Definition.   For a given function $z = f(x, y)$,

$$\Delta = \frac{\partial^2 z}{\partial x^2} \cdot \frac{\partial^2 z}{\partial y^2} - \left(\frac{\partial^2 z}{\partial x \partial y} \right)^2,$$

and $\Delta|_{(x_0, y_0)}$ denotes Δ evaluated at $x = x_0, y = y_0$.

Definition.   *The Δ test.* Let $z = f(x, y)$ be a function of two variables, and (x_0, y_0) such that

$$\frac{\partial z}{\partial x} \bigg|_{(x_0, y_0)} = 0, \text{ and}$$

$$\frac{\partial z}{\partial y} \bigg|_{(x_0, y_0)} = 0.$$

Then if $\Delta|_{(x_0, y_0)} > 0$ and $\frac{\partial^2 z}{\partial x^2} < 0$ or $\frac{\partial^2 z}{\partial y^2} < 0$, $f(x_0, y_0)$ is a maximum value of z. If $\Delta|_{(x_0, y_0)} > 0$ and $\frac{\partial^2 z}{\partial x^2} > 0$ or $\frac{\partial^2 z}{\partial y^2} > 0$, then $f(x_0, y_0)$ is a minimum value of z. If $\Delta|_{(x_0, y_0)} < 0$, then $f(x_0, y_0)$ is neither a maximum nor minimum value for z. If $\Delta|_{(x_0, y_0)} = 0$, the Δ test fails.

Notice that if $\frac{\partial^2 z}{\partial x^2}$ and $\frac{\partial^2 z}{\partial y^2}$ differ in sign then $\Delta < 0$ and we have neither a maximum nor minimum. When $\Delta = 0$ the test fails, meaning we cannot tell with this test if the point is a maximum or minimum. Some other method must be used in these cases.

Example.   If $z = (x - 1)^2 - (y - 2)^2$ as in a previous example, $(1, 2)$ is the only possibility for an extremum. What does the Δ test tell us about this function?

Solution. $\frac{\partial^2 z}{\partial x^2} = 2, \frac{\partial^2 z}{\partial y^2} = -2, \frac{\partial^2 z}{\partial x \partial y} = 0,$ thus

$$\Delta|_{(1, 2)} = (2)(-2) - (0)^2 = -4,$$

indicating that z has no maxima or minima.

Example. If $z = 2xy - 5y^2 - 2x^2 + 4x + 4y - 4$, $(\frac{4}{3}, \frac{2}{3})$ corresponds to the only possible extremum for z. Apply the Δ test.

Solution. $\dfrac{\partial^2 z}{\partial x^2} = -4$, $\dfrac{\partial^2 z}{\partial y^2} = -10$, and $\dfrac{\partial^2 z}{\partial x \partial y} = 2$.

Thus,

$$\Delta \left| \left(\frac{4}{3}, \frac{2}{3} \right) \right. = (-4)(-10) - (2)^2 = 36$$

Since $\dfrac{\partial^2 z}{\partial x^2} < 0$, this must correspond to a relative maximum. Thus

$f(\frac{4}{3}, \frac{2}{3}) = 0$ is the maximum value of z.

Example. Find the extrema of $f(x, y) = z = 7x^2 + y^2 - 5xy - 3x + 6y - 2$.

Solution. $\qquad\qquad\qquad \dfrac{\partial z}{\partial x} = 14x - 5y - 3$.

$$\dfrac{\partial z}{\partial y} = 2y - 5x + 6.$$

Setting these to zero and solving,

$$14x - 5y - 3 = 0, \text{ and}$$
$$-5x + 2y + 6 = 0;$$

or

$$28x - 10y - 6 = 0, \text{ and}$$
$$\underline{-25x + 10y + 30 = 0.}$$
$$3x + 24 = 0$$
$$x = 8.$$

Thus, $\qquad\qquad -5(-8) + 2y + 6 = 0$
$$40 + 2y + 6 = 0$$
$$2y = -46.$$
$$y = -23.$$

$$\dfrac{\partial^2 z}{\partial x^2} = 14.$$

$$\dfrac{\partial^2 z}{\partial y^2} = 2.$$

$$\frac{\partial^2 z}{\partial x \partial y} = -5.$$

$$\Delta|_{(-8,-23)} = (14)(2) - (-5)^2 = 3.$$

Since $\frac{\partial^2 z}{\partial x^2} = 14$, a positive value, we conclude

$$f(-8, -23) = 7(-8)^2 + (-23)^2 - 5(-8)(-23) - 3(-8) + 6(-23) - 2$$

$$= 448 + 529 - 920 + 24 - 138 - 2$$

$$= 1001 - 1060$$

$$= -59$$

is a minimum value for z.

Example.   Find any extrema of

$$z = f(x,y) = y \ln x - x.$$

Solution.

$$\frac{\partial z}{\partial x} = \frac{y}{x} - 1,$$

$$\frac{\partial^2 z}{\partial x^2} = \frac{-y}{x^2},$$

$$\frac{\partial z}{\partial y} = \ln x,$$

$$\frac{\partial^2 z}{\partial y^2} = 0, \text{ and}$$

$$\frac{\partial^2 z}{\partial x \partial y} = \frac{1}{x}.$$

Setting $\frac{\partial z}{\partial x}$ and $\frac{\partial z}{\partial y}$ equal to zero.

$$\frac{y}{x} - 1 = 0, \frac{y - x}{x} = 0, \text{ or } x = y.$$

$$\ln x = 0, \text{ therefore } x = 1.$$

Thus the only possibility for an extremum is at $(1,1)$.

$$\Delta|_{(1,1)} = \left(\frac{-1}{1^2}\right)(0) - \left(\frac{1}{1}\right)^2$$

$$= -1.$$

There are no maxima or minima.

Example.   Find the maximum and minimum values, if any, for

$$z = f(x,y) = 2x^4 - x^2 + 3y^2.$$

Solution.

$$\frac{\partial z}{\partial x} = 8x^3 - 2x,$$

$$\frac{\partial^2 z}{\partial x^2} = 24x^2 - 2,$$

$$\frac{\partial z}{\partial y} = 6y,$$

$$\frac{\partial^2 z}{\partial y^2} = 6, \text{ and}$$

$$\frac{\partial^2 z}{\partial x \partial y} = 0.$$

Setting $\dfrac{\partial z}{\partial x}$ and $\dfrac{\partial z}{\partial y}$ to zero,

$$8x^3 - 2x = 0, \text{ or } 2x(4x^2 - 1) = 0.$$

$$x = 0, \text{ or } x = \pm\tfrac{1}{2}.$$

$$6y = 0 \text{ or } y = 0.$$

Thus the criteria yield three possible points to test: $(0,0)$, $(\tfrac{1}{2},0)$, and $(-\tfrac{1}{2},0)$.

$$\Delta = (24x^2 - 2)(6) - 0$$

$$\Delta|_{(0,0)} = -12 \text{ no maximum or minimum}$$

$$\Delta|_{(\frac{1}{2},0)} = (24(\tfrac{1}{4}) - 2)(6) = 24.$$

$$\frac{\partial^2 z}{\partial x^2}\Big|_{(\frac{1}{2},0)} = (24x^2 - 2) = 6 - 2 = 4.$$

Thus z is a minimum at $(\tfrac{1}{2},0)$

$$\Delta|_{(-\frac{1}{2},0)} = 24, \text{ and}$$

$$\frac{\partial^2 z}{\partial x^2}\Big|_{(-\frac{1}{2},0)} = 4, \text{ indicating } (-\tfrac{1}{2},0)$$

also yields a relative minimum

$$f(\tfrac{1}{2},0) = 2(\tfrac{1}{2})^4 - (\tfrac{1}{2})^2 + 3(0)^2 = \tfrac{2}{16} - \tfrac{1}{4} = -\tfrac{1}{8}.$$

$$f(-\tfrac{1}{2},0) = 2(-\tfrac{1}{2})^4 - (-\tfrac{1}{2})^2 + 3(0)^2 = -\tfrac{1}{8}.$$

Problems of a less abstract nature can also be considered with this procedure.

Example.   Suppose that a long range economic model yields the conclusion that the return from a certain type of investment will be determined by two factors, one measured by x and a second by y, with R, the return, given by

$$R = ke^{-(x-2)^2-(y-3)^2}$$

where k is a positive constant. What values of x and y will produce a maximum return?

Solution. $R = ke^{-(x-2)^2} \cdot e^{-(y-3)^2}$

Therefore,

$$\frac{\partial R}{\partial x} = 2k(-(x-2))e^{-(x-2)^2} \cdot e^{-(y-3)^2}.$$

$$\frac{\partial R}{\partial y} = -2k(y-3)e^{-(x-2)^2} \cdot e^{-(y-3)^2}.$$

$$\frac{\partial^2 R}{\partial x^2} = -2k\left[(x-2)2(-(x-2))e^{-(x-2)^2} + e^{-(x-2)^2}\right]e^{-(y-3)^2}.$$

$$\frac{\partial^2 R}{\partial y^2} = -2k\left[(y-3)2[-(y-3)]e^{-(y-3)^2} + e^{-(y-3)^2}\right]e^{-(x-2)^2}.$$

$$\frac{\partial^2 R}{\partial x \partial y} = 4k(x-2)(y-3)e^{-(x-2)^2}e^{-(y-3)^2}.$$

When $\dfrac{\partial R}{\partial x}$ and $\dfrac{\partial R}{\partial y}$ are set equal to zero,

$$-2k(x-2)e^{-(x-2)^2}e^{-(y-3)^2} = 0, \ x = 2, \text{ and}$$

$$-2k(y-3)e^{-(x-2)^2}e^{-(y-3)^2} = 0, \ y = 3.$$

Thus the only possible maximum or minimum is $(2,3)$

$$\Delta|_{(2,3)} = \{-2k[(x-2)2(-(x-2))e^{-(x-2)^2} + e^{-(x-2)^2}]e^{-(y-3)^2}\}$$
$$\times \{-2k[(y-3)2(-(y-3))e^{-(y-3)^2} + e^{-(y-3)^2}]e^{-(x-2)^2}\}$$
$$- [4k(x-2)(y-3)e^{-(x-2)^2}e^{-(y-3)^2}]^2$$

$$= 4k^2.$$

Since,

$$\Delta|_{(2,3)} > 0 \text{ and } \frac{\partial^2 R}{\partial x^2} = -2k < 0$$

$(2,3)$ corresponds to a maximum value for R.

$$R|_{(2,3)} = ke^{-(2-2)^2-(3-3)^2} = k.$$

7-4   Exercises

(1-16)   Apply the Δ test to determine the extrema for each of the following if possible.

1. $z = f(x,y) = x^3 - 12xy + 8y^3$
2. $z = f(x,y) = x^2 - y^2 - 2xy - 4x$
3. $z = f(x,y) = x^2 + xy + y^2 - 3x + 2$
4. $z = f(x,y) = x^2 - xy + y^2 - x - y$
5. $z = f(x,y) = x^3 - 12x + y^2$
6. $z = f(x,y) = x^3 - 6x - 6xy + 6y + 3y^2$
7. $z = f(x,y) = x^3 + y^3 - 9xy$
8. $z = f(x,y) = 4 - x^{\frac{2}{3}} - y^{\frac{2}{3}}$

9. $z = f(x,y) = \dfrac{1}{x} + xy - \dfrac{8}{y}.$

10. $z = f(x,y) = x^4 + y^4 - 4xy$
11. $z = f(x,y) = x^2 + 9 + 6x \cos y$
12. $z = f(x,y) = 25 + (x - y)^4 + (x - 1)^4$
13. $z = f(x,y) = xy(4 - x - y)$
14. $z = f(x,y) = 4 \ln x + e^y - x - y$

15. $z = f(x,y) = \dfrac{xy}{2} - \ln(x^2 + y^2)^{\frac{1}{2}}$

16. $z = f(x,y) = \sin x + \sin y + \sin(x + y)$
17.   In a certain economic model, the cost, z, of a given item is related to two factors, measured in x and y, by the equation $z = x^2 + y^2 - \ln xy$, where $x > 0$ and $y > 0$. Determine the values of x and y which will correspond to a minimum value of z.
18.   The profit P from the sales of a certain commodity is related to cost, production factors, advertising costs, etc., by the equation

$$P = -4a^2 - 2b^2 - ab + 18b + 20a,$$

where a and b are variables describing actual costs in thousands of dollars. Determine how much should be invested in each factor to maximize profit.
19.   A sociological analysis indicates that a parameter measuring the crime rate, R, depends on the amount spent on welfare, as measured in w hundreds of millions of dollars, and on the amount spent on prisons as measured by p in hundreds of millions of dollars.

$$R = w^3 + 2p^3 - 6w + 6p - 6wp.$$

How much should be spent on each type of program to yield a minimum crime rate parameter?

20.   The profit P as a function of the prices, x and y, of two competing items is given by

$$P = 65 - 2(x - 7)^2 - 4(y - 7)^2 - 4x - 2y + 14.$$

Determine the values of x and y which maximize profits.

(21-24)   The method known as "least squares" is used to find the line $y = mx + b$ that best fits a set of experimental data, (x_1,y_1), (x_2,y_2), . . . , (x_n,y_n). If the line fits the data perfectly, then for any pair, (x_i,y_i), $y_i = mx_i + b$. In general, however, y_i will not be exactly $mx_i + b$. Thus, y_i will deviate from $mx_i + b$ by $y_i - (mx_i + b)$. We wish to choose m and b so that all the deviations will be minimum. Some of the deviations will be positive and others will be negative. If we take the squares of the deviations, they will all be positive or zero. Thus a negative deviation will "count" as much as a positive one. Since the experimental data are known, if we add the squares of all the deviations, we will have a function of two variables, m and b, which we wish to minimize. That is, the line $y = mx + b$ that best fits is the one for which

$$f(m,b) = \sum_{i=1}^{n} [y_i - (mx_i + b)]^2$$

is minimum. Find such a line for the data given below.

21. $(0,0)$, $(4,3)$, $(2,2)$
22. $(1,2)$, $(0,1)$, $(6,-2)$
23. $(2,0)$, $(0,1)$, $(-3,2)$
24. $(0,5)$, $(2,1)$, $(-1,3)$

7-5   THE CHAIN RULE AND TOTAL DIFFERENTIALS

Two very useful concepts related to the differentiation of a function of a single variable were the chain rule and the differential. Both of these ideas have parallels related to the functions of two variables. Suppose z is a function of two variables, x and y, while x and y, in turn, are functions of two more variables, u and v. That is,

$$z = f(x,y), \ x = h(u,v), \text{ and } y = g(u,v).$$

Then the chain rule for partial differentiation states

$$\frac{\partial z}{\partial u} = \frac{\partial z}{\partial x} \cdot \frac{\partial x}{\partial u} + \frac{\partial z}{\partial y} \cdot \frac{\partial y}{\partial u},$$

and

$$\frac{\partial z}{\partial v} = \frac{\partial z}{\partial x} \cdot \frac{\partial x}{\partial v} + \frac{\partial z}{\partial y} \cdot \frac{\partial y}{\partial v}.$$

Example. If $z = 3x^2 + 2y$, $x = u^2 v$ and $y = u^2 - v^3$ find $\dfrac{\partial z}{\partial u}$ and $\dfrac{\partial z}{\partial v}$.

Solution.
$$\frac{\partial z}{\partial x} = 6x.$$

$$\frac{\partial z}{\partial y} = 2.$$

$$\frac{\partial x}{\partial u} = 2uv.$$

$$\frac{\partial x}{\partial v} = u^2.$$

$$\frac{\partial y}{\partial u} = 2u.$$

$$\frac{\partial y}{\partial v} = -3v^2.$$

Thus,

$$\frac{\partial z}{\partial u} = (6x)(2uv) + 2(2u) = 12(u^2 v)uv + 4u = 12u^3 v^2 + 4u.$$

$$\frac{\partial z}{\partial v} = (6x)(u^2) + 2(-3v^2) = 6(u^2 v)u^2 - 6v^2 = 6u^4 v - 6v^2.$$

Example. If $z = 3x^2 y$ and $x = \dfrac{4u^2}{v}$ and $y = \ln\left(\dfrac{u}{v}\right)$ find $\dfrac{\partial z}{\partial u}$ and $\dfrac{\partial z}{\partial v}$.

Solution.
$$\frac{\partial z}{\partial x} = 6xy,$$

$$\frac{\partial z}{\partial y} = 3x^2,$$

$$\frac{\partial x}{\partial u} = \frac{8u}{v},$$

$$\frac{\partial y}{\partial u} = \frac{1}{u}, \text{ and}$$

$$\frac{\partial y}{\partial v} = -\frac{1}{v}.$$

$$\frac{\partial x}{\partial v} = \frac{-4u^2}{v^2},$$

Therefore,

$$\frac{\partial z}{\partial u} = \frac{\partial z}{\partial x}\frac{\partial x}{\partial u} + \frac{\partial z}{\partial y}\frac{\partial y}{\partial u}$$

$$= 6xy\left(\frac{8u}{v}\right) + 3x^2\left(\frac{1}{u}\right)$$

$$= 6\left(\frac{4u^2}{v}\right)\ln\left(\frac{u}{v}\right)\left(\frac{8u}{v}\right) + 3\left(\frac{4u^2}{v}\right)^2\frac{1}{u}.$$

$$= 192\frac{u^3}{v^2}\ln\left(\frac{u}{v}\right) + 48\frac{u^3}{v^2}.$$

$$\frac{\partial z}{\partial v} = \frac{\partial z}{\partial x}\frac{\partial x}{\partial v} + \frac{\partial z}{\partial y}\frac{\partial y}{\partial v}$$

$$= 6xy\left(\frac{-4u^2}{v^2}\right) + (3x^2)\left(-\frac{1}{v}\right)$$

$$= 6\left(\frac{4u^2}{v}\right)\ln\left(\frac{u}{v}\right)\left(\frac{-4u^2}{v^2}\right) + 3\left(\frac{4u^2}{v}\right)^2\left(-\frac{1}{v}\right)$$

$$= -96\frac{u^4}{v^3}\ln\left(\frac{u}{v}\right) - 48\frac{u^4}{v^3} = -48\left\{2\ln\left(\frac{u}{v}\right) + 1\right\}\frac{u^4}{v^3}.$$

Example.   If $z = x^2 \cos 2y$ and $x = \sqrt{u^2 + v^2}$ and $y = \tan^{-1}\left(\frac{u}{v}\right)$ find

$\dfrac{\partial z}{\partial u}$ and $\dfrac{\partial z}{\partial v}$.

Solution. $\dfrac{\partial z}{\partial x} = 2x \cos 2y.$

$$\frac{\partial z}{\partial y} = -2x^2 \sin(2y).$$

$$\frac{\partial x}{\partial u} = \frac{u}{\sqrt{u^2 + v^2}} = \frac{u}{x}.$$

$$\frac{\partial x}{\partial v} = \frac{v}{\sqrt{u^2 + v^2}} = \frac{v}{x}.$$

$$\frac{\partial y}{\partial u} = \frac{1}{1 + \left(\dfrac{u}{v}\right)^2} \cdot \frac{1}{v} = \frac{\dfrac{1}{v}}{\dfrac{v^2 + u^2}{v^2}} = \frac{v}{u^2 + v^2} = \frac{v}{x^2}.$$

$$\frac{\partial y}{\partial v} = \frac{1}{1 + \left(\dfrac{u}{v}\right)^2} \left(\frac{-u}{v^2}\right) = \frac{-u}{v^2 + u^2} = \frac{-u}{x^2}.$$

Thus,

$$\frac{\partial z}{\partial u} = \frac{\partial z}{\partial x} \frac{\partial x}{\partial u} + \frac{\partial z}{\partial y} \frac{\partial y}{\partial u}$$

$$= (2x \cos 2y)\left(\frac{u}{x}\right) + (-2x^2 \sin 2y)\left(\frac{v}{x^2}\right)$$

$$= 2u \cos 2y - 2v \sin 2y.$$

$$\frac{\partial z}{\partial v} = \frac{\partial z}{\partial x} \frac{\partial x}{\partial v} + \frac{\partial z}{\partial y} \frac{\partial y}{\partial v}$$

$$= (2x \cos 2y)\left(\frac{v}{x}\right) + (-2x^2 \sin 2y)\left(\frac{-u}{x^2}\right)$$

$$= 2v \cos 2y + 2u \sin 2y.$$

Now consider the case when x and y, instead of being functions of two variables, are functions of a single variable t. That is

$$z = f(x,y), \; x = h(t), \text{ and } y = g(t).$$

Then $\dfrac{\partial x}{\partial t}$ and $\dfrac{dx}{dt}$ are equal, as are $\dfrac{\partial y}{\partial t}$ and $\dfrac{dy}{dt}$. The chain rule becomes

$$\frac{\partial z}{\partial t} = \frac{dz}{dt} = \frac{\partial z}{\partial x} \cdot \frac{dx}{dt} + \frac{\partial z}{\partial y} \cdot \frac{dy}{dt}.$$

In this case, $\dfrac{dz}{dt}$ is called the total derivative of z.

Example. If $z = xe^y + y^2$, $x = t \cos t$, and $y = t \sin t$, find $\dfrac{dz}{dt}$.

Solution.

$$\frac{dx}{dt} = -t \sin t + \cos t, \text{ and}$$

$$\frac{dy}{dt} = t \cos t + \sin t.$$

Therefore,

$$\frac{dz}{dt} = \frac{\partial z}{\partial x}\frac{dx}{dt} + \frac{\partial z}{\partial y}\frac{dy}{dt}$$

$$= e^y(-t \sin t + \cos t) + (xe^y + 2y)(t \cos t + \sin t).$$

To obtain an expression in t alone, one would only have to substitute for x and y in the final expression.

The total differential can then be defined as follows.

> **Definition.** If $z = f(x,y)$, and dx and dy are differential changes in x and y, then
>
> $$dz = f_x dx + f_y dy = \frac{\partial z}{\partial x} dx + \frac{\partial z}{\partial y} dy.$$

Example.   If $z = 4x^3 y^2$, find dz.

Solution. $dz = (12x^2 y^2)dx + (8x^3 y)dy.$

Example.   If $z = \ln x^2 - y$, $dx = 0.3$, $dy = 0.4$, $x = 1$, and $y = 2$, calculate dz.

Solution. $dz = \left(\dfrac{2}{x}\right)dx - dy$

$$= \left(\frac{2}{1}\right)(0.3) - 0.4 = 0.6 - 0.4 = 0.2.$$

In the case of the function of a single variable $y = f(x)$, dy is interpreted as the change in y along the tangent line to $y = f(x)$, if x is changed by the amount dx. The actual change in y along $y = f(x)$ is given by $\Delta y = f(x + dx) - f(x)$ and if dx is small, Δy is approximated by dy. In a more complete development of three-dimensional analytic geometry than has been presented here, it would be necessary to supply an appropriate definition of the plane tangent to a surface $z = f(x,y)$ at a pair of values (x,y). If x and y are changed by an amount dx and dy then dz corresponds to the change in z along that tangent plane. The actual change in z along the surface is given by $\Delta z = f(x + dx, y + dy) - f(x,y)$. As in the function of a single variable Δz is approximated by dz, if dx and dy are small.

Example.   Suppose $z = f(x,y) = \sqrt{1 + xy}$. Estimate Δz when $x = 4$, $y = 2$, $dx = 0.1$, and $dy = 0.3$.

Solution. $dz = \dfrac{y}{2\sqrt{1 + xy}} dx + \dfrac{x}{2\sqrt{1 + xy}} dy$

$= \dfrac{2}{2\sqrt{1 + (2)4}} (0.1) + \dfrac{4}{2\sqrt{1 + (2)4}} (0.3)$

$= \dfrac{0.1}{3} + \dfrac{0.6}{3} = \dfrac{0.7}{3} = \dfrac{7}{30} \approx 0.23.$

7-5   Exercises

(1-10)   For the given functions, calculate the indicated derivatives.

1. $z = x^2 + y^2$, $x = u \cos v$, $y = u \sin v$ calculate $\dfrac{\partial z}{\partial u}$, $\dfrac{\partial z}{\partial v}$

2. $z = x^2 + xy + y^2$, $x = u + v$, $y = u - v$ calculate $\dfrac{\partial z}{\partial u}$, $\dfrac{\partial z}{\partial v}$

3. $z = e^{x+y} - e^{-x-y}$, $x = \ln u$, $y = \ln v$ calculate $\dfrac{\partial z}{\partial u}$ and $\dfrac{\partial z}{\partial v}$

4. $z = \tan^{-1}x + \sqrt{1 - y^2}$, $x = u^2$, $y = v - 1$ calculate $\dfrac{\partial z}{\partial u}$, $\dfrac{\partial z}{\partial v}$

5. $z = e^{x/y}$, $x = u + 2v$, $y = 2u - v$ calculate $\dfrac{\partial z}{\partial u}$ and $\dfrac{\partial z}{\partial v}$

6. $z = \cos(xy)$, $x = u^2 v$, $y = e^{uv}$ calculate $\dfrac{\partial z}{\partial u}$ and $\dfrac{\partial z}{\partial v}$

7. $z = \dfrac{x}{y} + y$, $x = t^2 - 1$, $y = t - 1$ calculate $\dfrac{dz}{dt}$

8. $z = \tan^{-1} \dfrac{r}{\theta}$, $r = x + \sin y$, $\theta = x - \sin y$ calculate $\dfrac{\partial z}{\partial x}$ and $\dfrac{\partial z}{\partial y}$

9. $w = u^2 + ve^u$, $u = x \sin x$, $v = x \cos x$ find $\dfrac{dw}{dx}$

10. $w = x^2y + y^2x$, $x = \ln\left(\dfrac{u}{v}\right)$, $y = \ln (uv)$ calculate $\dfrac{\partial w}{\partial u}$ and $\dfrac{\partial w}{\partial v}$

(11-15)   Calculate dz in each case.

11. $z = (x + 2y)^2$

12. $z = \ln(x - \ln y)$

13. $z = x^2 + 2xy + 2y^2 + x + y$

14. $z = e^{-x-y}$

15. $z = \sin^2(xy) + \cos^2(xy)$

16. If $z = 3x^2 + 2y$, $x = u^2 v$,   and $y = u^2 - v^3$,   verify   that

$$\frac{\partial z}{\partial u} = 12u^3 v^2 + 4u$$

$$\frac{\partial z}{\partial v} = 6u^4 v - 6v^2 \text{ by replacing } x \text{ and } y \text{ with their expressions in } u \text{ and } v$$

and calculating $\dfrac{\partial z}{\partial u}$ and $\dfrac{\partial z}{\partial v}$ directly.

17. If $z = 3x^2 y$, $x = \dfrac{4u^2}{v}$ and $y = \ln\left(\dfrac{u}{v}\right)$ verify by substitution and direct

calculation that $\dfrac{\partial z}{\partial u} = 192 \dfrac{u^3}{v^2} \ln\left(\dfrac{u}{v}\right) + 48 \dfrac{u^3}{v^2}$ and $\dfrac{\partial z}{\partial v} = -48 \cdot$

$\left[2\ln\left(\dfrac{u}{v}\right) + 1\right]\dfrac{u^4}{v^3}.$

18. If $z = x^2 \cos 2y$ and $x = \sqrt{u^2 + v^2}$ and $y = \tan^{-1}\left(\dfrac{u}{v}\right)$ as in the text

example verify by direct substitution and calculation that

$\dfrac{\partial z}{\partial u} = 2u \cos 2y - 2v \sin 2y$ and $\dfrac{\partial z}{\partial v} = 2v \cos 2y + 2u \sin 2y.$

19. For the example $z = \sqrt{1 + xy}$ with $x = 4$, $y = 2$, $dx = 0.1$, $dy = 0.3$
in the text calculate Δz, the actual value of the change in z.

20. If two sides of a triangle are measured and found to be $3 \pm .01$ inches
and $9 \pm .03$ inches, and the angle between the sides is known to be
exactly $60°$, estimate the area of the triangle and set limits on the
accuracy of the estimate. (*Hint*: find the area of the triangle, A, as a
function of the lengths of the sides and calculate dA).

(21-23) If $y = f(x)$ and $w = g(x)$ the following rules for differentials hold.

$$dy = f'(x)\, dx,$$

$$dw = g'(x)\, dx,$$

$$d(y + w) = dy + dw,$$

$$d(y \cdot w) = y\, dw + w\, dy, \text{ and}$$

$$d\left(\frac{y}{w}\right) = \frac{w\, dy - y\, dw}{w^2}.$$

Show that if $z = f(x,y)$, and $w = g(x,y)$:

21. $d(z + w) = dz + dw$

22. $d(z \cdot w) = z\,dw + w\,dz$

23. $d\left(\dfrac{z}{w}\right) = \dfrac{w\,dz - z\,dw}{w^2}$

Chapter 7   REVIEW

1. Give three examples of everyday quantities whose value depends on the value of two independent quantities.

2. What conventions normally apply to the domain of a function of two variables defined by an equation when the domain of the function is not specified?

(3-10) For each of the following defining expressions determine the domain of the function, and sketch that domain in an xy plane.

3. $f(x,y) = \dfrac{\sqrt{(x-2)^2 + 1}}{(y-2)(y+3)}$

4. $f(x,y) = \dfrac{\sin(x+y)}{\cos(x+y)}$

5. $f(x,y) = \sqrt{25 - x^2 - y^2}$

6. $f(x,y) = \ln xy$

7. $f(x,y) = \dfrac{e^x}{e^y}(x^2 + y^2)$

8. $f(x,y) = \dfrac{e^x + e^{-x}}{2}$

9. $f(x,y) = \dfrac{y^2 - x^2}{(x+y)(y-2)}$

10. $f(x,y) = \sin\left(\dfrac{1}{x+y}\right) \cdot e^{x+y}$

11. Restate the defining expression for each of the functions in problems 3-10 in the $f: (x,y) \rightarrow$ image form of section 7-1.

(12-16) Find each of the functional images indicated.

12. $f(x,y) = \dfrac{\sqrt{(x-2)^2 + 1}}{(y-2)(y+3)}$, find $f(0,0), f(1,4), f(4,1), f(2,2)$

13. $f(x,y) = \sqrt{25 - x^2 - y^2}$, find $f(0,0), f(3,4), f(-3,4), f(1,2), f(5,1)$

14. $f(x,y) = \dfrac{e^x}{e^y}(x^2 + y^2)$, find $f(1,1), f(3,\ln 2), f(0,1), f(-1,-2), f(x,x)$

15. $f(x,y) = \sin\left(\dfrac{1}{x+y}\right) \cdot e^{x+y}$, find $f\left(0,\dfrac{2}{\pi}\right), f\left(\dfrac{4}{\pi},\dfrac{2}{\pi}\right), f(1,-1)$

16. $f(x,y) = \dfrac{|x||y - x|}{|x| - 2}$, find $f(1,1), f(2,1), f(0,0), f(x,x)$, and $f(w,w)$

(17-25) Using traces sketch in three dimensions each of the following surfaces.

17. $z = x^2 + y^2$

18. $z = \sin x + 1 - y$

19. $z = 36 - (x - 2)^2 - (y - 2)^2$

20. $z = e^{\frac{1}{2}(x^2 + y^2)}$

21. $z = x^2 - y^2$

22. $z = (x - y)x^2$

23. $z = x^2 + 4x + 4 + y^2 + 6y + 9$

24. $z = x + 2y - 3$

25. $z = -x - y - 4$

(26-30) An alternate to the three-dimensional rectangular coordinates in a plane is cylindrical coordinates. These are defined by using polar coordinates in the xy plane rather than the usual coordinates, and retaining z as a measure of the distance above or below the xy plane.

Then $\qquad x = r\cos\theta, \; y = r\sin\theta$, and $z = z$

where (x,y,z) are the rectangular coordinates of a point, and (r,θ,z) the cylindrical coordinates. See figure 7-13.

26. Plot the following points in cylindrical coordinates: $(1,0,1)$, $(1,\pi,1)$, $(3,2\pi,2)$, $(-2,\pi,0)$, $\left(3,\dfrac{\pi}{4},1\right)$, $\left(3,-\dfrac{\pi}{4},1\right)$, and $\left(3,\dfrac{\pi}{3},1\right)$.

27. What is the three-dimensional surface described by the cylindrical coordinate equation $r = 5$?

28. Describe the surface defined by the cylindrical coordinate equation $\theta = \dfrac{\pi}{4}$.

29. Describe the surface defined by the cylindrical coordinate equation $z = \sqrt{25 - r^2}$.

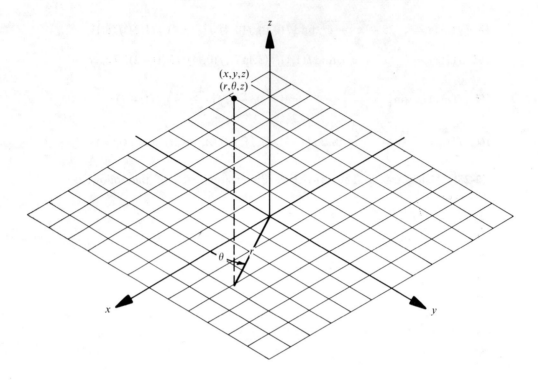

FIG. 7-13.   Cylindrical Coordinates

30.   Find the cylindrical coordinate equation for the surface described by the rectangular coordinate equation

$$z = \sqrt{25 - (x - 5)^2 + y^2}.$$

(31-40)   Find the indicated partial derivatives.

31. $z = e^{x/y}$, find $\dfrac{\partial z}{\partial x}, \dfrac{\partial^2 z}{\partial x^2}, \dfrac{\partial^3 z}{\partial x^2 \partial y}$

32. $z = \sqrt{x^2 + y^2}$, find $\dfrac{\partial z}{\partial x}, \dfrac{\partial z}{\partial y}, \dfrac{\partial^2 z}{\partial x^2}, \dfrac{\partial^2 z}{\partial x \partial y}$

33. $z = xe^y + ye^x$, find $\dfrac{\partial z}{\partial x}, \dfrac{\partial z}{\partial y}, \dfrac{\partial^2 z}{\partial x \partial y}$

34. $z = \dfrac{x^2 - y^2}{x^2 + y^2}$, find $\dfrac{\partial^3 z}{\partial x \partial y^2}$

35. $z = (x^2 + 3y^2 x)$, find $\dfrac{\partial^4 z}{\partial x^4}$.

36. If $z = \sin^{-1} xy$, $x = u + v$, and $y = u - v$, find $\dfrac{\partial z}{\partial u}$ and $\dfrac{\partial z}{\partial v}$.

37. $z = x^2 + y^2$, $x = \sin u \cos v$, and $y = \cos u \cos v$, find $\dfrac{\partial z}{\partial u}$ and $\dfrac{\partial z}{\partial v}$.

38. $z = \ln\left(\dfrac{x}{y}\right)$, $x = e^u$, and $y = e^{-v}$, find $\dfrac{\partial^2 z}{\partial u^2}$.

39. $z = \dfrac{x^2}{y^3}$, $x = u^2 v$, and $y = vu^2$, find $\dfrac{\partial^2 z}{\partial v^2}$.

40. $z = \sin\left(\dfrac{x}{y}\right)$, $y = u$, and $x = u \cos v$, find $\dfrac{\partial z}{\partial u}$ and $\dfrac{\partial z}{\partial v}$.

41. If $x = r \cos \theta$, $y = r \sin \theta$, and $z = f(x, y)$, show that

$$\left(\frac{\partial z}{\partial r}\right)^2 + \frac{1}{r^2}\left(\frac{\partial z}{\partial \theta}\right)^2 = \left(\frac{\partial z}{\partial x}\right)^2 + \left(\frac{\partial z}{\partial y}\right)^2.$$

42. Recalling Laplace's equation for a function of two variables, *i.e.*,

$$\frac{\partial^2 z}{\partial x^2} + \frac{\partial^2 z}{\partial y^2} = 0, \text{ show that}$$

$$z = e^x \sin y \text{ and } z = e^y \cos x$$

both satisfy Laplace's equation.

43. Show that if $z = f_1(x, y)$ and $z = f_2(x, y)$ both satisfy Laplace's equation, $z = f_1(x, y) + f_2(x, y)$ satisfies Laplace's equation.

(44-45) If $F(x, y) = 0$ implicitly defines y as a function of x, it can be shown that

$$\frac{dy}{dx} = \frac{-\dfrac{\partial F}{\partial x}}{\dfrac{\partial F}{\partial y}}. \text{ Find } \frac{dy}{dx} \text{ in each case.}$$

44. $F(x, y) = x^2 + y^2 - xy = 0$.

45. $F(x, y) = \sin(x + y) = 0$.

(46-51) Find the maxima and minima of the indicated functions.

46. $f(x, y) = 2xy^2 - x^3 + 3y$

47. $f(x, y) = \cos x - \sin y$, $0 \leq x \leq 2\pi$

48. $f(x, y) = x^2 y^2 - y$

49. $f(x,y) = 8x^3 - 12x - 12xy + 6y + 3y^2$

50. $f(x,y) = \dfrac{x^4}{16} + 16y^4 - 4xy$

51. $f(x,y) = x^2 + 4y^2 - 4x$

(52-54)   For the given function with $dx = \frac{1}{2}$ and $dy = -\frac{1}{3}$, calculate dz at the indicated point.

52. $z = x^2y^2 - y$ at $(2,1)$

53. $z = \sin x - \cos y$ at $\left(\dfrac{\pi}{2}, \dfrac{\pi}{3} \right)$

54. $z = 2xy^2 - x^3 + 3y$ at $(2,-1)$

CHAPTER EIGHT

Several Variables—Continued

The process of integration can also be extended to functions of more than one variable, and just as there were two approaches to the extension of differentiation there are two approaches to the extension of integration. One approach involves the extension of the basic concept of an integral by translating the interval of integration into a region of integration. This approach will be considered in the next section. The second approach involves a repeated application of the usual integration process, treating one of the variables as a constant.

8-1 REPEATED INTEGRATION

Example. Let $z = x^2 y^3$, and evaluate $\int_0^4 z \, dx$, where y is treated as a constant.

Solution.
$$\int_0^4 z\,dx = \int_0^4 x^2 y^3\,dx = \frac{x^3 y^3}{3}\Bigg]_0^4$$

$$= \frac{4^3 y^3}{3} - \frac{0^3 y^3}{3} = \frac{64}{3} y^3.$$

In this example, the final result is still a function of y. Therefore, it can be integrated with respect to y.

Example. Evaluate $\displaystyle\int_1^3 \int_0^4 z\,dx\,dy$, where $z = x^2 y^3$, and $\displaystyle\int_0^4 z\,dx$ is evaluated treating y as a constant.

Solution.
$$\int_1^3 \int_0^4 z\,dx\,dy = \int_1^3 \left\{ \int_0^4 x^2 y^3\,dx \right\} dy$$

$$= \int_1^3 \frac{64}{3} y^3\,dy$$

$$= \frac{64}{3}\left[\frac{y^4}{4} \right]_1^3$$

$$= \frac{64}{3}\left(\frac{1}{4} \right)[3^4 - 1^4]$$

$$= \frac{16}{3}[81 - 1] = \frac{16}{3}(80) = \frac{1280}{3}.$$

In general, if $z = f(x,y)$, then

$$\int_a^b \int_c^d z\,dx\,dy = \int_a^b \left\{ \int_c^d z\,dx \right\} dy,$$

where the inner integral is evaluated by treating y as a constant.

Example. Evaluate $\displaystyle\int_0^5 \int_1^e \frac{y}{x}\,dx\,dy = I$.

Solution.
$$\int_1^e \frac{y}{x}\,dx = y\left[\ln x \right]_1^e$$

$$= y[\ln e - \ln 1]$$

$$= y[1 - 0]$$

$$= y.$$

Thus,

$$I = \int_0^5 y\,dy$$

$$= \frac{y^2}{2}\bigg]_0^5$$

$$= \frac{25}{2}.$$

In the preceding examples and the ones that follow, we will assume z is sufficiently well-behaved that no improper integration is involved.

Also, integrals will be found using the fundamental theorem approach (antidifferentiation) rather than by the definition of an integral or by some numerical scheme.

Since the inner integration treats y as a constant, the limits of integration could contain y, and thus depend on y. The mechanics are straightforward.

Example.   Evaluate $\displaystyle\int_4^5 \int_0^{y^2} xy\,dx\,dy = I$.

Solution.

$$\int_0^{y^2} xy\,dx = \frac{x^2 y}{2}\bigg]_0^{y^2} = \frac{(y^2)^2 y}{2} - \frac{0^2 y}{2}$$

$$= \frac{y^4 y}{2} = \frac{y^5}{2}.$$

Thus,

$$I = \int_4^5 \frac{y^5}{2}\,dy$$

$$= \frac{y^6}{12}\bigg]_4^5$$

$$= \frac{5^6}{12} - \frac{4^6}{12} = \frac{1}{12}[15625 - 4096]$$

$$= \frac{11529}{12} = \frac{3843}{4}.$$

Example.   Evaluate $\displaystyle I = \int_0^2 \int_{2y-4}^0 \frac{2x-1}{y+1}\,dx\,dy.$

Solution.

$$\int_{2y-4}^0 \frac{2x-1}{y+1}\,dx = \frac{1}{y+1}\Big[x^2 - x\Big]_{2y-4}^0$$

$$= \frac{1}{y+1} [0 - \{(2y-4)^2 - (2y-4)\}]$$

$$= \frac{-1}{y+1} [(2y-4)^2 - (2y-4)]$$

$$= \frac{-1}{y+1} [4y^2 - 16y + 16 - 2y + 4]$$

$$= \frac{-1}{y+1} [4y^2 - 18y + 20]$$

$$= \frac{-2}{y+1} [(2y^2 - 9y + 10)]$$

$$= -2 \left[2y - 11 + \frac{21}{y+1} \right].$$

Therefore,

$$I = -2 \int_0^2 \left(2y - 11 + \frac{21}{y+1} \right) dy$$

$$= -2 \left[y^2 - 11y + 21 \ln(y+1) \right]_0^2$$

$$= -2[4 - 22 + 21 \ln 3 - (0 - 0 + 21 \ln 1)]$$

$$= -2[-18 + 21 \ln 3]$$

$$= 6[6 - 7 \ln 3].$$

There is no reason why the inner integration must be with respect to x. That is,

$$\int_a^b \int_c^d f(x,y) \, dy \, dx$$

is evaluated with respect to y by treating x as a constant in the innermost integration. In this case, c and d can be functions of x.

Example.   Evaluate $I = \int_0^2 \int_0^{\sqrt{x+1}} \sqrt{x+1} \, y^4 \, dy \, dx$.

Solution. $\int_0^{\sqrt{x+1}} \sqrt{x+1} \, y^4 \, dy = \sqrt{x+1} \dfrac{y^5}{5} \Bigg]_0^{\sqrt{x+1}}$

$$= \frac{\sqrt{x+1} \, (\sqrt{x+1})^5}{5}$$

$$= \frac{(\sqrt{x+1})^6}{5}$$

$$= \frac{(x+1)^3}{5}.$$

Therefore,

$$I = \int_0^2 \frac{(x+1)^3}{5} dx = \frac{(x+1)^4}{20} \Bigg]_0^2$$

$$= \frac{3^4}{20} - \frac{1^4}{20} = \frac{81-1}{20} = \frac{80}{20} = 4.$$

8-1   Exercises

(1-20)   Evaluate each of the following repeated integrals.

1. $\displaystyle\int_{-1}^2 \int_0^4 (2y - x + 4)\, dx\, dy$

2. $\displaystyle\int_0^4 \int_{-1}^2 (2y - x + 4)\, dy\, dx$

3. $\displaystyle\int_1^4 \int_{-2}^2 xy\, dy\, dx$

4. $\displaystyle\int_0^4 \int_0^{y^2} \sqrt{16 - x}\, dx\, dy$

5. $\displaystyle\int_0^{10} \int_{x-5}^x xy\, dy\, dx$

6. $\displaystyle\int_0^3 \int_x^{x^2-1} (x - 1)\, dy\, dx$

7. $\displaystyle\int_0^3 \int_{2y}^{y^2} (y - 2x)\, dx\, dy$

8. $\displaystyle\int_1^3 \int_0^{\ln x} e^y \sqrt{(x - 1)^2 + 4}\, dy\, dx$

9. $\displaystyle\int_0^{\ln 2} \int_0^{\ln 2} e^{x+y}\, dx\, dy$

10. $\displaystyle\int_{-5}^5 \int_0^{\sqrt{25-x^2}} dy\, dx$

11. $\displaystyle\int_{-1}^{1}\int_{0}^{1-y^2}(x+y)\,dx\,dy$

12. $\displaystyle\int_{0}^{1}\int_{0}^{1-y^2}(x+y)\,dx\,dy$

13. $\displaystyle\int_{\pi/2}^{\pi}\int_{0}^{1-\sin y}x\,dx\,dy$

14. $\displaystyle\int_{0}^{\pi}\int_{\sin x}^{1}y\,dy\,dx$

15. $\displaystyle\int_{-3}^{3}\int_{y}^{2y}\sqrt{xy-y^2}\,dx\,dy$

16. $\displaystyle\int_{0}^{2}\int_{\sqrt{x}}^{(x^2+4)/2}xy\,dy\,dx$

17. $\displaystyle\int_{-1}^{1}\int_{-\sqrt{1-y^2}}^{+\sqrt{1-y^2}}(x+y)\,dx\,dy$

18. $\displaystyle\int_{\pi/2}^{\pi}\int_{0}^{4\cos x}2y\,dy\,dx$

19. $\displaystyle\int_{0}^{2}\int_{0}^{\sqrt{4-y^2}}xy\sqrt{4-x^2}\,dx\,dy$

20. $\displaystyle\int_{0}^{2}\int_{x/2}^{\sqrt{x+2}-1}dy\,dx$

(21-23)   Consider $\displaystyle I_1 = 2\int_{0}^{1}\int_{0}^{x}xy^2\,dy\,dx$

and $\displaystyle I_2 = \int_{-1}^{1}\int_{0}^{x}xy^2\,dy\,dx$

21. Does $\displaystyle I_2 = \int_{-1}^{1}\int_{0}^{x}xy^2\,dy\,dx = \frac{I_1}{2}$?

22. Does $I_2 = I_1$?

23. In general if $a < b < c$ does

$$\int_{a}^{c}\int_{f_1(x)}^{f_2(x)}z\,dy\,dx = \int_{a}^{b}\int_{f_1(x)}^{f_2(x)}z\,dy\,dx + \int_{b}^{c}\int_{f_1(x)}^{f_2(x)}z\,dy\,dx,$$

where $z = f(x,y)$?

24. In general if b is exactly halfway between a and c does

$$\int_a^c \int_{f_1(x)}^{f_2(x)} z \, dy \, dx = 2 \int_b^c \int_{f_1(x)}^{f_2(x)} z \, dy \, dx?$$

25. If $\int_0^2 \int_0^{x^2} e^{y/x} \, dy \, dx = e^2 - 1$ what is $\int_0^{x^2} \int_0^2 e^{y/x} \, dx \, dy?$

8-2   MULTIPLE INTEGRATION

Repeated integration is one of the ways by which the concept of integration can be extended to a function of two variables. The alternate approach is an extension of the basic concept of an integral itself. The definition of an integral depended upon the idea of a Riemann sum of the function over some interval. Suppose that we have a function which is defined and continuous over a region in the xy plane. We can extend the idea of a Riemann sum to such a case.

We need a suitable notation for a Riemann sum over a region. Let $f(x,y)$ denote the function, and A stand for the region. Suppose A is partitioned into n subregions, of area $\Delta A_1, \Delta A_2, \Delta A_3, \ldots, \Delta A_n$. In other words, the ith subregion has area ΔA_i. Figure 8-1 illustrates the region. Let (x_i, y_i) be any point in the ith subregion. The corresponding Riemann sum would be

$$\sum_{i=1}^{n} f(x_i, y_i) \, \Delta A_i,$$

The limit of such sums will be denoted by

$$\lim_{\substack{n \to \infty \\ |\Delta A_i| \to 0}} \sum_{i=1}^{n} f(x_i, y_i) \, \Delta A_i,$$

where $|\Delta A_i|$ denotes the largest area of any of the subregions of the partition being considered. Further, it is required that $|\Delta A_i| \to 0$ as the number of subregions involved tends to infinity. This limit, if it exists, is the double or multiple integral of the function f over the region A. It is denoted as

$$\int_A f(x,y) \, dA$$

or as

$$\iint_A f(x,y) \, dA.$$

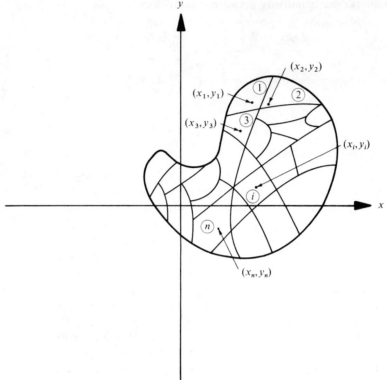

FIG. 8-1. A Region A Divided into n Sub-regions

In this text, we shall use the former notation for a multiple integral over a region. This is to remind us of the single sum nature of the double integral.

Example. As a very simple example, consider $f(x,y) = 1$, a constant function. Let A be the region bounded by the lines $x = 0$, $x = 2$, $y = 0$, and $y = 3$. This region is shown in figure 8-2. Find $\int_A f(x,y) \, dx$.

Solution. In order to find $\int_A f(x,y) \, dA$, it will be necessary to divide A into a number of subregions. Suppose that the interval from 0 to 2 along the x axis is divided into k equal length subintervals, and the interval from 0 to 3 along the y axis is also divided into k subintervals. This division is illustrated in figure 8-2. These two partitions will divide the total area into

$n = k^2$ subregions each with an area of

$$\left(\frac{2-0}{k}\right)\left(\frac{3-0}{k}\right) = \frac{6}{k^2}$$

square units. Thus $\Delta A = \dfrac{6}{k^2}$ for every subregion. The Riemann sum for a specific value of k is then given by

$$\underset{i=1}{\overset{n=k^2}{\sum}} (1)\frac{6}{k^2} = \underbrace{\frac{6}{k^2} + \frac{6}{k^2} + \cdots + \frac{6}{k^2}}_{k^2 \text{ terms}} = \frac{6}{k^2}k^2 = 6.$$

Thus, for any partition of this type, the Riemann sum is exactly 6 units,

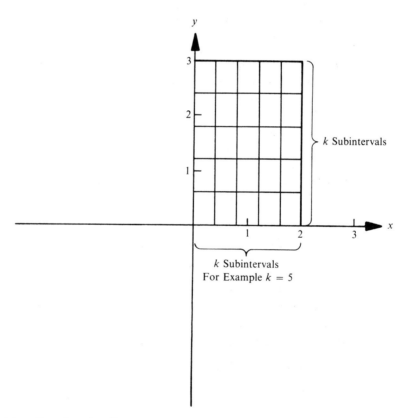

FIG. 8-2.   Division of an Area into Rectangular Subregions

and one can conclude that

$$\lim_{\substack{n \to \infty \\ |\Delta A_i| \to 0}} \sum_{i=1}^{n=k^2} \frac{6}{k^2} = 6,$$

or

$$\int_A 1 \, dA = 6.$$

It is not too surprising that this value is exactly the area of A.

Unless we are considering a carefully chosen simple case, like the example, it seems unlikely that we will be able to apply the definition of a multiple integral to find its value by taking a limit. What is needed is a method for multiple integrals analogous to that provided by the fundamental theorem of calculus for single integration. The method for multiple integration is repeated integration. What we hope to do is find for a given multiple integral a corresponding repeated integral which will have the value of the multiple integral. The repeated integral we find will involve boundaries of the region of integration of the multiple integral. Clearly, to do this we will require the mathematical description of the region of integration.

Consider a region A, bounded by the lines $x = a$, $x = b$, $y = c$, and $y = d$; a, b, c, and d are constants; $a < b$ and $c < d$. Such a region is illustrated in figure 8-3. A natural choice for a division of such a region would be to divide the region into rectangular subregions by a suitable partition of the interval from a to b along the x axis and a second partition of the interval c to d along the y axis. Suppose that the interval along the x axis is divided into k subintervals, while that along the y axis is divided into m subintervals.

Let Δx_i be the length of the ith subinterval along the x axis, and Δy_j be the length of the jth subinterval along the y axis. The area A has then been divided into $k \times m$ subregions. The areas of these subregions are $\Delta x_1 \Delta y_1$, $\Delta x_1 \Delta y_2, \Delta x_1 \Delta y_3, \ldots, \Delta x_1 \Delta y_m, \Delta x_2 \Delta y_1, \ldots, \Delta x_2 \Delta y_m, \ldots, \Delta x_k \Delta y_1, \ldots,$ $\Delta x_k \Delta y_m$. Let (x_i, y_j) be a point in the ijth subregion, $i.e.$, the subregion i from the left and j from the bottom. Following the definition of the double integral, form a Riemann sum. Figure 8-3 illustrates the problem.

Sum $= (f(x_1, y_1)\Delta x_1 \Delta y_1 + f(x_1, y_2)\Delta x_1 \Delta y_2 + \cdots + f(x_1, y_m)\Delta x_1 \Delta y_m)$

$\qquad + (f(x_2, y_1)\Delta x_2 \Delta y_1 + f(x_2, y_2)\Delta x_2 \Delta y_2 + \cdots + f(x_2, y_m)\Delta x_2 \Delta y_m)$

$\qquad \cdot$

$\qquad \cdot$

$\qquad \cdot$

$\qquad + (f(x_k, y_1)\Delta x_k \Delta y_1 + f(x_k, y_2)\Delta x_k \Delta y_2 + \cdots + f(x_k, y_m)\Delta x_k \Delta y_m).$

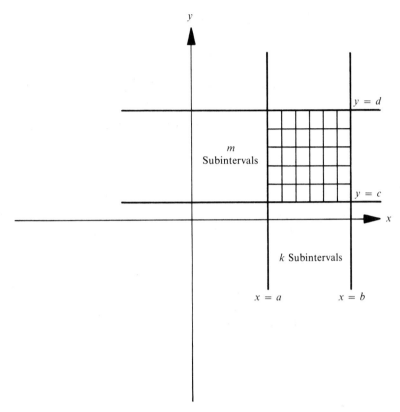

FIG. 8-3.   Division of an Interval into k × m Subregions

Using summation notation,

$$\text{Sum} = \sum_{j=1}^{m} f(x_1, y_j)\Delta x_1 \Delta y_j + \sum_{j=1}^{m} f(x_2, y_j)\Delta x_2 \Delta y_j + \cdots$$

$$+ \sum_{j=1}^{m} f(x_k, y_j)\Delta x_k \Delta y_j.$$

Using a double summation notation,

$$\text{Sum} = \sum_{i=1}^{k} \left\{ \sum_{j=1}^{m} f(x_i, y_j)\Delta y_j \Delta x_i \right\}$$

$$= \sum_{i=1}^{k} \left\{ \sum_{j=1}^{m} f(x_i, y_j)\Delta y_j \right\} \Delta x_i.$$

If $\displaystyle\int_A f(x,y)\,dA$ exists, it must be given by the limit of the sum as k and m tend to infinity. Specifically,

$$\int_A f(x,y)\,dA = \lim_{\substack{k\to\infty \\ |\Delta x_i|\to 0}}\left[\lim_{\substack{m\to\infty \\ |\Delta y_j|\to 0}}\left\{\sum_{i=1}^{k}\left(\sum_{j=1}^{m}f(x_i,y_j)\Delta y_j\right)\Delta x_i\right\}\right].$$

However, the limit as m tends to infinity does not affect the sum over k; thus

$$\int_A f(x,y)\,dA = \lim_{\substack{k\to\infty \\ |\Delta x_i|\to 0}}\sum_{i=1}^{k}\left\{\lim_{\substack{m\to\infty \\ |\Delta y_j|\to 0}}\sum_{j=1}^{m}f(x_i,y_j)\Delta y_j\right\}\Delta x_i.$$

If one compares the inner limit/sum combination with the definition of an ordinary integral, realizing that x_i is fixed as the sum is taken over j, and m tends to infinity, then,

$$\lim_{\substack{m\to\infty \\ |\Delta y_j|\to 0}}\sum_{j=1}^{m}f(x_i,y_j)\Delta y_j = \int_c^d f(x_i,y)\,dy.$$

That is, this limit is the integral of $f(x,y)$ with respect to y, holding x at a constant value of x_i. Then

$$\int_A f(x,y)\,dA = \lim_{\substack{k\to\infty \\ |\Delta x_i|\to 0}}\sum_{i=1}^{k}\left\{\int_c^d f(x_i,y)\,dy\right\}\Delta x_i.$$

However, $\displaystyle\int_c^d f(x_i,y)\,dy$ is a function of x_i; or x in the ordinary sense, therefore

$$\int_A f(x,y)\,dA = \int_a^b\left\{\int_c^d f(x,y)\,dy\right\}dx.$$

This is a repeated integral; specifically, it is a repeated integral whose limits of integration correspond to the boundaries of the region of the multiple integral.

Example. Let A be the region bounded by $x = 0$, $x = 2$, $y = 0$, and $y = 3$ as in the previous example, with $f(x,y) = 1$. Calculate $\displaystyle\int_A 1\,dA$.

Solution.
$$\int_A 1\,dA = \int_0^2\int_0^3 1\,dy\,dx$$

$$= \int_0^2 y\Big]_0^3 dx$$

$$= \int_0^2 3 \, dx$$

$$= 3x \Big]_0^2$$

$$= 3(2) = 6.$$

This agrees with the previous answer.

The above discussion does not constitute a proof, only a reasonable argument for the result. It also applies to a more general result involving regions with boundaries other than constants. Consider a function $f(x,y)$ and a region A bounded by $y = g_2(x)$, $y = g_1(x)$, $x = a$, $x = b$ with $g_2(x) > g_1(x)$ for all x, $a \leq x \leq b$. Such a region is shown in figure 8-4.

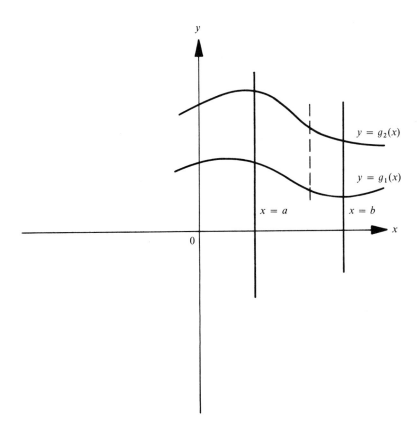

FIG. 8-4.   The Region Bounded by $y = g_1(x)$, $g_2(x)$, $x = a$, and $x = b$

Then

$$\int_A f(x,y)\, dA = \int_a^b \int_{g_1(x)}^{g_2(x)} f(x,y)\, dy\, dx.$$

This result is also a very reasonable one. The inner integration involves holding x constant. A typical constant value for x is shown as a dashed line in figure 8-4. Within the region, and along the dashed line, y varies from $g_1(x)$ to $g_2(x)$. To complete integration over the region, one then needs to integrate the inner result with respect to x from $x = a$ to $x = b$.

Example.   Consider the region A bounded by $y = x$ above and $y = x^2$ below, and by $x = \frac{1}{2}$ on the left and $x = \frac{3}{4}$ on the right. This region is shown in figure 8-5. If $f(x,y) = xy^2$ evaluate

$$\int_A f(x,y)\, dA.$$

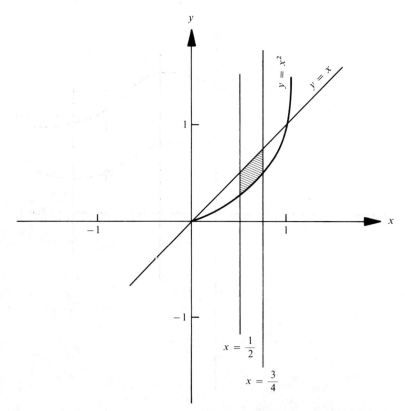

FIG. 8-5.   The Region Bounded by $y = x^2$, $y = x$, $x = \frac{1}{2}$, and $x = \frac{3}{4}$

Solution.   From figure 8-5

$$\int_A f(x,y)\,dA = \int_{1/2}^{3/4} \int_{x^2}^{x} xy^2\,dy\,dx$$

$$= \int_{1/2}^{3/4} \frac{xy^3}{3} \Big]_{x^2}^{x} dx$$

$$= \int_{1/2}^{3/4} \left(\frac{x^4}{3} - \frac{x^7}{3} \right) dx$$

$$= \frac{1}{3} \left[\frac{x^5}{5} - \frac{x^8}{8} \right]_{1/2}^{3/4}$$

$$= \frac{1}{3} \left[\frac{1}{5}\left(\frac{3}{4}\right)^5 - \frac{1}{8}\left(\frac{3}{4}\right)^8 \right] - \frac{1}{3}\left[\frac{1}{5}\left(\frac{1}{2}\right)^5 - \frac{1}{8}\left(\frac{1}{2}\right)^8 \right]$$

$$= \frac{1}{15} \cdot \frac{3^5}{2^{10}} - \frac{1}{(3)2^3} \cdot \frac{3^8}{2^{16}} - \frac{1}{3(5)} \cdot \frac{1}{2^5} + \frac{1}{(3)2^3} \cdot \frac{1}{2^8}$$

$$= \frac{3^5 \cdot 2^9 - 3^8(5) - 2^{14} + (5)2^8}{3(5)(2)^{19}} = \frac{76{,}507}{7{,}864{,}320}.$$

Example.   If $f(x,y) = 1$, then $\displaystyle\int_A 1\,dA$ will yield the area of A. Find the area of the region bounded by $y = x^2$ and $y = 9 - x^2$.

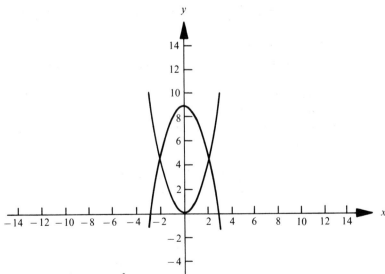

FIG. 8-6.   The Area Bounded by $y = x^2$ and $y = 9 - x^2$

Solution. The area in question is shown in figure 8-6. The points of intersection are given by

$$x^2 = 9 - x^2$$

$$2x^2 = 9$$

$$x = \pm \frac{3}{\sqrt{2}}, y = \frac{9}{2}.$$

The area is given by

$$\int_A dA = \int_{-3/\sqrt{2}}^{3/\sqrt{2}} \int_{x^2}^{9-x^2} dy\, dx \quad \text{since} \int dy = y$$

$$= \int_{-3/\sqrt{2}}^{3/\sqrt{2}} y \Big]_{x^2}^{9-x^2} dx$$

$$= \int_{-3/\sqrt{2}}^{3/\sqrt{2}} (9 - 2x^2)\,dx \quad \text{since} \int (9 - 2x^2)\,dx = 9x - \frac{2x^3}{3}$$

$$= 9x - \frac{2x^3}{3} \Big]_{-3/\sqrt{2}}^{3/\sqrt{2}}$$

$$= \left((9)\frac{3}{\sqrt{2}} - \frac{2\left(\frac{3}{\sqrt{2}}\right)^3}{3} \right) - \left(-(9)\frac{3}{\sqrt{2}} + \frac{2\left(\frac{3}{\sqrt{2}}\right)^3}{3} \right)$$

$$= 2\left(\frac{27}{\sqrt{2}} - \frac{9}{\sqrt{2}} \right) = \frac{2}{\sqrt{2}}(18) = \frac{36}{\sqrt{2}} = 18\sqrt{2}.$$

When the region is bounded by curves where x is given as a function of y only minor changes must be made in the method.

Example. Find the area bounded by $y = 0$, $x = e^y$, and $x = 2$.
Solution. This region is shown in figure 8-7. This time a dashed line has been used to indicate a constant y value. Notice that for a constant y, x varies from e^y to 2.

$$\int_A dA = \int_0^{\ln 2} \int_{e^y}^2 dx\, dy$$

$$= \int_0^{\ln 2} x \Big]_{e^y}^2 dy$$

$$= \int_0^{\ln 2} (2 - e^y)\,dy$$

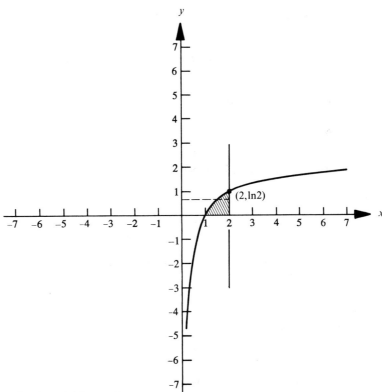

FIG. 8-7.   The Region Bounded by $y = 0$,
$y = \ln x$, and $x = 2$

$$= 2y - e^y \Big]_0^{\ln 2}$$

$$= 2\ln 2 - e^{\ln 2} - (0 - e^0)$$

$$= 2\ln 2 - 2 + 1 = 2\ln 2 - 1.$$

8-2   Exercises

(1-20)   For each function and region given find $\displaystyle\int_A f(x,y)\,dA$.

1. $f(x,y) = 3x^2y + y$, A bounded by $x = 0$, $x = 1$, $y = 1$, and $y = 3$
2. $f(x,y) = xy$, A bounded by $y = 0$, $x = y^{\frac{1}{2}}$, and $x = 2 - y^{\frac{1}{2}}$

3. $f(x,y) = x + y$, A bounded by $y = 0$, $y = \dfrac{x}{2}$, $x = 0$, $x = 6$

4. $f(x,y) = \dfrac{y^2}{x}$, A bounded by $y = 1$, $y = x$, $x = 1$, $x = e$

5. $f(x,y) = 2y$, A bounded by $y = 0$, $y = \cos x$, $x = 0$, $x = \dfrac{\pi}{6}$

6. $f(x,y) = x$, A bounded by $y = 2x$, $y = x^2$

7. $f(x,y) = e^x \cdot e^y$, A bounded by $x = 0$, $x = \ln y$, and $y = \ln 4$

8. $f(x,y) = 1$, A bounded by $y = 1$, $y = e^x$, $x = 0$, and $x = 2$

9. $f(x,y) = 1$, A bounded by $x = \ln y$, $x = 2$, $y = 1$, $y = e^2$

10. $f(x,y) = x \sin y$, A bounded by $y = 0$, $y = x$, $x = 0$, $x = \dfrac{\pi}{2}$

11. $f(x,y) = \dfrac{x^2}{1 + y^2}$, A bounded by $y = -1$, $y = 1$, $x = 0$, $x = 2$

12. $f(x,y) = 2x^2 y - x + 2$, A bounded by $y = \dfrac{x}{3}$, $y = 4 - x$, $x = -1$, and $x = 0$

13. $f(x,y) = 2xy - y^2 + 1$, A bounded by $x = 2y + 2$, $x = 3 - 3y$, and $y = 0$

14. $f(x,y) = 2y$, A bounded by $y = +9 - x^2$ and $y = 0$

15. $f(x,y) = 2xy$, A bounded by $y = x^2 + 4$, $y = 3x + 2$, $x = -2$, and $x = 1$

16. $f(x,y) = 1$, A bounded by $y = x^2$ and $y = x + 2$

17. $f(x,y) = 1$, A bounded by $y = \sqrt{25 - x^2}$, $y = 0$

18. $f(x,y) = 1$, A bounded by $x = -y$ and $y = x - x^2$

19. $f(x,y) = 1$, A bounded by $y = \sqrt{x + 4}$ and $y = \frac{3}{5}x$

20. $f(x,y) = 2x$, A bounded by $x = 0$, $x = 2 \sin y \cos y$, $y = 0$, and $y = \dfrac{\pi}{3}$

(21-25) Multiple integrals are required to change the order of repeated integration.

$$\int_a^b \int_{f(x)}^{g(x)} f(x,y)\, dy\, dx = \int_A f(x,y)\, dA,$$

where A depends on the expressions for $f(x)$ and $g(x)$.

Once A has been found a second repeated integral can be found, with reversed order of integration but the same value by finding new limits of integration for $\int_A f(x,y)\,dA$ with a reversed order of integration. For each of the integrals given find a second repeated integral with reversed order of integration but the same value.

For example, consider $\int_0^{\ln 2} \int_{e^y}^2 dx\,dy$ as shown in figure 8-7. A is bounded by $x = e^y$, $y = 0$, and $x = 2$. Therefore we could attempt to set up integration with respect to y first, holding x constant. If we are considering a value within the region, with x constant it is clear that y varies from 0 to its value along the curve. Here $x = e^y$; however we want y as a function of x. That means that we will have to view the curve as $y = \ln x$. Then:

$$\int_0^{\ln 2} \int_{e^y}^2 dx\,dy = \int_A dA = \int_1^2 \int_0^{\ln x} dy\,dx$$

where A is the region bounded by $y = 0$, $x = 2$, $y = \ln x$, or $x = e^y$.

21. $\displaystyle\int_0^1 \int_{y^3}^{y^2} dx\,dy$

22. $\displaystyle\int_0^3 \int_0^{\sqrt{9-x^2}} dy\,dx$

23. $\displaystyle\int_{-1}^1 \int_{-1}^y \sqrt{1 + y^2}\,dx\,dy$

24. $\displaystyle\int_0^{\sqrt 2} \int_{x^2-1}^1 x \ln x\,dy\,dx$

25. $\displaystyle\int_{-1}^4 \int_0^{2y} e^{-x^2}\,dx\,dy$

(26-29) If $z = f(x,y) \geq 0$ for all (x,y) in a region A, then $\int_A z\,dA$ yields the volume bounded by the region A in the xy plane and the surface $z = f(x,y)$ with walls vertical lines on the boundaries of A. In each case below find the volume indicated using double integration.

26. The volume bounded by $z = 0$ and $z = 4$, $x = 1$, $x = 3$, $y = 2$, and $y = 5$.

27. The volume in the first octant bounded by the plane $z = -x - y + 3$.

28. The volume bounded by $z = 25 - x^2 - y^2$ and $z = 0$.

29. The volume bounded by $z = 0$, $z = \dfrac{1}{\sqrt{2\pi}} e^{\frac{-x^2}{2}}$, $y = 0$, and $y = 1$.

8-3   FUNCTIONS OF MORE THAN TWO VARIABLES

The concept of a function extends to functions of more than two variables. In a realistic sense it is probable that the more variables we can handle, the more useful the approach, as most real phenomena are controlled by a large number of factors. Functions such as

$$w = f(x,y,z) = xy^3z,$$

$$\frac{\partial w}{\partial x}, \frac{\partial w}{\partial y}, \frac{\partial w}{\partial z}, \frac{\partial^4 w}{\partial x \partial y^2 \partial z}, \text{ and}$$

$$\int_1^3 \int_2^5 \int_7^1 xy^3z \, dz \, dx \, dy$$

can be evaluated following the patterns we have established.

Example.   If $w = f(x,y,z)$ is a function of three variables x, y, and z, and

$$f(x,y,z) = \frac{x \sin(\pi y)}{z^3}$$

find $f(1,\frac{1}{2},8), f(0,\frac{1}{4},-1)$, and $f(-1,-\frac{1}{2},2)$.

Solution. $f(1,\tfrac{1}{2},8) = \dfrac{1 \sin(\pi \cdot \frac{1}{2})}{8^3} = \dfrac{1(1)}{512} = \dfrac{1}{512}.$

$$f(0,\tfrac{1}{4},-1) = \frac{(0)\sin\left(\dfrac{\pi}{4}\right)}{(-1)^3} = 0.$$

$$f(-1,-\tfrac{1}{2},2) = \frac{(-1)\sin\left(-\dfrac{\pi}{2}\right)}{2^3}$$

$$= \frac{-1(-1)}{8} = \frac{1}{8}.$$

Example.   If $w = f(x,y,z) = \dfrac{x \sin(\pi y)}{z^3}$ find $\dfrac{\partial w}{\partial x}, \dfrac{\partial w}{\partial y}$, and $\dfrac{\partial w}{\partial z}$.

Solution.   Each of these partials is evaluated by treating all of the other variables as constants.

$$\frac{\partial w}{\partial x} = \frac{\sin(\pi y)}{z^3},$$

$$\frac{\partial w}{\partial y} = \frac{\pi x \cos(\pi y)}{z^3},$$

and

$$\frac{\partial w}{\partial z} = \frac{-3x \sin(\pi y)}{z^4}.$$

Example.   Evaluate the three-fold repeated integral

$$J = \int_0^1 \int_{-2}^{3x} \int_0^{xy^2} z^2 \, dz \, dy \, dx.$$

Solution. $\displaystyle \int_0^{xy^2} z^2 \, dz = \frac{z^3}{3} \bigg]_0^{xy^2} = \frac{(xy^2)^3}{3} = \frac{x^3 y^6}{3}.$

$$J = \int_0^1 \int_{-2}^{3x} \frac{x^3 y^6}{3} \, dy \, dx.$$

However,

$$\int_{-2}^{3x} \frac{x^3 y^6}{3} \, dy = \frac{x^3 y^7}{21} \bigg]_{-2}^{3x}$$

$$= \frac{x^3}{21}[(3x)^7 - (-2)^7]$$

$$= \frac{x^3}{21}[2{,}187x^7 + 128].$$

Thus,

$$J = \int_0^1 \left[\frac{2{,}187}{21} x^{10} + \frac{128}{21} x^3 \right] dx$$

$$= \frac{2{,}187}{(21)11} x^{11} + \frac{128}{(21)4} x^4 \bigg]_0^1$$

$$= \frac{2{,}187}{231} + \frac{32}{21}\left(\frac{11}{11}\right)$$

$$= \frac{2{,}187 + 352}{231}$$

$$= \frac{2{,}539}{231}.$$

We have seen how the chain rule extends to the more complex case of partial derivatives. That is, if $w = f(x,y,z)$, $x = h(u,v)$, $y = g(u,v)$, and $z = j(u,v)$, then

$$\frac{\partial w}{\partial u} = \frac{\partial w}{\partial x} \cdot \frac{\partial x}{\partial u} + \frac{\partial w}{\partial y} \cdot \frac{\partial y}{\partial u} + \frac{\partial w}{\partial z} \cdot \frac{\partial z}{\partial u},$$

and so forth.

Example.   If $w = x^2 + y^2 + z^2$, $x = uv^3$, $y = vu^4$, and $z = u^5 v^5$, find $\dfrac{\partial w}{\partial v}$.

Solution. $\dfrac{\partial w}{\partial v} = \dfrac{\partial w}{\partial x} \cdot \dfrac{\partial x}{\partial v} + \dfrac{\partial w}{\partial y} \cdot \dfrac{\partial y}{\partial v} + \dfrac{\partial w}{\partial z} \cdot \dfrac{\partial z}{\partial v}$

$$= 2x(3uv^2) + 2y(u^4) + 2z(5u^5 v^4).$$

It is often useful to find a general approach to various related concepts. For example, consider n independent variables denoted by $x_1, x_2, x_3, \ldots, x_n$. Then $z = f(x_1, x_2, \ldots, x_n)$ indicates z is a function of these n variables, and one can consider partial derivatives of z with respect to each of these variables.

$$\frac{\partial z}{\partial x_1} \text{ or } \frac{\partial z}{\partial x_7} \text{ or } \frac{\partial^2 z}{\partial x_3^{\,2}} \text{ or } \frac{\partial^2 z}{\partial x_1 \partial x_7} \text{ or } \frac{\partial z}{\partial x_i}$$

Or it may be useful to consider an n-fold repeated integral. It may be denoted by

$$\int_{a_1}^{b_1} \int_{a_2}^{b_2} \int_{a_3}^{b_3} \cdots \int_{a_n}^{b_n} f(x_1, x_2, \ldots, x_n)\, dx_n\, dx_{n-1} \cdots dx_2\, dx_1,$$

where a_n and b_n may be a function of $x_1 \ldots x_{n-1}$, and a_{n-1} and b_{n-1} may be functions of $x_1 \ldots x_{n-2}$, etc. Clearly, the outermost integration must have constant limits, whereas a_2 and b_2, at their worst, are functions only of x_1.

The summation notation provides a compact form of the chain rule. Suppose that $z = f(x_1, x_2, \ldots, x_n)$ while $x_i = g(y_1, \ldots, y_k)$ where each x_i is a function of k variables y_1 to y_k. Then,

$$\frac{\partial z}{\partial y_i} = \sum_{j=1}^{n} \frac{\partial z}{\partial x_j} \frac{\partial x_j}{\partial y_i}, \quad i = 1, 2, \ldots, k.$$

As obscure as these ideas may seem, they do have many useful applications. For example, one encounters n-fold repeated integrals, and an n-variable chain rule in advanced mathematical statistics. Specifically, the mathematical expression for the statistical expectation with respect to a six-tuple valued random phenomenon takes the form

$$\int_{-\infty}^{\infty} \int_{-\infty}^{\infty} \int_{-\infty}^{\infty} \int_{-\infty}^{\infty} \int_{-\infty}^{\infty} \int_{-\infty}^{\infty} g(x_1, x_2, x_3, x_4, x_5, x_6)$$

$$\cdot f(x_1, x_2, x_3, x_4, x_5, x_6)\, dx_1\, dx_2\, dx_3\, dx_4\, dx_5\, dx_6,$$

where $f(x_1, x_2, x_3, x_4, x_5, x_6)$ is a probability density function, and $g(x_1, x_2, x_3, x_4, x_5, x_6)$ is any continuous function. Specific examples of this type of analysis can be found in *Introduction to Mathematical Statistics* by Paul G. Hoel, John Wiley & Sons, 1962, and *Modern Probability Theory and*

Its Applications by Emanuel Parzen, John Wiley & Sons, 1960. The exercises below will assist in clarifying the concepts involved.

8-3   Exercises

(1-10)   For the given functions find the indicated partial derivatives.

1. $f(x,y,z) = x^2 \ln y - y \ln z + zy, \dfrac{\partial f}{\partial x}, \dfrac{\partial^2 f}{\partial x^2}, \dfrac{\partial f}{\partial z}, \dfrac{\partial^2 f}{\partial x \partial y}$

2. $f(x,y,z) = \sin(x^2 - y + z), \dfrac{\partial f}{\partial x}, \dfrac{\partial f}{\partial y}, \dfrac{\partial f}{\partial z}, \dfrac{\partial^2 f}{\partial x \partial y}$

3. $f(x,y,z) = e^{\frac{x+y+z}{2}}, \dfrac{\partial f}{\partial x}, \dfrac{\partial f}{\partial y}, \dfrac{\partial f}{\partial z}, \dfrac{\partial^3 f}{\partial x \partial y \partial z}$

4. $f(x,y,z) = \dfrac{\sqrt{x^2 + y^2 + z^2}}{x}, \dfrac{\partial f}{\partial x}, \dfrac{\partial f}{\partial y}, \dfrac{\partial f}{\partial z}, \dfrac{\partial^2 f}{\partial z^2}$

5. $f(x,y,z,w) = \ln(xyzw), \dfrac{\partial f}{\partial x}, \dfrac{\partial f}{\partial y}, \dfrac{\partial f}{\partial z}, \dfrac{\partial f}{\partial w}, \dfrac{\partial^2 f}{\partial x \partial y}$

6. $f(x,y,z,w) = \tan^{-1}(x) - \sin y + \sin^{-1} z + w^3,$

$$\dfrac{\partial^2 f}{\partial x \partial y}, \dfrac{\partial^2 f}{\partial x \partial z}, \dfrac{\partial^2 f}{\partial x \partial w}, \dfrac{\partial^2 f}{\partial y \partial z}$$

7. $f(x_1,x_2,x_3,x_4,x_5) = \displaystyle\sum_{i=1}^{5} x_i^2 + \sin(x_1 x_2)$

$$\dfrac{\partial f}{\partial x_2}, \dfrac{\partial^2 f}{\partial x_3^2}, \dfrac{\partial^2 f}{\partial x_1 \partial x_3}$$

8. $f(x_1,x_2,x_3,x_4,x_5) = \sin(x_1 + x_2 - x_3 - x_4 + x_5)$

$$\dfrac{\partial^2 f}{\partial x_1 \partial x_2}, \dfrac{\partial^2 f}{\partial x_4^2}, \dfrac{\partial f}{\partial x_5}$$

9. $f(u,v,w) = \dfrac{u^2 - v^2}{w}, \dfrac{\partial f}{\partial u}, \dfrac{\partial f}{\partial v}, \dfrac{\partial f}{\partial w}, \dfrac{\partial^3 f}{\partial w^3}$

10. $f(r,\theta,\psi) = r \tan^{-1}\left(\dfrac{\theta}{\psi}\right), \dfrac{\partial f}{\partial r}, \dfrac{\partial f}{\partial \theta}, \dfrac{\partial f}{\partial \psi}, \dfrac{\partial^2 f}{\partial r^2}$

(11-19)   Find the indicated repeated integrals.

11. $\displaystyle\int_0^1 \int_1^2 \int_2^3 2xyz \, dy \, dz \, dx$

12. $\displaystyle\int_0^1 \int_1^2 \int_2^3 2\,xyz\ dz\,dy\,dx$

13. $\displaystyle\int_{-\pi/2}^{\pi/2} \int_0^{2\pi} \int_0^5 r^2 \sin\psi\ dr\,d\theta\,d\psi$

14. $\displaystyle\int_0^{2\pi} \int_0^5 \int_{-\sqrt{25-r^2}}^{\sqrt{25-r^2}} r\,dz\,dr\,d\theta$

15. $\displaystyle\int_0^2 \int_0^{2w} \int_0^{2z} \int_0^{2y} 2x\,dx\,dy\,dz\,dw$

16. $\displaystyle\int_1^2 \int_0^{y^2} \int_1^{e^2} \frac{1}{x}\,dx\,dz\,dy$

17. $\displaystyle\int_0^{2\pi} \int_0^{2\pi} \int_0^{2\pi} \sin x \sin y \cos z\ dz\,dy\,dx$

18. $\displaystyle\int_1^2 \int_{\sqrt{\pi/4}}^{\sqrt{\pi/2}} \int_0^x \sin x^2\ dy\,dx\,dz$

19. $\displaystyle\underbrace{\int_0^3 \int_0^3 \int_0^3 \dots \int_0^3}_{n \text{ times}} dx_1\,dx_2 \dots dx_n$

(20-21) If $w = \sin(x^2)\sin y \cos z$, $x = u^2v - 1$, $y = \dfrac{u}{v}\pi$, and $z = \sqrt{u^2 - v^2}$ find

20. $\dfrac{\partial w}{\partial u}$

21. $\dfrac{\partial w}{\partial v}$

(22-24) If $z = e^{\sum_{i=1}^{5} x_i}$, $x_1 = y_1$, $x_2 = y_1 + y_2{}^2$, $x_3 = \displaystyle\sum_{i=1}^{3} y_i{}^i$, $x_4 = \displaystyle\sum_{i=1}^{4} y_i{}^i$

and $x_5 = \displaystyle\sum_{i=1}^{5} y_i{}^i$ find

22. $\dfrac{\partial z}{\partial y_1}, \dfrac{\partial z}{\partial y_2}$

23. $\dfrac{\partial z}{\partial y_3}, \dfrac{\partial z}{\partial y_5}$

24. $\dfrac{\partial^2 z}{\partial y_i{}^2}$

25. Consider $\displaystyle\int_V f(x,y,z)\,dV$ where $f(x,y,z) = 1$. Why do you think this integral should be the volume V?

26. What form should the three-fold repeated integral used to evaluate a triple integral like $\displaystyle\int_V f(x,y,z)\,dV$ be? What kinds of limits of integration are involved?

8-4 LINEAR PROGRAMMING

If $z = f(x,y) = ax + by + c$ for a, b, and c constants, then $f(x,y)$ will graph in three dimensions as a plane. Such a plane in general has no maximum or minimum value for z. However, in a number of practical problems the allowable values of x and y are restricted to a small region in the xy plane, and the plane $z = f(x,y) = ax + by + c$ will have a maximum and minimum value over this region. Finding such maximum and minimum values is called linear programming. Since its discovery in the early 1940s linear programming has grown steadily in its application to economics. We will present the basic theory for the three-dimensional case. However linear programming can be extended to n-dimensional space and can include a number of sophisticated techniques for finding maxima or minima.

Figure 8-8 shows a shaded region in the xy plane and the portion of the plane $z = f(x,y) = ax + by + c$ above the region. The maximum and minimum value of z on the plane and above the region will occur when the coordinates of one of the vertices of the region are substituted into $ax + by + c$. In this case the maximum value of $f(x,y)$ occurs above the point A and the minimum above point B.

When the function to be maximized or minimized is linear (graphs as a plane) the maximum or minimum value will always occur at one of the vertices of the region in the xy plane. Therefore it is not necessary to graph the plane. Simply graph the region in the xy plane and test its vertices to discover maximum or minimum values above the region.

Example.   Find the maximum value of z and the minimum value of z for $z = 4x + 3y$ given the following conditions on x and y.

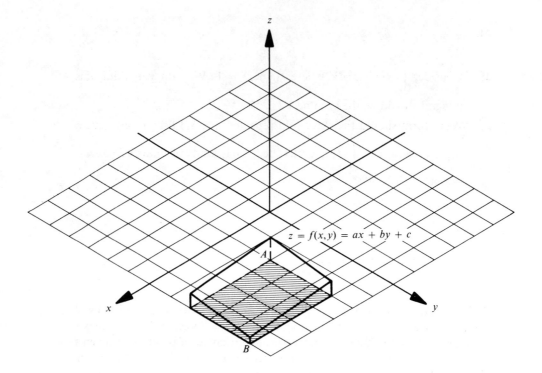

FIG. 8-8.   Maximum or Minimum Values
of $z = f(x,y) = ax + by + c$ Over a Region
in the x-y Plane

$$x \geq 0, y \geq 0$$

$$x + y \leq 6, 2x + y \leq 8$$

Solution. The intersection of the constraints on x and y is graphed as the
shaded region in figure 8-9. Now we test the four vertices of the region,
$(0,0)$, $(4,0)$, $(2,4)$, and $(0,6)$ in $z = 4x + 3y$ to find the maximum and
minimum values of $f(x,y)$.

$$z = f(0,0) = 4(0) + 3(0) = 0$$

$$z = f(4,0) = 4(4) + 3(0) = 16$$

$$z = f(2,4) = 4(2) + 3(4) = 20$$

$$z = f(0,6) = 4(0) + 3(6) = 18$$

Therefore the maximum value of z is 20 and occurs when $x = 2$ and $y = 4$
and the minimum value of z is 0 and occurs when $x = y = 0$.

Example. A company produces two types of food supplements, called types A and B. Type A yields a profit of $10.00 per ounce and type B yields a profit of $20.00 per ounce. The supplements are manufactured in two different departments. Department I requires 2 hours to manufacture one ounce of A and 3 hours to manufacture one ounce of B. Department II requires 1 hour to manufacture a single ounce of A and 4 hours to manufacture an ounce of B. How many ounces of A and B should be produced to give maximum profit if Department I has 20 hours of time available for production and Department II has 15 hours available?

Solution. Let x be the number of ounces of supplement A produced and y be the number of ounces of B produced. The profit, P, is

$$P = 10x + 20y.$$

We will graph the constraints on x and y and then test the coordinates of the vertices thus discovered in the profit function to find which gives maximum profit. It is clear that x and y must be nonnegative, that is,

$$x \geq 0 \quad \text{and} \quad y \geq 0.$$

The information on production in Departments I and II is given in the following table.

	Hours Available	Hours required to produce one ounce	
		A	B
Dept. I	20	2	3
Dept. II	15	1	4

Using the data from Department I

$$2x + 3y \leq 20.$$

The information on Department II implies

$$x + 4y \leq 15.$$

Thus, the constraints on x and y are

$$x \geq 0,$$

$$y \geq 0,$$

$$2x + 3y \leq 20, \text{ and}$$

$$x + 4y \leq 15.$$

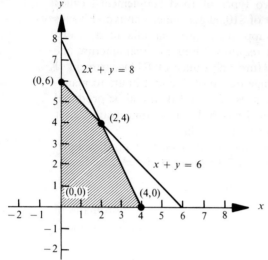

FIG. 8-9. $x \geq 0$, $y \geq 0$, $x + y \leq 6$, and $2x + y \leq 8$

These are graphed in figure 8-10. The vertices' coordinates substituted into the profit function $P = 10x + 20y$ give:

$$\text{for } (0,0), \quad P = 0,$$

$$\text{for } (10,0), \quad P = 10(10) + 20(0) = \$100,$$

$$\text{for } (7,2), \quad P = 10(7) + 20(2) \quad = \$110,$$

$$\text{for } (0,3\tfrac{3}{4}), \quad P = 10(0) + 20(3\tfrac{3}{4}) = \$75.$$

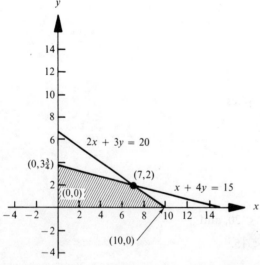

FIG. 8-10.   The Region Bounded by $x \geq 0$, $y \geq 0$, $2x + 3y \leq 20$, and $x + 4y \leq 15$

The maximum profit of $110 will occur when 7 ounces of supplement A and 2 ounces of supplement B are produced.

The linear programming presented here involves a function of x and y that is linear and that we wish to maximize or minimize based upon certain restrictions on x and y. The next example will, at first glance, appear to be more complicated than this. It will appear as if the income function is a function of three variables. However, the example is such that one of the variables can be represented as a function of the other two.

Example. During the spring season a resort operator rents bicycles for $12 per day, skidoos for $40 per day, and motorcycles for $25 per day. He has storage space for a combined total of 50 bicycles, skidoos, and motorcycles. In order to satisfy certain regular customers he must have at least 10 bicycles, but he will never need more than 20. He is certain to rent 5 skidoos every day while the greatest demand for skidoos was 35 in one day. How many bicycles, skidoos, and motorcycles should he have for maximum income?

Solution. Let m be the number of motorcycles, b the number of bicycles, and s the number of skidoos. We will use the fact that $b + m + s = 50$ to solve for m in terms of b and s. In this way, the income can be represented as a function of just two variables. The income, I, is

$$I = 12b + 40s + 25m.$$

Substituting

$$m = 50 - b - s,$$

$$I = 12b + 40s + 25(50 - b - s).$$

$$I = 12b + 40s + 1250 - 25b - 25s.$$

$$I = 1250 - 13b + 15s.$$

We chose to write m in terms of b and s in the income function, because most of the information in the problem concerned skidoos and bicycles. The constraints on b and s are:

$$b \geq 10, b \leq 20,$$

$$s \geq 5, s \leq 35, \text{ and}$$

$$b + s \leq 50.$$

These constraints are graphed in figure 8-11.

Testing the coordinates of the vertices in the income function $I = 1{,}250 - 13b + 15s$ yields:

$$\text{for } (10,5), \quad I = 1{,}250 - 13(10) + 15(5)$$

$$= 1{,}250 - 130 + 75 \ = \$1{,}195,$$

$$\text{for } (20,5), \quad I = 1{,}250 - 13(20) + 15(5)$$

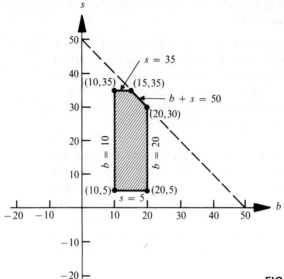

FIG. 8-11.   The Region Bounded by $b \geq 10$, $b \leq 20$, $s \geq 5$, $s \leq 35$, and $b + s \leq 50$

$$= 1{,}250 - 260 + 75 \ = \$1{,}065,$$

$$\text{for } (20,30), \ I = 1{,}250 - 13(20) + 15(30)$$

$$I = 1{,}250 - 260 + 450 = \$1{,}440,$$

$$\text{for } (15,35), \ I = 1{,}250 - 13(15) + 15(35)$$

$$= 1{,}250 - 195 + 525 = \$1{,}580, \text{ and}$$

$$\text{for } (10,35), \ I = 1{,}250 - 13(10) + 15(35)$$

$$= 1{,}250 - 130 + 525 = \$1{,}645.$$

The maximum income is $1,645 and occurs when there are 10 bicycles, 35 skidoos, and 5 motorcycles.

8-4   Exercises

1. Find the maximum value of z for $z = 2x + 5y$ given:

$$x \geq 2$$

$$y \geq 1$$

$$x + y \leq 8$$

2.   Find the maximum value of z for $z = 2x - 5y$ if:

$$x \geq 2$$
$$y \geq 2$$
$$x + y \leq 10$$

3.   Find the minimum value of P for $P = 2x + 4y$ if:

$$x \geq 0$$
$$y \geq 0$$
$$x + y \geq 8$$
$$2x + 3y \geq 19$$

4.   Find the minimum value of P for $P = 2x + 6y - 8$ if:

$$0 \leq x \leq 10$$
$$y \geq 0$$
$$2x + y \geq 16$$
$$x + 5y \geq 26$$

5.   Find the maximum and minimum values of z for $z = 6x + 3y$ if:

$$x + y \leq 6$$
$$x - y \leq 2$$
$$2y - 3x \leq 12$$

6.   Find the minimum value of z for $z = 4x - y$ if:

$$x - y \geq -1$$
$$3x + 2y \geq 17$$
$$x + 4y \geq 9$$

7.   Find the maximum and minimum values of I for $I = 3x + 10y$ if:

$$x + 2y \leq 6$$
$$x - y \leq 6$$
$$x \geq -6$$
$$y \leq 1$$

8.   Find the maximum and minimum values of I for $I = x + y$ if:

$$x + 3y \geq 9$$
$$2x - y \geq 4$$

$$y \geq 0$$

$$x \leq 15$$

9. A company produces Vitamin A and Vitamin B. The profit on Vitamin A is $150 a pound and Vitamin B yields a profit of $200 per pound. Vitamin A takes 5 hours per pound to manufacture and 3 hours per pound to package. Vitamin B requires 6 hours per pound to manufacture and 2 hours per pound to package. 60 hours of manufacturing time is available, while only 30 hours of packaging time is available. How many pounds of Vitamins A and B should be manufactured to maximize profits?

10. A special diet requires a daily intake of at least 10 ounces of protein and 14 ounces of carbohydrates. The protein and carbohydrate are to come from two grain mixtures. Mixture I contains 3 ounces of protein and 6 ounces of carbohydrate per pound and costs $2.00 per pound. Mixture II contains 1 ounce of protein and 5 ounces of carbohydrate per pound and costs $1.50 per pound. How much of mixtures I and II should be purchased to satisfy the dietary requirements at minimum cost?

11. Two types of hammers, claw and sledge, go through three distinct manufacturing phases: stamping, assembly, and finishing. The time, in hours, required for each phase is given below:

	stamping	assembly	finishing
claw	$\frac{1}{4}$	$\frac{1}{4}$	1
sledge	$\frac{1}{4}$	$\frac{1}{2}$	$\frac{1}{2}$

The times available are 20 hours for stamping, 25 hours for assembly, and 50 hours for finishing. What is the maximum profit that can be made under these conditions if a claw hammer makes $1.00 in profit and a sledge hammer $1.50?

12. A winery can deliver 2,500 fifths of wine or brandy. The winery must deliver 1,500 fifths of wine to satisfy certain regular customers, and 800 fifths of brandy. How many fifths of wine and brandy should be delivered to maximize the profit if the profit from a single fifth of wine is $0.80 and from a fifth of brandy is $1.50?

13. An airliner will hold 400 passengers. The liner is designed to carry passengers in three compartments: first class, second class, and tourist. By moving partitions, the size of the compartments can be changed but the first class compartment will hold at least 50 people, the second

class compartment at least 25, and the tourist compartment at least 25. On a charter flight, with all seats occupied, a tourist fare is $100, a second class fare is $150, and a first class fare is $200. How should the plane be loaded to maximize the gross income?

14. A retailer is setting up a business to sell television sets, stereos, and portable dishwashers. He wants a combined total of 100 of all three items. To satisfy certain customers he must have at least 10 stereos but he cannot sell more than 30 in the immediate future (which is all he is worried about). He wants fewer than 60 television sets but the number of these must equal or exceed the number of stereos. His investment averages $250 for a television set, $150 for a stereo, and $100 for a dishwasher. How many of each should he order to minimize his investment?

15. Suppose that you wish to give a party. You have $250 to spend on liquid refreshments, which, due to the idiosyncrasies of your guests, must be beer and Scotch. You need at least 750 drinks. Beer costs $0.60 a quart, is 4% alcohol, and a quart contains 4 drinks. Scotch costs $7.00 a quart, is 50% alcohol, and each quart contains 20 drinks. How many quarts of beer and Scotch should be purchased so that the party will have maximum alcoholic content?

Chapter 8 REVIEW

(1-10) Evaluate each of the following double integrals.

1. $\displaystyle \int_0^{\pi/2} \int_1^2 \frac{1}{x} \, dx \, dy$

2. $\displaystyle \int_0^{2\pi} \int_0^2 y^2 \sin^2 x \, dy \, dx$

3. $\displaystyle \int_0^5 \int_0^{\sqrt{25-x^2}} y^3 \, dy \, dx$

4. $\displaystyle \int_0^2 \int_0^{2-x} x(x^2 + 3y^2) \, dy \, dx$

5. $\displaystyle \int_{\pi/2}^{\pi} \int_0^{4\cos x} 2y \, dy \, dx$

6. $\displaystyle \int_0^2 \int_1^{\tan x} \frac{1}{(1 + y^2)} \, dy \, dx$

7. $\displaystyle \int_0^1 \int_0^2 xe^{xy} \, dy \, dx$

8. $\displaystyle\int_0^{\pi/4}\int_0^{2\sin x}\cos^2 x\,dy\,dx$

9. $\displaystyle\int_1^2\int_1^{e^y}yx^{-1}\,dx\,dy$

10. $\displaystyle\int_0^\pi\int_0^{\pi/2}\sin x\cos y\,dx\,dy$

(11-15) Find the $\displaystyle\int_A f(x,y)\,dA$, for the $f(x,y)$ and A indicated.

11. $f(x,y) = \dfrac{4}{x^2+1}$, A bounded by $y = x$, $y = 0$ and $x = 3$

12. $f(x,y) = y^{\frac{1}{2}}$, A bounded by $x = y^{\frac{1}{2}}$, $x = 1$, $y = 0$
13. $f(x,y) = y$, A bounded by $y = x^2$ and $x = y^2$
14. $f(x,y) = (3x^2 - xy)$, A bounded by $x = 2y$ and $x = 2y^2$
15. $f(x,y) = 1$, A bounded by $y = x^2$ and $y = x + 2$.

(16-20) For the given function find the indicated partial derivatives.

16. $w = f(x,y,z) = \dfrac{x^2\ln y^2 - y^2\ln z^2}{z}$, find $\dfrac{\partial w}{\partial x}, \dfrac{\partial w}{\partial y}$, and $\dfrac{\partial w}{\partial z}$

17. $w = f(x,y,z) = xyz - x^2y^2z^2$, find $\dfrac{\partial w}{\partial x}, \dfrac{\partial^2 w}{\partial x^2}$, and $\dfrac{\partial^2 w}{\partial x\partial z}$

18. $w = f(x,y,z) = \ln x - \ln y + \ln z + \ln\dfrac{xy}{z}$

   find $\dfrac{\partial^2 w}{\partial z^2}, \dfrac{\partial^2 w}{\partial x^2}$, and $\dfrac{\partial^2 w}{\partial y^2}$

19. $u = f(x,y,z,w)$, $x = v^2 - r^{-2}$, $y = vr^3$, $z = \dfrac{v^2}{r^2}$, $w = \dfrac{1}{v^2}$

   find $\dfrac{\partial u}{\partial v}$ and $\dfrac{\partial u}{\partial r}$

20. $f(x) = \displaystyle\sum_{i=1}^{100}\dfrac{1}{i^2}x^{i^2-1}$ find $\dfrac{df(x)}{dx}$

(21-25) Evaluate the indicated triple integrals.

21. $\displaystyle\int_0^{2\pi}\int_0^1\int_0^{\sqrt{1-x^2}}xz\,dz\,dx\,dy$

22. $\displaystyle\int_0^\pi\int_0^\pi\int_0^\pi xy\sin yz\,dz\,dy\,dx$

23. $\displaystyle\int_{-\ln 3}^{\ln 3} \int_{0}^{\sqrt{y}} \int_{0}^{y+z^2} z\, e^x \, dx \, dz \, dy$

24. $\displaystyle\int_{0}^{5} \int_{0}^{\sqrt{25-z^2}} \int_{0}^{5-z} x \, dy \, dx \, dz$

25. $\displaystyle\int_{-1}^{1} \int_{0}^{1-x^2} \int_{0}^{y} \frac{xy}{z^2} \, dz \, dy \, dx$

26. Describe the analogies that would exist if the *concept* of integration is extended to provide a definition for $\displaystyle\int_{V} f(x,y,z) \, dV$ (i.e., the integral of a function of three variables over a volume V, what does dV represent, what sum does one take, etc.?).

27. Discuss the weakness of geometric interpretations of partial differentiation and multiple integration when the concept is extended to functions of four, five, or more variables.

28. A farmer wishes to ship tomatoes, lettuce, and onions to the city. He can load 800 boxes on a truck, and must ship at least 200 boxes of tomatoes, at least 100 boxes of lettuce, and at least 200 boxes of onions. If the profit on tomatoes is \$2 per box, on lettuce is \$3 per box, and on onions is \$1 per box, how should the truck be loaded for a maximum profit?

29. A newspaper containing 60 pages is to contain at least 30 pages of news articles and at most 15 pages of advertising. Photographs are limited to one-fourth the number of pages for news articles. If the cost per page is \$30 per page of photographs, \$50 per page of news articles, and \$30 per page of advertisements what should the composition of the newspaper be for minimum cost?

CHAPTER NINE

Series and Sequences

To this point in the study of functions and their properties, the nature of a function's functional rule has determined the classification of the function. That is, functions have been classified according to the nature of the rule used to determine functional images. Algebraic functions and rational functions are defined in terms of polynomial functions. In turn, a polynomial function is one whose functional rule involves sums of integral powers of the function's argument. If a functional rule involved a circle and an arclength rule in a certain way it was called a trigonometric function. The logarithmic function was defined by a rule involving integration, while the exponential function made use of the inverse concept. In each case, it was a feature of the image-finding rule that determined the type of function being considered.

In this chapter we will examine types of functions that share a domain rather than a type of rule as their common characteristic. These functions will, in turn, lead to the concept of a series. Series are very valuable in the evaluation of tables, the solution of differential equations, and the representation of nonelementary functions which cannot be expressed in simpler terms.

9-1 SEQUENCES, CONVERGENCE, AND DIVERGENCE

The common characteristic of the functions considered in this chapter will be their domain of definition. The nature of the functional rule will be secondary. In each case, the domain will be taken from the set of nonnegative integers.

Definition. A real-valued function whose domain of definition is a subset or portion of the nonnegative integers is called a *sequence*.

Example. Let $f(n) = \dfrac{1}{n}$, with a domain, $n = 1, 2, 3, 4, 5, 6, 7, 8,$ or 9.

Find the values of the function over its domain.

Solution.
$$f(1) = \tfrac{1}{1} = 1,$$
$$f(2) = \tfrac{1}{2},$$
$$f(3) = \tfrac{1}{3},$$
$$f(4) = \tfrac{1}{4},$$
$$f(5) = \tfrac{1}{5},$$
$$f(6) = \tfrac{1}{6},$$
etc.

Example. Let $f(n) = n^2$, with a domain of the nonnegative integers. Find the value of the function for $n = 3, 1{,}000,$ and 2.7.
Solution.

$$f(3) = 3^2 = 9$$

$$f(1{,}000) = 1{,}000^2 = 1{,}000{,}000$$

$f(2.7)$ is undefined, because 2.7 is not in the domain of f.

Because of the special nature of the domain of a sequence a special notation is usually adopted for image values. For a given sequence, the image of an integer n will be denoted by a_n or b_n, that is, by means of a subscript rather than the usual $f(n)$ or $g(n)$ notation. The sequence as a whole, that is the totality of the image values, will be indicated by $\{a_n\}$ or $\{b_n\}$. The individual values are called the terms of the sequence.

Example. List according to this notation the two sequences given as examples earlier.

Solution. $a_n = \dfrac{1}{n}$, with $n = 1, 2, 3, 4, 5, 6, 7, 8, 9$, thus,

$$a_1 = \tfrac{1}{1} = 1, a_2 = \tfrac{1}{2}, a_3 = \tfrac{1}{3}, a_4 = \tfrac{1}{4}, \text{ etc.};$$

and

$$b_n = n^2, n \text{ any nonnegative integer}$$

$$b_0 = 0^2 = 0, b_1 = 1^2 = 1, b_2 = 2^2 = 4,$$

$$\ldots b_{1,000} = 1,000^2 = 1,000,000, \text{ etc.}$$

When dealing with a sequence, it is conventional to consider the images of the sequence arranged in order of ascending argument. That is, given a sequence denoted by $\{a_n\}$, it is natural to examine $a_0, a_1, a_2, \ldots, a_i,$ $a_{i+1}, \ldots$, etc., where the argument of the ith term is less than the $(i + 1)$th term. It is also informative to consider the behavior of terms as one goes further and further "out" this chain of terms. While studies of this kind can be interesting and useful for any type of sequence, we shall restrict our attention to sequences with an infinite number of terms.

For our discussion $\{a_n\}$ will be assumed to be an infinite sequence, *i.e.*, a sequence with an infinite number of terms. The domain of $\{a_n\}$ will be assumed to be the positive integers.

> **Definition.**   Let $\{a_n\}$ be a sequence. If there exists a number L such that for any positive number, denoted by ϵ, one can find an integer M dependent on ϵ such that
>
> $|a_n - L| < \epsilon$ provided $n > M$, then L is called *the limit of the sequence* $\{a_n\}$.

In other words, if $\lim\limits_{n \to \infty} a_n$ exists and is equal to L, then L is the limit of the sequence.

> **Definition.**   If $\{a_n\}$ has a limit, then it is said to *converge*; otherwise $\{a_n\}$ is said to *diverge*.

In actual practice, we shall not attempt to apply the formal definition of a limit of a sequence, but rather will depend on an intuitive evaluation, or upon convergence/divergence tests which will be considered later.

Example.   Let $\{a_n\}$ be a sequence such that $a_n = \dfrac{1}{n}$. Is $\{a_n\}$ convergent?

Solution. $$\lim_{n \to \infty} a_n = \lim_{n \to \infty} \frac{1}{n} = 0.$$

Thus, $\{a_n\}$ is a convergent sequence.

Example. Let $\{a_n\}$ be a sequence such that $a_n = n^2$. Is this sequence convergent?

Solution. $\lim\limits_{n\to\infty} a_n = \lim\limits_{n\to\infty} n^2 = \infty$.

Therefore, $\{a_n\}$ is a divergent sequence.

Example. Let $\{b_n\}$ be such that $b_n = \dfrac{n}{n+1}$. Is this sequence convergent?

Solution.
$$\lim\limits_{n\to\infty} b_n = \lim\limits_{b\to\infty} \frac{n}{n+1}$$

$$= \lim\limits_{n\to\infty} \frac{\dfrac{n}{n}}{\dfrac{n}{n} + \dfrac{1}{n}}$$

$$= \lim\limits_{n\to\infty} \frac{1}{1 + \dfrac{1}{n}} = 1.$$

Therefore, $\{b_n\}$ is convergent.

From the examples, it seems that sequences are defined by describing the functional rule, *i.e.*, the nature of the general term of the sequence $\{a_n\}$. This is the usual method used in defining ordinary functions. While in general this is the way sequences will be defined, a second, equally useful way, makes use of their special domain. Instead of giving the form of a general term of the sequence, one gives the specific value of one term, usually the first term of the sequence, and then one describes how successive terms are related. That is, one describes how the $(i + 1)$th term is related to the ith term. This type of definition is called a *recursive definition*.

Example. Consider the sequence $\{a_n\}$, where $a_1 = 3$ and $a_{i+1} = a_i + 2$. What are the first five terms of this sequence?

Solution. $a_1 = 3,$

$$a_2 = a_1 + 2 = 3 + 2 = 5,$$

$$a_3 = a_2 + 2 = 5 + 2 = 7,$$

$$a_4 = a_3 + 2 = 7 + 2 = 9, \text{ and}$$

$$a_5 = a_4 + 2 = 9 + 2 = 11.$$

Often, when a sequence is defined recursively it is possible to recover the more usual functional rule-defining equation.

Example. Given $\{a_n\}$, $a_1 = 3$, and $a_{i+1} = a_i + 2$, find the functional rule-defining equation and test for convergence.

Solution. $a_1 = 3,$

$$a_2 = a_1 + 2 = 3 + 2,$$

$$a_3 = a_2 + 2 = 3 + 2 + 2,$$

$$a_4 = a_3 + 2 = 3 + 2 + 2 + 2, \text{ and}$$

$$a_5 = a_4 + 2 = 3 + 2 + 2 + 2 + 2.$$

It follows that

$$a_n = 3 + \underbrace{2 + 2 + \cdots + 2}_{n-1}$$

$$= 3 + 2(n - 1) = 2n + 1.$$

Therefore,

$$\lim_{n \to \infty} a_n = \lim_{n \to \infty} (2n + 1)$$

$$= \infty.$$

Thus, $\{a_n\}$ is divergent.

A sequence of the type just considered, where each term is the previous term plus a fixed amount, is called an *arithmetic sequence*. A second type of sequence given a special name is the *geometric sequence*. In a geometric sequence, each term in the sequence is a constant factor times the previous term.

Example.   Consider $\{a_n\}$ where $a_1 = 1$ and $a_{i+1} = a_i(\frac{1}{2})$. Is this geometric sequence convergent?

Solution. $a_1 = 1,$

$$a_2 = \tfrac{1}{2},$$

$$a_3 = a_2(\tfrac{1}{2}) = (\tfrac{1}{2})^2,$$

$$a_4 = a_3(\tfrac{1}{2}) = (\tfrac{1}{2})^2(\tfrac{1}{2}) = (\tfrac{1}{2})^3, \text{ and}$$

$$a_5 = a_4(\tfrac{1}{2}) = (\tfrac{1}{2})^3(\tfrac{1}{2}) = (\tfrac{1}{2})^4.$$

It seems

$$a_n = (\tfrac{1}{2})^{n-1}$$

$$\lim_{n \to \infty} a_n = \lim_{n \to \infty} (\tfrac{1}{2})^{n-1} = \lim_{n \to \infty} \frac{1}{2^{n-1}}$$

$$= \lim_{n \to \infty} \frac{2}{2^n} = 0.$$

This series is convergent.

Example.   If $\{a_n\}$ is such that $a_1 = 1$ and $a_{i+1} = 3a_i$, is $\{a_n\}$ convergent?
Solution. $a_1 = 1,$

$$a_2 = a_1(3) = 3,$$

$$a_3 = a_2(3) = 3^2, \text{ and}$$

$$a_4 = a_3(3) = (3^2)3 = 3^3.$$

Therefore,

$$a_n = (3)^{n-1};$$

$$\lim_{n \to \infty} a_n = \lim_{n \to \infty} 3^{n-1} = \infty;$$

and $\{a_n\}$ is divergent.

9-1   Exercises

(1-10)   In each case a sequence $\{a_n\}$ has been given. Find values for a_1, a_2, a_3, and a_{20}, and determine if the sequence is convergent or divergent.

1. $\{a_n\}$ where $a_n = \dfrac{n + 3}{n^2}$

2. $\{a_n\}$ where $a_n = \dfrac{\cos n\pi}{n^2}$

3. $\{a_n\}$ where $a_n = \left(1 + \dfrac{1}{n}\right)^{1/n}$

4. $\{a_n\}$ where $a_n = \dfrac{(-1)^{n-2}}{\ln(n + 1)}$

5. $\{a_n\}$ where $a_n = \dfrac{1}{\sqrt{n + 1} - \sqrt{n}}$

6. $\{a_n\}$ where $a_n = \dfrac{\sqrt{n} - \sqrt{n + 2}}{n}$

7. $\{a_n\}$ where $a_n = \dfrac{3n^3 - 1}{2n^3 + 2}$

8. $\{a_n\}$ where $a_n = n \sin n\pi$
9. $\{a_n\}$ where $a_n = (\tfrac{1}{2})^n 2^{n-2}$

10. $\{a_n\}$ where $a_n = \dfrac{e^n}{n}$

(11-15)   In each case a sequence has been defined by giving a_{n+1} in terms of a_n. Find a_n in each case, and determine if the indicated sequence is convergent.

11. $a_{n+1} = a_n(\tfrac{1}{4})$, $a_1 = 1$

12. $a_{n+1} = a_n \cdot \dfrac{1}{n + 1}$, $a_1 = 1$

13. $a_{n+1} = a_n + (n + 1)$, $a_1 = 1$

14. $a_{n+1} = a_n + 1$, $a_1 = 1$

15. $a_{n+1} = a_n + \dfrac{1}{n + 1}$, $a_1 = 1$

(16-25) In each case the sum of the first n terms of a sequence is given. In each case determine the form of the general terms by finding the difference between $\displaystyle\sum_{i=1}^{n-1} a_i$ and $\displaystyle\sum_{i=1}^{n} a_i$ of the sequence and determine if the sequence is convergent.

16. $\displaystyle\sum_{i=1}^{n} a_i = \dfrac{n}{2n + 1}$

17. $\displaystyle\sum_{i=1}^{n} a_i = \dfrac{1}{2^n}$

18. $\displaystyle\sum_{i=1}^{n} a_i = \dfrac{1}{n + 1}$

19. $\displaystyle\sum_{i=1}^{n} a_i = \dfrac{n(n + 1)}{2}$

20. $\displaystyle\sum_{i=1}^{n} a_i = \ln(n + 1)$

21. $\displaystyle\sum_{i=1}^{n} a_i = 2[1 - (\tfrac{1}{2})^n]$

22. $\displaystyle\sum_{i=1}^{n} a_i = \dfrac{(1 - 3^n)}{-2}$

23. $\displaystyle\sum_{i=1}^{n} a_i = 3 + 4(n - 1)$

24. $\displaystyle\sum_{i=1}^{n} a_i = \dfrac{n^2}{n + 1}$

25. $\displaystyle\sum_{i=1}^{n} a_i = \dfrac{n}{n + 1}$

26. Present an argument supporting the hypothesis that all arithmetic sequences $\{a_n\}$ where $a_{i+1} = a_i + c$, $c \neq 0$, must be divergent.

27. Consider a general geometric sequence $\{a_n\}$ with $a_1 = a$, $a_{i+1} = ra_i$, where r is the constant ratio between terms. Determine what conditions must be placed on r to assure that the sequence is convergent.

(28-31) Consider $\{a_n\}$ and $\{b_n\}$, two convergent sequences. Discuss the convergence or divergence of the sequences formed from $\{a_n\}$ and $\{b_n\}$. Justify your answer in each case.

28. $\{c_n\}$ where $c_n = a_n + b_n$

29. $\{c_n\}$ where $c_n = a_n \cdot b_n$

30. $\{c_n\}$ where $c_n = \dfrac{a_n}{b_n}$

31. $\{c_n\}$ where $c_n = ka_n$, k a constant

(32-35) Consider $\{a_n\}$ and $\{b_n\}$, divergent sequences. Discuss the convergence and divergence of the sequence formed from $\{a_n\}$ and $\{b_n\}$. Justify your answer.

32. $\{c_n\}$ where $c_n = a_n - b_n$

33. $\{c_n\}$ where $c_n = a_n \cdot b_n$

34. $\{c_n\}$ where $c_n = \dfrac{a_n}{b_n}$

35. $\{c_n\}$ where $c_n = ka_n$, k a constant

9-2 SERIES

An idea very closely related to the concept of a sequence is that of a series. A series is nothing more than the sum formed from the terms of a sequence.

Example. List a few of the series formed from the sequence $\{a_n\}$ with $a_n = \dfrac{1}{2^n}$.

Solution. Some of the series which can be formed from this sequence are:

$$a_1 + a_2 + a_3 = \frac{1}{2} + \frac{1}{2^2} + \frac{1}{2^3},$$

$$\sum_{i=1}^{10} a_i = a_1 + a_2 + a_3 + a_4 + a_5 + a_6 + a_7 + a_8 + a_9 + a_{10}$$

$$= \frac{1}{2} + \frac{1}{2^2} + \frac{1}{2^3} + \frac{1}{2^4} + \frac{1}{2^5} + \frac{1}{2^6} + \frac{1}{2^7} + \frac{1}{2^8} + \frac{1}{2^9} + \frac{1}{2^{10}}$$

$$\sum_{k=3}^{7} a_{2k+1} = a_{2(3)+1} + a_{2(4)+1} + a_{2(5)+1} + a_{2(6)+1} + a_{2(7)+1}$$

$$= a_7 + a_9 + a_{11} + a_{13} + a_{15}$$

$$= \frac{1}{2^7} + \frac{1}{2^9} + \frac{1}{2^{11}} + \frac{1}{2^{13}} + \frac{1}{2^{15}}, \text{ and}$$

$$\sum_{i=1}^{1,000} a_i = a_1 + a_2 + a_3 + \cdots + a_{1,000}$$

$$= \frac{1}{2} + \frac{1}{2^2} + \frac{1}{2^3} + \cdots + \frac{1}{2^{1,000}}$$

Since we were interested in infinite sequences, it is natural to consider infinite series, *i.e.*, a series with an infinite number of terms.

Example.   Consider the sequence $\{a_n\}$ with $a_n = \dfrac{1}{2^n}$. The corresponding infinite series is

$$a_1 + a_2 + a_3 + \cdots + a_i + a_{i+1} + \cdots$$

$$= \frac{1}{2} + \frac{1}{2^2} + \frac{1}{2^3} + \cdots + \frac{1}{2^i} + \frac{1}{2^{i+1}} + \cdots.$$

Definition.   For a given infinite sequence $\{a_n\}$, the corresponding infinite series will be denoted by

$$\sum_{i=1}^{\infty} a_i = \lim_{n \to \infty} \sum_{i=1}^{n} a_i.$$

If

$$\sum_{i=1}^{\infty} a_i \left(i.e. \lim_{n \to \infty} \sum_{i=1}^{n} a_i \right)$$

exists, the series is said to be *convergent*. Otherwise the series is said to be *divergent*.

Example.   Consider a geometric sequence $\{a_n\}$ with $a_1 = a$ and $a_{i+1} =$

$ra_i = ar^i$. The corresponding geometric series is given by

$$\sum_{i=1}^{\infty} a_i = \sum_{i=1}^{\infty} ar^{i-1} = a + ar + ar^2 + \cdots$$

Under what conditions is this series convergent?
Solution.   To determine if this series is convergent, consider

$$S_n = \sum_{i=1}^{n} a_i = a + ar + ar^2 + \cdots + ar^{n-1}.$$

S_n is called a *partial sum* of the series. A trick can be used to find a compact form for S_n.
   Since

$$S_n = a + ar + ar^2 + \cdots + ar^{n-1}, \text{ and}$$
$$rS_n = ar + ar^2 + ar^3 + \cdots + ar^n,$$
$$S_n - rS_n = a - ar^n$$
$$= a(1 - r^n),$$

because all of the inner terms cancel.
Therefore,

$$S_n(1 - r) = a(1 - r^n),$$

or

$$S_n = \frac{a(1 - r^n)}{1 - r},$$

and

$$\sum_{i=1}^{\infty} a_i = \lim_{n \to \infty} \sum_{i=1}^{n} a_i = \lim_{n \to \infty} S_n$$
$$= \lim_{n \to \infty} \frac{a(1 - r^n)}{1 - r}.$$

If $|r| < 1$, then $\lim_{n \to \infty} r^n = 0$, and

$$\lim_{n \to \infty} S_n = \lim_{n \to \infty} \frac{a(1 - r^n)}{1 - r} = \frac{a}{1 - r};$$

and the series is convergent.
   If $|r| > 1$, then $\lim_{n \to \infty} r^n$ does not exist, and

$$\lim_{n \to \infty} S_n = \lim_{n \to \infty} \frac{a(1 - r^n)}{1 - r}$$

does not exist; therefore

$$\sum_{i=1}^{\infty} a_i \text{ is divergent.}$$

If $|r| = 1$, then $r = +1$ or $r = -1$.
If $r = 1$,

$$S_n = \sum_{i=1}^{n} a_i = na,$$

$$\text{and } \lim_{n \to \infty} S_n = \lim_{n \to \infty} na = \pm \infty,$$

whereas if $r = -1$,

$$S_n = \sum_{i=1}^{n} a(-1)^i = 0 \text{ or } a,$$

depending on whether n is odd or even. In either case, $\lim_{n \to \infty} S_n$ does not exist.

Therefore, we can conclude that a geometric series $\sum_{i=1}^{\infty} a_i$ with $a_i = ar^{i-1}$ is convergent if $|r| < 1$ and divergent if $|r| \geq 1$. Further, if $\sum_{i=1}^{\infty} a_i$ is convergent, it converges to $\dfrac{a}{1-r}$.

That is,

$$\sum_{i=1}^{\infty} a_i = \frac{a}{1-r},$$

where a is the first term and r the common factor.

Example.   Is $\displaystyle\sum_{i=1}^{\infty} \frac{1}{2^i}$ convergent?

Solution.   Yes, it is a geometric series with $|r| = |\frac{1}{2}| = \frac{1}{2} < 1$. Furthermore, since the first term is $\dfrac{1}{2^1} = \frac{1}{2}$,

$$\sum_{i=1}^{\infty} \frac{1}{2^i} = \frac{\frac{1}{2}}{1 - \frac{1}{2}} = \frac{\frac{1}{2}}{\frac{1}{2}} = 1.$$

A discussion of series may be viewed as the study of two sequences, the original sequence whose terms are the terms of the series, and the sequence of partial sums. That is, $\{a_n\}$ leads to the series $\displaystyle\sum_{i=1}^{\infty} a_i$, which in turn leads to the second sequence $\{S_n\}$ where

$$S_1 = a_1$$

$$S_2 = a_1 + a_2 = S_1 + a_2$$

$$S_3 = a_1 + a_2 + a_3 = S_2 + a_3$$

$$S_4 = a_1 + a_2 + a_3 + a_4 = S_3 + a_4$$

$$\cdots$$

$$S_n = \sum_{i=1}^{n} a_i = S_{n-1} + a_n$$

$$\cdots$$

The definition for convergence can be restated in terms of the convergence of a sequence.

Definition. $\sum_{i=1}^{\infty} a_i$ *converges* if its sequence of partial sums, $\{S_n\}$, where

$S_n = \sum_{i=1}^{n} a_i$, converges; otherwise $\sum_{i=1}^{\infty} a_i$ *diverges.*

The difference in the two definitions is only one of notation, not of concept.

Example. Test the series $\sum_{i=1}^{\infty} i$ for convergence.

Solution. $S_n = \sum_{i=1}^{n} i = 1 + 2 + 3 + 4 + \cdots + n.$

Using the standard method for finding this sum,

$$S_n = \underbrace{1 + 2 + 3 + 4 + \cdots + (n-1) + n,}_{n \text{ terms}}$$

or, writing in reversed order,

$$S_n = n + (n-1) + (n-2) + \cdots + 2 + 1.$$

Therefore, adding left and right sides,

$$2S_n = \underbrace{1 + n + [2 + (n-1)] + [3 + (n-2)] + \cdots + [(n-1) + 2] + [n+1]}_{n \text{ terms}}$$

$$= \underbrace{[1 + n] + [n+1] + [n+1] + \cdots + [n+1] + [n+1].}_{n \text{ terms}}$$

$$= n(n+1).$$

Then, dividing both sides by 2,

$$S_n = \frac{n(n + 1)}{2}.$$

Then,

$$\lim_{n \to \infty} S_n = \lim_{n \to \infty} \frac{n(n + 1)}{2} = \infty.$$

Therefore, $\{S_n\}$ is a divergent sequence, and $\sum_{i=1}^{\infty} i$ is a divergent series.

Although we will consider a number of tests for the convergence and divergence of a series in later sections, a simple test for divergence can be considered here.

TEST: Consider $\sum_{i=1}^{\infty} a_i$; if $\lim_{n \to \infty} a_n \neq 0$ the series is divergent. If $\lim_{n \to \infty} a_n = 0$ the series may be either convergent or divergent; in other words, the test fails to give any information.

The conclusion that a necessary condition for convergence is that the nth term of a series tend to zero as n tends to infinity is reasonable, but a simple illustration will demonstrate that this condition is not sufficient to guarantee convergence. The series $\sum_{i=1}^{\infty} \frac{1}{i} = 1 + \frac{1}{2} + \frac{1}{3} + \frac{1}{4} + \cdots$ meets the condition that $\lim_{n \to \infty} a_n = \lim_{n \to \infty} \frac{1}{n} = 0$, but it will be shown to be divergent with a later test. This series is called the *harmonic series*. However, some examples of the use of this test can be given.

Example. What is the $\lim_{n \to \infty} a_n$ of the convergent ($|r| < 1$) geometric series

$$\sum_{i=1}^{\infty} \frac{1}{2^i} \quad \left(i.e., a_n = \frac{1}{2^n}\right)?$$

Solution.
$$\lim_{n \to \infty} a_n = \lim_{n \to \infty} \frac{1}{2^n} = 0.$$

Example. What is the $\lim_{n \to \infty} a_n$ of the divergent geometric series ($|r| > 1$)

$$\sum_{i=1}^{\infty} 2^i \quad (i.e., a_n = 2^n)?$$

Solution.
$$\lim_{n \to \infty} a_n = \lim_{n \to \infty} 2^n = \infty.$$

Example. Are all arithmetic series divergent?

Solution. In any arithmetic series, *i.e.*, one formed from an arithmetic sequence $\{a_n\}$ with $a_1 = a$ and $a_{i+1} = a_i + b$, where b is a nonzero constant,

$$a_n = a + b(n - 1), \text{ and}$$

$$\lim_{n \to \infty} a_n = \lim_{n \to \infty} \{a + b(n - 1)\} = \pm \infty,$$

depending on the sign of b. Thus all arithmetic series are divergent.

Example. Is $\displaystyle\sum_{i=1}^{\infty} \frac{i}{i + 1}$ divergent?

Solution.
$$a_n = \frac{n}{n + 1},$$

and
$$\lim_{n \to \infty} a_n = \lim_{n \to \infty} \frac{n}{n + 1} = 1.$$

Thus,
$$\sum_{i=1}^{\infty} a_i = \sum_{i=1}^{\infty} \frac{i}{i + 1}$$

is divergent.

Example. Is the series $\displaystyle\sum_{i=2}^{\infty} \frac{1}{\ln (i)}$ convergent?

Solution.
$$a_n = \frac{1}{\ln n}.$$

$$\lim_{n \to \infty} a_n = \lim_{n \to \infty} \frac{1}{\ln n} = 0.$$

Thus,
$$\sum_{i=2}^{\infty} \frac{1}{\ln (i)}$$

may be either convergent or divergent. This test provides no conclusions about this series.

Notice that in all of preceding discussions, all these notations have the same meaning.

$$\lim_{i \to \infty} a_i = \lim_{n \to \infty} a_n = \lim_{k \to \infty} a_k, \text{ etc.}$$

and

$$\sum_{i=1}^{\infty} a_i = \sum_{n=1}^{\infty} a_n = \sum_{l=2}^{\infty} a_{l-1} = \sum_{k=7}^{\infty} a_{k-6} = \sum_{k=1}^{\infty} a_k, \text{ etc.}$$

This "change of index" is a useful device and will be used on occasion. The index of the sum, or the variable in the limit process, is a "dummy" and can be changed.

In the case of some series, we will know S_n, i.e., $\sum_{i=1}^{n} a_i$, rather than a specific form for a_n. It is usually a simple matter to recover a_n, since

$$S_n = S_{n-1} + a_n$$

or

$$a_n = S_n - S_{n-1}.$$

Example. Suppose $S_n = \sum_{i=1}^{n} a_n = \dfrac{n}{n+1}$; find a_n.

Solution. $a_n = S_n - S_{n-1}.$

$$S_n = \frac{n}{n+1}; S_{n-1} = \frac{n-1}{n-1+1} = \frac{n-1}{n}.$$

$$a_n = \frac{n}{n+1} - \frac{n-1}{n}$$

$$= \frac{n^2 - (n-1)(n+1)}{n(n+1)}$$

$$= \frac{n^2 - n^2 + 1}{n(n+1)}$$

$$= \frac{1}{n(n+1)}.$$

The infinite series is

$$\sum_{i=1}^{\infty} \frac{1}{i(i+1)}$$

and is convergent to 1, since

$$\lim_{n \to \infty} S_n = \lim_{n \to \infty} \frac{n}{n+1} = 1.$$

9-2 Exercises

(1-6) For each series determine if $\lim_{n \to \infty} a_n = 0$ and draw any possible conclusions about the convergence or divergence of the series.

1. $\displaystyle\sum_{i=1}^{\infty} \frac{i}{i+1}$

2. $\displaystyle\sum_{i=1}^{\infty} \frac{1}{\sqrt{i}}$

3. $\displaystyle\sum_{i=1}^{\infty} \frac{1}{4^i}$

4. $\displaystyle\sum_{i=0}^{\infty} (-1)^i$

5. $\displaystyle\sum_{i=0}^{\infty} (\tfrac{3}{2})^i$

6. $\displaystyle\sum_{i=0}^{\infty} i(-1)^i$

(7-12) In each case an expression has been given for $\displaystyle\sum_{i=1}^{n} a_i$. Use this expression to determine if $\displaystyle\sum_{i=1}^{\infty} a_i$ is convergent.

7. $\displaystyle\sum_{i=1}^{n} a_i = \frac{2n}{6n+1}$

8. $\displaystyle\sum_{i=1}^{n} a_i = \frac{n^3-2}{n^3}$

9. $\displaystyle\sum_{i=1}^{n} a_i = \frac{n^2}{2n+1}$

10. $\displaystyle\sum_{i=1}^{n} a_i = 2^n$

11. $\displaystyle\sum_{i=1}^{n} a_i = -3(1-2^n)$

12. $\displaystyle\sum_{i=1}^{n} a_i = \ln(n+1)$

(13-20) In each case an expression has been given for $S_n = \displaystyle\sum_{i=1}^{n} a_i$. Find the specific form for a_n.

13. $S_n = \dfrac{n^2}{n+1}$

14. $S_n = \dfrac{1}{2^n}$

15. $S_n = \dfrac{5n}{4n + 1}$

16. $S_n = \dfrac{n^2}{n^2 + 2}$

17. $S_n = \dfrac{n}{n + 1}$

18. $S_n = \ln\left(\dfrac{1}{n + 1}\right)$

19. $S_n = 3^n$

20. $S_n = \dfrac{n + 1}{n - 1}$

(21-26)   Any repeating decimal can be written as an infinite series. For example,

$$.23232323\ldots\ldots = 23\left(\frac{1}{100} + \frac{1}{10,000} + \frac{1}{1,000,000} + \cdots\right)$$

$$= 23\sum_{i=1}^{\infty}\frac{1}{10^{2i}} = 23\sum_{i=1}^{\infty}\left(\frac{1}{10^2}\right)^{i}$$

However, $\displaystyle\sum_{i=1}^{\infty}\left(\frac{1}{10^2}\right)^{i}$ is a convergent geometric series, which converges to

$$\frac{\dfrac{1}{10^2}}{1 - \dfrac{1}{10^2}} = \frac{\dfrac{1}{10^2}}{\dfrac{99}{100}} = \frac{1}{99}.$$

Therefore,

$$23\sum_{i=1}^{\infty}\frac{1}{10^{2i}} = \frac{23}{99},$$

or $.2323\ldots = \dfrac{23}{99}.$

Use this method to convert the following repeating decimals to rational numbers.

21. $.3333333\ldots$

22. $1.41414141\ldots$

23. 3.142857142857142857...

24. $-.371371371...$

25. 10.371371371...

26. .4444244424442...

27. Let R_n denote the remainder of a series if the series is truncated after n terms.

That is,
$$R_n = \sum_{i=n+1}^{\infty} a_i.$$

If $\sum_{i=1}^{\infty} a_i$ is convergent, what value must $\lim_{n \to \infty} R_n$ have? Justify your answer.

(28-29)   A ball is dropped from a height of 100 feet. Each time it hits the ground it bounces $\frac{2}{3}$ of the height from which it fell.

28. Find an infinite series representing the distance the ball travels as it bounces.

29. Based on your analysis of the infinite series of problem 28, how far will the ball travel before it comes to rest?

(30-33)   Consider two convergent infinite series
$$\sum_{i=1}^{\infty} a_i \quad \text{and} \quad \sum_{i=1}^{\infty} b_i.$$

30. What are $\lim_{n \to \infty} a_i$ and $\lim_{n \to \infty} b_i$?

31. Is the series $\sum_{i=1}^{\infty} c_i$, where $c_i = a_i + b_i$ for all i, convergent? Justify your answer.

32. Is the series $\sum_{i=1}^{\infty} c_i$, where $c_i = a_i \cdot b_i$, convergent?

33. Is the series $\sum_{i=1}^{\infty} \dfrac{a_i}{b_i}$ convergent? Justify your answer.

(34-36)   Consider two divergent series, $\sum_{i=1}^{\infty} a_i$ and $\sum_{i=1}^{\infty} b_i$.

34. What are $\lim_{n \to \infty} a_n$ and $\lim_{n \to \infty} b_n$?

35. If $c_i = a_i - b_i$, is $\sum_{i=1}^{\infty} c_i$ convergent or divergent? Justify your answer.

36. If $c_i = \dfrac{a_i}{b_i}$, is $\displaystyle\sum_{i=1}^{\infty} c_i$ convergent or divergent? Justify your answer.

37. How does the convergence or divergence of $\displaystyle\sum_{i=1}^{\infty} a_i$ relate to that of $\displaystyle\sum_{i=7}^{\infty} a_i$, to that of $\displaystyle\sum_{i=100,000}^{\infty} a_i$, to that of $\displaystyle\sum_{i=m}^{\infty} a_i$ where m is any positive integer?

38. A car rolling down a hill moves 2 feet in the first second, 5 feet in the second second, and 8 feet in the third second. At this rate, how far will the car move in 30 seconds?

39. Mr. Jones starts a regular savings plan by depositing $1,000 in the Get-Rich Savings and Loan Company. At the beginning of the second year his account is credited with $53 interest, so he deposits only $947. At the beginning of the third year he is credited with $106 and deposits $894. At the beginning of the fourth year he is credited with $159, and deposits $841. If he continues to receive interest and deposit in this manner, how much total interest will he have received by the end of the tenth year?

9-3   TESTS FOR CONVERGENCE AND DIVERGENCE

The definition of a convergent infinite series requires preknowledge of the limit of the series. On the other hand, many of the uses of infinite series involve the evaluation of a numerical quantity, whose decimal representation is otherwise unknown, as the limit of a convergent infinite series. To make infinite series useful it will be necessary to consider some tests which can tell if an infinite series is convergent without knowing the exact nature of the limit of the series.

The tests in this section will be structured for series with positive terms only. However, they will also take care of series with all negative terms, for they would then apply to the positive-termed series found by factoring out a common factor of negative one. Second, it is clear that the convergence or divergence of an infinite series does not depend on the values of any finite number of finite-valued terms. If one ignores the first term, the first thousand terms, or the first million terms, the series still converges or diverges on the basis of the behavior of the remaining infinite terms. This means that any test of convergence of a series $\displaystyle\sum_{i=1}^{\infty} a_i$ must assume $a_{i+1} \leq a_i$, that is, the terms of the series are descending in value, with $a_i \geq 0$ for all i. Further, we may assume

$$\lim_{n \to \infty} a_n = 0,$$

for, from the previous section, we know that without this condition the series must be divergent.

We can construct a graphical representation of an infinite series, which can help us visualize the relationships between the tests and the series. Suppose we construct a graph of the series by constructing a series of rectangular columns. Each column will be 1 unit wide and a_i units high; the left-hand side of the column is at the integer i. Such a graph is illustrated in figure 9-1. Clearly, if $\sum_{i=1}^{\infty} a_i$ exists, it must equal the total area of the columns.

The fact $\sum_{i=1}^{\infty} a_i$ corresponds to an area suggests that we should be able to use some features of integration, our area-finding tool, to test our series for convergence or divergence. But what do we integrate, and after we are done, what does the result tell us?

Consider an infinite series $\sum_{i=1}^{\infty} a_i$ and a function $f(x)$ such that $f(i) = a_i$ for all integers i. Further suppose that $f(x)$ is continuous for $x \geq 1$. The graph of $f(x)$ in figure 9-1 compares $f(x)$ to the rectangular columns of

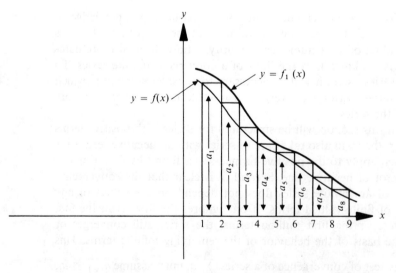

FIG. 9-1.   The Integral Test

$\sum\limits_{i=1}^{\infty} a_i$. The graph of $f(x)$ passes through $(1,a_1)$, $(2,a_2)$, ..., (i,a_i), etc., the upper left-hand corner of each column. Now consider a second function $f_1(x) = f(x - 1)$, where $f(x)$ is defined the same as before. In this case, $f_1(2) = f(1) = a_1$, $f_1(3) = f(2) = a_2$, etc. That is, $f_1(i) = a_{i-1}$ for any integer $i \geq 2$. That graph of $f_1(x)$ is shown in figure 9-1 as a dark line, and passes through the upper right-hand corners of the columns corresponding to $\sum\limits_{i=2}^{\infty} a_i$. Consider the two improper integrals

$$\int_2^{\infty} f(x)\, dx \qquad \text{and} \qquad \int_2^{\infty} f_1(x)\, dx.$$

Both of these exist, or fail to exist together, since $f_1(x)$ is only $f(x)$ shifted to the right. However, $\sum\limits_{i=2}^{\infty} a_i$ is trapped between these integrals. That is,

$$\int_2^{\infty} f(x)\, dx \leq \sum_{i=2}^{\infty} a_i \leq \int_2^{\infty} f_1(x)\, dx.$$

Therefore, it is reasonable to conclude that if the integrals converge, the series $\sum\limits_{i=2}^{\infty} a_i$ must also, and if $\sum\limits_{i=2}^{\infty} a_i$ diverges, so do the integrals. However, $\sum\limits_{i=1}^{\infty} a_i$ and $\sum\limits_{i=2}^{\infty} a_i$ differ only by a_1; therefore they must converge or diverge together. The summary of this result takes the form of the integral test for convergence and divergence.

THE INTEGRAL TEST: Consider an infinite series $\sum\limits_{i=1}^{\infty} a_i$ and a function $f(x)$ such that for some integer n, $f(i) = a_i$ for all integers $i \geq n$. Then $\int_n^{\infty} f(x)\, dx$ and $\sum\limits_{i=1}^{\infty} a_i$ converge or diverge together.

Stating that the function need only match the terms of the series from some integer n on and need not match the series for a finite number of terms preceding the nth, is only a restatement, in an alternative form, of the statement that the series' convergence or divergence is not affected by the behavior of a finite number of terms. The preceding discussion does not constitute a formal proof, and it is only presented to make the result seem reasonable. A more complete presentation of the subject of series would include a formal proof.

Example. Consider the convergent geometric series $\sum\limits_{i=1}^{\infty} \dfrac{1}{2^i}$. Apply the integral test to this series.

Solution. $a_i = \dfrac{1}{2^i}$; therefore the appropriate function is

$$f(x) = \frac{1}{2^x} = 2^{-x}.$$

The improper integral is then

$$\int_1^{\infty} 2^{-x}\, dx = \lim_{b \to \infty} \int_1^b 2^{-x}\, dx$$

$$= \lim_{b \to \infty} \frac{2^{-x}}{-\ln 2}\Bigg]_1^b$$

$$= \lim_{b \to \infty} \left[\frac{1}{-\ln 2} \left\{ \frac{1}{2^b} - \frac{1}{2} \right\} \right]$$

$$= \frac{1}{-\ln 2}\left(-\frac{1}{2}\right) = \frac{1}{2 \ln 2}.$$

The integral exists. Therefore the integral test verifies the convergence of the series.

Example. Consider the harmonic series $\sum\limits_{i=1}^{\infty} \dfrac{1}{i}$. Test this for convergence using the integral test.

Solution. Let $f(x) = \dfrac{1}{x}$. The improper integral corresponding to this series is

$$\int_1^{\infty} \frac{1}{x}\, dx = \lim_{b \to \infty} \int_1^b \frac{1}{x}\, dx$$

$$= \lim_{b \to \infty} \left[\ln x \right]_1^b$$

$$= \lim_{b \to \infty} \left[\ln b - \ln 1 \right]$$

$$= \lim_{b \to \infty} \left[\ln b \right] = \infty.$$

This harmonic series must diverge.

Example.   Consider the series $\sum\limits_{i=1}^{\infty} \dfrac{1}{i^p}$. This series is called a "*p* series." De-

termine the restrictions on p required to make the series convergent.
Solution.   If $p = 1$ then the series is the harmonic series, which we know
to be divergent. If $p \neq 1$ then we may apply the integral test, with $f(x) = x^{-p}$.

$$\int_{1}^{\infty} f(x)\, dx = \lim_{b \to \infty} \int_{1}^{b} x^{-p}\, dx$$

$$= \lim_{b \to \infty} \frac{x^{-p+1}}{-p+1} \bigg]_{1}^{b}$$

$$= \lim_{b \to \infty} \left[\frac{1}{1-p} \{ b^{-p+1} - 1 \} \right].$$

Whether this limit exist or not depends on the sign of $-p + 1$.
If $-p + 1 < 0$, *i.e.*, $p > 1$, then

$$\lim_{b \to \infty} (b^{-p+1}) = 0,$$

while if $-p + 1 > 0$, *i.e.*, $p < 1$,

$$\lim_{b \to \infty} (b^{-p+1}) = \infty.$$

Correspondingly, if $p > 1$ then the integral exists and $\sum\limits_{i=1}^{\infty} \dfrac{1}{i^p}$ converges,

and if $p \leq 1$ the integral fails to exist and $\sum\limits_{i=1}^{\infty} \dfrac{1}{i^p}$ diverges. In conclusion

$\sum\limits_{i=1}^{\infty} \dfrac{1}{i^p}$ converges if $p > 1$ and diverges if $p \leq 1$.

Although the integral test compares the series in question with an
integral, it is just as reasonable to construct a test that compares an unknown series with a known series.

COMPARISON TEST I: Consider   an infinite series $\sum\limits_{i=1}^{\infty} a_i$ with $a_i \geq 0$ and

$a_{i+1} \leq a_i$. Suppose that there exists a second series $\sum\limits_{i=1}^{\infty} b_i$ such that $b_i \geq a_i$

for all integers i. Then if $\sum\limits_{i=1}^{\infty} b_i$ converges, so does $\sum\limits_{i=1}^{\infty} a_i$.

A graph similar to figure 9-1 can be used to convince us of the validity of

the test. Consider figure 9-2. $\sum\limits_{i=1}^{\infty} b_i$ represents the total area of the *b* columns,

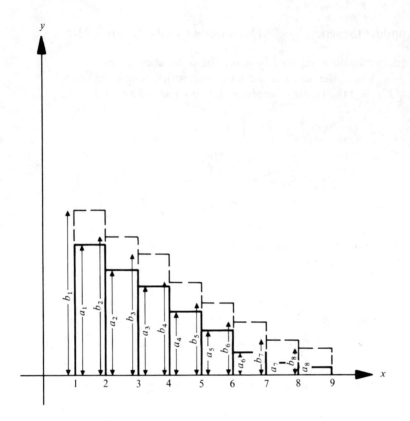

FIG. 9-2.   The Comparison Test I

whereas $\displaystyle\sum_{i=1}^{\infty} a_i$ represents that of the a columns, $a_i \le b_i$. If the total area of

the b columns is finite, *i.e.*, if $\displaystyle\sum_{i=1}^{\infty} b_i$ converges, then the total area of the

a columns must also be finite; that is, $\displaystyle\sum_{i=1}^{\infty} a_i$ converges.

A similar figure would lead to the conclusion that a comparison can be made to prove divergence. The construction of the figure is left as an exercise.

COMPARISON TEST II: Consider an infinite series $\displaystyle\sum_{i=1}^{\infty} a_i$. Suppose that there exists another infinite series $\sum\limits_{i=1}^{\infty} b_i$ with $b_i \leq a_i$ for all integers i. Then if

$\sum\limits_{i=1}^{\infty} b_i$ diverges, so does $\sum\limits_{i=1}^{\infty} a_i$.

The key to the use of the comparison tests is that one must decide which way a series goes before deciding which test to use. If the series tested seems to be convergent, then one tries to find a known convergent series which is term by term larger than the series to be tested. If one feels the unknown series is divergent, then one sets out to find a known divergent series that is term by term smaller than the series being tested. If you make the wrong guess, nothing results.

Example.   Use the comparison tests to determine the convergence of the series $\sum\limits_{i=3}^{\infty} \dfrac{1}{\ln i}$. For all integers $i \geq 3$, $\ln i < i$. Therefore, $\dfrac{1}{\ln i} > \dfrac{1}{i}$.

Since $\sum\limits_{i=3}^{\infty} \dfrac{1}{i}$ is part of the harmonic series, it is known to be divergent. There-

fore $\sum\limits_{i=3}^{\infty} \dfrac{1}{\ln i}$ is term by term larger than a known divergent series, and thus it

is divergent.

Notice we had to guess how the series behaved. Such guesses are usually based on a feel of what the series looks like.

Example.   Test $\sum\limits_{i=1}^{\infty} \dfrac{1}{(i + 1)(i + 2)}$ for convergence.

Solution. $\dfrac{1}{(i + 1)(i + 2)} = \dfrac{1}{i^2 + 3i + 2}$, it is reasonable to assume that for

i large enough, this behaves like $\dfrac{1}{i^2}$. Therefore we will try to compare this

series with

$$\sum\limits_{i=1}^{\infty} \dfrac{1}{i^2},$$

which is a p series with $p = 2 > 1$. Therefore it is convergent. Fortunately,

$$i^2 + 3i + 2 > i^2,$$

thus $\dfrac{1}{i^2 + 3i + 2} < \dfrac{1}{i^2}$, and $\sum\limits_{i=1}^{\infty} \dfrac{1}{(i + 1)(i + 2)}$

is term by term smaller than a known convergent series, and must be convergent.

9-3 Exercises

1. Construct a figure similar to figure 9-2 to justify the comparison test for divergence.

(2-7) Establish the convergence or divergence of each of the following series with use of the integral test.

2. $\displaystyle\sum_{i=1}^{\infty} \frac{1}{i^2 + 1}$

3. $\displaystyle\sum_{i=1}^{\infty} \frac{i}{(i^2 + 1)^{\frac{3}{2}}}$

4. $\displaystyle\sum_{i=1}^{\infty} \frac{i}{e^{2i}}$

5. $\displaystyle\sum_{i=1}^{\infty} \frac{1}{\sqrt{i^2 + 1}}$

6. $\displaystyle\sum_{i=1}^{\infty} \frac{1}{(i + 1)(i + 2)}$

7. $\displaystyle\sum_{i=2}^{\infty} \frac{1}{i(\ln i)^2}$

(8-13) Establish the convergence or divergence of each of the following series using a comparison test.

8. $\displaystyle\sum_{i=1}^{\infty} \frac{1}{(i + 1)(i + 2)}$

9. $\displaystyle\sum_{i=3}^{\infty} \frac{i}{(i - 1)(i - 2)}$

10. $\displaystyle\sum_{i=1}^{\infty} \frac{1}{3^i + 2}$

11. $\displaystyle\sum_{i=1}^{\infty} \frac{1}{3^i - 2}$

12. $\displaystyle\sum_{i=2}^{\infty} \frac{1}{i - 1}$

13. $\displaystyle\sum_{i=1}^{\infty} \frac{3}{2^i + 1}$

(14-25)   Determine if each of the following series is convergent or divergent.

14. $\displaystyle\sum_{i=1}^{\infty} \frac{1}{(i + 1)\ln(i + 1)}$

15. $\displaystyle\sum_{i=1}^{\infty} \frac{1}{\sqrt{i^2 + 2i + 2}}$

16. $\displaystyle\sum_{i=1}^{\infty} \frac{1}{(3i)^2}$

17. $\displaystyle\sum_{i=1}^{\infty} \frac{1}{(3i)^{\frac{1}{2}}}$

18. $\displaystyle\sum_{i=1}^{\infty} \frac{2 + \cos i}{i^2}$

19. $\displaystyle\sum_{i=1}^{\infty} \frac{\ln i}{i^2}$

20. $\displaystyle\sum_{i=1}^{\infty} \frac{i}{(i + 1)^2}$

21. $\displaystyle\sum_{i=1}^{\infty} \frac{i}{(i + 1)^3}$

22. $\displaystyle\sum_{i=1}^{\infty} \frac{i}{i + 1}$

23. $\displaystyle\sum_{i=1}^{\infty} \frac{i + 1}{(i + 1)3^i}$

24. $\displaystyle\sum_{i=1}^{\infty} i^2 \sin(\pi i)$

25. $\displaystyle\sum_{i=1}^{\infty} \frac{(-1)^i}{\cos(\pi(i + 1))}$

26.   Must two series be in the proper relationship for every term of both series when using the comparison tests? Modify the statements of the comparison tests to reflect your answer.

(27-30)   An alternate form of the comparison test is stated as follows: If

$\displaystyle\sum_{i=1}^{\infty} a_i$ and $\displaystyle\sum_{i=1}^{\infty} b_i$ are two positive-termed series and if

$$\lim_{n \to \infty} \frac{a_n}{b_n} = L, L > 0 \text{ and finite,}$$

then
$$\sum_{i=1}^{\infty} a_i \text{ and } \sum_{i=1}^{\infty} b_i$$

both converge or both diverge. Use this version to test the following series.

27. $\displaystyle\sum_{i=1}^{\infty} \frac{i}{i^2 + 1}$

28. $\displaystyle\sum_{i=1}^{\infty} \frac{1}{\sqrt{i^2 + 1}}$

29. $\displaystyle\sum_{i=1}^{\infty} \frac{1}{i^2 + 2i + 3}$

30. $\displaystyle\sum_{i=1}^{\infty} \frac{i^7 - 2i^3}{i^8 + 2i^7 - 4}$

9-4 THE RATIO TEST AND L'HÔSPITAL'S RULES

The integral test and the comparison test relate the terms of a series to other quantities outside of the original series. The ratio test analyzes the convergence or divergence of a series by examining how consecutive terms of the series itself relate to each other.

THE RATIO TEST: The series $\displaystyle\sum_{i=1}^{\infty} a_i$ is convergent if

$$\lim_{n \to \infty} \frac{a_{n+1}}{a_n} \text{ is less than 1.}$$

The series is divergent if

$$\lim_{n \to \infty} \frac{a_{n+1}}{a_n} \text{ is greater than 1.}$$

If
$$\lim_{n \to \infty} \frac{a_{n+1}}{a_n} = 1,$$

the ratio test fails, *i.e.*, no conclusion can be drawn.
To establish the result consider

$$\lim_{n \to \infty} \frac{a_{n+1}}{a_n} = L.$$

Now suppose that $L < 1$. Then there is a number r such that

$$L < r < 1,$$

and further, if n is large enough, say greater than some fixed number N, we can be sure that

$$\frac{a_{n+1}}{a_n} < r.$$

Thus, $a_{n+1} < ra_n,$

$$a_{n+2} < ra_{n+1} < r(ra_n) = r^2 a_n,$$

$$a_{n+3} < ra_{n+2} < r(r^2 a_n) = r^3 a_n.$$

Thus, the series $\sum\limits_{i=n+1}^{\infty} a_i$ is term by term less than $\sum\limits_{i=2}^{\infty} r^{i-1} a_n$. Since $\sum\limits_{i=2}^{\infty} r^{i-1} a_n$

is a geometric series, when $r < 1$, it is convergent. Thus, $\sum\limits_{i=n+1}^{\infty} a_i$ is convergent

by the comparison test. If $\sum\limits_{i=n}^{\infty} a_i$ converges so does $\sum\limits_{i=1}^{\infty} a_i$, since they differ

only by a finite number of terms. Similarly, if $\lim\limits_{n\to\infty} \dfrac{a_{n+1}}{a_n} = L$ and $L > 1$, the

comparison test can be used to establish that the series is divergent. This

approach also makes it clear why the ratio test fails if $\lim\limits_{n\to\infty} \dfrac{a_{n+1}}{a_n} = 1$. The ap-

plication of the ratio test is simpler than that of the comparison test as we don't have to guess the result in advance.

Example.   Apply the ratio test to the convergent geometric series

$$\sum_{i=1}^{\infty} \frac{1}{3^i}.$$

Solution. $a_n = \dfrac{1}{3^n}$, and $a_{n+1} = \dfrac{1}{3^{n+1}}$, thus

$$\lim_{n\to\infty} \frac{a_{n+1}}{a_n} = \lim_{n\to\infty} \frac{\dfrac{1}{3^{n+1}}}{\dfrac{1}{3^n}}$$

$$= \lim_{n\to\infty} \frac{3^n}{3^{n+1}}$$

$$= \lim_{n\to\infty} \frac{1}{3} = \frac{1}{3}.$$

Since $\dfrac{1}{3} < 1$ the ratio test indicates that $\displaystyle\sum_{i=1}^{\infty} \dfrac{1}{3^i}$ converges.

Example.   Consider the series

$$\frac{1}{1} + \frac{1}{2(1)} + \frac{1}{3(2)(1)} + \frac{1}{4(3)(2)(1)} + \cdots + \frac{1}{n(n-1)(n-2)\ldots(3)(2)(1)} + \cdots,$$

or

$$\sum_{i=1}^{\infty} \frac{1}{i(i-1)\ldots(3)(2)(1)}.$$

Test this series for convergence using the ratio test.

Solution. $a_n = \dfrac{1}{n(n-1)(n-2)\ldots(3)(2)(1)}$

$$a_{n+1} = \frac{1}{(n+1)(n)(n-1)\ldots(3)(2)(1)}$$

$$\frac{a_{n+1}}{a_n} = \frac{\dfrac{1}{(n+1)(n)(n-1)\ldots(3)(2)(1)}}{\dfrac{1}{n(n-1)(n-2)\ldots(3)(2)(1)}}$$

$$= \frac{n(n-1)(n-2)\ldots(3)(2)(1)}{(n+1)(n)(n-1)\ldots(3)(2)(1)}$$

$$= \frac{1}{n+1}.$$

Thus,

$$\lim_{n\to\infty} \frac{a_{n+1}}{a_n} = \lim_{n\to\infty} \frac{1}{n+1}$$

$$= 0 < 1.$$

Thus, this series has been shown convergent by use of the ratio test.

Factors like $n(n-1)(n-2)\ldots(3)(2)(1)$ are sufficiently common and useful to warrant a special notation. $n! = n(n-1)\ldots(3)(2)(1)$ for $n \geq 2$ and n an integer. $n!$ is read "n factorial." In general,

$$n! = n(n-1)! = n(n-1)(n-2)!, \text{ etc.}$$

$$(n+1)! = (n+1)n!$$

The definition of $n!$ does not reasonably apply if $n = 0$ or $n = 1$. For that reason these are defined as special cases, just as $a^0 = 1$ is defined as a special case.

Definition. $0! = 1! = 1.$

Using factorials in the previous series example we have:

Example.   Test $\sum\limits_{i=1}^{\infty} \dfrac{1}{i!}$ for convergence.

Solution.
$$a_n = \frac{1}{n!}$$

$$a_{n+1} = \frac{1}{(n+1)!}$$

$$\frac{a_{n+1}}{a_n} = \frac{\dfrac{1}{(n+1)!}}{\dfrac{1}{n!}} = \frac{n!}{(n+1)!}$$

$$= \frac{n!}{(n+1)n!}$$

$$= \frac{1}{n+1},$$

and

$$\lim_{n \to \infty} \frac{a_{n+1}}{a_n} = \lim_{n \to \infty} \frac{1}{n+1} = 0.$$

Thus by the ratio test the series is convergent.

Example.   Test the series $\sum\limits_{i=1}^{\infty} \dfrac{2^i}{i!}$ for convergence.

Solution.
$$a_n = \frac{2^n}{n!}$$

$$a_{n+1} = \frac{2^{n+1}}{(n+1)!}$$

$$\frac{a_{n+1}}{a_n} = \frac{\dfrac{2^{n+1}}{(n+1)!}}{\dfrac{2^n}{n!}} = \frac{2^{n+1}}{2^n} \cdot \frac{n!}{(n+1)!} = \frac{2}{n+1}.$$

And,

$$\lim_{n \to \infty} \frac{a_{n+1}}{a_n} = \lim_{n \to \infty} \frac{2}{n+1} = 0 < 1.$$

Thus, the series has been shown to be convergent by the ratio test.

Example.   Test $\sum\limits_{i=1}^{\infty} \dfrac{2^i}{\ln i^2}$ for convergence.

Solution.

$$a_n = \frac{2^n}{\ln n^2} = \frac{2^n}{2\ln n} = \frac{2^{n-1}}{\ln n}$$

$$a_{n+1} = \frac{2^n}{\ln(n+1)}$$

$$\frac{a_{n+1}}{a_n} = \frac{\dfrac{2^n}{\ln(n+1)}}{\dfrac{2^{n-1}}{\ln n}}$$

$$= \frac{2^n}{2^{n-1}}\left(\frac{\ln n}{\ln(n+1)}\right)$$

$$= 2\frac{\ln n}{\ln(n+1)}$$

However,

$$\lim_{n\to\infty} \frac{a_{n+1}}{a_n} = \lim_{n\to\infty} 2\frac{\ln n}{\ln(n+1)} = \,?$$

This seems to be a dead end unless we can establish the limit. We shall come back to this after considering L'Hôspital's rules.

To aid in finding limits such as the one in the preceeding example, two very useful rules involving just such cases were developed by L'Hôspital.

Guillaume Francois Marquis de L'Hôspital was a French disciple of Leibniz and a student of one of the great names in the development of calculus, John Bernoulli. L'Hôspital was also the author of the first published textbook on differential calculus, *Analyse des infiniments petits pour l'intelligence des lignes courbes*. The following are L'Hôspital's rules.

I.   Let $f(x)$ and $g(x)$ be two functions such that

$$\lim_{x\to a} f(x) = \infty \text{ and } \lim_{x\to a} g(x) = \infty.$$

Then

$$\lim_{x\to a} \frac{f(x)}{g(x)} = \lim_{x\to a} \frac{f'(x)}{g'(x)},$$

where a may be either finite or infinite.

II.   Let $f(x)$ and $g(x)$ be two functions such that

$$\lim_{x \to a} f(x) = 0 \text{ and } \lim_{x \to a} g(x) = 0,$$

Then,

$$\lim_{x \to a} \frac{f(x)}{g(x)} = \lim_{x \to a} \frac{f'(x)}{g'(x)},$$

where a may be either finite or infinite.

In both cases it is assumed that f and g are differentiable functions over the values in question except possibly at $x = a$.

These rules of L'Hôspital, which are really theorems, are stated without proof. However, a simple proof of the following restricted form is given to provide some insight and credibility.

Proof.   Suppose $f(a) = g(a) = 0$. Then

$$\lim_{x \to a} \frac{f(x)}{g(x)} = \lim_{x \to a} \frac{f(x) - f(a)}{g(x) - g(a)}$$

$$= \lim_{x \to a} \frac{\dfrac{f(x) - f(a)}{x - a}}{\dfrac{g(x) - g(a)}{x - a}}$$

$$= \frac{f'(a)}{g'(a)}.$$

Example.   Since $\lim_{x \to 0} \sin x = 0$, $\lim_{x \to 0} x = 0$,

$$\frac{d}{dx} \sin x = \cos x, \frac{d}{dx} x = 1, \text{ and } \lim_{x \to 0} \cos x = 1,$$

$$\lim_{x \to 0} \frac{\sin x}{x} = \lim_{x \to 0} \frac{\cos x}{1} = 1,$$

Example.   Complete the previous series example.

Solution. $\lim\limits_{x \to \infty} 2 \dfrac{\ln(x)}{\ln(x + 1)} = \lim\limits_{x \to \infty} 2 \dfrac{\dfrac{1}{x}}{\dfrac{1}{x + 1}},$

since $\dfrac{d}{dx} \ln x = \dfrac{1}{x}, \dfrac{d}{dx} \ln(x + 1) = \dfrac{1}{x + 1},$

and $\lim\limits_{x \to \infty} \ln x = \lim\limits_{x \to \infty} \ln(x + 1) = \infty.$

Therefore,

$$\lim\limits_{x \to \infty} (2) \frac{\ln x}{\ln(x + 1)} = \lim\limits_{x \to \infty} (2) \frac{x + 1}{x}$$

$$= \lim\limits_{x \to \infty} (2) \frac{1}{1} = 2,$$

since $\dfrac{d}{dx}(x + 1) = 1, \dfrac{d}{dx}x = 1,$ and

$$\lim\limits_{x \to \infty} (x + 1) = \infty = \lim\limits_{x \to \infty} x.$$

Here L'Hôspital's Rules have been applied twice. Since

$$\lim\limits_{n \to \infty} \frac{a_{n+1}}{a_n} = 2,$$

the ratio test concludes $\sum\limits_{i=1}^{\infty} \dfrac{2^i}{\ln i^2}$ is divergent.

Example.   Use the ratio test to test the harmonic series $\sum\limits_{i=1}^{\infty} \dfrac{1}{i}$.

Solution. $a_n = \dfrac{1}{n}, a_{n+1} = \dfrac{1}{n + 1}$

$$\lim\limits_{n \to \infty} \frac{a_{n+1}}{a_n} = \lim\limits_{n \to \infty} \frac{\dfrac{1}{n + 1}}{\dfrac{1}{n}} = \lim\limits_{n \to \infty} \frac{n}{n + 1}$$

$$= \lim\limits_{n \to \infty} \frac{1}{1} = 1.$$

The ratio test fails to draw any conclusion.

Example.   Use the ratio test on the series $\sum\limits_{i=1}^{\infty} \dfrac{1}{n^2}$, a convergent p series.

Solution. $a_n = \dfrac{1}{n^2}$

$$a_{n+1} = \frac{1}{(n + 1)^2}$$

$$\lim_{n \to \infty} \frac{a_{n+1}}{a_n} = \lim_{n \to \infty} \frac{\dfrac{1}{(n+1)^2}}{\dfrac{1}{n^2}}$$

$$= \lim_{n \to \infty} \frac{n^2}{(n+1)^2}$$

$$= \lim_{n \to \infty} \frac{2n}{2(n+1)}$$

$$= \lim_{n \to \infty} \frac{2}{2} = 1.$$

Again the ratio test fails.

From the latter two examples, it is clear that with either a convergent or a divergent series the ratio test can fail. Also, in both cases, L'Hôspital's rules were used in the evaluation of the limit. The alert reader may have noticed there is a conceptual problem applying L'Hôspital's rules in these cases. $\dfrac{d}{dn} n^2$ is not defined, since we are considering n^2 defined only for integer values for n. However, x^2, x a real number, is defined and takes the same values as n^2 when $x = n$. Further, $f(x) = x^2$ is differentiable for all real numbers, not just integers. L'Hôspital's rules can be applied by treating expressions like n^2 or $\ln n$ as functions of a continuous real variable. That is, we may treat the factors as differentiable functions and differentiate using the usual rules. This practice can be formally established in a more complete presentation.

9-4   Exercises

(1-10)   Find the indicated limits.

1. $\displaystyle\lim_{x \to 0} \frac{\sin x - 2x}{x}$

2. $\displaystyle\lim_{x \to 0} \frac{\tan x}{4x}$

3. $\displaystyle\lim_{x \to \infty} \frac{2^x}{x^2}$

4. $\displaystyle\lim_{x \to \infty} \frac{x^{12}}{e^x}$

5. $\lim\limits_{x \to \infty} \dfrac{\ln x}{x}$

6. $\lim\limits_{x \to \infty} \dfrac{x}{\ln x}$

7. $\lim\limits_{x \to \infty} \dfrac{\sin \dfrac{1}{x}}{\tan^{-1}\left(\dfrac{1}{x}\right)}$

8. $\lim\limits_{x \to \infty} \dfrac{\ln\left(\dfrac{e^{2x}}{x}\right)}{\sqrt{x}}$

9. $\lim\limits_{x \to \infty} \dfrac{1 + \cos 2x}{1 - \sin x}$

10. $\lim\limits_{x \to 3} \dfrac{x^3 - 3x^2 + 9x - 27}{x - 3}$

(11-25)   Use the ratio test to determine if the following series are convergent.

11. $\displaystyle\sum_{i=1}^{\infty} \dfrac{i}{2^i}$

12. $\displaystyle\sum_{i=2}^{\infty} \dfrac{1}{\ln (i)^2}$

13. $\displaystyle\sum_{i=1}^{\infty} \dfrac{i + 2}{i(i + 1)}$

14. $\displaystyle\sum_{i=1}^{\infty} \sin\left(\dfrac{\pi}{i}\right)$

15. $\displaystyle\sum_{i=1}^{\infty} \dfrac{2^i}{i!}$

16. $\displaystyle\sum_{i=1}^{\infty} \dfrac{1(3)(5)(7)(9) \ldots (2i - 1)}{2(4)(6)(8)(10) \ldots (2i)}$

17. $\displaystyle\sum_{i=1}^{\infty} \dfrac{i!}{2^i}$

18. $\displaystyle\sum_{i=1}^{\infty} \dfrac{e^i}{i^3}$

19. $\displaystyle\sum_{i=1}^{\infty} \dfrac{e^{-1}}{i^2}$

20. $\displaystyle\sum_{i=1}^{\infty} \frac{\ln i}{i^3}$

21. $\displaystyle\sum_{i=1}^{\infty} \frac{1}{3^{i-1}}$

22. $\displaystyle\sum_{i=1}^{\infty} \frac{i}{i^2 - 1}$

23. $\displaystyle\sum_{i=1}^{\infty} \frac{i - 1}{i!}$

24. $\displaystyle\sum_{i=1}^{\infty} \frac{i!}{(2i)!}$

25. $\displaystyle\sum_{i=1}^{\infty} \frac{i}{2i!}$

26. Suppose $\displaystyle\sum_{i=1}^{\infty} a_i$ can be shown to be convergent by the ratio test. Does this mean $\displaystyle\sum_{i=1}^{\infty} [a_i]^2$ is convergent? Justify your answer.

27. Show that $\displaystyle\sum_{i=1}^{\infty} a_i$ may converge, but $\displaystyle\sum_{i=1}^{\infty} \sqrt{a_i}$ may still diverge.

28. In problem 26, the condition was given that the series could be shown convergent by the ratio test. Is this condition necessary to guarantee that if $\displaystyle\sum_{i=1}^{\infty} a_i$ is convergent so is $\displaystyle\sum_{i=1}^{\infty} [a_i]^2$? Justify your answer.

9-5   ALTERNATING SERIES AND ABSOLUTE CONVERGENCE

All of the series considered so far have included only terms with the same sign. The simplest kind of series with terms which differ in algebraic sign is one where the terms alternate in sign. Such series are called *alternating series*.

Examples.

$$\sum_{i=1}^{\infty} \frac{(-1)^{i+1}}{i} = 1 - \tfrac{1}{2} + \tfrac{1}{3} - \tfrac{1}{4} + \tfrac{1}{5} - \tfrac{1}{6} + \cdots,$$

$$\sum_{i=1}^{\infty} \frac{(-1)^{i+1}}{i^2} = 1 - \tfrac{1}{4} + \tfrac{1}{9} - \tfrac{1}{16} + \cdots, \text{ and}$$

$$\sum_{i=1}^{\infty} \frac{(-1)^i}{i!} = \frac{-1}{1} + \frac{1}{2(1)} - \frac{1}{3(2)(1)} + \frac{1}{4(3)(2)(1)} - \cdots.$$

The convergence of an alternating series is a much simpler matter to examine.

TEST FOR THE CONVERGENCE OF ALTERNATING SERIES: Consider the alternating series $\sum_{i=1}^{\infty} (-1)^{i+1} a_i$, where $a_i \geq 0$ for all i. This series converges if $a_{i+1} < a_i$ for all i, and $\lim_{i \to \infty} a_i = 0$.

To establish this test, consider a series meeting the conditions of the test,

$$\sum_{i=1}^{\infty} (-1)^{i+1} a_i \text{ with } \lim_{n \to \infty} a_n = 0 \text{ and } a_{i+1} < a_i \text{ for all } i.$$

Then

$$\sum_{i=1}^{2n} (-1)^{i+1} a_i = a_1 - a_2 + a_3 - a_4 \cdots - a_{2n}$$

$$= (a_1 - a_2) + (a_3 - a_4) \ldots (a_{2n-1} - a_{2n}).$$

Each term in a parenthesis is positive because of the condition that $a_{i+1} < a_i$. Hence, the sum is positive.

On the other hand

$$\sum_{i=1}^{2n} (-1)^{i+1} a_i = a_1 - (a_2 - a_3) - (a_4 - a_5) - (a_6 - a_7) \cdots - (a_{2n}).$$

Thus, although $\sum_{i=1}^{2n} (-1)^{i+1} a_i$ is positive, it is less than a_1, since it has been shown to be a_1 minus a number of positive terms.

Consider the fact that

$$\sum_{i=1}^{2n} (-1)^{i+1} a_i < \sum_{i=1}^{2n+2} (-1)^{i+1} a_i,$$

because

$$\sum_{i=1}^{2n+2} (-1)^{i+1} a_i = \sum_{i=1}^{2n} (-1)^{i+1} a_i + (a_{2n+1} - a_{2n+2}),$$

and $a_{2n+1} - a_{2n+2}$ is positive.

$$\sum_{i=1}^{2n} (-1)^{i+1} a_i < \sum_{i=1}^{2n+2} (-1)^{i+1} a_i < \sum_{i=1}^{2n+4} (-1)^{i+1} a_i < \cdots < a_1$$

So,
$$\lim_{n\to\infty} \sum_{i=1}^{2n} (-1)^{i+1} a_i$$

gets bigger as n tends to infinity but it is always less than a_1, the first term. Therefore we can conclude that
$$\lim_{n\to\infty} \sum_{i=1}^{2n} (-1)^{i+1} a_i$$

exists hence
$$\lim_{n\to\infty} \sum_{i=1}^{n} (-1)^{i+1} a_i$$

exists, and the series converges.

Example.   Does the alternating harmonic series converge?

Solution. $\displaystyle\sum_{i=1}^{\infty} \frac{(-1)^{i+1}}{i}$. Since $a_n = \dfrac{1}{n}$, $a_{n+1} = \dfrac{1}{n+1}$, and $\dfrac{1}{n+1} \le \dfrac{1}{n}$

for all n, and $\lim_{n\to\infty} a_n = \lim_{n\to\infty} \dfrac{1}{n} = 0$, the series is convergent.

Example.   Does the alternating p series $\displaystyle\sum_{i=1}^{\infty} \frac{(-1)^{i+1}}{i^2}$ converge?

Solution.   Here $a_n = \dfrac{1}{n^2}$, $a_{n+1} = \dfrac{1}{(n+1)^2}$, and $\dfrac{1}{(n+1)^2} \le \dfrac{1}{n^2}$ for all positive integers n. Therefore,
$$\lim_{n\to\infty} a_n = \lim_{n\to\infty} \frac{1}{n^2} = 0,$$

and the series is convergent.

The last two examples illustrate an interesting feature of alternating series. Associated with the two convergent alternating series are two regular series found by leaving out the alternating feature. These are
$$\sum_{i=1}^{\infty} \frac{1}{i} \quad\text{and}\quad \sum_{i=1}^{\infty} \frac{1}{i^2}.$$

The first, $\displaystyle\sum_{i=1}^{\infty} \frac{1}{i}$, is the harmonic series, and is divergent. The second,

$\displaystyle\sum_{i=1}^{\infty} \frac{1}{i^2}$, is a p series with $p > 1$, and is convergent. It would seem that without

the alternating feature, some convergent alternating series would fail to converge. For that reason convergent alternating series are classified according to whether or not they require the alternating feature for their convergence.

Definition. Consider a convergent alternating series $\sum\limits_{i=1}^{\infty} (-1)^{i+1} a_i$, with

$a_i \geq 0$ for all i. Associated with this series is a second positive

termed series, $\sum\limits_{i=1}^{\infty} a_i$. If $\sum\limits_{i=1}^{\infty} a_i$ converges then $\sum\limits_{i=1}^{\infty} (-1)^{i+1} a_i$

is said to be *absolutely* convergent. If $\sum\limits_{i=1}^{\infty} a_i$ diverges then

$\sum\limits_{i=1}^{\infty} (-1)^{i+1} a_i$ is said to be *conditionally convergent*.

In other words, if a convergent alternating series does not converge without the alternating feature it is called a conditionally convergent series. If it would still converge without the alternating signs it is called absolutely convergent.

Example. $\sum\limits_{i=1}^{\infty} \dfrac{(-1)^{i+1}}{i^2}$ is absolutely convergent, because $\sum\limits_{i=1}^{\infty} \dfrac{1}{i^2}$ is convergent.

Example. $\sum\limits_{i=1}^{\infty} \dfrac{(-1)^{i+1}}{i}$ is conditionally convergent, because $\sum\limits_{i=1}^{\infty} \dfrac{1}{i}$ is
divergent.

Fortunately, if an alternating series is absolutely convergent, it is con-vergent. This means that a possible first step in testing an alternating series for convergence is to test the associated positive term series for convergence.

Example. Test the series $\sum\limits_{i=1}^{\infty} \dfrac{(-1)^{i+1} 3^i}{i^2}$ for convergence and absolute
convergence.

Solution.
$$a_n = \frac{3^n}{n^2}, \; a_{n+1} = \frac{3^{n+1}}{(n+1)^2}.$$

$$\frac{a_{n+1}}{a_n} = \frac{\dfrac{3^{n+1}}{(n+1)^2}}{\dfrac{3^n}{(n)^2}} = (3) \frac{n^2}{(n+1)^2}$$

Using the ratio test,

$$\lim_{n \to \infty} \frac{a_{n+1}}{a_n} = \lim_{n \to \infty} \frac{3n^2}{(n + 1)^2}$$

$$\lim_{n \to \infty} \frac{6n}{2(n + 1)} = \lim_{n \to \infty} 3 = 3.$$

The series $\sum\limits_{i=1}^{\infty} a_i = \sum\limits_{i=1}^{\infty} \frac{3^i}{i^2}$ is divergent, thus, although $\sum\limits_{i=1}^{\infty} \frac{(-1)^{i+1}3^i}{i^2}$ may be conditionally convergent, it cannot be absolutely convergent. Testing for conditional convergency:

$$\lim_{n \to \infty} a_n = \lim_{n \to \infty} \frac{3^n}{n^2} = \lim_{n \to \infty} \frac{\ln (3)3^n}{2n}$$

$$= \lim_{n \to \infty} \frac{(\ln 3)^2(3)^n}{2} = \infty.$$

The series is divergent.

The last example suggests a more practical approach in the order in which one tests the features of an alternating series. First, one should check $\lim\limits_{n \to \infty} a_n$ to see whether it is zero. If this condition has been met, the ratio or some other test can be applied to the series to check for absolute convergence. Finally, if the series is not absolutely convergent the original series can be checked for conditional convergence by checking if $a_{n+1} < a_n$.

Example. Check the convergence of $\sum\limits_{i=1}^{\infty} \frac{(-1)^{i+1}}{i \, 3^i}$.

Solution. $a_n = \dfrac{1}{n(3)^n}$ and $\lim\limits_{n \to \infty} a_n = \lim\limits_{n \to \infty} \dfrac{1}{n(3)^n} = 0$. Using the ratio test,

$$a_{n+1} = \frac{1}{(n + 1)3^{n+1}}$$

$$\frac{a_{n+1}}{a_n} = \frac{\dfrac{1}{(n + 1)3^{n+1}}}{\dfrac{1}{n(3)^n}}$$

$$= \frac{n(3)^n}{(n + 1)3^{n+1}} = \frac{n}{(n + 1)(3)}$$

$$\lim_{n \to \infty} \frac{a_{n+1}}{a_n} = \lim_{n \to \infty} \frac{n}{3(n+1)} = \lim_{n \to \infty} \frac{1}{3} < 1.$$

Therefore, $\sum_{i=1}^{\infty} \frac{1}{i\,3^i}$ is convergent; thus

$$\sum_{i=1}^{\infty} \frac{(-1)^{i+1}}{i\,3^i}$$

is absolutely convergent.

Example. Test the series $\sum_{i=2}^{\infty} \frac{(-1)^i}{i \ln i}$ for convergence.

Solution. $\qquad\qquad a_n = \dfrac{1}{n \ln n} \qquad$ and

$$\lim_{n \to \infty} a_n = \lim_{n \to \infty} \frac{1}{n \ln n} = 0.$$

$$a_{n+1} = \frac{1}{(n+1) \ln (n+1)}.$$

$$\frac{a_{n+1}}{a_n} = \frac{\dfrac{1}{(n+1) \ln (n+1)}}{\dfrac{1}{n \ln n}} = \frac{n \ln n}{(n+1) \ln (n+1)}.$$

$$\lim_{n \to \infty} \frac{a_{n+1}}{a_n} = \lim_{n \to \infty} \frac{n \ln n}{(n+1) \ln (n+1)}$$

$$= \lim_{n \to \infty} \left(\frac{n}{n+1} \right) \cdot \lim_{n \to \infty} \frac{\ln n}{\ln (n+1)}$$

$$= \lim_{n \to \infty} \frac{1}{1} \cdot \lim_{n \to \infty} \frac{\dfrac{1}{n}}{\dfrac{1}{n+1}}$$

$$= \lim_{n \to \infty} \frac{n+1}{n} = \lim_{n \to \infty} \frac{1}{1} = 1.$$

The ratio test fails!
Perhaps the integral test will work.

$f(x) = \dfrac{1}{x \ln x}$, and the improper integral is

$$\int_2^\infty \frac{1}{x \ln x} \, dx = \lim_{b \to \infty} \int_2^b \frac{1}{x \ln x} \, dx.$$

If $u = \ln x$, then $du = \dfrac{1}{x} \, dx.$

Therefore,

$$\int \frac{1}{x \ln x} \, dx = \int \frac{1}{u} \, du = \ln u.$$

Thus,

$$\lim_{b \to \infty} \int_2^b \frac{1}{x \ln x} \, dx = \lim_{b \to \infty} \left\{ \ln (\ln x) \Big]_2^b \right\}$$

$$= \lim_{b \to \infty} \big[\ln (\ln b) - \ln (\ln 2) \big] = \infty.$$

The integral, and thus the series, diverges. However,

$$\frac{1}{(i + 1) \ln (i + 1)} < \frac{1}{i \ln i}.$$

Thus, $\displaystyle\sum_{i=2}^\infty \frac{(-1)^i}{i \ln i}$ is conditionally convergent.

9-5   Exercises

(1-20)   Test each of the following alternating series for convergence and absolute convergence.

1. $\displaystyle\sum_{i=1}^\infty \frac{(-1)^{i+1}}{i^2 + 1}$

2. $\displaystyle\sum_{i=1}^\infty \frac{(-1)^{i+1} e^i}{i}$

3. $\displaystyle\sum_{i=1}^\infty (-1)^{i+1} \frac{\ln i}{i}$

4. $\displaystyle\sum_{i=1}^\infty \frac{(-1)^{i+1}}{2^{2i}}$

5. $\displaystyle\sum_{i=1}^\infty \frac{(-1)^i}{i!}$

6. $\displaystyle\sum_{i=1}^\infty (-1)^{i+1}$

7. $\displaystyle\sum_{i=1}^{\infty} \frac{(-1)^i}{i(3)^i}$

8. $\displaystyle\sum_{i=1}^{\infty} \frac{(-4)^{i+1}}{i^4}$

9. $\displaystyle\sum_{i=1}^{\infty} \frac{(-1)^{i+1}}{(2i-1)!}$

10. $\displaystyle\sum_{i=1}^{\infty} (-1)^{i+1} \cdot \frac{i^2+1}{i^3}$

11. $\displaystyle\sum_{i=1}^{\infty} (-1)^{i+1} i \left(\frac{2}{3}\right)^i$

12. $\displaystyle\sum_{i=1}^{\infty} \frac{(-1)^i 7^i}{2(4)(6)\ldots(2i)}$

13. $\displaystyle\sum_{i=1}^{\infty} (-1)^{i+1} \frac{7^{i+2}}{5^{i+1}}$

14. $\displaystyle\sum_{i=1}^{\infty} \frac{(-1)^{i+1} 9^{i+4}}{10^{i+3}}$

15. $\displaystyle\sum_{i=1}^{\infty} \frac{(-1)^{i+1}(3+2i)}{7^i}$

16. $\displaystyle\sum_{i=1}^{\infty} \frac{(-1)^{i+1}}{i+1} \cdot i$

17. $\displaystyle\sum_{i=1}^{\infty} \frac{(-1)^{i+1}}{\cos \pi i}$

18. $\displaystyle\sum_{i=1}^{\infty} \frac{(-1)^{i+1}}{\sin (i\pi)}$

19. $\displaystyle\sum_{i=1}^{\infty} \frac{\sin (i\pi)}{(-1)^{i+1}}$

20. $\displaystyle\sum_{i=3}^{\infty} \frac{\cos (i\pi)}{\ln i}$

(21-30) It can be shown that the error in approximating the infinite sum of a convergent alternating series with a finite number of terms is no more, in absolute value, than the value of the first omitted term. That is, if one estimates

$$\sum_{i=1}^{\infty} (-1)^i a_i \qquad \text{as approximately} \qquad \sum_{i=1}^{n} (-1)^i a_i,$$

the maximum possible error is a_{n+1}.

(21-25) In each case estimate the error in approximating the indicated sum with the first four terms of the series.

21. $\displaystyle\sum_{i=1}^{\infty} \frac{(-1)^{i+1}}{i}$

22. $\displaystyle\sum_{i=1}^{\infty} \frac{(-1)^{i+1}}{i!}$

23. $\displaystyle\sum_{i=1}^{\infty} \frac{(-1)^{i+1}}{i\,2^i}$

24. $\displaystyle\sum_{i=1}^{\infty} \frac{(-1)^{i+1}}{(3i+1)^3}$

25. $\displaystyle\sum_{i=1}^{\infty} \frac{(-1)^{i+1}\cdot i}{2^i}$

(26-30) Determine how many terms one would have to include in order that the estimated sum have no more than 0.001 error.

26. $\displaystyle\sum_{i=1}^{\infty} \frac{(-1)^{i+1}}{i}$

27. $\displaystyle\sum_{i=1}^{\infty} \frac{(-1)^{i+1}}{i!}$

28. $\displaystyle\sum_{i=1}^{\infty} \frac{(-1)^{i+1}}{i^i}$

29. $\displaystyle\sum_{i=1}^{\infty} \frac{(-1)^{i+1}i!}{3^i}$

30. $\displaystyle\sum_{i=1}^{\infty} \frac{(-1)^{i+1}\sin(\pi i)}{i^3}$

9-6   POWER SERIES

The terms of a series have so far been terms of a sequence; that is, real-valued functions whose domains have been the non-negative integers. Suppose that these terms are functions of an independent variable, say x, in addition to being functions of integers. In other words, suppose that the terms of a series are functions of two variables, x and n, where n has only integer values. Such terms may be denoted

$$f(n,x) \qquad \text{or} \qquad f_n(x).$$

Examples.
$$f_n(x) = nx^n,$$
$$f_n(x) = n^3 \sin nx - e^x, \text{ and}$$
$$f_n(x) = \frac{\ln x}{n}.$$

In terms of sequences, we consider a sequence of functions

$$f_0(x), f_1(x), f_2(x), \ldots, f_n(x),$$

and form a series by summing these terms. Although there are infinitely many possibilities for such functions, the simplest ones involve only powers of x. In this type of function, $f_n(x)$ takes the form of a numerical coefficient dependent on n times an nth power of x. In general,

$$f_n(x) = a_n(x - c)^n,$$

where c is a constant. The corresponding infinite series is

$$a_0 + \sum_{i=1}^{\infty} a_i(x - c)^i.$$

Such a series is called a *power series*.

$a_0 + \sum_{i=1}^{\infty} a_i(x - c)^i$ will be denoted by $\sum_{i=0}^{\infty} a_i(x - c)^i$ where it is understood that the first term is a_0 rather than $a_0(x - c)^0$. $(x - c)^0$ does not present any problems unless $x = c$, in which case $(x - c)^0 = 0^0$, which is undefined.

Examples.

$$\sum_{i=0}^{\infty} \frac{x^i}{i!} = 1 + x + \frac{x^2}{2!} + \frac{x^3}{3!} + \cdots.$$

$$\sum_{i=0}^{\infty} i^2(x - 3)^i = 0 + (x - 3) + 2^2(x - 3)^2 + \cdots.$$

$$\sum_{i=1}^{\infty} \frac{(-1)^{i+1}}{i}\left(x - \frac{\pi}{2}\right)^i = \left(x - \frac{\pi}{2}\right) - \frac{\left(x - \frac{\pi}{2}\right)^2}{2} + \frac{\left(x - \frac{\pi}{2}\right)^3}{3} - \cdots.$$

$$\sum_{i=0}^{\infty} x^i = 1 + x + x^2 + x^3 + \cdots.$$

The question of convergence and divergence of such series clearly depends on the actual value assumed by x.

Example.   The series $\sum\limits_{i=0}^{\infty} x^i$ is a convergent geometric series if $x = \frac{1}{2}$, whereas it is a divergent geometric series if $x = 3$. In fact, if $-1 < x < 1$, the series is a convergent geometric series, and if $|x| \geq 1$, the series is a divergent geometric series.

> **Definition.**   The set of values of x for which the infinite series
>
> $$\sum_{i=0}^{\infty} a_i(x - c)^i$$
>
> converges is called the *interval of convergence* of the series.

Example.   The interval of convergence for the series

$$\sum_{i=0}^{\infty} x^i$$

is the set of all x values such that $-1 < x < 1$.

For a given power series, the ratio test can usually be relied upon to determine the interval of convergence; however, the endpoints of the interval usually correspond to values of x for which the ratio test fails, and as such must be tested by some other means. In applying the ratio test, we will have to consider the absolute value of the terms since, unlike the series considered earlier, we cannot guarantee all of the terms of the series are positive.

Example.   For what values of x does the series $\sum\limits_{i=0}^{\infty} x^i$ converge?

Solution. $a_n = |x^n|, \; a_{n+1} = |x^{n+1}|.$

$$\frac{a_{n+1}}{a_n} = \left| \frac{x^{n+1}}{x^n} \right| = |x|.$$

Therefore,

$$\lim_{n \to \infty} \frac{a_{n+1}}{a_n} = \lim_{n \to \infty} |x| = |x|.$$

Clearly if $|x| < 1$ the series is convergent, and if $|x| > 1$, the series is divergent. If $|x| = 1$,

$$\lim_{n \to \infty} a_n \neq 0,$$

and the series is divergent.

Hence, $\sum\limits_{i=0}^{\infty} x^i$ is convergent if $-1 < x < 1$.

In order to make the form of our series agree with the indicated form of a power series, we shall let

$$u_n = |a_n(x - c)^n|$$

where n is the appropriate power for $(x - c)$. Then the ratio test would be applied to $\lim\limits_{n \to \infty} \dfrac{u_{n+1}}{u_n}$.

Example. Determine the interval of convergence of the series

$$\sum_{i=1}^{\infty} \frac{(x - 2)^{i-1}}{3^i i^2}.$$

Solution. $u_n = \left| \dfrac{(x - 2)^{n-1}}{3^n n^2} \right|$

$$u_{n+1} = \left| \frac{(x - 2)^n}{3^{n+1}(n + 1)^2} \right|$$

$$\frac{u_{n+1}}{u_n} = \left| \frac{\dfrac{(x - 2)^n}{3^{n+1}(n + 1)^2}}{\dfrac{(x - 2)^{n-1}}{3^n n^2}} \right| = \left| \frac{(x - 2)^n (3)^n n^2}{(x - 2)^{n-1}(3)^{n+1}(n + 1)^2} \right|$$

$$= \frac{|x - 2|}{3} \cdot \frac{n^2}{(n + 1)^2}.$$

$$\lim_{n \to \infty} \frac{u_{n+1}}{u_n} = \lim_{n \to \infty} \left[\frac{|x - 2|}{3} \cdot \frac{n^2}{(n + 1)^2} \right]$$

$$= \lim_{n \to \infty} \frac{|x - 2|}{3} \cdot \frac{2n}{2(n + 1)}$$

$$= \lim_{n \to \infty} \frac{|x - 2|}{3} = \frac{|x - 2|}{3}.$$

If $\dfrac{|x - 2|}{3} < 1$, the series is convergent. Thus the series is convergent if $\dfrac{|x - 2|}{3} < 1$, $|x - 2| < 3$, $-3 < x - 2 < 3$, or $-1 < x < 5$. The series is divergent if $x > 5$ or $x < -1$, as then the ratio would be greater than 1. What happens if $x = -1$ or $x = 5$? In the first case, $x = -1$, the series becomes

$$\sum_{i=1}^{\infty} \frac{(-3)^{i-1}}{3^i\,i^2} = \sum_{i=1}^{\infty} \frac{(-1)^{i-1}}{3i^2} = \frac{1}{3} \sum_{i=1}^{\infty} \frac{(-1)^{i-1}}{i^2},$$

which is a convergent alternating p series. In the case $x = 5$, the series becomes

$$\sum_{i=1}^{\infty} \frac{3^{i-1}}{3^i\,i^2} = \sum_{i=1}^{\infty} \frac{1}{3i^2} = \frac{1}{3} \sum_{i=1}^{\infty} \frac{1}{i^2},$$

which is also a convergent p series. In either case, the series is convergent; thus the interval of convergence is $-1 \le x \le 5$.

Example.   Determine the interval of convergence for the series

$$\sum_{i=0}^{\infty} \frac{x^{2i}}{i!}.$$

Solution.
$$u_n = \left| \frac{x^{2n}}{n!} \right|.$$

$$u_{n+1} = \left| \frac{x^{2(n+1)}}{(n+1)!} \right|.$$

$$\frac{n_{n+1}}{u_n} = \left| \frac{\dfrac{x^{2n+2}}{(n+1)!}}{\dfrac{x^{2n}}{n!}} \right| = \left| \frac{x^{2n+2}(n)!}{x^{2n}(n+1)!} \right|$$

$$= \frac{x^2}{n+1}.$$

$$\lim_{n \to \infty} \frac{u_{n+1}}{u_n} = \lim_{n \to \infty} \frac{x^2}{n+1} = 0.$$

Therefore, if x is any finite number, the series converges. The interval of convergence is $-\infty < x < \infty$.

Example.   Find the interval of convergence for

$$\sum_{i=0}^{\infty} i!\,x^i.$$

Solution.
$$u_n = |n!\,x^n|.$$

$$u_{n+1} = |(n+1)!\,x^{n+1}|.$$

$$\frac{u_{n+1}}{u_n} = \left| \frac{(n+1)!\,x^{n+1}}{n!\,x^n} \right| = (n+1)|x|.$$

$$\lim_{n \to \infty} \frac{u_{n+1}}{u_n} = \lim_{n \to \infty} (n + 1)|x| = \infty,$$

unless $x = 0$. This series converges only if $x = 0$.

An interesting variation on the interval of convergence of a power series is involved in the following theorem.

Theorem. $\displaystyle\sum_{i=1}^{\infty} a_i x^i$ and $\displaystyle\sum_{i=1}^{\infty} i a_i x^{i-1}$ have the same interval of convergence except possibly at their endpoints.

Argument. All that is required to illustrate this result is to show that the ratio test yields the same conditions on x. First let us apply the ratio test to

$$\sum_{i=1}^{\infty} a_i x^i.$$

$$u_n = |a_n x^n|$$

$$u_{n+1} = |a_{n+1} x^{n+1}|$$

$$\lim_{n \to \infty} \frac{u_{n+1}}{u_n} = \lim_{n \to \infty} \left| \frac{a_{n+1} x^{n+1}}{a_n x^n} \right|$$

$$= \lim_{n \to \infty} \left| \frac{a_{n+1}}{a_n} \right| |x|.$$

Thus, $\displaystyle\sum_{i=1}^{\infty} a_i x^i$ converges if

$$\lim_{n \to \infty} \frac{a_{n+1}}{a_n} |x| < 1,$$

and diverges if

$$\lim_{n \to \infty} \frac{a_{n+1}}{a_n} |x| > 1.$$

Now consider the ratio test applied to $\displaystyle\sum_{i=1}^{\infty} i a_i x^{i-1}$.

$$u_n = |n a_n x^{n-1}|.$$

$$u_{n+1} = |(n + 1) a_{n+1} x^n|.$$

$$\lim_{n \to \infty} \frac{u_{n+1}}{u_n} = \lim_{n \to \infty} \left| \frac{(n + 1) a_{n+1} x^n}{n a_n x^{n-1}} \right|$$

$$= \lim_{n \to \infty} \left(\frac{n+1}{n} \right) \lim_{n \to \infty} \frac{a_{n+1}}{a_n} |x|$$

$$= \lim_{n \to \infty} \frac{a_{n+1}}{a_n} |x|.$$

Then

$$\sum_{i=1}^{\infty} i a_i x^{i-1}$$

also converges if

$$\lim_{n \to \infty} \frac{a_{n+1}}{a_n} |x| < 1$$

and diverges if

$$\lim_{n \to \infty} \frac{a_{n+1}}{a_n} |x| > 1.$$

Example.   Since $\sum_{i=1}^{\infty} x^i$ converges for $-1 < x < 1$, so does

$$\sum_{i=1}^{\infty} i x^{i-1}.$$

For that matter, since $\sum_{i=1}^{\infty} i x^{i-1}$ converges for $-1 < x < 1$, so does

$\sum_{i=1}^{\infty} i(i-1) x^{i-2}$ and so does $\sum_{i=1}^{\infty} i(i-1)(i-2) x^{i-3}$, etc.

9-6   Exercises

(1-20)   Determine the interval of convergence for each of the following power series.

1. $\sum_{i=0}^{\infty} \dfrac{x^i}{i!}$

2. $\sum_{i=1}^{\infty} i(x-2)^i$

3. $\sum_{i=1}^{\infty} \dfrac{2^i x^i}{i^2}$

4. $\sum_{i=0}^{\infty} \dfrac{(x-2)^i}{2^i}$

5. $\sum_{i=0}^{\infty} \dfrac{(x-10)^i}{i!}$

6. $\displaystyle\sum_{i=0}^{\infty} x^i (\tfrac{3}{2})^i$

7. $\displaystyle\sum_{i=1}^{\infty} \frac{(-1)^{i+1} x^i}{3^i i^2}$

8. $\displaystyle\sum_{i=0}^{\infty} \frac{(x+1)^i}{(i+1)}$

9. $\displaystyle\sum_{i=1}^{\infty} \frac{x^i}{\ln(i+1)}$

10. $\displaystyle\sum_{i=1}^{\infty} \frac{(3x-1)^i}{i^2}$

11. $\displaystyle\sum_{i=1}^{\infty} \frac{(2x+1)^i}{(-i)^3}$

12. $\displaystyle\sum_{i=0}^{\infty} \frac{(-1)^i x^{2i+1}}{(2i+1)!}$

13. $\displaystyle\sum_{i=0}^{\infty} \frac{(-1)^i x^{2i}}{(2i)!}$

14. $\displaystyle\sum_{i=0}^{\infty} \frac{(-1)^i (x-8)^i}{i}$

15. $\displaystyle\sum_{i=0}^{\infty} \frac{(-1)^i (2x-1)^i}{(2i)^2}$

16. $\displaystyle\sum_{i=0}^{\infty} \frac{(-1)^i (x+2)^i}{i+1}$

17. $\displaystyle\sum_{i=0}^{\infty} \frac{x^i}{(i+3)^2}$

18. $\displaystyle\sum_{i=0}^{\infty} \frac{x^i}{(i+1)^5}$

19. $\displaystyle\sum_{i=0}^{\infty} x^i i$

20. $\displaystyle\sum_{i=0}^{\infty} \frac{(-1)^{i+1} (x-3)^i i}{i+3}$

(21-26) In each case $\displaystyle\sum_{i=0}^{\infty} a_i x^i$ and $\displaystyle\sum_{i=1}^{\infty} i a_i x^{i-1}$ have been given. Verify by

determining the interval of convergence involved that the two series have the
same interval of convergence. Do they both necessarily converge at the endpoints of their intervals?

21. $\displaystyle\sum_{i=1}^{\infty} \frac{x^i}{\ln(i+1)}$ and $\displaystyle\sum_{i=2}^{\infty} \frac{ix^{i-1}}{\ln(i+1)}$

22. $\displaystyle\sum_{i=0}^{\infty} i!\, x^i$ and $\displaystyle\sum_{i=1}^{\infty} i(i)!\, x^{i-1}$

23. $\displaystyle\sum_{i=0}^{\infty} \frac{(x+2)^i}{(i+2)2^i}$ and $\displaystyle\sum_{i=1}^{\infty} \frac{i(x+2)^{i-1}}{(i+2)2^i}$

24. $\displaystyle\sum_{i=0}^{\infty} \frac{(-1)^{i+1}x^{2i+1}}{(2i+1)!}$ and $\displaystyle\sum_{i=1}^{\infty} \frac{(-1)^{i+1}(2i+1)x^{2i}}{(2i+1)!}$

25. $\displaystyle\sum_{i=0}^{\infty} 8^i x^i$ and $\displaystyle\sum_{i=1}^{\infty} i8^i x^{i-1}$

26. $\displaystyle\sum_{i=0}^{\infty} \frac{(x-1)^i}{2^i \sqrt{i+1}}$ and $\displaystyle\sum_{i=1}^{\infty} \frac{i(x-1)^{i-1}}{2^i \sqrt{i+1}}$

(27-30)   For a power series of the form $\displaystyle\sum_{i=0}^{\infty} a_i x^i$ the interval of convergence
can often be stated in the form $|x| < R, |x| \le R, -R \le x < R,$ or $R < x \le R.$
In this case, R is called the radius of convergence of the series. Find the radius
of convergence for each of the following series.

27. $\displaystyle\sum_{i=0}^{\infty} \frac{(-1)^i x^{2i}}{(2i)!}$

28. $\displaystyle\sum_{i=0}^{\infty} (-1)^i x^i i$

29. $\displaystyle\sum_{i=0}^{\infty} \frac{(-1)^i x^i}{(2i)}$

30. $\displaystyle\sum_{i=0}^{\infty} \frac{x^i}{5^i}$

31. Find any power series whose interval of convergence is from -2 to $+2$.

32. Find any power series whose interval of convergence is from 28 to 32.

33. Find any power series whose interval of convergence is from $C - R$ to
$C + R$ where C is some real number and R is a given positive real
number.

9-7 FUNCTIONS DEFINED BY POWER SERIES

If x is a value within the interval of convergence of a given power series,

$$\sum_{i=0}^{\infty} a_i x^i,$$

then we can be sure that the series converges. Clearly, the actual value to which the series converges depends on the value selected for x. Therefore, it is appropriate to indicate

$$\sum_{i=0}^{\infty} a_i x^i = f(x).$$

That is, the series is a function of x. A number of questions arise. For example, what kind of functional properties does a function defined as an infinite power series have? Under what conditions does such a function defined in terms of a power series behave like some well-known function? When can a "regular" function also be represented by an infinite power series? For example, can we represent the sine function as an infinite power series? If we can, then that series could be used to find actual sine values.

Some theorems can help answer these questions.

Theorem 9.1. If $f(x) = \displaystyle\sum_{i=0}^{\infty} a_i(x - c)^i$ then

$$f'(x) = \sum_{i=1}^{\infty} i a_i(x - c)^{i-1}$$

for all values x within the interval of convergence.

We have already seen in section 9-6 that these two series must share a common interval of convergence. Although the two series do not have the same starting point, it is clear that the deletion or addition of any finite number of terms will not affect the convergence of the series. Such convergence or divergence depends on the behavior of terms as the index of the terms tends to infinity. In particular, this theorem states that the series obtained by formal term-by-term differentiation of a series is indeed the derivative of the function defined by the original series.

Theorem 9.2. If $f(x) = \displaystyle\sum_{i=0}^{\infty} a_i(x - c)^i$, then

$$\int_c^x f(t)\,dt = \int_c^x \sum_{i=0}^{\infty} a_i(t - c)^i\,dt$$

$$= \sum_{i=0}^{\infty} \int_c^x a_i(t - c)^i \, dt$$

$$= \sum_{i=0}^{\infty} \left[\frac{a_i(t - c)^{i+1}}{i + 1} \right]_c^x$$

$$= \sum_{i=0}^{\infty} \left[\frac{a_i(x - c)^{i+1}}{i + 1} \right],$$

for a value of x within the interval of convergence.

In other words, the formal term-by-term integration of an infinite power series does result in the integral of the original function.

These two theorems are useful in obtaining infinite power series representations for a given function. These are especially useful when coupled with the fact that ordinary algebraic procedures are valid as long as the arguments involved are restricted to values within the interval of convergence, and that a power series representation of a function is essentially unique.

Example.   Represent the functions $f(x) = \dfrac{1}{1 - x}$ and $\ln|1 - x|$ by power series.

Solution.   Consider the following long division,

$$\frac{1}{1 - x} = 1 + x + x^2 \cdots$$

It appears that

$$\frac{1}{1 - x} = \sum_{i=0}^{\infty} x^i$$

provided $|x| < 1$, *i.e.*, x is within the interval of convergence of the series. Now consider,

$$\int_0^x \frac{1}{1 - t} \, dt.$$

Applying the integration theorem,

$$\int_0^x \frac{1}{1 - t} \, dt = \int_0^x \sum_{i=0}^{\infty} t^i \, dt$$

$$= \sum_{i=0}^{\infty} \frac{x^{i+1}}{i + 1}.$$

On the other hand,

$$\int_0^x \frac{1}{1 - t} \, dt = -\ln(1 - t) \Big]_0^x$$

$$= -\ln(1 - x).$$

Thus

$$-\ln(1 - x) = \sum_{i=0}^{\infty} \frac{x^{i+1}}{i + 1},$$

or

$$\ln(1 - x) = -\sum_{i=0}^{\infty} \frac{x^{i+1}}{i + 1}$$

provided $|x| < 1$.

Example. Show that for the function

$$f(x) = \sum_{i=0}^{\infty} \frac{x^i}{i!},$$

$$f'(x) = f(x).$$

Solution. $\quad f(x) = \sum_{i=0}^{\infty} \frac{x^i}{i!},$

therefore

$$f'(x) = \sum_{i=1}^{\infty} \frac{ix^{i-1}}{i!}$$

Both series are convergent for all real values for x (see section 9-6).

$$f'(x) = \sum_{i=1}^{\infty} \frac{ix^{i-1}}{i!} = \sum_{i=1}^{\infty} \frac{x^{i-1}}{(i - 1)!}.$$

Let $k = i - 1$.

$$f'(x) = \sum_{k=0}^{\infty} \frac{x^k}{k!} = \sum_{i=0}^{\infty} \frac{x^i}{i!} = f(x).$$

This suggests that if

$$f(x) = \sum_{i=0}^{\infty} \frac{x^i}{i!},$$

then $f(x) = e^x$, because e^x is the only function we have seen where

$$f'(x) = f(x).$$

Example. Find an infinite power series for $\cos x$ assuming that

$$\sin x = \sum_{i=0}^{\infty} \frac{(-1)^i x^{2i+1}}{(2i + 1)!}.$$

Solution. $\dfrac{d}{dx} \sin x = \cos x$, and

$$\frac{d}{dx}\left\{ \sum_{i=0}^{\infty} \frac{(-1)^i x^{2i+1}}{(2i+1)!} \right\} = \sum_{i=0}^{\infty} \frac{(-1)^i (2i+1) x^{2i}}{(2i+1)!}$$

$$= \sum_{i=0}^{\infty} \frac{(-1)^i x^{2i}}{(2i)!}.$$

Thus, if

$$\sin x = \sum_{i=0}^{\infty} \frac{x^{2i+1}(-1)^i}{(2i+1)!},$$

then

$$\cos x = \sum_{i=0}^{\infty} \frac{(-1)^i x^{2i}}{(2i)!}$$

$$= 1 - \frac{x^2}{2!} + \frac{x^4}{4!} - \frac{x^6}{6!} + \cdots.$$

The interval of convergence for these series is left as an exercise.

Example.   Find an infinite series to represent $\tan^{-1} x$.

Solution. $\dfrac{d}{dx}(\tan^{-1} x) = \dfrac{1}{1+x^2}.$

However,

$$\frac{1}{1+x^2} = 1 - x^2 + x^4 - x^6 + \cdots$$

$$= \sum_{i=0}^{\infty} (-1)^i x^{2i}$$

by long division, and is valid if $x^2 < 1$. Thus,

$$\tan^{-1} x = \int_0^x \frac{1}{1+t^2}\, dt$$

$$= \int_0^x \sum_{i=0}^{\infty} (-1)^i t^{2i}\, dt$$

$$= \sum_{i=0}^{\infty} \int_0^x (-1)^i t^{2i}\, dt$$

$$= \sum_{i=0}^{\infty} \frac{(-1)^i t^{2i+1}}{2i+1} \Bigg]_0^x$$

$$= \sum_{i=0}^{\infty} \frac{(-1)^i x^{2i+1}}{2i+1},$$

or

$$\tan^{-1} x = x - \frac{x^3}{3} + \frac{x^5}{5} - \frac{x^7}{7} + \cdots.$$

As a simple variation, consider the following.

Example.   Find a power series for $\dfrac{\tan^{-1} x}{x}$ valid for $0 < x < 1$.

Solution.   Within the specified interval

$$\tan^{-1} x = \sum_{i=0}^{\infty} \frac{(-1)^i x^{2i+1}}{2i + 1}.$$

Hence

$$\frac{\tan^{-1} x}{x} = \frac{1}{x} \sum_{i=0}^{\infty} \frac{(-1)^i x^{2i+1}}{2i + 1}$$

$$= \sum_{i=0}^{\infty} \frac{(-1)^i x^{2i}}{2i + 1}.$$

9-7   Exercises

(1-10)   Using any of the methods indicated in this section find a power series representing the indicated function. Determine the interval of convergence in each case.

1. $\dfrac{1}{1 + x}$

2. $\dfrac{1}{1 - x^2}$

3. $\dfrac{x}{1 + x^3}$

4. $\ln (1 + x)$

5. $\ln (1 + x)^2$

6. $\ln (1 + x)^x$

7. $\ln (1 + x)^{1/x}$

8. $\tan^{-1}(x^2)$ (*Hint*: use the series for $\tan^{-1} x$, with x replaced by x^2.)

9. $\ln \left(\dfrac{1 + x}{1 - x} \right)$ $\left(Hint: \ln \left(\dfrac{1 + x}{1 - x} \right) = \ln (1 + x) - \ln (1 - x). \right)$

10. $\dfrac{1 + x}{1 - x}$

11.   Show that $\displaystyle\sum_{i=1}^{\infty} a_i(x - c)^i$ and $\displaystyle\sum_{i=1}^{\infty} \frac{a_i(x - c)^{i+1}}{i + 1}$

have the same radius of convergence.

(12-17)   A very useful method of finding power series is the generalized form of the binomial series.

$$(a + x)^n = a^n + na^{n-1}x + \frac{n(n-1)a^{n-2}x^2}{2!} + \frac{n(n-1)(n-2)a^{n-3}x^3}{3!}$$

$$+ \cdots + \frac{n(n-1)(n-2)\ldots(n-i+1)a^{n-i}x^i}{i!} + \cdots$$

For example,

$$\frac{1}{\sqrt{1+x}} = (1+x)^{-\frac{1}{2}} = 1^{-\frac{1}{2}} + (-\tfrac{1}{2})1^{-\frac{3}{2}}x$$

$$+ \frac{(-\tfrac{1}{2})(-\tfrac{3}{2})1^{-\frac{5}{2}}x^2}{2!} + \frac{(-\tfrac{1}{2})(-\tfrac{3}{2})(-\tfrac{5}{2})1^{-\frac{7}{2}}x^3}{3!} + \cdots$$

$$= 1 - \frac{1}{2}x + \frac{1(3)}{2(2)(2)!}x^2 - \frac{1(3)(5)}{(2)^3(3)!}x^3 + \cdots$$

$$= 1 - \frac{1}{2}x + \frac{1(3)}{2(4)}x^2 - \frac{1(3)(5)}{2(4)(6)}x^3 + \frac{1(3)(5)(7)}{2(4)(6)(8)}x^4 - \cdots$$

12. Determine the interval of convergence for the power series for

$$\frac{1}{\sqrt{1+x}}.$$

13. By replacing x by $-x$ in the power series for $\dfrac{1}{\sqrt{1+x}}$ one gets a series

for $\dfrac{1}{\sqrt{1-x}}$. Find this series and establish its interval of convergence.

14. By replacing x by $-x^2$ in the power series for $\dfrac{1}{\sqrt{1+x}}$ one gets a

power series for $\dfrac{1}{\sqrt{1-x^2}}$. Find this series and determine its interval

of convergence.

15. Use the results of problem 14, together with the fact that

$$\int_0^x \frac{1}{\sqrt{1-t^2}}\, dt = \sin^{-1} x$$

to find an infinite power series for $\sin^{-1} x$.

16. By replacing x by x^2 in the series for $\dfrac{1}{\sqrt{1+x}}$ find a series for $\dfrac{1}{\sqrt{1+x^2}}$,

together with its interval of convergence.

17. Since $\displaystyle\int_0^x \frac{dt}{\sqrt{1 + t^2}} = \ln(x + \sqrt{1 + x^2})$ use the results of problem 16

to find an infinite series for $\ln(x + \sqrt{1 + x^2})$.

18. Assume that $\displaystyle\sin x = \sum_{i=0}^{\infty} \frac{(-1)^i x^{2i+1}}{(2i + 1)!}$

Find a power series for $\dfrac{\sin x}{x}$.

Discuss the behavior of the series derived as $\displaystyle\lim_{x\to 0} \frac{\sin x}{x}$ is considered.

19. Since $\cot^{-1} x = \dfrac{\pi}{2} - \tan^{-1} x$ find an infinite series for $\cot^{-1} x$.

20. Since $\csc^{-1} x = \sin^{-1}\left(\dfrac{1}{x}\right)$ use the infinite series for $\sin^{-1} x$ to

find an infinite series for $\csc^{-1} x$ by replacing x by $\dfrac{1}{x}$. Is this a power

series?

9-8 TAYLOR'S SERIES

Sometimes, if we have been lucky, we have been able to find an infinite series representing a known function. It is natural to wonder if it is possible to find, in a systematic way without some good guess or lucky break, an infinite power series for a given function. To approach this problem, let us consider what is involved.

Given a function $f(x)$. Since power series are differentiable over and over again, at least within their interval of convergence, we should assume that if the series is an alternative representation of $f(x)$, $f(x)$ is also. Then can we find an infinite power series of the form

$$\sum_{i=0}^{\infty} a_i(x - c)^i,$$

which for a given value of x and within some interval around c, has the property

$$f(x) = \sum_{i=0}^{\infty} a_i(x - c)^i?$$

Clearly the problem is one of finding the proper form for the a_i's. If $f(x) = \sum_{i=0}^{\infty} a_i(x - c)^i$, then in expanded form

$$f(x) = a_0 + a_1(x - c) + a_2(x - c)^2 + a_3(x - c)^3$$
$$+ \cdots + a_n(x - c)^n + \cdots$$

Then

$$f'(x) = a_1 + 2a_2(x - c) + 3a_3(x - c)^2 + 4a_4(x - c)^3$$
$$+ \cdots + na_n(x - c)^{n-1} + \cdots .$$

$$f''(x) = 2a_2 + (3)2a_3(x - c) + (4)3a_4(x - c)^2 + \cdots$$
$$+ n(n - 1)(x - c)^{n-2} + \cdots .$$

$$f'''(x) = (3)2a_3 + (4)(3)2a_4(x - c) + (5)(4)(3)a_5(x - c)^2 + \cdots$$
$$+ n(n - 1)(n - 2)(x - c)^{n-3} + \cdots .$$

In general,

$$f^{(n)}(x) = n(n - 1)(n - 2) \ldots (3)2a_n$$
$$+ (n + 1)(n)(n - 1) \ldots 2a_{n+1}(x - c) + \cdots$$
$$= n! \, a_n + (n + 1)(n)(n - 1) \ldots 2a_{n+1}(x - c).$$

where $f^{(n)}(x) = \dfrac{d^n f(x)}{dx^n} = $ the nth derivative of $f(x)$.

If $x = c$ then each of these equations reduces to a single term of the series, because $(c - c) = 0$. Specifically

$$f(c) = a_0,$$
$$f'(c) = a_1,$$
$$f''(c) = 2a_2 \qquad \text{or} \qquad a_2 = \frac{f''(c)}{2},$$
$$f'''(c) = 3(2)a_3 \qquad \text{or} \qquad a_3 = \frac{f'''(c)}{3!},$$

or, in general,

$$f^{(n)}(c) = n! \, a_n \qquad \text{or} \qquad a_n = \frac{f^{(n)}(c)}{n!}$$

The conclusion of this analysis is *if* there is a power series for a given function in terms of powers of $(x - c)$, then the coefficients must be given by

$$a_n = \frac{f^{(n)}(c)}{n!}.$$

This result is called *Taylor's Formula*, and the series is called *Taylor's series*. In the special case where $c = 0$, the result is called *Maclaurin's series*.

Example. Find the Maclaurin's series representing e^x.
Solution. If $f(x) = e^x$, then

$$f'(x) = e^x,$$

$$f''(x) = e^x, \text{ and}$$

in general

$$f^{(n)}(x) = e^x.$$

At $c = 0$,

$$f(c) = e^0 = 1,$$

$$f'(c) = e^0 = 1, \text{ and}$$

$$f^{(n)}(c) = e^0 = 1.$$

Therefore,

$$a_0 = 1 = f(0).$$

$$a_1 = f'(0) = 1.$$

$$a_2 = \frac{f''(0)}{2!} = \frac{1}{2!}.$$

$$a_3 = \frac{f'''(0)}{3!} = \frac{1}{3!}.$$

$$\cdots$$

$$a_n = \frac{f^{(n)}(0)}{n!} = \frac{1}{n!}.$$

Thus,

$$e^x = a_0 + a_1 x + a_2 x^2 + a_3 x^3 + \cdots$$

$$= 1 + x + \frac{x^2}{2!} + \frac{x^3}{3!} + \frac{x^4}{4!} + \cdots$$

$$= \sum_{i=0}^{\infty} \frac{x^i}{i!}.$$

This was the expected result. The interval of convergence for this series is from $-\infty$ to $+\infty$.

It can be shown that if a Taylor's series representing a given function is truncated after a finite number of terms, say n, the error made by estimating the function with the finite series can be estimated by

$$R_n(x) = \frac{f^{(n+1)}(z)}{(n+1)!}(x-c)^{n+1}.$$

where $R_n(x)$ is the remainder term for the series, and z is a number between x and c.

Example.   Estimate the error made in assuming that e is given by the first 11 terms of its Taylor's series.
Solution.   Considering 11 terms implies that $n = 10$, then $n + 1 = 11$, and

$$f^{(11)}(0) = e^0 = 1,$$

since

$$e^x = \sum_{i=0}^{\infty} \frac{x^i}{i!}, \text{ and thus } e = \sum_{i=0}^{\infty} \frac{1}{i!}.$$

If

$$e \approx 1 + 1 + \frac{1}{2!} + \frac{1}{3!} + \frac{1}{4!} + \frac{1}{5!} + \frac{1}{6!} + \frac{1}{7!} + \frac{1}{8!} + \frac{1}{9!} - \frac{1}{10!},$$

the error, $R_{11}(1) = \dfrac{e^z}{11!}$, where $0 \le z \le 1$. But $\dfrac{e^z}{11!} \le \dfrac{3^1}{11!}$, therefore the

error is less than $\dfrac{3}{11!}$.

Example.   Find the Maclaurin's series for $\sin x$.
Solution. $f(x) = \sin x,$

$$f'(x) = \cos x,$$

$$f''(x) = -\sin x,$$

$$f'''(x) = -\cos x,$$

$$f^{(4)}(x) = \sin x = f(x),$$

$$f^{(5)}(x) = \cos x = f'(x),$$

$$f^{(6)}(x) = -\sin x = f''(x),$$

$$f^{(7)}(x) = -\cos x = f'''(x), \text{ and}$$

$$f^{(8)}(x) = \sin x = f(x) = f^{(4)}(x).$$

In general,

$$f^{(4n)}(x) = \sin x,$$

$$f^{(4n+1)}(x) = \cos x,$$

$$f^{(4n+2)}(x) = -\sin x, \text{ and}$$

$$f^{(4n+3)}(x) = -\cos x$$

for $n = 0, 1, 2, 3, \ldots$.
If $c = 0$,

$$f^{(4n)}(0) = \sin 0 = 0,$$

$$f^{(4n+1)}(0) = \cos 0 = 1,$$

$$f^{(4n+2)}(0) = -\sin 0 = 0, \text{ and}$$

$$f^{(4n+3)}(0) = -\cos 0 = -1.$$

Therefore,

$$a_{4n} = 0,$$

$$a_{4n+1} = \frac{1}{(4n+1)!}$$

$$a_{4n+2} = 0, \text{ and}$$

$$a_{4n+3} = \frac{-1}{(4n+3)!},$$

for $n = 0, 1, 2, 3, 4, \ldots$.
In other words, a's with even subscripts are zero, whereas those with odd subscripts alternate in sign. Thus,

$$\sin x = 0 + \frac{x}{1!} + 0 - \frac{x^3}{3!} + 0 + \frac{x^5}{5!} + 0 - \frac{x^7}{7!} + \cdots = \sum_{i=0}^{\infty} \frac{(-1)^i x^{2i+1}}{(2i+1)!}.$$

It is a simple matter to verify that this series converges for all real values of x.

Example.   If $\sin x = \sum_{i=0}^{\infty} \frac{(-1)x^{2i+1}}{(2i+1)!}$, find the Maclaurin's series for $\cos x$.

Solution.   Using term by term differentiation as was done in an example in section 9-7,

$$\cos x = \sum_{i=0}^{\infty} \frac{(-1)^i x^{2i}}{(2i)!}.$$

Would we have obtained the same series directly from Taylor's series?

For $f(x) = \cos x$ the verification is left as an exercise. However, it will be informative to verify by an example the fact that Taylor's series agrees with series obtained other ways.

Example. Verify by use of Taylor's series that

$$\frac{1}{1 - x} = 1 + x + x^2 + x^3 + \cdots$$

$$= \sum_{i=0}^{\infty} x^i,$$

if $|x| < 1$.

Solution. Here $c = 0$ and $a_n = \dfrac{f^{(n)}(0)}{n!}$.

$$f(x) = \frac{1}{1 - x},$$

$$f'(x) = \frac{-1}{(1 - x)^2}(-1) = \frac{1}{(1 - x)^2},$$

$$f''(x) = \frac{-2}{(1 - x)^3}(-1) = \frac{2}{(1 - x)^3}, \text{ and}$$

$$f'''(x) = \frac{+2(-3)}{(1 - x)^4}(-1) = \frac{2(3)}{(1 - x)^4}.$$

In general,

$$f^{(n)}(x) = \frac{n!}{(1 - x)^{n+1}}.$$

At $x = 0$,

$$f^{(n)}(0) = n!.$$

Therefore,

$$a_n = \frac{f^{(n)}(0)}{n!} = \frac{n!}{n!} = 1$$

for all n.

Here,

$$\frac{1}{1 - x} = \sum_{i=0}^{\infty} a_i x^i = \sum_{i=0}^{\infty} x^i.$$

When a series is known, or found by using some method other than Taylor's formula, it is often useful in evaluating derivatives.

Example.   Find $\dfrac{d^7}{dx^7}\tan^{-1}x\Big|_{x=0}$

Solution.   Using term by term integration, we found that

$$\tan^{-1}x = x - \frac{x^3}{3} + \frac{x^5}{5} - \frac{x^7}{7} + \frac{x^9}{9}.$$

Using Maclaurin's series,

$$\tan^{-1}x = a_0 + a_1 x + a_2 x^2 + a_3 x^3 + a_4 x^4 + a_5 x^5 + a_6 x^6 + a_7 x^7 + \cdots,$$

where $a_n = \dfrac{f^{(n)}(0)}{n!}$.

Comparing the two series, it is apparent that

$$a_7 = \frac{\dfrac{d^7}{dx^7}\tan^{-1}x\Big|_{x=0}}{7!},$$

while, at the same time, $a_7 = -\frac{1}{7}$ from the actual series.

Thus,

$$\frac{\dfrac{d^7}{dx^7}\tan^{-1}(x)\Big|_{x=0}}{7!} = -\frac{1}{7},$$

or

$$\frac{d^7}{dx^7}\tan^{-1}(x)\Big|_{x=0} = \frac{-7!}{7} = -6! = -720.$$

   Actually the most important applications of infinite series relate to solving equations like

$$\frac{d^2y}{dx^2} - xy = 0.$$

One can assume that $y = \sum\limits_{i=0}^{\infty} a_i x^i$. Then

$$y' = \sum_{i=1}^{\infty} a_i i x^{i-1},$$

$$y'' = \sum_{i=2}^{\infty} a_i i(i-1)x^{i-2},$$

and

$$xy = \sum_{i=0}^{\infty} a_i x^{i+1}.$$

In terms of the power series, the equation becomes

$$\sum_{i=2}^{\infty} i(i-1)a_i x^{i-2} - \sum_{i=0}^{\infty} a_i x^{i+1} = 0,$$

$$2(1)a_2 + 3(2)a_3 x + 4(3)a_4 x^2 + 5(4)a_5 x^3 + \cdots$$

$$- \{a_0 x + a_1 x^2 + a_2 x^3 + \cdots\} = 0,$$

or
$$2a_2 + (6a_3 - a_0)x + (12a_4 - a_1)x^2 + \cdots = 0.$$

To satisfy the equation, all of the coefficients must vanish. Hence,

$$a_2 = 0, \qquad 6a_3 - a_0 = 0, \qquad 12a_4 - a_1 = 0, \text{ etc.},$$

or
$$a_3 = \frac{a_0}{6}, \qquad a_4 = \frac{a_1}{12}, \qquad a_5 = 0, \text{ etc.}$$

Hence,

$$y = a_0 + a_1 x + \frac{a_0}{6}x^3 + \frac{a_1}{12}x^4 + \frac{a_0}{2(3)(5)(6)}x^6 + \cdots.$$

Thus, if a solution exists it must be represented by the indicated power series.

In attempting to solve differential equations, equations involving an unknown function and its derivatives as above, it is often possible to find an infinite power series representing the function. It frequently happens in these cases that the function found has no counterpart among the algebraic functions. This leads to a whole class of functions, defined only in terms of a power series, that represent nonelementary functions. Often it is only with functions found in terms of an infinite series that suitable mathematical models of real world phenomena can be found.

9-8   Exercises

1. Use Taylor's formula to find a Maclaurin's series for $\ln |x + 1|$. Determine the radius of convergence.

2. If $f(x) = \dfrac{e^x + e^{-x}}{2}$ find a series in powers of x for $f(x)$ using Taylor's formula.

3. Using the series developed for e^x find a series for $f(x) = \dfrac{e^x + e^{-x}}{2}$.

4. $f(x) = \dfrac{e^x + e^{-x}}{2}$ is called the *hyperbolic cosine* of x and is usually

    denoted as $\cosh(x) = \dfrac{e^x + e^{-x}}{2}$. Verify, using the infinite series repre-

    sentation of $\cosh(x)$, that $\dfrac{d^2}{dx^2}\cosh(x) = \cosh x$.

5. Verify by direct calculation that $\dfrac{d^2}{dx^2}\cosh(x) = \cosh(x)$.

6. Find a Taylor's series with $c = \dfrac{\pi}{2}$ for $\cos x$.

7. Find a Taylor's series with $c = \dfrac{\pi}{2}$ for $\sin x$.

8. Develop the Maclaurin's series for $\tan^{-1}x$.
9. Develop the Maclaurin's series for $\sin^{-1}x$.
10. Find, by any method, a Maclaurin's series for e^{x^2}.
11. Find, using the result of problem 10,

$$\left. \frac{d^7}{dx^7} e^{x^2} \right|_{x=0}.$$

12. Find a Taylor's series for e^x in powers of $(x - 1)$, *i.e.*, with $c = 1$.

13. Find a Taylor's series with $c = 1$ for $f(x) = \sqrt{x}$.
14. What problems would one encounter if one tried to find a Maclaurin's series for $f(x) = \sqrt{x}$?
15. Test the validity of the binomial expansion

$$(a + x)^n = a^n + na^{n-1}x + \frac{n(n-1)a^{n-2}x^2}{2!} + \frac{n(n-1)(n-2)a^{n-3}x^3}{3!} + \cdots$$

$$+ \frac{n(n-1)(n-2)\cdots(n-i+1)a^{n-i}x^i}{i!} + \cdots$$

    by finding the first four terms of the Maclaurin's series for $f(x) = (a + x)^n$, where n is some rational number.
16. Consider $f(x) = (4 - x)^3$. Find the Taylor's series for $f(x)$. Does this result agree with the ordinary expansion of $(4 - x)^3$ by the usual rules of algebra?
17. Estimate the error made in equating $\sin(1)$, to the first four terms of the Maclaurin's expansion for $\sin x$, with $x = 1$.
18. Estimate the error one would make if one said that $\cos x$ was exactly

equal to the first three terms of the Maclaurin's series for $\cos x$ provided $0 \le x < \dfrac{\pi}{4}$.

19. Since $\tan^{-1} 1 = \dfrac{\pi}{4}$ how many terms would be necessary to estimate $\dfrac{\pi}{4}$ using the series developed for $\tan^{-1} x$, so that the error would be less than 0.005.

(20-23) Find the first three terms of the Maclaurin's series for each of the indicated functions.

20. $f(x) = \sec x$
21. $f(x) = \ln[\sec x]$
22. $f(x) = e^x \sin x$
23. $f(x) = x \ln(1 + x)$
24. Find a power series such that

$$y = \sum_{i=0}^{\infty} a_i x^i$$

is a solution to the equation $\dfrac{dy}{dx} - y = 0$. Does the power series you find appear to be one of the known functions? Which one?

Chapter 9   REVIEW

1. Define a sequence.
2. Define a series.
3. Define convergence and divergence for a sequence.
4. Define convergence and divergence for a series.
5. What is a sequence of partial sums? How does it relate to the concept of an infinite series?

(6-10) Determine if the following sequences are convergent or divergent. Find a_1, a_2, and a_7 in each case.

6. $\{a_n\}$, where $a_n = \dfrac{\ln(n + 1)}{n}$

7. $\{a_n\}$, where $a_n = 3^n$

8. $\{a_n\}$, where $a_n = \dfrac{n^2 - 1}{(n + 3)^2}$ 10. $\{a_n\}$, where $a_n = \dfrac{\ln(n^2)}{2n^3}$

9. $\{a_n\}$, where $a_n = 3^{-n}$

(11-13) In each case below a sequence $\{a_n\}$ is defined recursively. Find a general form for a_n, and test the sequence for convergence.

11. $a_{n+1} = a_n\left(\dfrac{1}{n + 1}\right)$, $a_1 = 1$

12. $a_{n+1} = a_n + (n + 1)$, $a_1 = 1$
13. $a_{n+1} = a_n + 1$, $a_1 = 1$
14. State the integral test for convergence of a series. What are the principal problems encountered in applying the integral test?

(15-18) Test the following series for convergence using the integral test.

15. $\displaystyle\sum_{i=1}^{\infty} \dfrac{1}{i\sqrt{i}}$ 17. $\displaystyle\sum_{i=2}^{\infty} \dfrac{\ln i}{i^2}$

16. $\displaystyle\sum_{i=1}^{\infty} \dfrac{1}{3i + 1}$ 18. $\displaystyle\sum_{i=1}^{\infty} \dfrac{i^2}{e^i}$

19. State the comparison tests for convergence or divergence. What are the principal problems one encounters in attempting to use the comparison test?

(20-23) Use the comparison test to establish the convergence or divergence of the following series.

20. $\displaystyle\sum_{i=1}^{\infty} \dfrac{1}{(3i)^4}$ 22. $\displaystyle\sum_{i=1}^{\infty} \dfrac{1}{2^{1/i}}$

21. $\displaystyle\sum_{i-1}^{\infty} \dfrac{|\sin i|}{i^2}$ 23. $\displaystyle\sum_{i=1}^{\infty} \dfrac{(i + 1)!}{(i + 2)!}$

24. State the ratio test for the convergence of an infinite series. What problems can one expect to encounter in attempting to apply it?

(25-28) Using the ratio test, test the following series for convergence.

25. $\displaystyle\sum_{i=1}^{\infty} \dfrac{i!}{2^i}$

26. $\displaystyle\sum_{i=1}^{\infty} \dfrac{1(3)(5)(7)(9)\ldots(2i + 1)}{2(4)(6)(8)(10)\ldots 2i(2i + 2)}\left(\dfrac{2}{3}\right)^i$

27. $\displaystyle\sum_{i=1}^{\infty} \frac{2^i}{i^2}$

28. $\displaystyle\sum_{i=1}^{\infty} \frac{i^2}{2^i}$

29. Under what conditions does an alternating series converge?

30. What are absolute and conditional convergence?

(31-34) Test the following series for absolute convergence.

31. $\displaystyle\sum_{i=1}^{\infty} \frac{(-1)^{i+1}}{i(i+2)}$

33. $\displaystyle\sum_{i=1}^{\infty} \frac{(-1)^i}{i 3^i}$

32. $\displaystyle\sum_{i=1}^{\infty} \frac{(2i-1)(-1)^{i+1}}{5i+1}$

34. $\displaystyle\sum_{i=1}^{\infty} \frac{(-1)^{i+1}}{i+5}$

(35-40) Test the following series for convergence by any method.

35. $\displaystyle\sum_{i=1}^{\infty} \frac{i}{i^4+1}$

38. $\displaystyle\sum_{i=1}^{\infty} \left[i - \left(\frac{2}{3}\right)^{i+1}\right]$

36. $\displaystyle\sum_{i=1}^{\infty} \frac{1}{(2i+2)^3}$

39. $\displaystyle\sum_{i=1}^{\infty} \frac{2+6\sqrt{i}}{i}$

37. $\displaystyle\sum_{i=3}^{\infty} \frac{1}{i(\ln i)^{3/2}}$

40. $\displaystyle\sum_{i=1}^{\infty} \frac{(-1)(-2)(-3)\ldots(-i)}{(2)(4)(6)(8)\ldots(2i)}$

41. For a given series $\displaystyle\sum_{i=1}^{\infty} a_i$ with S_n, the partial sum, $S_n \cdot S_{n+1} < 0$. How can this happen? Can you find an example where this takes place?

42. What is a power series?

43. Does a power series converge for all values of the argument?

(44-50) Determine the interval of convergence for each of the following series.

44. $\displaystyle\sum_{i=1}^{\infty} i(x-2)^i$

45. $\displaystyle\sum_{i=2}^{\infty} \frac{x^i}{\ln(i)}$

46. $\displaystyle\sum_{i=1}^{\infty} (-1)^i \frac{1(3)(5)(7)(9)\ldots(2i+1)}{2(4)(6)(8)(10)\ldots(2i)} x^i$

47. $\displaystyle\sum_{i=1}^{\infty} \frac{i!}{i^i} x^i$

48. $\displaystyle\sum_{i=1}^{\infty} \frac{(x+3)^i}{i 2^i}$

49. $\displaystyle\sum_{i=1}^{\infty} \frac{(x+1)^i}{4^i}$ **50.** $\displaystyle\sum_{i=1}^{\infty} \frac{(x^2+2x+1)^i}{i}$

51. Does the concept of an interval of convergence apply to a series like

$$\sum_{i=1}^{\infty} \frac{1}{ix^i}?$$ If it does, what is the interval of convergence?

52. If a function $f(x)$ can be represented by a power series, what advantage does such a series representation have over the more usual and more compact representation?

53. Use the idea of partial sums or term by term differentiation to argue that if

$$\sum_{i=0}^{\infty} a_i x^i \text{ and } \sum_{i=0}^{\infty} b_i x^i$$

have the same interval of convergence, and

$$\sum_{i=0}^{\infty} a_i x^i = \sum_{i=0}^{\infty} b_i x^i$$

for every x in that interval, then $a_n = b_n$ for all n.

(54-60)   Find by any method a series of the form

$$\sum_{i=0}^{\infty} a_i (x-c)^i$$

for the indicated value of c. Determine the interval of convergence in each case.

54. $f(x) = \sin x, c = \dfrac{\pi}{4}$.

55. $f(x) = \ln\left(\dfrac{1-x}{1-x^2}\right), c - 0$

56. $f(x) = e^{-x^2}, c = 0$

57. $f(x) = \sinh x = \dfrac{e^x - e^{-x}}{2}$ ($\sinh x$ is read "hyperbolic sine of x"), $c = 0$

58. $f(x) = (1+x)^{\frac{1}{3}}, c = 0$

59. $f(x) = \dfrac{1}{x}, c = 1$

60. $f(x) = \sec x, c = 0$

(61-62) Assume $e^{\cos x} = e\left(1 - \dfrac{x^2}{2} + \dfrac{x^4}{4} - \dfrac{31x^6}{720} + \cdots\right)$

61. Find $\dfrac{d^4}{dx^4} e^{\cos x}\Big|_{x=0}$

62. Find $\dfrac{d^5}{dx^5} e^{\cos x}\Big|_{x=0}$

63. If $\dfrac{\ln(1 + x)}{1 + x} = x - \left(1 + \dfrac{1}{2}\right)x^2 + \left(1 + \dfrac{1}{2} + \dfrac{1}{3}\right)x^3$

$$- \left(1 + \dfrac{1}{2} + \dfrac{1}{3} + \dfrac{1}{4}\right)x^4 + \cdots$$

find $\dfrac{d^{10}}{dx^{10}} \dfrac{\ln(1 + x)}{1 + x}\Big|_{x=0}.$

64. Estimate $\sin\left(\dfrac{\pi}{4}\right)$ with 4 nonzero terms of the Maclaurin's series for $\sin x$. What error is involved in this estimate?

Appendix

TABLE I

Values of $\dfrac{1}{\sqrt{2\pi}} \displaystyle\int_0^z e^{-x^2/2}\, dx$ or Normal Curve or Gaussian Areas

z	0.00	.01	.02	.03	.04	.05	.06	.07	.08	.09
0.0	0.0000	0.0040	0.0080	0.0120	0.0160	0.0199	0.0239	0.0279	0.0319	0.0359
0.1	.0398	.0438	.0478	.0517	.0557	.0596	.0636	.0675	.0714	.0753
0.2	.0793	.0832	.0871	.0910	.0948	.0987	.1026	.1064	.1103	.1141
0.3	.1179	.1217	.1255	.1293	.1331	.1368	.1406	.1443	.1480	.1517
0.4	.1554	.1591	.1628	.1664	.1700	.1736	.1772	.1808	.1844	.1879
0.5	.1915	.1950	.1985	.2019	.2054	.2088	.2123	.2157	.2190	.2224
0.6	.2257	.2291	.2324	.2357	.2389	.2422	.2454	.2486	.2517	.2549
0.7	.2580	.2611	.2642	.2673	.2704	.2734	.2764	.2794	.2823	.2852
0.8	.2881	.2910	.2939	.2967	.2995	.3023	.3051	.3078	.3106	.3133
0.9	.3159	.3186	.3212	.3238	.3264	.3289	.3315	.3340	.3365	.3389
1.0	.3413	.3438	.3461	.3485	.3508	.3531	.3554	.3577	.3599	.3621
1.1	.3643	.3665	.3686	.3708	.3729	.3749	.3770	.3790	.3810	.3830
1.2	.3849	.3869	.3888	.3907	.3925	.3944	.3962	.3980	.3997	.4015
1.3	.4032	.4049	.4066	.4082	.4099	.4115	.4131	.4147	.4162	.4177
1.4	.4192	.4207	.4222	.4236	.4251	.4265	.4279	.4292	.4306	.4319
1.5	.4332	.4345	.4357	.4370	.4382	.4394	.4406	.4418	.4429	.4441
1.6	.4452	.4463	.4474	.4484	.4495	.4505	.4515	.4525	.4535	.4545
1.7	.4554	.4564	.4573	.4582	.4591	.4599	.4608	.4616	.4625	.4633
1.8	.4641	.4649	.4656	.4664	.4671	.4678	.4686	.4693	.4699	.4706
1.9	.4713	.4719	.4726	.4732	.4738	.4744	.4750	.4756	.4761	.4767
2.0	.4772	.4778	.4783	.4788	.4793	.4798	.4803	.4808	.4812	.4817
2.1	.4821	.4826	.4830	.4834	.4838	.4842	.4846	.4850	.4854	.4857
2.2	.4861	.4864	.4868	.4871	.4875	.4878	.4881	.4884	.4887	.4890
2.3	.4893	.4896	.4898	.4901	.4904	.4906	.4909	.4911	.4913	.4916
2.4	.4918	.4920	.4922	.4925	.4927	.4929	.4931	.4932	.4934	.4936
2.5	.4938	.4940	.4941	.4943	.4945	.4946	.4948	.4949	.4951	.4952
2.6	.4953	.4955	.4956	.4957	.4959	.4960	.4961	.4962	.4963	.4964
2.7	.4965	.4966	.4967	.4968	.4969	.4970	.4971	.4972	.4973	.4974
2.8	.4974	.4975	.4976	.4977	.4977	.4978	.4979	.4979	.4980	.4981
2.9	.4981	.4982	.4982	.4983	.4984	.4984	.4985	.4985	.4986	.4986
3.0	.4987	.4987	.4987	.4988	.4988	.4989	.4989	.4989	.4990	.4990

TABLE II

Natural Logarithms

x	$\ln x$	x	$\ln x$	x	$\ln x$
0.1	−2.303	3.5	1.253	6.9	1.932
.2	−1.609	3.6	1.281	7.0	1.946
.3	−1.204	3.7	1.308	7.1	1.960
.4	−.916	3.8	1.335	7.2	1.974
.5	−.693	3.9	1.361	7.3	1.988
.6	−.511	4.0	1.386	7.4	2.001
.7	−.357	4.1	1.411	7.5	2.015
.8	−.223	4.2	1.435	7.6	2.028
.9	−.105	4.3	1.459	7.7	2.041
1.0	0.000	4.4	1.482	7.8	2.054
1.1	.095	4.5	1.504	7.9	2.067
1.2	.182	4.6	1.526	8.0	2.079
1.3	.262	4.7	1.548	8.1	2.092
1.4	.336	4.8	1.569	8.2	2.104
1.5	.405	4.9	1.589	8.3	2.116
1.6	.470	5.0	1.609	8.4	2.128
1.7	.531	5.1	1.629	8.5	2.140
1.8	.588	5.2	1.649	8.6	2.152
1.9	.642	5.3	1.668	8.7	2.163
2.0	.693	5.4	1.686	8.8	2.175
2.1	.742	5.5	1.705	8.9	2.186
2.2	.788	5.6	1.723	9.0	2.197
2.3	.833	5.7	1.740	9.1	2.208
2.4	.875	5.8	1.758	9.2	2.219
2.5	.916	5.9	1.775	9.3	2.230
2.6	.956	6.0	1.792	9.4	2.241
2.7	.993	6 1	1.808	9.5	2.251
2.8	1.030	6.2	1.825	9.6	2.262
2.9	1.065	6.3	1.841	9.7	2.272
3.0	1.099	6.4	1.856	9.8	2.282
3.1	1.131	6.5	1.872	9.9	2.293
3.2	1.163	6.6	1.887	10.0	2.303
3.3	1.194	6.7	1.902		
3.4	1.224	6.8	1.917		

TABLE III. e^x

x	e^x	x	e^x	x	e^x
0.00	1.0000	.37	1.4477	.74	2.0959
.01	1.0101	.38	1.4623	.75	2.1170
.02	1.0202	.39	1.4770	.76	2.1383
.03	1.0305	.40	1.4918	.77	2.1598
.04	1.0408	.41	1.5068	.78	2.1815
.05	1.0513	.42	1.5220	.79	2.2034
.06	1.0618	.43	1.5373	.80	2.2255
.07	1.0725	.44	1.5527	.81	2.2479
.08	1.0833	.45	1.5683	.82	2.2705
.09	1.0942	.46	1.5841	.83	2.2933
.10	1.1052	.47	1.6000	.84	2.3164
.11	1.1163	.48	1.6161	.85	2.3396
.12	1.1275	.49	1.6323	.86	2.3632
.13	1.1388	.50	1.6487	.87	2.3869
.14	1.1503	.51	1.6653	.88	2.4109
.15	1.1618	.52	1.6820	.89	2.4351
.16	1.1735	.53	1.6989	.90	2.4596
.17	1.1853	.54	1.7160	.91	2.4843
.18	1.1972	.55	1.7333	.92	2.5093
.19	1.2092	.56	1.7507	.93	2.5345
.20	1.2214	.57	1.7683	.94	2.5600
.21	1.2337	.58	1.7860	.95	2.5857
.22	1.2461	.59	1.8040	.96	2.6117
.23	1.2586	.60	1.8221	.97	2.6379
.24	1.2712	.61	1.8404	.98	2.6645
.25	1.2840	.62	1.8589	.99	2.6912
.26	1.2969	.63	1.8776	1.	2.7183
.27	1.3100	.64	1.8965	2.	7.3891
.28	1.3231	.65	1.9155	3.	20.0855
.29	1.3364	.66	1.9348	4.	54.5981
.30	1.3499	.67	1.9542	5.	148.4132
.31	1.3634	.68	1.9739	6.	403.4288
.32	1.3771	.69	1.9937	7.	1096.6331
.33	1.3910	.70	2.0138	8.	2980.9579
.34	1.4049	.71	2.0340	9.	8103.0839
.35	1.4191	.72	2.0544	10.	22026.4650
.36	1.4333	.73	2.0751		

TABLE IV. Trigonometric Functions

Rad.	Deg.	Sin	Tan	Sec	Csc	Cot	Cos	Deg.	Rad.
0.000	0°	0.000	0.000	1.000	——	——	1.000	90°	1.571
.017	1°	.017	.017	1.000	57.30	57.29	1.000	89°	1.553
.035	2°	.035	.035	1.001	28.65	28.64	0.999	88°	1.536
.052	3°	.052	.052	1.001	19.11	19.08	.999	87°	1.518
.070	4°	.070	.070	1.002	14.34	14.30	.998	86°	1.501
.087	5°	.087	.087	1.004	11.47	11.43	.996	85°	1.484
.105	6°	.105	.105	1.006	9.567	9.514	.995	84°	1.466
.122	7°	.122	.123	1.008	8.206	8.144	.993	83°	1.449
.140	8°	.139	.141	1.010	7.185	7.115	.990	82°	1.431
.157	9°	.156	.158	1.012	6.392	6.314	.988	81°	1.414
.175	10°	.174	.176	1.015	5.759	5.671	.985	80°	1.396
.192	11°	.191	.194	1.019	5.241	5.145	.982	79°	1.379
.209	12°	.208	.213	1.022	4.810	4.705	.978	78°	1.361
.227	13°	.225	.231	1.026	4.445	4.331	.974	77°	1.344
.244	14°	.242	.249	1.031	4.134	4.011	.970	76°	1.326
.262	15°	.259	.268	1.035	3.864	3.732	.966	75°	1.309
.279	16°	.276	.287	1.040	3.628	3.487	.961	74°	1.292
.297	17°	.292	.306	1.046	3.420	3.271	.956	73°	1.274
.314	18°	.309	.325	1.051	3.236	3.078	.951	72°	1.257
.332	19°	.326	.344	1.058	3.072	2.904	.946	71°	1.239
.349	20°	.342	.364	1.064	2.924	2.747	.940	70°	1.222
.367	21°	.358	.384	1.071	2.790	2.605	.934	69°	1.204
.384	22°	.375	.404	1.079	2.669	2.475	.927	68°	1.187
.401	23°	.391	.424	1.086	2.559	2.356	.921	67°	1.169
.419	24°	.407	.445	1.095	2.459	2.246	.914	66°	1.152
.436	25°	.423	.466	1.103	2.366	2.145	.906	65°	1.134
.454	26°	.438	.488	1.113	2.281	2.050	.899	64°	1.117
.471	27°	.454	.510	1.122	2.203	1.963	.891	63°	1.100
.489	28°	.469	.532	1.133	2.130	1.881	.883	62°	1.082
.506	29°	.485	.554	1.143	2.063	1.804	.875	61°	1.065
.524	30°	.500	.577	1.155	2.000	1.732	.866	60°	1.047
.541	31°	.515	.601	1.167	1.942	1.664	.857	59°	1.030
.559	32°	.530	.625	1.179	1.887	1.600	.848	58°	1.012
.576	33°	.545	.649	1.192	1.836	1.540	.839	57°	0.995
.593	34°	.559	.675	1.206	1.788	1.483	.829	56°	0.977
.611	35°	.574	.700	1.221	1.743	1.428	.819	55°	0.960
.628	36°	.588	.727	1.236	1.701	1.376	.809	54°	0.942
.646	37°	.602	.754	1.252	1.662	1.327	.799	53°	0.925
.663	38°	.616	.781	1.269	1.624	1.280	.788	52°	0.908
.681	39°	.629	.810	1.287	1.589	1.235	.777	51°	0.890
.698	40°	.643	.839	1.305	1.556	1.192	.766	50°	0.873
.716	41°	.656	.869	1.325	1.524	1.150	.755	49°	0.855
.733	42°	.669	.900	1.346	1.494	1.111	.743	48°	0.838
.750	43°	.682	.933	1.367	1.466	1.072	.731	47°	0.820
.768	44°	.695	.966	1.390	1.440	1.036	.719	46°	0.803
.785	45°	.707	1.000	1.414	1.414	1.000	.707	45°	0.785
Rad.	Deg.	Cos	Cot	Csc	Sec	Tan	Sin	Deg.	Rad.

TABLE V. Table of Integrals

(*Note*: It is understood that every integral in this table has a constant of integration to be supplied by the reader.)

1. $\displaystyle\int du = u$

2. $\displaystyle\int u^n\, du = \frac{u^{n+1}}{n+1}, n \neq -1$

3. $\displaystyle\int \frac{du}{u} = \ln|u|$

4. $\displaystyle\int u\, dv = uv - \int v\, du$

5. $\displaystyle\int \frac{dx}{ax+b} = \frac{1}{a}\ln|ax+b|$

6. $\displaystyle\int \frac{dx}{x(ax+b)} = \frac{1}{b}\ln\left|\frac{x}{ax+b}\right|$

7. $\displaystyle\int x(ax+b)^n\, dx = \frac{1}{a^2(n+2)}(ax+b)^{n+2} - \frac{b}{a^2(n+1)}(ax+b)^{n+1}$

$$(n \neq -1, -2)$$

8. $\displaystyle\int x\sqrt{ax+b}\, dx = \frac{2}{15a^2}(ax+b)^{3/2}(3ax-2b)$

9. $\displaystyle\int \frac{\sqrt{ax+b}}{x}\, dx = 2\sqrt{ax+b} + \sqrt{b}\ln\left|\frac{\sqrt{ax+b}-\sqrt{b}}{\sqrt{ax+b}+\sqrt{b}}\right|, (b > 0)$

10. $\displaystyle\int \frac{\sqrt{ax+b}}{x}\, dx = 2\sqrt{ax+b} - 2\sqrt{-b}\tan^{-1}\sqrt{\frac{ax+b}{-b}}, (b < 0)$

11. $\displaystyle\int \frac{dx}{x\sqrt{ax+b}} = \frac{1}{\sqrt{b}}\ln\left|\frac{\sqrt{ax+b}-\sqrt{b}}{\sqrt{ax+b}+\sqrt{b}}\right|, (b > 0)$

12. $\displaystyle\int \frac{dx}{x\sqrt{ax+b}} = \frac{2}{\sqrt{-b}}\tan^{-1}\sqrt{\frac{ax+b}{-b}}, (b < 0)$

13. $\displaystyle\int \frac{du}{a^2+u^2} = \frac{1}{a}\tan^{-1}\left(\frac{u}{a}\right)$

14. $\displaystyle\int \frac{du}{a^2-u^2} = \frac{1}{2a}\ln\left|\frac{a+u}{a-u}\right|$

15. $\displaystyle\int \frac{du}{\sqrt{a^2-u^2}} = \sin^{-1}\left(\frac{u}{a}\right)$

16. $\displaystyle\int \frac{du}{\sqrt{u^2\pm a^2}} = \ln\left|u + \sqrt{u^2\pm a^2}\right|$

Table of Integrals (*continued*)

17. $\displaystyle \int \frac{du}{u\sqrt{a^2 \pm u^2}} = -\frac{1}{a} \ln \left| \frac{a + \sqrt{a^2 \pm u^2}}{u} \right|$

18. $\displaystyle \int \frac{du}{|u|\sqrt{u^2 - a^2}} = \frac{1}{a} \sec^{-1} \frac{u}{a}$

19. $\displaystyle \int \frac{\sqrt{u^2 - a^2}}{u} du = \sqrt{u^2 - a^2} - a \sec^{-1}\left(\frac{u}{a}\right)$

20. $\displaystyle \int \frac{\sqrt{u^2 + a^2}}{u} du = \sqrt{u^2 + a^2} - a \ln \left| \frac{a + \sqrt{u^2 + a^2}}{u} \right|$

21. $\displaystyle \int \sqrt{a^2 - u^2}\, du = \frac{u}{2}\sqrt{a^2 - u^2} + \frac{a^2}{2} \sin^{-1}\left(\frac{u}{a}\right)$

22. $\displaystyle \int \frac{dx}{ax^2 + bx + c} = \frac{2}{\sqrt{4ac - b^2}} \tan^{-1}\left(\frac{2ax + b}{\sqrt{4ac - b^2}}\right), \; (b^2 < 4ac)$

23. $\displaystyle \int \frac{dx}{ax^2 + bx + c} = \frac{1}{\sqrt{b^2 - 4ac}} \ln \left| \frac{2ax + b - \sqrt{b^2 - 4ac}}{2ax + b + \sqrt{b^2 - 4ac}} \right|, \; (b^2 > 4ac)$

24. $\displaystyle \int \frac{dx}{ax^2 + bx + c} = -\frac{2}{2ax + b}, \; (b^2 = 4ac)$

25. $\displaystyle \int \sin ax\, dx = -\frac{1}{a} \cos ax$

26. $\displaystyle \int \cos ax\, dx = \frac{1}{a} \sin ax$

27. $\displaystyle \int \sin^2 ax\, dx = \frac{x}{2} - \frac{\sin(2ax)}{4a}$

28. $\displaystyle \int \cos^2 ax\, dx = \frac{x}{2} + \frac{\sin(2ax)}{4a}$

29. $\displaystyle \int \frac{dx}{\sin ax} = \frac{1}{a} \ln \left| \tan\left(\frac{ax}{2}\right) \right| = \frac{1}{a} \ln |\csc ax - \cot ax|$

30. $\displaystyle \int \frac{dx}{\cos ax} = \frac{1}{a} \ln |\tan ax + \sec ax|$

31. $\displaystyle \int \sin ax \sin bx\, dx = \frac{1}{2}\left[\frac{\sin(a - b)x}{(a - b)} - \frac{\sin(a + b)x}{(a + b)} \right] (a^2 \neq b^2)$

32. $\displaystyle \int \sin ax \cos bx\, dx = -\frac{1}{2}\left[\frac{\cos(a - b)x}{(a - b)} + \frac{\cos(a + b)x}{(a + b)} \right] (a^2 \neq b^2)$

33. $\displaystyle \int \cos ax \cos bx\, dx = \frac{1}{2}\left[\frac{\sin(a - b)x}{(a - b)} + \frac{\sin(a + b)x}{(a + b)} \right] (a^2 \neq b^2)$

Table of Integrals (*continued*)

34. $\displaystyle \int \sin^n u \, du = \frac{-\sin^{n-1} u \cos u}{n} + \frac{n-1}{n} \int \sin^{n-2} u \, du$

35. $\displaystyle \int \cos^n u \, du = \frac{\cos^{n-1} u \sin u}{n} + \frac{n-1}{n} \int \cos^{n-2} u \, du$

36. $\displaystyle \int \tan^n u \, du = \frac{\tan^{n-1} u}{n-1} - \int \tan^{n-2} u \, du$

37. $\displaystyle \int \cot^n u \, du = \frac{-\cot^{n-1} u}{n-1} - \int \cot^{n-2} u \, du$

38. $\displaystyle \int \sec^n u \, du = \frac{\tan u \sec^{n-2} u}{n-1} + \frac{n-2}{n-1} \int \sec^{n-2} u \, du. \ (n \neq 1)$

39. $\displaystyle \int \csc^n u \, du = \frac{-\cot u \csc^{n-2} u}{n-1} + \frac{n-2}{n-1} \int \csc^{n-2} u \, du, \ (n \neq 1)$

40. $\displaystyle \int x^n \sin ax \, dx = -\frac{1}{a} x^n \cos ax + \frac{n}{a} \int x^{n-1} \cos ax \, dx$

41. $\displaystyle \int x^n \cos ax \, dx = \frac{1}{a} x^n \sin ax - \frac{n}{a} \int x^{n-1} \sin ax \, dx$

42. $\displaystyle \int e^u \, du = e^u$

43. $\displaystyle \int x^n e^{ax} \, dx = \frac{1}{a} x^n e^{ax} - \frac{n}{a} \int x^{n-1} e^{ax} \, dx \quad (n > 0)$

44. $\displaystyle \int \frac{e^{ax}}{x^n} \, dx = -\frac{e^{ax}}{(n-1)x^{n-1}} + \frac{a}{n-1} \int \frac{e^{ax}}{x^{n-1}} \, dx \quad (n > 0)$

45. $\displaystyle \int a^u \, du = \frac{a^u}{\ln a}$

46. $\displaystyle \int x^n a^{bx} \, dx = \frac{x^n a^{bx}}{b \ln a} - \frac{n}{b \ln a} \int x^{n-1} a^{bx} \, dx \quad (n > 0)$

47. $\displaystyle \int \ln u \, du = u \ln u - u$

48. $\displaystyle \int \frac{du}{u \ln u} = \ln |\ln u|$

49. $\displaystyle \int x^n \ln(ax) \, dx = x^{n+1} \left[\frac{\ln(ax)}{n+1} - \frac{1}{(n+1)^2} \right] \quad (n \neq -1)$

50. $\displaystyle \int x^n (\ln ax)^m \, dx = \frac{x^{n+1}}{n+1} (\ln ax)^m - \frac{m}{n+1} \int x^n [\ln(ax)]^{m-1} \, dx \quad (n \neq -1)$

Table of Integrals (*continued*)

51. $\int x\,e^{ax}\,dx = \dfrac{ax-1}{a^2}\,e^{ax}$

52. $\int_0^\infty e^{-ax^2}\,dx = \dfrac{1}{2}\sqrt{\dfrac{\pi}{a}},\ a > 0$

53. $\int_0^\infty x^{n-1}e^{-x}\,dx = (n-1)!,\ n > 0$

54. $\int e^{ax}\sin(bx)\,dx = \dfrac{e^{ax}}{a^2+b^2}\left[a\sin(bx) - b\cos(bx)\right]$

55. $\int e^{ax}\cos(bx)\,dx = \dfrac{e^{ax}}{a^2+b^2}\left[a\cos(bx) + b\sin(bx)\right]$

56. $\int \sin^{-1}ax\,dx = x\sin^{-1}ax + \dfrac{1}{a}\sqrt{1 - a^2x^2}$

57. $\int \tan^{-1}ax\,dx = x\tan^{-1}ax - \dfrac{1}{2a}\ln(1 + a^2x^2)$

Answers to

Odd-Numbered Exercises

CHAPTER 1

1-1 Exercises

1. $\{3,5,7,9,\ldots\}$
3. $\{-6,-5,-4,-3,-2,-1,0,1,2,3,4,5,6\}$
5. $\{-1,0,1,2,3,4,5,6,7\}$
7. $\{3,4,5,\ldots\}$
9. $\{x \mid x = 2n,\ 1 \le n \le 5,\ n \text{ is a natural number}\}$
11. $\{x \mid |x| \le 4,\ x \text{ is an integer}\}$
13. $\{x \mid x = 3n + 1,\ n \text{ is a natural number}\}$
15. $\left\{ x \mid x = \dfrac{2}{2n + 1} \quad \text{or} \quad x = \dfrac{1}{n + 1},\ n \text{ is a natural number} \right\}$
17. $\{-2,-1,0,1,2,3,4,5\}$
19. $\{1,2,3,4,5,6\}$

21. $\{1,2,3,4,5\} = S$

23. $\{1,2,3,4,5\} = S$

25. $A = \{1,3,5,7,\ldots\} = \{x \mid x = 2n + 1, n \geq 0, n \in I\}$
$B = \{1,4,9,16,\ldots\} = \{x \mid x = n^2, n \in N\}$
$C = \{4,5,6,\ldots\} = \{x \mid x = n + 3, n \in N\}$
$D = \{7,9,11,\ldots\} = \{x \mid x = 2n + 5, n \in N\}$
$E = \{1,8,27,64,\ldots\} = \{x \mid x = n^3, n \in N\}$

1-2 Exercises

1. function; domain $= \{1,3,5,7\}$; range $= \{2,4,6,8\}$

3. function; domain $=$ the real numbers; range $=$ the real numbers

5. function; domain $= \{2,3,4,5\}$; range $= \{1\}$

7. function; domain $= \{x \mid x^2 \geq 3\}$; range $= \{y \mid y \geq 0\}$

9. function; domain $= \{x \mid x \neq (2k + 1)\dfrac{\pi}{2}, \ k \ \text{an integer}\}$; range $=$ $\{y \mid y \geq 0\}$

11. $f(0) = 1$

13. $f(-1) = 6$

15. $3a^2 - 2a + 1$

17. $6xh + 3h^2 - 2h$

19. 4

21. $\frac{1}{3}(x + 1)^3 - 2(x + 1) + 4$ or $\frac{1}{3}x^3 + x^2 - x + \frac{7}{3}$

23. $x^2 + hx + \frac{1}{3}h^2 - 2$

25. Yes.

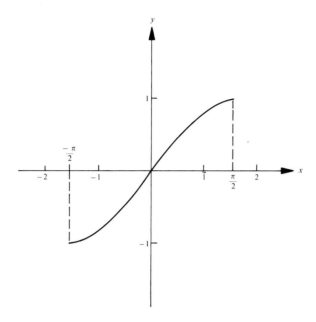

27. Yes.

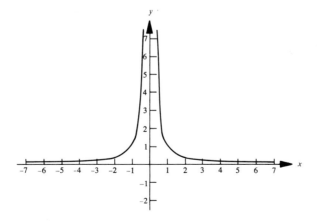

29. Yes.

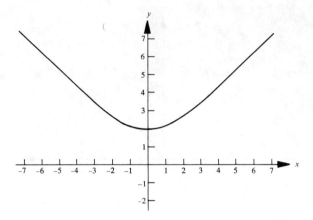

31. Yes.

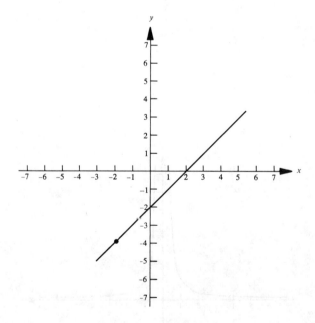

33. If C = cost in minutes and t = time, then
$$C = 55\left(\frac{t}{3}\right)$$

35. $f(1000) = -\$150$
$f(10,000) = \$3000$
$f(100,000) = \$34,500$
$f(x) = 0$ when
$x = \frac{10000}{7}$

A profit is realized when the 1429th item is produced.

37.

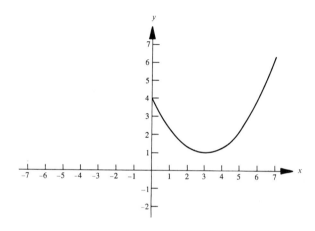

domain: $\{x \mid x \geq 0\}$

39.

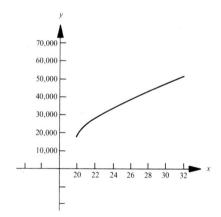

domain: $\{x \mid x \geq 20\}$

41. Function.

43. Nonfunction.

1-3   Exercises

1. $f(x) + g(x) = x^2 + 5x + 1$
   domain: {all reals}
   $f(x) - g(x) = x^2 + x - 1$
   domain: {all reals}
   $f(x) \cdot g(x) = 2x^3 + 7x^2 + 3x$
   domain: {all reals}
   $$\frac{f(x)}{g(x)} = \frac{x^2 + 3x}{2x + 1}$$
   domain: $\{x | x \neq -\frac{1}{2}\}$

3. $f(x) + g(x) = \sqrt{x^2 - 1} + x + 2$
   domain: $\{x | |x| \geq 1\}$

   $f(x) - g(x) = \sqrt{x^2 - 1} - x - 2$
   domain: $\{x | |x| \geq 1\}$

   $f(x) \cdot g(x) = (x + 2)\sqrt{x^2 - 1}$
   domain: $\{x | |x| \geq 1\}$

   $$\frac{f(x)}{g(x)} = \frac{\sqrt{x^2 - 1}}{x + 2}$$
   domain: $\{x | |x| \geq 1, x \neq -2\}$

5. $f(x) + g(x) = 1 - \sqrt{x} + \cos x$
   domain: $\{x | x \geq 0\}$

   $f(x) - g(x) = 1 - \sqrt{x} - \cos x$
   domain: $\{x | x \geq 0\}$

   $f(x) \cdot g(x) = (1 - \sqrt{x}) \cos x$
   domain: $\{x | x \geq 0\}$

   $$\frac{f(x)}{g(x)} = \frac{1 - \sqrt{x}}{\cos x}$$
   domain: $\left\{ x \,\middle|\, x \geq 0, x \neq \frac{(2n - 1)\pi}{2}, n \text{ a natural number} \right\}$

7. $f \circ g = \dfrac{1}{1 - \sqrt{x}}$
   domain: $\{x | x \geq 0, x \neq 1\}$

9. $f \circ g = \sin(1 + \sqrt{x})$
   domain: $\{x | x \geq 0\}$

11. $g \circ f = 2(x^2 + 3x) + 1$
$= 2x^2 + 6x + 1$
domain: {all reals}

13. $g \circ f = \sqrt{x^2 - 1} + 2$
domain: $\{x \mid |x| \geq 1\}$

15. $g \circ f = \cos(1 - \sqrt{x})$
domain: $\{x \mid x \geq 0\}$

17. -1

19. Undefined.

21. $\dfrac{1}{1 - \sqrt{x + h}}$

23. $f(x) = \dfrac{1}{\sqrt{1 - x^2}}$

25.

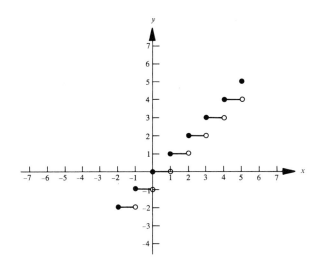

27.

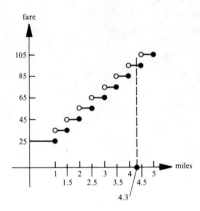

fare = 95 cents

1-4 Exercises

1. 0.2
3. 14.25
5. $2ah + h^2$
7. $6x(\Delta x) + 3(\Delta x)^2 + 2(\Delta x)$
9. $3x^2h + 3xh^2 + h^3$
11. 2
13. $2\sqrt{17} - 8$
15. $2ax + ah + b$
17. $6a^2 + 6ah + 2h^2$
19. 144
21. 96.016
23. 15.3
25. $\frac{225}{14}$
27. 45 dollars
29. Marginal cost is the average rate of change of cost.

1-5 Exercises

1. 0.4, 0.6, 0.8, 1.4, 1.2   5. 0
3. $\lim\limits_{x \to 3} f(x) = 1$ 7. 2

9. 132
11. 2
13. -1
15. -7
17. 12
19. Undefined.

21. $\dfrac{1}{\sqrt{a} + a}$

23. $2\sqrt{a}$
25. 11
27. 6
29. $3x^2$

1-6 Exercises

1. 2

3. $\dfrac{2}{\pi}$

5. $-\infty$
7. $+\infty$
9. 1
11. 0
13. $-\infty$

15. 1
17. 3
19. 1

21. $\dfrac{b}{a}$

23. 0
25. Undefined.

1-7 Exercises

1. 0
3. $\frac{1}{2}$
5. $\frac{3}{5}$
7. -3
9. ∞
11. 0
13. $-\frac{1}{3}$

15. 2
17. $-\frac{5}{4}$
19. 0
21. 1
23. $-\frac{2}{5}$
25. Undefined.
27. -1

Chapter 1   REVIEW

1. $\{-1, 0\}$
3. $\{1,2,3,4,6,12\}$
5. $\{1,\frac{1}{4},\frac{1}{9},\frac{1}{16}, \ldots\}$
7. $\{3\}$
9. $\{1,2,3,4\}$
11. domain: $\{2,3,5,7\}$; range: $\{3,4,6,8\}$

13. domain: $\{x|x \geq \frac{1}{2}\}$; range: $\{f(x)|f(x) \geq 0\}$
15. domain: $\{x|x \neq 0\}$; range: $\{-1,1\}$
17. 5
19. $3x^2h + 3xh^2 + h^3 - 2h$
21. $3x^2 + 2x$
    domain: $\{$all reals$\}$
23. $x - 1; x \neq -\frac{2}{3}$
25. $9x^2 - 3x - 4$
    domain: $\{$all reals$\}$
27. $3x^2 + 3x + 1$
29. $-8b - 4h$
31. Undefined.
33. $-\frac{1}{2}$
35. $\frac{5}{2}$
37. $-\infty$
39. 0
41. -5
43. 129.6

CHAPTER 2

2-1 Exercises

1. $\frac{5}{4}$
3. $-\frac{5}{7}$
5. Undefined.
7. $-3, 5$
9. $\frac{4}{3}, \frac{7}{3}$
11. $0, 4$
13. $y = x$
15. $3x - 4y = -13$
17. $y = 2$
19. $y = x$
21. $7x + 4y = -1$
23. $y = -5$
25. $x = -5$
27. $m =$ marginal cost
    $b =$ fixed cost

29. (a) $90
    (b) $9
    (c) $40
    (d) $50
    (e) $5
31. (a) $650
    (b) $8.125
    (c) $10
    (d) $640
    (e) $8
33. (a) $7,000
    (b) $58.33
    (c) $1,000
    (d) $6,000
    (e) $50

2-2 Exercises

1. $\dfrac{dy}{dx} = 2x$

3. $\dfrac{dy}{dx} = -6$

5. $D_x y = -2x$

7. $D_x y = -\dfrac{2}{x^3}$

9. $f'(3) = -\frac{1}{9}$

11. $h'(-1) = -5$

13. $f'(0) = 0$

15. $-\frac{1}{36}$

17. 1

19. 0.99

21. $6I - 2$

2-3 Exercises

1. $3x^2$

3. $35x^4$

5. $-36x^{-4}$

7. $\dfrac{1}{2\sqrt{x}}$

9. $15x^{\frac{2}{3}}$

11. $6x - 6$

13. $6x - 4$

15. $2ax + b$

17. -20

19. -4

21. $\dfrac{3x^5 - 2}{x^3}$

23. $\dfrac{5x^2 + 9x + 1}{2\sqrt{x}}$

25. $3x^2 + 8x + 3$

27. $y' = -\dfrac{2}{x^2}$

29. $y' = \dfrac{30x - 50}{x^3}$

2-4 Exercises

1. $30x + 11$

3. $3t^2 + 10t + 4$

5. $24x^3 + 30x^2 + 24x + 20$

7. $48t^3 + 42t^2 + 28t - 12$

9. $108x^5 + 165x^4 + 114x^2 + 38x + 2$

11. $3t^2 + 10t + 3$

13. $3x^2 - 1$

15. $-\dfrac{2}{(x - 1)^2}$

17. $\dfrac{1 - t^2}{(t^2 + 1)^2}$

19. $\dfrac{x^2 + 2x - 5}{(x + 1)^2}$

21. $\dfrac{-4(t + 1)}{(t - 1)^3}$

23. $\dfrac{-3x^2}{(x^3 - 1)^2}$

25. $-\dfrac{1}{3t^{\frac{4}{3}}(t^{\frac{1}{3}} - 1)^2}$

27. $-\dfrac{1}{\sqrt{x}\,(1 + \sqrt{x})^2}$

29. $-\dfrac{29}{625}$

2-5 Exercises

1. $6(x + 5)^5$

3. $(2x + 1)^{-\frac{1}{2}}$

5. $x(x^2 + 1)^{-\frac{1}{2}}$

7. $\dfrac{-2}{3(x + 4)^{\frac{5}{3}}}$

9. $\dfrac{-(3x^2 + 2)}{3(x^3 + 2x)^{\frac{4}{3}}}$

11. $\dfrac{9x + 4}{2\sqrt{3x + 2}}$

13. $\dfrac{5x^3 + 90x}{(x^2 + 9)^{\frac{3}{2}}}$

15. $\frac{1}{3}(x + \sqrt{x})^{-\frac{2}{3}}\left(1 + \dfrac{1}{2\sqrt{x}}\right)$

17. $\dfrac{2x - 5}{(x + 2)^2\sqrt{x^2 + 5}}$

19. $\dfrac{-x^2 - x}{(x^2 - 1)^{\frac{3}{2}}(x^3 + 1)^{\frac{2}{3}}}$

21. $\dfrac{2\sqrt{x^2 + 1} + x}{2\sqrt{(x^2 + 1)(2x + \sqrt{x^2 + 1})}}$

23. Undefined.

25. $\sqrt{2x}^{\sqrt{2}-1}$

2-6 Exercises

1. $5 \cos 5x$

3. $-4 \sin 4x$

5. $3 \cos t$

7. $24 \sin 6t$

9. $\cos x + \sin x$

11. $-2 \cos x \sin x = -\sin 2x$

13. $\cos x^2 - 2x^2 \sin x^2$

15. $\cos^2 x - \sin^2 x = \cos 2x$

17. $\dfrac{\cos x}{2\sqrt{\sin x}}$

19. $\dfrac{x \cos x - \sin x}{x^2}$

21. $\dfrac{-2 \cos t}{(1 + \sin t)^2}$

23. $\dfrac{-\cos \sqrt{x} \sin \sqrt{x}}{\sqrt{x}}$

25. $-\pi^2$

27. $\approx 10^3(3(3.14)^2) \approx \$29{,}600/\text{year}$

29. 0

2-7 Exercises

1. $3 \sec 3x \tan 3x$

3. $6 \sec^2 2x$

5. $-2x \csc^2 x^2$

7. $+8x \csc x^2 \cot x^2$

9. $2 \tan t \sec^2 t$

11. $6t + 7 + 2t \sec t^2 \tan t^2$

13. $2t \csc \sqrt{t} - \dfrac{t^2 \csc \sqrt{t} \cot \sqrt{t}}{2\sqrt{t}}$

15. $\cos t \sec^2 (\sin t)$

17. $\dfrac{2 \tan x \cos 2x - \sin 2x \sec^2 x}{\tan^2 x} = -2 \sin 2x$

19. $\dfrac{2 \sec^2 x}{\sec^2 x + 2 \tan x}$

2-8   Exercises

1. 0

3. 4

5. $\dfrac{2}{x^3}$

7. $-\sin x$

9. $\dfrac{1}{(x^2 + 1)^{\frac{3}{2}}}$

11. $\dfrac{12}{(x - 2)^3}$

13. $\dfrac{2}{x^{\frac{3}{2}}}$

15. 24

17. $-\dfrac{6}{(x - 1)^4}$

19. $\dfrac{6}{(x + 1)^4}$

21. $\sin x$

23. $\sin x$

25. When $n < a$, $a(a - 1)(a - 2) \ldots (a - n + 1)x^{a-n}$. When $n > 0$, the nth derivative of x^n is 0.

27.

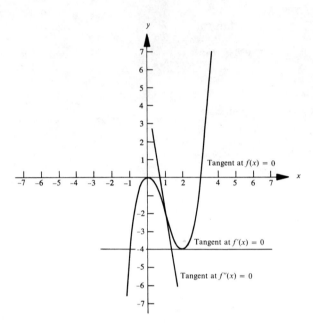

Tangent at $f(x) = 0$

Tangent at $f'(x) = 0$

Tangent at $f''(x) = 0$

Chapter 2 REVIEW

1. 20

3. 3

5. 230

7. $-\dfrac{1}{x^{\frac{3}{2}}}$

9. $\dfrac{4t^4 + 9t^2 + 3}{\sqrt{t^2 + 1}}$

11. $\dfrac{x \cos x - 2 \sin x}{x^3}$

13. $6 \sec^2 3x \tan 3x$

15. 0

17. $2 \sec^2 x \tan x$

19. $\dfrac{-3x}{(x^2 + 1)^{\frac{5}{2}}}$

21. 0.72 g/hr

CHAPTER 3

3-1 Exercises

1. If $x_1 = 1$, then $x_3 = 1.75$.

3. If $x_1 = 2.5$, then $x_3 = 2.16$.

5. 1, -2.67

7. No real roots.

9. 7.32, 1.37, -0.70

11. -7.20

13. 2.83, 2.83

15. $-0.414, -0.492$

3-2   Exercises

  1. Decreasing, concave upward.
  3. Decreasing, concave upward.
  5. Neither, concave upward.
  7. Increasing, neither.
  9. Not defined at $x = 0$.
 11. Increasing, concave downward.
 13. Increasing: $x > -1$.
         Decreasing: $x < -1$.
         Concave up: for all x.

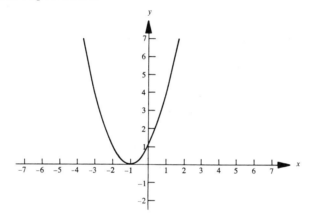

 15. Increasing: $t < \frac{5}{2}$ or $t > 5$.
         Decreasing: $+\frac{5}{2} < t < 5$.
         Concave up: $t > \frac{15}{4}$.
         Concave down: $t < \frac{15}{4}$.

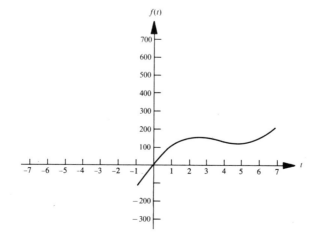

17. Increasing: never.
Decreasing: $x > 0$ or $x < 0$.
Concave up: $x > 0$.
Concave down: $x < 0$.

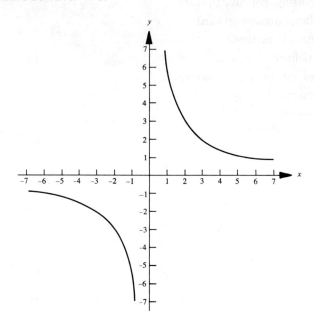

19. $(0, 0)$

21. $(0, 0)$

23.

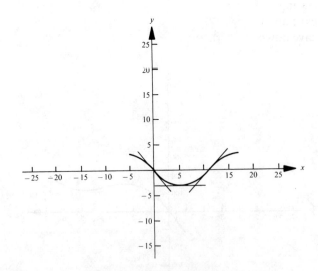

3-3 Exercises

1. $(-2, -5)$ min
3. None.
5. None.
7. $(1, -8)$ min
$(-1, 8)$ max
9. $(3, -77)$ min
$(-2, 48)$ max
11. $(1, 11)$ min
$(-1, 11)$ min
$(0, 12)$ max

13. No max or min.
15. $(1, 2)$ min
$(-1, -2)$ max
17. $(\frac{1}{8}, \frac{-3}{4})$ min
19. No max or min.
21. $(\frac{-8}{27}, \frac{4}{27})$ max, $(0,0)$ min
23. $(-\frac{1}{2}, f(-\frac{1}{2}))$ max

3-4 Exercises

1. 15, 15
3. 5, 25
5. 90.7 in^3
7. 160×160
9. $6 \times 6 \times 15$
11. $(5\sqrt{2} + 4) \times (10\sqrt{2} + 8)$ or 11.1×22.1
13. $r = 2, h = \dfrac{16}{\pi}$
15. rt. angles.
17. \$275
19. 175
21. $s = 20\sqrt{5} \approx 44.2$ mph
23. $\left(10 - \dfrac{8\sqrt{3}}{3}\right)$ miles ≈ 5.3 miles from A.
25. 250 items.

3-5 Exercises

1. $dy = 16x\,dx$
3. $dy = \dfrac{x\,dx}{\sqrt{x^2 + 25}}$
5. $dy = (\sec^3 x + \sec x \tan^2 x)\,dx$
7. $dy = \dfrac{dx}{(x + 1)^2}$
9. 0.14
11. 3×10^{-5}
13. $dy = 2, \Delta y = 2.04$

15. $dy = 1.2, \Delta y = 1.261$

17. $\frac{82}{27}$

19. 6.085

21. $V \approx 226.8$ cu. in.

23. $\sqrt{100 + dx} = 10 + \dfrac{dx}{20}$

25. $2\sqrt{\dfrac{3}{\pi}}$

3-6 Exercises

1. $\dfrac{dy}{dx} = \dfrac{x}{y}$

3. $\dfrac{dy}{dx} = \dfrac{-1 - y}{x}$

5. $\dfrac{dy}{dx} = \dfrac{y - 3x^2}{2y - x}$

7. $\dfrac{dy}{dx} = \dfrac{-y}{2(x + 1)}$

9. $\dfrac{dy}{dx} = \sec y$

11. $\dfrac{dy}{dx} = \dfrac{\cos(xy) - xy\sin(xy)}{x^2 \sin(xy)}$

13. $\frac{4}{3}$

15. $\frac{1}{3}$

17. $\frac{6}{5}$

19. $-\dfrac{1}{y^3}$

21. $-\dfrac{16}{9y^3}$

23. 0

25. $\dfrac{3x^2 + 4xy + y^2}{(y + 2x)^3}$

3-7 Exercises

1. $3

3. $0

5. 26,000

7. $1,400

9. $1,600

11. $-12\pi, -2\pi$

13. $\dfrac{5}{36\pi}$

15. $\dfrac{230}{\sqrt{61}}$ knots.

17. $5/\pi$ ft/min

3-8 Exercises

1. $y = x$

3. $y = \dfrac{x - 5}{4}$

5. $y = \dfrac{1 - x}{6}$

7. $y = x^2 - 25; y \geq -25, x \geq 0$

9. $y = \pm \sqrt{x} - 4$ (not a function).

11. $y = x^{\frac{3}{2}}$

13. $\dfrac{\pi}{2}$

15. $-\dfrac{\pi}{3}$

17. $\dfrac{3\pi}{4}$

19. 0

21. $-\dfrac{\pi}{6}$

23. $\frac{1}{2}$

25. Undefined.

27. $\dfrac{\pi}{2}$

29. -1

31. $f^{-1}(x) = \dfrac{x-2}{3}, f(f^{-1}(x)) = x$

33.

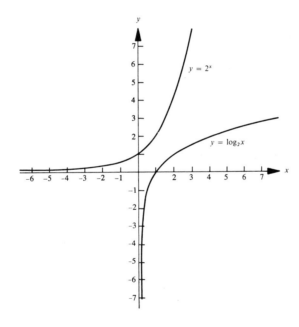

35. 2

37. 3

39. 6

41. 1,000

3-9 Exercises

5. $\dfrac{2x}{\sqrt{1-x^4}}$

7. $\dfrac{3 - 12x^2}{1 + (3x - 4x^3)^2}$

9. $2x \cot^{-1}(2x) - \dfrac{2x^2}{1 + 4x^2}$

11. 1

13. $\dfrac{64x \tan^{-1} x^2}{1 + x^4}$

15. $\dfrac{-x}{(1 - x^2)^{\frac{3}{2}}}$

17. $\dfrac{2x}{(1 + x^2)^2}$

19. $\dfrac{|x|}{x}\left(\dfrac{2x^2 - 1}{x^2(x^2 - 1)^{\frac{3}{2}}}\right)$, $|x| > 1$

21. $\frac{1}{4}$

23. 40π mi/min

3-10   Exercises

1. $c = \frac{7}{2}$

3. $c = \dfrac{\pi}{4}$ or $c = \dfrac{3\pi}{4}$

5. $f\left(\dfrac{3\pi}{2}\right) \neq 0$. Therefore Rolle's theorem does not apply.

7. $\dfrac{f(3) - f(0)}{3 - 0} = 0$

$d = 2$

$0 < 2 < 3$

9. $\dfrac{f\left(-\dfrac{\pi}{2}\right) - f\left(\dfrac{\pi}{2}\right)}{-\dfrac{\pi}{2} - \dfrac{\pi}{2}} = 0$

$d = 0$

$-\dfrac{\pi}{2} < 0 < \dfrac{\pi}{2}$

11.

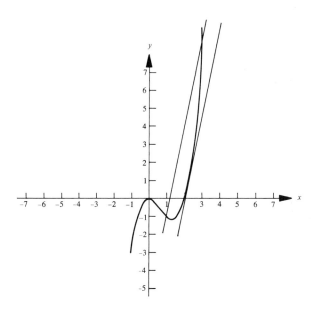

13. $f(0) = 1 \neq 0$

15. Not continuous at $x = 1$.

17. Not continuous at $x = 0$.

19. Not continuous over the interval

$$-\frac{\pi}{2} \leq x \leq \frac{\pi}{2}$$

(undefined when $x = 0$).

Chapter 3   REVIEW

1. 1.74 and -5.74

3. Increasing: $x > -2$.
Decreasing: $x < -2$.
Always concave upward.
Minimum: $(-2, -3)$.
No max or inflection pts.

5. $\dfrac{dy}{dx} = \dfrac{3x}{4y}$

7. $\dfrac{dy}{dx} = \dfrac{3x^2 - 4y + 2x}{4x}$

9. $\dfrac{dy}{dx} = \dfrac{1}{2\sqrt{x+1}\,(x+2)}$

11. $y'' = -\dfrac{4}{y^3}$

13. $y'' = \dfrac{|x|}{x}\left(\dfrac{2x^2 - 1}{x^2(x^2 - 1)^{\frac{3}{2}}}\right)$

$|x| > 1$

15. 20

17. $dy = (6x + 8)\,dx$
$\Delta y = 6x(\Delta x) + 3(\Delta x)^2 + 8(\Delta x)$

19. 125×125 feet

21. 911 feet from A

23. $\dfrac{-1 + \sqrt{19}}{3} = c$

25. $\dfrac{f(b) - f(a)}{b - a} = \dfrac{9}{34}$

$d = 1.9$

CHAPTER 4

4-1 Exercises

1. 30

3. 28

5. 13

7. 16.83

9. 5.18

11. $\dfrac{\pi}{8}$

4-2 Exercises

1. $-1 + 1 + 3 + 5 + 7 = 15$

3. $1 + \frac{1}{2} + \frac{1}{3} + \frac{1}{4} + \frac{1}{5} + \frac{1}{6} = 2.45 \ (\text{or } 2\frac{9}{20})$

5. $(1 - \frac{1}{2}) + (\frac{1}{2} - \frac{1}{3}) + (\frac{1}{3} - \frac{1}{4}) + (\frac{1}{4} - \frac{1}{5}) = \frac{4}{5}$

7. $\dfrac{n^3 + 6n^2 + 8n}{3}$

9. $\dfrac{4n^3 + 27n^2 + 59n}{6}$

11. $\dfrac{64}{3}$

13. $\dfrac{14}{3}$

15. $\dfrac{27}{2}$

17. 73,200

4-3   Exercises

1. $c = \dfrac{4\sqrt{3}}{3}$

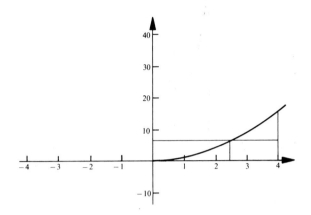

3. $c = \dfrac{2\sqrt{3}}{3}$

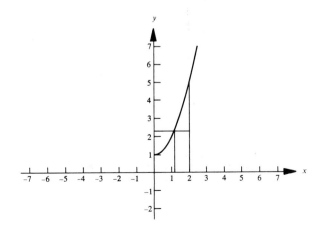

5. $c = \dfrac{-1 \pm \sqrt{13}}{4}$

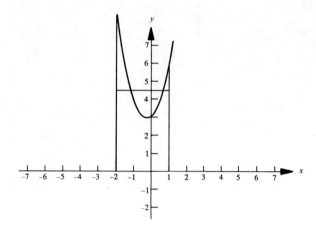

7. $\frac{8}{3}$

9. $-\frac{7}{3}$

11. $\frac{17}{12}$

13. No, not continuous at $x = 1$.

15. f is not nonnegative over the entire interval.

17. f is not nonnegative over the entire interval.

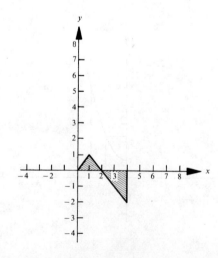

4-4 Exercises

1. 22
3. $14\frac{1}{2}$
5. 15.29

7. .99
9. .99
11. $2\frac{1}{16}$

4-5 Exercises

1. $\dfrac{3x^2}{2} + C$

3. $\dfrac{x^{11}}{11} - \dfrac{2x^7}{7} + \dfrac{x^4}{4} + C$

5. $2\sqrt{x} + C$

7. $\frac{1}{3}(x^2 + 5)^{\frac{3}{2}} + C$

9. $-\dfrac{2}{x} - \dfrac{3}{2x^2} + C$

11. $\frac{1}{4}(4x^2 + 2x + 1)^4 + C$

13. $\frac{1}{10}(6x + 9)^5 + C$

15. $\dfrac{x^{2a+1}}{2a + 1} + C$

17. $-\dfrac{1}{x} - \dfrac{2}{\sqrt{x}} + C$

19. $\frac{3}{13}(x - 1)^{\frac{13}{3}} + C$

21. $x^3 + \dfrac{x^2}{2} - 3x + C$

23. $\frac{1}{2}(x^4 - 1)^{\frac{1}{2}} + C$

4-6 Exercises

1. $\frac{1}{2}\sin 2x + C$

3. $2\tan\left(\dfrac{\theta}{2}\right) + C$

5. $\frac{1}{4}\tan^4 x + C$

7. $-\cot x + C$

9. $\frac{1}{3}\sin^3\theta + C$

11. $\dfrac{1}{\sqrt{3}}\sin^{-1}\sqrt{3}x + C$

13. $-\tan^{-1}x + C$

15. $\frac{1}{6}\tan^{-1}\left(\dfrac{3x}{2}\right) + C$

17. $\sin^{-1}\left(\dfrac{x - 1}{\sqrt{2}}\right) + C$

19. $\tan^{-1}(\sin x) + C$

21. $-\sec\left(\dfrac{1}{x}\right) + C$

Chapter 4   REVIEW

1. (a) $\frac{15}{4}$
   (b) $\frac{11}{4}$
   (c) $\frac{8}{3}$

3. (a) 28
   (b) $21\frac{1}{2}$
   (c) 22

5. (a) 0.72
   (b) 0.98
   (c) 1

7. 12

9. $\dfrac{x^6}{2} + \dfrac{x^4}{2} - \dfrac{x^3}{3} + x + C$

11. $\frac{2}{5}x^{\frac{5}{2}} + \frac{2}{3}x^{\frac{3}{2}} - 3x + C$

13. $\frac{1}{2}\sqrt{1 + 2x^2} + C$

15. $\frac{2}{3}(x - 2)^{\frac{3}{2}} + C$

17. $\frac{1}{15}(x^3 + 3x + 4)^5 + C$

19. $\frac{1}{9}\sin^3 3x + C$

21. $-\cos(2x + 3) + C$

23. $\frac{1}{2}\sin(x^2) + C$

25. $\frac{1}{3}\tan^3 x + C$

CHAPTER 5

5-1   Exercises

1. The closed interval from a to b cannot contain 0.

3. The closed interval from a to b cannot contain an odd multiple of $\dfrac{\pi}{2}$.

5. The closed interval from a to b cannot contain 1 or -2.

7. $10\frac{2}{3}$

9. $37\frac{1}{3}$

11. $\frac{7}{27}$

13. 2

15. -1

17. $\dfrac{4a^{\frac{3}{2}}}{15}$

19. $3\frac{7}{12}$

21. Not defined at $x = 1$; therefore fundamental theorem does not apply.

23. To interpret as area, take $\displaystyle\int_{-2}^{1} (2x - 2)\,dx + \int_{1}^{6} (2x - 2)\,dx = 34$,

the integral $\displaystyle\int_{-2}^{6} (2x - 2)\,dx - 16$.

5-2   Exercises

1. $\dfrac{3}{3x + 2}$

3. $\dfrac{4x}{x^2 + 3}$

5. $\dfrac{-14x}{(x^2 + 3)(2x^2 - 1)}$

7. $1 + \ln x$

9. $\sec x$

11. $\dfrac{1}{\sqrt{x^2 + 1}}$

13. $\dfrac{x^2 + 1}{x^3 + 3x}$

15. $\dfrac{-2}{(2x + 1)(2x - 1)}$

17. $\ln 5$

19. $\ln |\sin x| + c$

21. $x^2 - x + \frac{3}{2} \ln |2x + 1| + c$

23. $\ln |2x^2 + x + 5| + c$

25. $\frac{1}{2} \ln 8 = \frac{3}{2} \ln 2$

27. $\frac{14}{3} + \frac{2}{9} \ln 2$

29. $\ln |2x - \cos x| + c$

31. $\ln |\sec x + \tan x| + c$

33. $\eta = \frac{2}{3}$; demand is inelastic.

35. $\eta = 2$; demand is elastic.

5-3 Exercises

1. $2x e^{x^2}$

3. $\frac{1}{2}(e^x + e^{-x})$

5. $-2x e^{-x^2}$

7. ex^{e-1}

9. 1

11. $\dfrac{1}{x}$

13. $2x \, 3^{x^2} \ln 3$

15. $\dfrac{2}{x \ln 10}$

17. $e^x + ex^{e-1}$

19. $\frac{1}{2}e^{x^2} + c$

21. $\dfrac{2^{3x+2}}{3 \ln 2}$

23. $\ln(1 + e^x) + c$

25. $-e^{-x} + c$

27. $\frac{1}{2}(e^x - e^{-x}) + c$

29. $e^{\tan^{-1} x} + c$

31. $\dfrac{x^2}{2} + c$

5-4 Exercises

1. $\dfrac{-xe^{-ax}}{a} - \dfrac{e^{-ax}}{a^2} + c$

3. $x \tan x + \ln |\cos x| + c$

5. $\dfrac{x^3}{3}(\ln x - \frac{1}{3}) + c$

7. $e^x(x^2 - 2x + 2) + c$

9. $x \sin^{-1}(2x) + \frac{1}{2}(\sqrt{1 - 4x^2}) + c$

11. $\dfrac{e^{ax}}{a^2 + b^2}(a \sin bx - b \cos bx) + c$

13. $x \ln(x + 1) - x + \ln |x + 1| + c$

15. $-\dfrac{e^{-x^2}}{2}(x^2 + 1) + c$

17. $\dfrac{\pi^2}{4} - 2 - \dfrac{\pi^2 \sqrt{2}}{32} - \dfrac{\pi \sqrt{2}}{4} + \sqrt{2}$

19. $-\dfrac{5}{e^4} + \dfrac{2}{e}$

5-5 Exercises

1. $\frac{1}{2}\left[x\sqrt{1 + x^2} + \ln\left|x + \sqrt{x^2 + 1}\right|\right] + c$

3. $\dfrac{1}{2}\left[x\sqrt{4 - x^2} + 4\sin^{-1}\left(\dfrac{x}{2}\right)\right] + c$

5. $-\sqrt{9 - x^2} + \sin^{-1}\left(\dfrac{x}{3}\right) + c$

7. $\frac{1}{2}(\tan\theta - \theta) + c$

9. $\sqrt{x^2 + 1} - \ln\left|\dfrac{\sqrt{x^2 + 1} + 1}{x}\right| + c$

11. $\frac{1}{4}\ln\left|\dfrac{3 + x}{1 - x}\right| + c$

13. $x - \tan^{-1}x + c$

15. $\frac{1}{2}\left[x\sqrt{x^2 - 1} - \ln\left|x + \sqrt{x^2 - 1}\right|\right] + c$

17. $\dfrac{\pi}{4}$

19. $\dfrac{\pi + 2}{8}$

21. $\frac{52}{9}$

23. $\frac{1}{4}\ln(3)$

5-6 Exercises

1. $\frac{1}{4}\tan^4 x - \frac{1}{2}\tan^2 x - \ln|\sec x| + c$

3. $\dfrac{1}{3\sqrt{5}}\ln\left|\dfrac{\sqrt{2x + 5} - \sqrt{5}}{\sqrt{2x + 5} + \sqrt{5}}\right| + c$

5. $\frac{1}{28}(2x + 5)^7 - \frac{5}{24}(2x + 5)^6 + c$

7. $\tan^{-1}(x + 2) + c$

9. $\frac{1}{3}\left[\frac{1}{4}\tan^4 3x - \frac{1}{2}\tan^2 3x - \ln|\sec 3x|\right] + c$

11. $\dfrac{x^3 a^{2x}}{2\ln a} - \dfrac{3x^2 a^{2x}}{4(\ln a)^2} + \dfrac{3x\,a^{2x}}{4(\ln a)^3} - \dfrac{3a^{2x}}{8(\ln a)^4} + c$

13. $x^5 \left[\dfrac{\ln x}{5} - \dfrac{1}{25} \right] + c$

15. $\ln \left| \dfrac{2x(2x + \sqrt{4x^2 + 1})^2}{1 + \sqrt{4x^2 + 1}} \right| + c$

17. $\dfrac{e^{-x}}{5} \left[-\cos(2x) + 2\sin(2x) \right] + c$

19. $\dfrac{x}{2} + \dfrac{\sin 6x}{12} + c$

21. $\dfrac{x^3}{3}(\ln 2x)^3 - \dfrac{x^3}{3}(\ln 2x)^2 + \dfrac{2x^3}{3}\left(\dfrac{\ln 2x}{3} - \dfrac{1}{9} \right) + c$

23. $3! = 6$

25. $-\dfrac{1}{\sqrt{2}} \ln \left| \dfrac{\tan\left(\dfrac{x}{2}\right) - 1 - \sqrt{2}}{\tan\left(\dfrac{x}{2}\right) - 1 + \sqrt{2}} \right| + c$

5-7 Exercises

1. 2

3. Diverges.

5. Diverges.

7. Diverges.

9. 2

11. $\displaystyle\int_0^\infty e^{-ax}\, dx = \lim_{b \to \infty} \int_0^b e^{-ax}\, dx$

$$= -\dfrac{1}{a} \lim_{b \to \infty} e^{1/ax} \Big]_0^b$$

$$= -\dfrac{1}{a} \lim_{b \to \infty} \left(\dfrac{1}{e^{ab}} - 1 \right) = \dfrac{1}{a}$$

13. Yes, when $n < 0$.

15. 2

17. 2

19. $\frac{3}{2}(\sqrt[3]{4} - 1)$

Chapter 5   REVIEW

1. 184

3. $\dfrac{2e^4 - 10}{e^2}$

5. $\dfrac{7}{\ln 2}$

7. $-\dfrac{\pi}{4} + \dfrac{1}{2} \ln 2$

9. $\ln 2$

11. $\tan \theta + \sec \theta + c$

13. $\dfrac{x^2}{2} \sin^{-1} x - \dfrac{1}{4} \sin^{-1}(x) + \dfrac{x}{4} \sqrt{1 - x^2} + c$

15. $\tan^{-1}(e^x) + c$

17. $-2 \cos \sqrt{x} + c$

19. $\dfrac{x^2}{4} + \dfrac{x}{4} \sin(2x) + \dfrac{1}{8} \cos(2x) + c$

21. 8

23. $\dfrac{\pi}{4}$

25. Diverges.

6-1   Exercises

1. $\frac{65}{4}$

3. $\ln 2$

5. 6

7. $2 + 3\pi$

9. $\frac{1}{6}$

11. $\dfrac{3\sqrt{3} - \pi}{3}$

13. $190 \ln 10 - 90 - 90 \ln 3$

15. $\dfrac{5\pi}{12} - \dfrac{\sqrt{3}}{2}$

17. $\displaystyle\int_0^3 e^{-x^2} \, dx$

19. $4 \displaystyle\int_0^2 \sqrt{4 - x^2} \, dx$

6-2   Exercises

1. For a sufficiently large number of 70-year-old men, 4 out of 9 may expect to reach their 80th birthday.

3. No; there are two red aces.

5. $\dfrac{\sqrt{2}}{2}$

7. $\frac{1}{2}$

9. $\frac{5}{14}$

11. $\frac{1}{2}$

13. $\frac{1}{6}$

15. $\approx \dfrac{1}{4} + \dfrac{1.24}{\pi}$

17. 4

19. $\dfrac{\pi}{6}$

21. $P(x) = \frac{3}{8}x^2 ; \frac{7}{8}$

23. $P(x) = \dfrac{3x^2}{(x^3 + 1)^2} ; \dfrac{1}{4}$

25. $P(x) = \dfrac{1}{2x^{\frac{3}{2}}} ; \dfrac{2}{3}$

27. Does not define a P function.

29. $\dfrac{\pi}{6}$

31. 1

33. $a = \dfrac{\pi}{3}, b = \dfrac{\pi}{2}, c = \dfrac{2\pi}{3}$

6-3 Exercises

1. $\frac{45}{14}$

3. 0

5. $\frac{53}{34}$

7. $\dfrac{5}{1 - e^{\frac{5}{2}}}$

9. 0

11. $\mu = \frac{4}{5}$
$\sigma^2 = \frac{76}{525}$

13. $\mu = \frac{3}{2}$
$\sigma^2 = \frac{9}{20}$

15. $\mu = 5$
$\sigma^2 = \frac{27}{5}$

17. $\mu = 0$

19. $\mu = \dfrac{1}{2e\sqrt{2\pi}}$

6-4 Exercises

1. 0.4772

3. 0.4772

5. 0.5328

7. 0.8185

9. 0.0228

11. 0.7062
(See figure 6-11)
Each toss has a width of 1, therefore to include 190 must include $189\frac{1}{2}$–$190\frac{1}{2}$.

13. 0.6736

15. 0.5394

17. (a) 1.44
(b) -0.92

19. (a) 0.84
    (b) 0.67

21. (a) Not possible.
    (b) Not possible.

6-5   Exercises

1. $6,000(\sqrt[3]{4} - 1)$

3. $9,333 $\frac{1}{3}$

5. $500 \ln \left(\frac{18}{13}\right)$

7. $3,547.67

9. $\approx \$79,700$

11. $\approx 5,000$

13. $\approx 12,360$

15. $\approx 10,300$

17. 32,000

19. 3,600

6-6   Exercises

1. The integral of marginal revenue is total revenue.

3. $10

5. 257.5

7. $\dfrac{51e^6 - 1}{2e^6}$

9. $\frac{3}{4}10^{\frac{4}{3}} - (\frac{1}{3})10^{\frac{3}{2}} + 3$

11. $\frac{4}{3}$

13. 100

15. 5,627 tons

6-7   Exercises

1. $c = \displaystyle\int_b^d g(y)\, dy$, where $g(d) = 0$

3. $60\frac{3}{4}$

5. 5.6

7. $\frac{1}{2}(5 - \ln 6)$

9. $4 - \ln 5$

11. $7e^3 - 1$

13. 14.89

15. $3 \ln 3 - 2 \approx 1.297$

17. selling price $= 9$ units
    $c = \frac{2}{3}$
    $P = 4$

19. selling price $= 3$ units

$c = \frac{1}{3}$

$P = \frac{1}{3}$

6-8   Exercises

1. (a) $\dfrac{20}{\sqrt[100]{2}}$ gm

   (b) $\dfrac{5}{256}$ gm

   (c) $\dfrac{20}{2^{100}}$ gm $= \dfrac{5}{2^{98}}$ gm

3. $\approx 74{,}300$ yrs old

   (too old for accurate measurement—see problem 4)

5. 7.6×10^8

7. 2112 A.D.

9. 1,992 A.D.

   Human population growth is limited and dependent on factors which must be accounted for.

11. 2110 A.D.

13. 1.71 hr

15. $k = \dfrac{-\ln(2)}{t}$ for growth

   whereas

   $k = \dfrac{\ln 2}{t_h}$ for half life when $(-)$ is included in expression.

19. Never.

6-9   Exercises

1. 1

3. $3 - 2\ln 2$

5. 2

7. $\ln(1.5)$

9. $\cos 1 - \dfrac{\sqrt{2}}{2}$

11. 8π

13. 39π

15. $\dfrac{128\pi}{3}$

17. $\dfrac{\pi^2}{2}$

19. $\dfrac{3\pi}{8}$

21. $\dfrac{\pi}{2}$

23. Undefined.

25. $\pi \displaystyle\int_c^d [f(y)]^2 \, dy$

27. $\dfrac{8\pi}{3}$

29. $\dfrac{256\pi}{15}$

Chapter 6   REVIEW

1. 39

3. $\frac{1}{3}$

5. $\dfrac{2 - \sqrt{3}}{2}$

7. $\dfrac{3\pi^2}{32} + \dfrac{\pi}{4} + \dfrac{\sqrt{2}}{2}$

11. At least one possible result will happen 100% of the time.

13. 0.3794

15. $\dfrac{1}{\pi}\left[\tan^{-1}\left(\tfrac{1}{3}\right) - \tan^{-1}\left(-\tfrac{1}{2}\right)\right]$

17. $\mu = \tfrac{4}{7},\ \sigma^2 = \tfrac{18}{245}$

19. 0.7938

21. 0.5468

23. 0.1539

25. 0.36

27. $1{,}000 \ln 5 \approx \$1{,}609$

29. 5,000

31. $\approx \$13{,}600$

33. $\approx \$13{,}350$

35. $1{,}000 \ln 6 = \$1{,}790$

37. price = 5 units
$P = \tfrac{1}{2}(\ln 2)^2$
$c = 5(1 - \ln 2)$

39. price = 36 units
$P = 213\tfrac{1}{3}$
$c = 341\tfrac{1}{3}$

41. 150.15 or $\left(\dfrac{601e^6 - 1}{4e^6}\right)$

43. $8\sqrt[4]{10} - \tfrac{25}{6}\sqrt[5]{10} + 3$

45. ≈ 510 yrs

47. $K = 0.66\%$ or $\frac{2}{3}$ of one percent

49. $2e^3 - e^2$

51. $\ln |\sec 1|$

53. $\pi(\ln 4 + \frac{145}{6})$

55. $2\pi e^2$

CHAPTER 7

7-1 Exercises

3. $f(0,0) \to 2$

$f(1,1) \to \sqrt{\frac{5}{2}}$

$f(2,2) \to 2\sqrt{\frac{2}{3}}$

$f(4,1) \to 2$

$f(2x,3) \to \sqrt{x^2 + 1}$

$f(u,v) \to \dfrac{\sqrt{u^2 + 4}}{\sqrt{v + 1}}$

$f(x^2 + y^2, x) \to \dfrac{\sqrt{(x^2 + y^2)^2 + 4}}{\sqrt{x + 1}}$

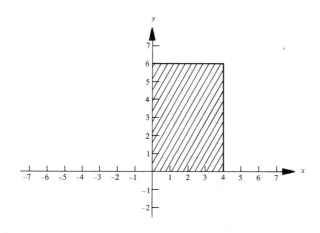

5. $f(0,0)$ meaningless
$f(1,1) \to 1$
$f(2,2)$ meaningless
$f(4,1)$ meaningless

$$f(2x,3) \to \frac{1}{36x^2}$$

$$f(u,v) \to \frac{1}{u^2v^2}$$

$$f(x^2 + y^2, x) \to \frac{(x^2 + y^2)^2}{y^2}, \text{ where } (x^2 + y^2)x = 1$$

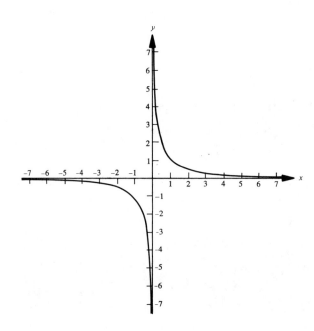

7. $D = \{(x,y) | x \text{ and } y \text{ are real}\}$

9. $D = \{(x,y) | x > 0, y > 0\}$

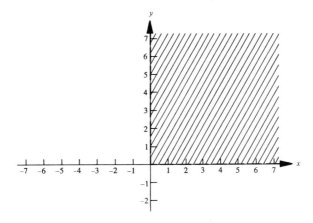

11. No value of x or y makes this a real-valued function.

13. $D = \{(x,y) | x^2 + y^2 \leq 25\}$

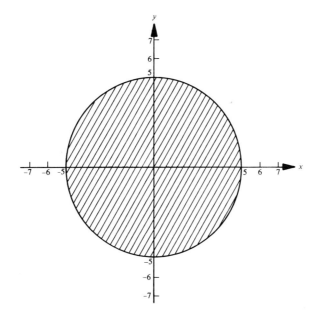

15. $D = \{(x,y) \mid x \text{ and } y \text{ are real}\}$

17. 1

19. $\frac{4}{9}$

21. e^2

23. 25

25. e^2

29. $\dfrac{2}{\sqrt{3}}$

31. 1

33. 2

35. 1

37. Within 9 units.

39. Within 9 units.

7-2 Exercises

1. $\sqrt{41}$

3. $2\sqrt{2}$

5. 2

7.

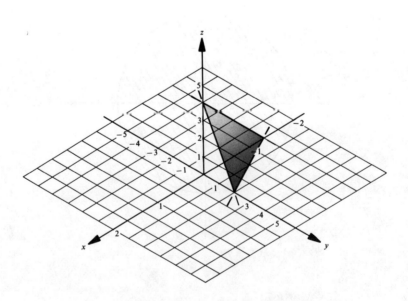

9.

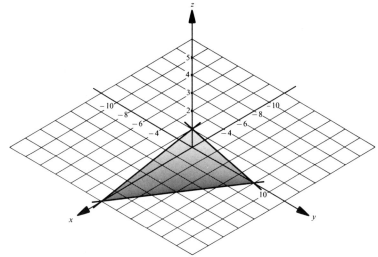

11.

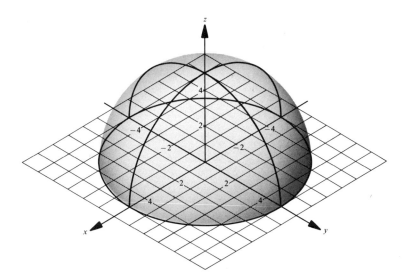

13.

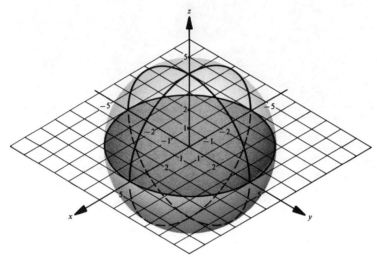

15.

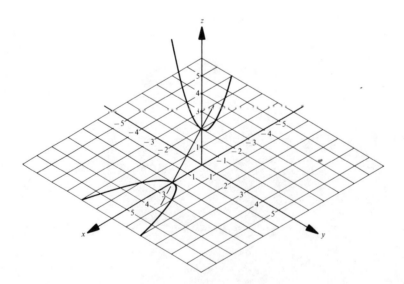

17.

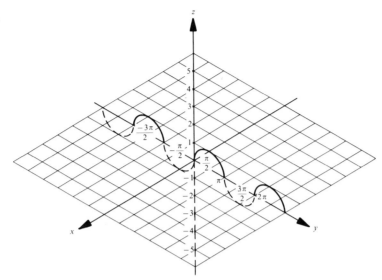

19.

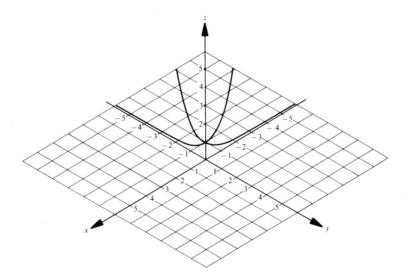

21. $(0,0,4), (0,0,-4)$

23.

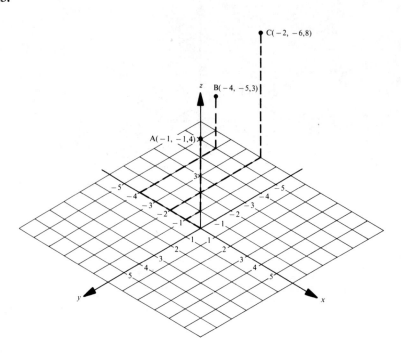

7-3 Exercises

1. $-\dfrac{2}{x^3y^2}, -\dfrac{2}{x^2y^3}$

3. $\dfrac{2}{x}, \dfrac{1}{y}$

5. $2x \cos (x^2 + 2 \cos y), -2 \sin y \cos (x^2 + 2 \cos y)$

7. $\dfrac{y}{2x^2\sqrt{x^2 - y^2}}, \dfrac{-x}{2y^2\sqrt{x^2 - y^2}}$

9. $2y - 4x + 4, 2x - 10y + 4$

11. $\dfrac{\partial^2 z}{\partial x^2} = \dfrac{6}{x^4y^2}, \dfrac{\partial^2 z}{\partial y^2} = \dfrac{6}{x^2y^4}$

$\dfrac{\partial^2 z}{\partial y \partial x} = \dfrac{4}{x^3y^3}, \dfrac{\partial^2 z}{\partial x \partial y} = \dfrac{4}{x^3y^3}$

13. $\dfrac{\partial^2 z}{\partial x^2} = \dfrac{2(y^2 + 2)(3x^2 - 15x + 17)}{(x^2 - 5x + 8)^3}, \dfrac{\partial^2 z}{\partial y^2} = \dfrac{2}{x^2 - 5x + 8}$

$\dfrac{\partial^2 z}{\partial y \partial x} = \dfrac{-2y(2x - 5)}{(x^2 - 5x + 8)^2}, \dfrac{\partial^2 z}{\partial y \partial x} = \dfrac{-2y(2x - 5)}{(x^2 - 5x + 8)^2}$

15. $\dfrac{\partial^2 z}{\partial x^2} = 2, \dfrac{\partial^2 z}{\partial y^2} = 2$

$\dfrac{\partial^2 z}{\partial y \, \partial x} = 1 \qquad \dfrac{\partial^2 z}{\partial x \, \partial y} = 1$

17. $f_{yyy}(x,y) = \dfrac{4}{y^3}, \qquad f_{xyx}(x,y) = 0$

19. $f_{xxy}(x,y) = ye^{xy}(xy + 2)$
$f_{xyx}(x,y) = ye^{xy}(xy + 2)$
$f_{yxx}(x,y) = ye^{xy}(xy + 2)$

21. $4y$
25. $(\frac{4}{3}, \frac{2}{3})$
27. $\sin(xy) - x^5 + y^3 + c$
29. $xy + y \ln(xy) + c$

7-4 Exercises

1. $f(2,1) = -8$, min
3. $f(2,-1) = -1$, min
5. $f(2,0) = -16$, min
7. $f(3,3) = -27$, min
9. $f(-\frac{1}{2},4) = -8$, max
11. $f(-3,2k\pi) = 36$, min, $\quad f(3, (2k + 1)\pi) = 36$, min
13. no max or min
15. no max or min

17. $f\left(\dfrac{\sqrt{2}}{2}, \dfrac{\sqrt{2}}{2}\right) = 1 + \ln 2$

19. 200 million dollars on welfare
100 million dollars on prisons

21. $y = \frac{3}{4}x + \frac{1}{6}$
23. $y = \frac{-15}{38}x + \frac{33}{38}$

7-5 Exercises

1. $\dfrac{\partial z}{\partial u} = 2x \cos v + 2y \sin v$

   $\dfrac{\partial z}{\partial v} = -2xu \sin v + 2yu \cos v$

   $= -2xy + 2xy = 0$

3. $\dfrac{\partial z}{\partial u} = \dfrac{1}{u}\left(e^{x+y} + e^{-x-y}\right)$

   $= v + \dfrac{1}{u^2 v}$

   $\dfrac{\partial z}{\partial v} = \dfrac{1}{v}\left(e^{x+y} + e^{-x-y}\right)$

   $= u + \dfrac{1}{uv^2}$

5. $\dfrac{\partial z}{\partial u} = \dfrac{1}{y}\, e^{x/y}\left(1 - \dfrac{2x}{y}\right)$

   $\dfrac{\partial z}{\partial v} = \dfrac{1}{y}\, e^{x/y}\left(2 + \dfrac{x}{y}\right)$

7. $\dfrac{dz}{dt} = \dfrac{2t}{y} - \dfrac{x}{y^2} + 1 = 2$

9. $\dfrac{dw}{dx} = (2u + ve^u)(\sin x + v) + e^u (\cos x - u)$

11. $dz = 2(x + 2y)\, dx + 4(x + 2y)\, dy$

13. $dz = (2x + 2y + 1)\, dx + (2x + 4y + 1)\, dy$

15. $dz = 0$

19. 0.2295

Chapter 7 REVIEW

3. $D = \{(x,y) \mid x \text{ is a real number}, y \neq 2, y \neq -3\}$

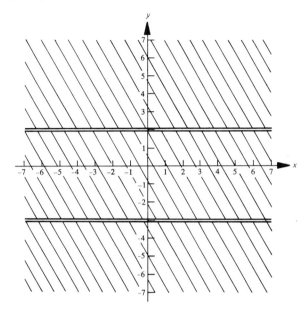

5. $D = \{(x,y) \mid x^2 + y^2 \leq 25\}$

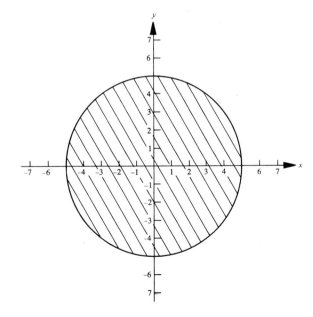

7. $D = \{(x,y) \mid x \text{ and } y \text{ are real}\}$

9. $D = \{(x,y) \mid y \neq 2, \; x \neq -y\}$

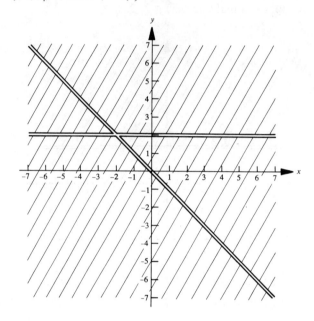

13. $f(0,0) \quad = 5$

$f(3,4) \quad = 0$

$f(-3,4) = 0$

$f(1,2) \quad = 2\sqrt{5}$

$f(5,1)$ no real solution

15. $f\!\left(0, \dfrac{2}{\pi}\right) = e^{2/\pi}$

$f\!\left(\dfrac{4}{\pi}, \dfrac{2}{\pi}\right) = \tfrac{1}{2}e^{6/\pi}$

$f(1,-1)$ meaningless

17.

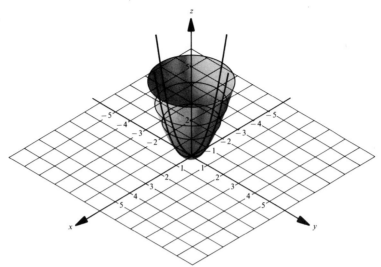

19.

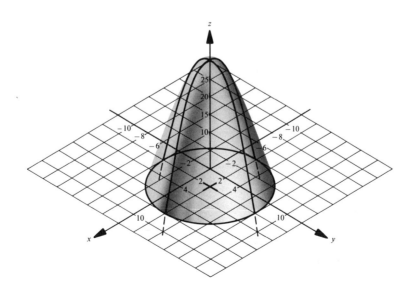

21.

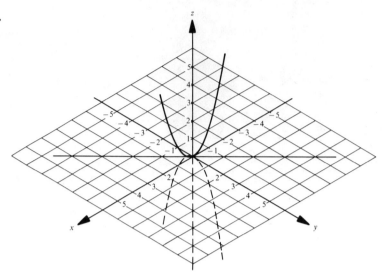

23.

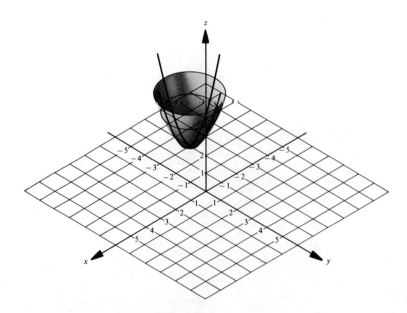

25.

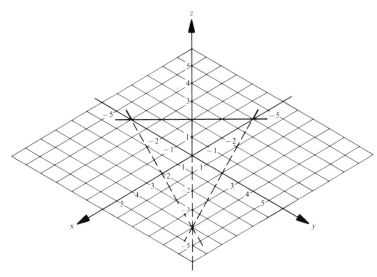

27. Right circular cylinder, radius 5, z axis as center line.

29. Hemisphere above the xy plane; center at origin, radius 5.

31. $\dfrac{\partial z}{\partial x} = \dfrac{1}{y} e^{x/y}$

$\dfrac{\partial^2 z}{\partial x^2} = \dfrac{1}{y^2} e^{x/y}$

$\dfrac{\partial^3 z}{\partial x^2 \, \partial y} = \dfrac{x}{y^2} e^{x/y} - \dfrac{2}{y^3} e^{x/y}$

33. $\dfrac{\partial z}{\partial x} = e^y + ye^x, \qquad \dfrac{\partial z}{\partial y} = xe^y + e^x, \qquad \dfrac{\partial^2 z}{\partial x \, \partial y} = e^y + e^x$

35. $\dfrac{\partial^4 z}{\partial x^4} = 0$

37. $\dfrac{\partial z}{\partial u} = 2x \cos u \cos v - 2y \sin u \cos v = 0$

$\dfrac{\partial z}{\partial v} = -2 \cos v \sin v$

39. $\dfrac{\partial^2 z}{\partial v^2} = \dfrac{2}{u^2 v^3}$

45. $\dfrac{dy}{dx} = 1$

47. $f\left(\pi, \dfrac{\pi}{2}\right) = -2,\ \text{min}$

  $f\left(0, \dfrac{3\pi}{2}\right) = 2,\ \text{max}$

49. $f(1,1) = -7,\ \text{min}$

51. $f(2,0) = -4,\ \text{min}$

53. $-\dfrac{\sqrt{3}}{6}$

CHAPTER 8

8-1   Exercises

1. 36

3. 0

5. $\frac{3125}{3}$

7. $-\frac{207}{20}$

9. 1

11. $\frac{8}{15}$

13. $\dfrac{3\pi}{8} - 1$

15. 12

17. 0

19. $\frac{16}{5}$

21. No.

23. Yes.

25. Notation is meaningless as outer limits must be constants

8-2   Exercises

1. 8

3. 45

5. $\dfrac{\pi}{12} + \dfrac{\sqrt{3}}{8}$

7. $(4\ln 4) - 8 + e$

9. $e^2 - 3$

11. $\dfrac{4\pi}{3}$

13. $\frac{33}{250}$

15. $-\frac{243}{4}$

17. $\dfrac{25\pi}{2}$

19. $\frac{21}{2}$

21. $\displaystyle\int_0^1 \int_{\sqrt{x}}^{\sqrt[3]{x}} dy\, dx$

23. $\displaystyle\int_{-1}^1 \int_x^1 \sqrt{1 + y^2}\, dy\, dx$

25. $\displaystyle\int_{-2}^0 \int_{-1}^{x/2} e^{-x^2}\, dy\, dx + \int_0^8 \int_{x/2}^4 e^{-x^2}\, dy\, dx$

27. $\frac{9}{2}$

29. 1

8-3 Exercises

1. $\dfrac{\partial f}{\partial x} = 2x \ln y$

$\dfrac{\partial^2 f}{\partial x^2} = 2 \ln y$

$\dfrac{\partial f}{\partial z} = \dfrac{-y}{z} + y$

$\dfrac{\partial^2 f}{\partial x \partial y} = \dfrac{2x}{y}$

3. $\dfrac{\partial f}{\partial x} = \frac{1}{2} e^{\,(x+y+z)/2}$

$\dfrac{\partial f}{\partial y} = \frac{1}{2} e^{\,(x+y+z)/2}$

$\dfrac{\partial f}{\partial z} = \frac{1}{2} e^{\,(x+y+z)/2}$

$\dfrac{\partial^3 f}{\partial x \partial y \partial z} = \frac{1}{8} e^{(x+y+z)/2}$

5. $\dfrac{\partial f}{\partial x} = \dfrac{1}{x}$

$\dfrac{\partial f}{\partial y} = \dfrac{1}{y}$

$\dfrac{\partial f}{\partial z} = \dfrac{1}{z}$

$\dfrac{\partial f}{\partial w} = \dfrac{1}{w}$

$\dfrac{\partial^2 f}{\partial x \, \partial y} = 0$

7. $\dfrac{\partial f}{\partial x_2} = x_1 \cos(x_1 x_2) + 2x_2$

$\dfrac{\partial^2 f}{\partial x_3^2} = 2$

$\dfrac{\partial^2 f}{\partial x_1 \, \partial x_3} = 0$

9. $\dfrac{\partial f}{\partial u} = \dfrac{2u}{w}$

$\dfrac{\partial f}{\partial v} = \dfrac{-2v}{w}$

$\dfrac{\partial f}{\partial w} = \dfrac{v^2 - u^2}{w^2}$

$\dfrac{\partial^3 f}{\partial w^3} = \dfrac{6(v^2 - u^2)}{w^4}$

11. $\frac{15}{4}$

13. 0

15. $\dfrac{2^{12}}{15}$

17. 0

19. 3^n

21. $2u^2x \cos(x^2) \sin y \cos z - \dfrac{u\pi}{v^2} \sin(x^2) \cos y \cos z +$

$$\dfrac{v \sin(x^2) \sin y \sin z}{\sqrt{u^2 - v^2}}$$

23. $\dfrac{\partial z}{\partial y_3} = 9y_3^2 z$

$\dfrac{\partial z}{\partial y_5} = 5y_5^4 z$

8-4　Exercises

1. $z = 34$

3. $P = 19$

5. $z = 30,$ max, $\qquad z = -150,$ min

7. $I = 22,$ max, $\qquad I = -138,$ min

9. No vitamin A; 10 lbs. vitamin B.

11. \$82.50

13. 350 first class, $\qquad$ 25 second class, $\qquad$ 25 tourist

15. 34 qt Scotch, $\qquad$ 20 qt beer

Chapter 8　REVIEW

1. $\dfrac{\pi}{2} \ln 2$

3. $\frac{1250}{3}$

5. 4π

7. $\dfrac{e^2 - 3}{2}$

9. $\frac{7}{3}$

11. $2 \ln 10$

13. $\frac{3}{20}$

15. $\frac{9}{2}$

17. $\dfrac{\partial w}{\partial x} = yz - 2xy^2z^2$

$\dfrac{\partial^2 w}{\partial x^2} = -2y^2z^2$

$\dfrac{\partial^2 w}{\partial x\,\partial z} = y - 4xy^2z$

19. $\dfrac{\partial u}{\partial v} = 2v\,\dfrac{\partial u}{\partial x} + r^3\,\dfrac{\partial u}{\partial y} + \dfrac{2v}{r^2}\,\dfrac{\partial u}{\partial z} - \dfrac{2}{v^3}\,\dfrac{\partial u}{\partial w}$

$\dfrac{\partial u}{\partial r} = \dfrac{2}{r^3}\,\dfrac{\partial y}{\partial x} + 3vr^2\,\dfrac{\partial u}{\partial y} - \dfrac{2v^2}{r^3}\,\dfrac{\partial u}{\partial z}$

21. $\dfrac{\pi}{4}$

23. $\frac{20}{9} - \ln 3$

25. Undefined at $z = 0$ (diverges).

29. 36 pages news,   15 pages advertising,   9 pages photos

CHAPTER 9

9-1   Exercises

1. $a_1 = 4,$ $a_2 = \frac{5}{4},$ $a_3 = \frac{2}{3},$ $a_{20} = \frac{23}{400},$ Convergent.

3. $a_1 = 2,$ $a_2 = \left(\frac{3}{2}\right)^{\frac{1}{2}},$ $a_3 = \left(\frac{4}{3}\right)^{\frac{1}{3}},$ $a_{20} = \left(\frac{21}{20}\right)^{\frac{1}{20}}$
Convergent.

5. $a_1 = \dfrac{1}{\sqrt{2} - 1}$

$a_2 = \dfrac{1}{\sqrt{3} - \sqrt{2}}$

$a_3 = \dfrac{1}{2 - \sqrt{3}}$

$a_{20} = \dfrac{1}{\sqrt{21} - \sqrt{20}}$

Divergent.

7. $a_1 = \frac{1}{2},$ $a_2 = \frac{23}{18},$ $a_3 = \frac{10}{7}$

$a_{20} = \dfrac{3(20)^3 - 1}{2(20)^3 + 2}$

$= \dfrac{2399}{16002}$

Convergent.

9. $a_1 = \frac{1}{4},$ $a_2 = \frac{1}{4},$ $a_3 = \frac{1}{4},$ $a_{20} = \frac{1}{4},$ Convergent.

11. $a_n = \dfrac{1}{4^{n-1}}$

Convergent.

13. $a_n = \dfrac{n(n + 1)}{2}$

Divergent.

15. $a_n = 1 + \displaystyle\sum_{i=2}^{n} \dfrac{1}{i}$

Divergent. (This will be shown to be divergent in the next section.)

17. $a_n = \dfrac{-1}{2^n}, n > 1$

Convergent.

19. $a_n = n$

Divergent.

21. $a_n = (\tfrac{1}{2})^{n-1}$

Convergent.

23. $a_n = 4$

Convergent.

25. $a_n = \dfrac{1}{n(n + 1)}$

Convergent.

27. $|r| < 1$

29. Convergent.

31. Convergent.

33. Divergent.

35. Divergent.

9-2 Exercises

1. $\displaystyle\lim_{n \to \infty} \dfrac{n}{n + 1} = 1 \neq 0$

Divergent.

3. $\displaystyle\lim_{n \to \infty} \dfrac{1}{4^n} = 0$

May or may not converge.

5. $\displaystyle\lim_{n \to \infty} (\tfrac{3}{2})^n \neq 0$

Divergent.

7. Convergent.

9. Divergent.

11. Divergent.

13. $a_n = \dfrac{n^2 + n - 1}{n(n + 1)}$

15. $a_n = \dfrac{5}{(4n + 1)(4n - 3)}$

17. $a_n = \dfrac{1}{n(n + 1)}$

19. $a_n = 2(3)^{n-1}$

21. $\tfrac{1}{3}$

23. $\tfrac{22}{7}$

25. $10\tfrac{371}{999}$

27. 0

29. 500 ft

31. Yes; $\displaystyle\sum_{i=1}^{\infty} c_i = \sum_{i=1}^{\infty} a_i + \sum_{i=1}^{\infty} b_i$

where $c_i = a_i + b_i$

33. Unknown.

35. Could be either.

37. If any of the series converge, the rest do also.

39. $2,915

9-3 Exercises

3.	Convergent.	**17.**	Divergent.
5.	Divergent.	**19.**	Convergent.
7.	Convergent.	**21.**	Convergent.
9.	Convergent.	**23.**	Convergent.
11.	Convergent.	**25.**	Divergent.
13.	Convergent.	**27.**	Divergent.
15.	Divergent.	**29.**	Convergent.

9-4 Exercises

1. -1

3. ∞

5. 0

7. 1

9. No limit.

11. Convergent.

13. Ratio test fails.

15. Convergent.

17. Divergent.

19. Test fails.

21. Convergent.

23. Convergent.

25. Test fails.

27. Let $a_i = \dfrac{1}{i^2}$; then $\sqrt{a_i} = \dfrac{1}{i}$ and $\displaystyle\sum_{i=1}^{\infty} \dfrac{1}{i^2}$ converges, whereas

$\displaystyle\sum_{i=1}^{\infty} \dfrac{1}{i}$ diverges.

9-5　Exercises

1. Absolutely convergent.
3. Conditionally convergent.
5. Absolutely convergent.
7. Absolutely convergent.
9. Absolutely convergent.
11. Absolutely convergent.
13. Divergent.
15. Absolutely convergent.

17. Divergent.
19. Absolutely convergent.
21. $\frac{1}{5}$
23. $\frac{1}{160}$
25. $\frac{5}{32}$
27. 7
29. Divergent series.

9-6　Exercises

1. $-\infty < x < \infty$
3. $-\frac{1}{2} \le x \le \frac{1}{2}$
5. $-\infty < x < \infty$
7. $-3 \le x \le 3$
9. $-1 \le x < 1$
11. $-1 \le x \le 0$
13. $-\infty < x < \infty$
15. $0 \le x \le 1$
17. $-1 \le x \le 1$
19. $-1 < x < 1$

21. $-1 < x < 1$, yes
23. $-4 \le x < 0$, yes
25. $-\frac{1}{8} < x < \frac{1}{8}$, yes
27. $R = \infty$
29. $R = 1$
31. $\displaystyle\sum_{i=1}^{\infty} \left(\frac{x}{2}\right)^i$
33. $\displaystyle\sum_{i=1}^{\infty} \frac{(x - c)^i}{R^i}$

9-7　Exercises

1. $1 + \displaystyle\sum_{i=1}^{\infty} (-x)^i$
   $|x| < 1$

3. $\displaystyle\sum_{i=1}^{\infty} x^{3i-2}(-1)^{i+2}$
   $|x| < 1$

5. $2 \displaystyle\sum_{i=1}^{\infty} \frac{(-1)^{i-1}x^i}{i}$
   $R = 1$

7. $\displaystyle\sum_{i=1}^{\infty} \frac{(-1)^{i-1}x^{i-1}}{i}$
   $-1 < x < 1$ and $x \ne 0$

9. $2 \sum_{i=1}^{\infty} \dfrac{x^{2i-1}}{2i-1}$

$R = 1$

13. $\dfrac{1}{\sqrt{1-x}} = 1 + \dfrac{x}{2} + \dfrac{1(3)}{2(4)}x^2 + \dfrac{1(3)(5)}{2(4)(6)}x^3 + \cdots, R = 1$

15. $\sin^{-1} x = x + \dfrac{1}{2} \cdot \dfrac{x^3}{3} + \dfrac{1(3)}{2(4)} \cdot \dfrac{x^5}{5} + \dfrac{1(3)(5)}{2(4)(6)} \cdot \dfrac{x^7}{7} + \cdots, R = 1$

17. $\ln(x + \sqrt{1 + x^2}) = x - \dfrac{1}{2} \cdot \dfrac{x^3}{3} + \dfrac{1(3)}{2(4)} \cdot \dfrac{x^5}{5} - \dfrac{1 \cdot 3 \cdot 5}{2 \cdot 4 \cdot 6} \cdot \dfrac{x^7}{7} + \cdots$

$R = 1$

19. $\cot^{-1} x = \dfrac{\pi}{2} - x + \dfrac{x^3}{3} - \dfrac{x^4}{5} + \cdots$

9-8   Exercises

1. $\ln(1 + x) = x - \dfrac{x^2}{2} + \dfrac{x^3}{3} - \dfrac{x^4}{4} + \cdots + (-1)^{n-1}\dfrac{x^n}{n} - \cdots, R = 1$

3. $\sum_{i=0}^{\infty} \dfrac{x^{2i}}{(2i)!}$

7. $1 - \dfrac{\left(x - \dfrac{\pi}{2}\right)^2}{2!} + \dfrac{\left(x - \dfrac{\pi}{2}\right)^4}{4!} - \dfrac{\left(x - \dfrac{\pi}{2}\right)^6}{6!} + \cdots$

9. $\sin^{-1} x = x + \dfrac{x^3}{2(3)} + \dfrac{3x^5}{2(4)(5)} + \dfrac{1(3)(5)x^7}{2(4)(6)(7)} + \cdots$

11. 1

13. $1 + \dfrac{(x-1)}{2} + \sum_{i=2}^{\infty} (-1)^{i+1} \dfrac{1(3)(5) \ldots (2i-3)}{2^i i!}(x-1)^i$

17. $\dfrac{1}{9!}$

19. 200 terms

21. $\ln(\sec x) = \dfrac{x^2}{2} + \dfrac{x^4}{12} + \dfrac{x^6}{45}$

23. $x \ln(x + 1) = x^2 - \dfrac{x^3}{2} + \dfrac{x^4}{3}$

Chapter 9   REVIEW

7. $a_1 = 3,$ $a_2 = 9,$ $a_7 = 3^7,$ Divergent.

9. $a_1 = \frac{1}{3},$ $a_2 = \frac{1}{9},$ $a_7 = \dfrac{1}{3^7},$ Convergent.

11. $a_n = \dfrac{1}{n!}$, convergent.

13. $a_n = n$; divergent.

15. Convergent.

17. Convergent.

21. Convergent.

23. Divergent.

25. Divergent.

27. Divergent.

31. Absolutely convergent.

33. Absolutely convergent.

35. Convergent.

37. Convergent.

39. Divergent.

41. An alternating divergent series.

43. No.

45. $-1 \leq x < 1$

47. $-e < x < e$

49. $-5 < x < 3$

51. Yes; $x > 1$ or $x \leq -1$.

55. $-x + \dfrac{x^2}{2} - \dfrac{x^3}{3} + \dfrac{x^4}{4} - \cdots, \; -1 < x \leq 1$

57. $\displaystyle\sum_{i=0}^{\infty} \dfrac{x^{(2i+1)}}{(2i+1)!}, \; -\infty < x < \infty$

59. $-(x-1) + (x-1)^2 - (x-1)^3 + (x-1)^4, \; 0 < x < 2$

61. $3!e$

63. $10! \left(\displaystyle\sum_{i=1}^{10} \dfrac{1}{i} \right)$

INDEX